Mathematics
in Elementary
Education

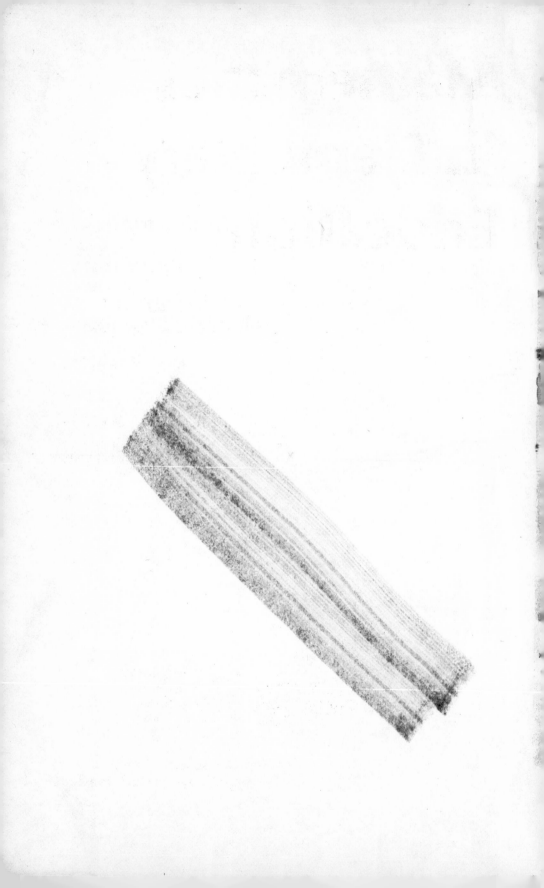

Mathematics in Elementary Education

Selected Readings

Edited by

Nicholas J. Vigilante

The Macmillan Company
Collier-Macmillan Limited, London

Library of Congress catalog card number:
69–11407

The Macmillan Company
Collier-Macmillan Canada, Ltd., Toronto,
Ontario

Printed in the United States of America

Preface

In these cybernetic days of the knowledge explosion, complex storage facilities, and instantaneous retrieval and processing of information along with the communication revolution, when admittedly the medium has become the message, the human mind must be adaptive as never before. When in an earlier period of mankind it took 2,000 years to reverse an Aristotelian truism, even now Einstein's theory is relative. The age of the revolutionary, of the idea generator, of the think tank has now been recognized as a natural phenomenon of man that encourages the individual to seek those ideals which place him on the threshold of developmental inquiry. One of the most distinctive forces affecting the schools in the last ten years has been the "modern mathematics" movement. This movement introduced not only a core of new content to elementary school programs but also a new pedagogical approach based on heuristic developments which recognize the cognitive and affective forces that influence the learner. The teaching of mathematics without a deep concern for the learner is now passé; instead, both factors are inextricably interwoven as we attempt to build programs and teach children who are attending the schools of today.

This new and exciting approach to the teaching of mathematics continues to attract the attention of teachers from all disciplines. The upsurge of interest in the new mathematics, which has led to the largest "back to school" movement ever witnessed in the history of mankind, has affected the general citizenry as well as the teacher and the researcher. The viewing of mathematics as developmental in nature rather than an immutable phenomenon makes the discipline of mathematics considerably more attractive to the imagination of both the young and the old—the young who uncover the power inherent in the mathematics of today, and the old who see the excitement among the children as they display reasoning powers beyond those with which children have been traditionally credited.

In the parlance of a Pythagorean colony, we hear mathematics discussed in terms of at least three different types of subject matter: pure (logical relationships), applied (translation of the relations of the physical world expressed by equations and formulas), and the mechanical, dealing with aspects of computation.

A parallel can be uncovered in discussing mathematics for elementary school children or in reading the literature related to elementary school mathematics. We recognize the pure as being those concerns (as exemplified by Piaget) which attempt to formulate a relationship between mathematics development and children's learning. We also see the applied program as evidenced by the Madison Project, the Cuisenaire materials, and so on. The mechanics of computation can be paralleled to those conditions which are necessary for teacher practice as we recognize the society in which our children reside.

The collection of readings in this book is specifically prepared for use in the undergraduate classroom, the in-service program, and the graduate seminar—that is, for everyone learning to teach mathematics in the elementary school. Although the articles were selected specifically with this group in mind, I would also expect other liberally educated individuals to profit from the topics included.

This book of readings is not intended to include only recent publications; it is generally accepted that much can be gleaned from the past. Therefore, the intent of this book is to place some of the current articles next to those which appeared during an earlier period of elementary school program development. The editor hopes this juxtaposition will generate viable insights among the readers. The authoritative, conveniently arranged articles are intended to inform, encourage, and reveal insights pertaining to working with children and mathematics in today's elementary schools.

This book pays special attention to viable constructs that will allow the preservice and in-service classroom teachers to implement a mathematics program for their children which will be challenging as well as pedagogically sound. The intent is to develop a program that is undergirded by a teacher's understanding of the subject and its place in the curriculum, by insights into how children learn, and by familiarity with the order and nature of experience for effective learning.

A book of readings is a work of prejudice in the sense that the works included have been chosen by one person. This is no less true when the book is about mathematics for elementary school children than when it concerns history or literature. I make no apology for any seeming prejudices indicated by my choice of readings but only for the limitations of space. Many more outstanding references could not be included. It will be obvious to some readers that I have included topics which might have been omitted by other writers. The intent, however, was to include a cross section of references that are representative of the many exciting phases related to teaching mathematics to children attending elementary schools.

In conclusion I wish to reiterate that the object throughout has been to combine what knowledge we have about children, about elementary school mathematics programs, and about learning how to prepare children for the mathematical world. How well this objective has been reached is submitted to those engaged in the most rewarding labor of all—teaching mathematics to elementary school children.

N. J. V.

Contents

Developmental Mathematics

In a most complex world, there are many important questions asked in their simplest form, but very few are answered without revealing the complicated patterns that exist in nature and in man's cognitive facilities. As we continue to examine nature in its awesomeness in an attempt to identify more readily the existing patterns, we grow more dependent upon that form of science which attempts to explain patterns that exist in our environment. Man has used mathematics to explain the obvious as well as those patterns that are not obvious to the uninitiated. Mathematical patterns exist in every form, every object, every idea that nature and man have been able to conceive—some obvious, some not. It is not surprising that a larger segment of the population is not familiar with the vast possibilities that mathematics offers. This in part is explained as never before by the growing complexity of the discipline.

If we were to ask what is mathematics, we might get a vast array of responses, some of which would be most complicated. The liberally educated individuals would most probably list such classifications as pure, applied, and adaptive. However, these classifications might be codified and, adding the dimension of time, would reveal an insight which must be considered and which also offers some direction for the individual interested in mathematics.

Mathematics insights continue to evolve through man's careful and intricate pursuits. The developmental nature of mathematics places its character as an ever-ending exposure of patterns. When viewed in perspective, mathematics no longer exists as a set of immutable statements establishing exact truths. The accomplished mathematician has the benefit of accumulated mathematics insights at his disposal; they are there not in order to make his thinking rigid but to offer the individual full license to develop new patterns from this vast storehouse of information. For the nonmathematician, it is consoling to hear that contemporary great minds are not in agreement on certain mathematical statements. Bertrand Russell's summation that "the subject in which we never know what we are talking about nor whether what we are saying is true" reflects the contemporary view of mathematics to some degree.

Mathematics is a growing, changing "language" that man uses to explain his environment. As the world continues to change in a physical, political, and social nature, so the nature of mathematics will change, allowing man to explain his world as being of a developmental nature.

The Nature of Mathematics

Carl B. Allendoerfer

Before you can make sense of the current recommendations for the reform of mathematics teaching, you must have an understanding of the nature of mathematics. To many of you mathematics probably means ordinary arithmetic with its set rules for computation. Others may remember algebra as a collection of special procedures which, by some sort of magic, can be used to get the answer in the book. And geometry is a mysterious subject full of theorems to memorize and outrageous tricks by means of which we prove the truth of perfectly obvious relationships in nature. It is no wonder that parents ask me, "How can there be anything new in mathematics? Are the old formulas not still true?" So that you can fit your present recollection of mathematics into the whole picture as a mathematician sees it, I shall begin with a description of the nature of our subject. Later we shall discuss the details of its separate branches.

Let me begin by describing the structure of a mathematical theory in a mature form. In other words, let me show you how a piece of mathematics looks when it has been completed and polished and written up (or is it "embalmed"?) in textbooks. As we shall see, this picture is quite different from that of a mathematical theory in the process of development.

I begin our story with "nature," a word which I wish to use in the broadest possible sense (see Fig. 1). Under this heading I shall include all physical and biological aspects of nature as well as human disciplines such as economics, psychology, anthropology, business, and warfare. The scholars in these various fields have initially gone to very great trouble to describe their subjects as best they can in words, and as their scholarship matures they begin

Reprinted with permission of The Macmillan Company from *Mathematics for Parents* by Carl B. Allendoerfer. Copyright © Carl B. Allendoerfer 1965.

to investigate the quantitative aspects of their domains. Then they join with mathematicians to build what is currently called a *mathematical model* of their portion of nature. This model is incomplete in many ways, for first it contains only the quantitative and geometric aspects of nature, and, moreover, like all models it is only an imperfect copy and not the real thing. Extant models differ in their degree of excellence; they are remarkably exact for the physical sciences, but are just emerging in hesitant form in the social sciences. But whatever the value of the model, it is the beginning of a mathematical theory.

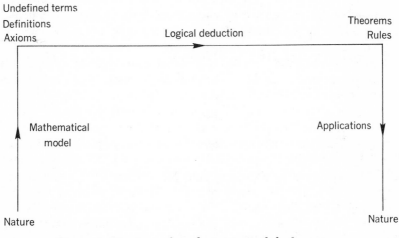

Undefined terms
Definitions
Axioms

Logical deduction

Theorems
Rules

Mathematical model

Applications

Nature

Nature

Figure 1. Structure of mathematics—polished version.

Let us examine the character of such a model. In the first place, it is necessary to settle upon a technical vocabulary to describe the observed phenomena. It is surprising to most nonmathematicians to be told that the basic words in this vocabulary cannot be defined. In order to appreciate this point, consider the plight of an American who tries to read a French text with only the aid of a French language dictionary. He can look up each word, but finds that the definitions are in terms of other French words which have no meaning for him. The case is hopeless unless in some other fashion he learns the meaning of a basic collection of French words. In mathematics we have no way of assigning meanings to this basic collection of technical words, and must leave them undefined. Thus in geometry the words *point, line,* and *plane,* are taken as undefined. I agree that we may well have mental pictures of what these words connote, but this is quite another matter from giving them satisfactory definitions. The rest of the technical vocabulary is built up from these words by the familiar process of definition.

Next we wish to use these words to say something about our observations of nature, and so we form sentences which we believe to be true. Actually sentences such as "Two points determine a straight line" cannot be shown to be true by any form of reasoning, for how can one establish the truth of a sentence containing two words which are not defined? This sentence is in fact an abstraction from the observation that there is a unique straight road between a pair of towns, and thus it is part of our model of nature. Sentences of this kind which describe basic observed facts of nature are called *axioms* and by assumption they are *true*.

Our model, then, consists of a collection of abstractions: undefined words, words defined in terms of these, and statements called axioms which are assumed to be true. The construction of such a model is a creative act of the highest order. In many ways it compares with the landscape of the artist or the novel of the writer, each of whom is expressing in his own way aspects of nature which appear important to him at the time. Let us examine a few models of this kind.

The first illustration of a mathematical model that a child meets is that of the concept of *number*. In his early years he learns to count and is able to understand phrases such as: "three blocks," "three trees," "three boys," and the like. But what does "three" mean all by itself? Primitive tribes have difficulty answering this question, and some of them use different words for "three" when they are counting different kinds of objects. As a matter of fact there is a trace of this in our own language, for we use different words to describe groups of various kinds of animals, such as: *flock* of sheep, *herd* of cattle, *pack* of wolves, or *covey* of quail. There is no need for all these separate names for the idea involved, and you can see the confusion that would result if we extended this practice to our ordinary counting operations.

But what is "three?" It is an abstraction derived from our experience in actual counting. When we abstract the other counting numbers and formulate the rules for computing with these, we have constructed the mathematical model which we call *arithmetic*. The troubles which young children have in arithmetic have their origin in this process of abstraction, for this is the first time the youngsters have met anything abstract. Now that we understand the nature of the difficulties, we can consider what needs to be done to help the children over this hurdle.

Another illustration of a mathematical model is the usual formulation of plane geometry. As you will remember, geometry begins logically with a set of axioms, or postulates, and a set of undefined terms. These are obtained by abstraction from the physical process of measuring parcels of land. A farmer's field has corners, boundaries, and the land area itself. The corners may be marked with posts and the boundaries with fences which are only approximately straight. In our model these posts become points, the fences become lines, and the field itself becomes a plane. Point, line, and plane are our abstractions. Now we look at the field and observe, for instance, that there is a single fence between every pair of corner posts. In our abstraction this becomes the axiom: there is a unique line passing through any pair of distinct points. By this process we build up the model which we use as our foundation of plane geometry.

A further example of the construction of a model is Newton's invention of the calculus. His concern was with an appropriate theory to explain the observed motions of the planets in our solar system. Quantitative measurements and elementary mathematical descriptions of the planetary orbits were at hand, but there was no systematic theory which accounted for them. Newton's first task was to develop an adequate vocabulary which included the definitions of words such as *velocity* and *acceleration*. These definitions are now the basic ideas of the differential calculus. He did not lay a solid foundation of undefined terms and axioms, and these had to be supplied at a later date. Like all model builders, he painted with a broad brush and left the details to be filled in by lesser men. Nevertheless, he did state the most essential axioms, which are currently known as Newton's laws of motion. On this foundation he built his theory of gravity and planetary motion. One of Einstein's great contributions is the construction of a different model for this same portion of nature.

A most exciting development at the present time is the construction of similar models in the social and biological sciences. Although these models are far from ideal, they are bold attempts to put these subjects on a firm mathematical foundation and are the forerunners of great things to come.

Once the model is constructed, the mathematician proceeds to prove theorems. These are statements about his subject which can be deduced logically from his assumed axioms. To say that a mathematical statement is *true* is to mean that this statement is a logical consequence of a set of axioms, and nothing more. The notion of absolute truth is entirely foreign to mathematics in spite of the worship of mathematics by laymen who are seeking something that is unchangeable and eternal. If mathematicians were to apply the method of reasoning of their own subject to their personal philosophy of ethics and values, they would be (and frequently are) pure relativists.

The chain is now closed by the applied mathematician who takes the general theorems so deduced, puts numbers in them, and attempts to discover new relationships in nature. Of course, he can prove nothing about nature in this way. Nevertheless, he can arrive at statements about nature which can probably be verified by observation of nature if his original model is reasonably good. Of course, his objective is to find new facts about nature which had not been previously observed, or better, to predict what would be found if a certain measurement or observation were to be made.

I fear that I have misled you into believing that a mathematical theory is built by following these three steps in order; nothing could be farther from the truth. Mathematicians often perform the magical feat of building the fifth storey without first establishing a foundation or even thinking about the first four stories. We start at both ends and the middle and only after decades of effort bring forth the beautiful, logical, and polished gems which we dangle before our students.

More often we follow a different path. Beginning with nature as before, we seek to find as many relationships within it as we can. If we can systematize these we do so, but a lack of organization of our material does not keep us from pushing forward. On the basis of what we have observed, we *guess* theorems and use these to derive other theorems. Immediately we rush to apply these back again to nature and proceed headlong if our predictions are successful. Axioms, logic, and rigor are thrown to the winds, and we become intoxicated with our success and open to dreadful errors.

This process is called *intuition,* and its nature is in no way understood. Several great mathematicians have written accounts of their experiences in this phase of mathematical discovery, but the psychologists are baffled by their testimony. The successful unraveling of this process should be a major contribution to the understanding of the human mind. But explained or not, it is by this means that the great majority of mathematical theorems are first discovered. One of my teachers in graduate school was good for about one hundred such discoveries a week, with an average of only about one which stood up under careful analysis. Yet those that were correct made him one of the great mathematicians of the past generation

The procedure is then as in Fig. 2. By means of intuition we guess theorems, test them against applications, organize those that survive, find axioms on the basis of which they can be proved and thus build our mathematical model. A little-known trade secret is that in this process theorems come first and axioms second. A good example of this is the re-examination of Euclidean geometry in the past century. It was discovered that many of Euclid's theorems could not be proved from his axioms. Yet we all believed these theorems to be true, and a number of different systems of axioms were developed which had these theorems as their consequences. This process of justifying a belief by trying to find premises from which it can be deduced is shockingly similar to much reasoning in our daily lives, and I am embarrassed to have to let you know that mathematicians are experts at this art.

After the model has been constructed in this way we then prove theorems by deduction and finally seek for applications to nature. There are, then, four key words in the process of constructing a mathematical theory:

> Intuition
> Organization
> Deduction
> Application

We shall see that this same pattern applies to the learning of mathematics, and that any good course in our subject must include all four of these features.

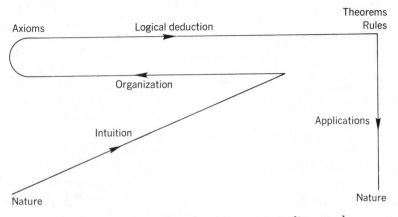

Figure 2. Structure of mathematics—as it is discovered.

This description of mathematics would have seemed reasonably accurate until something more than one hundred years ago, but it omits the most significant development in our subject during the past century. The breakthrough which stimulated this new point of view was the construction of non-Euclidean geometry. One of Euclid's axioms stated that there exists a unique line through a given point which is parallel to a given line which does not pass through this point (Fig. 3). This axiom was never fully accepted by mathematicians on the ground that it did not have the "self-evident" quality of Euclid's other axioms, and many attempts were made to prove it on the basis of the other axioms. Although no such proofs were obtained, everyone believed that this axiom was true, and in fact Euclidean geometry was given the aura of absolute truth commonly associated with the Bible.

In the early part of the nineteenth century attempts were made to prove this axiom by the method of contradiction. In conformity with this method mathematicians assumed that the axiom was false and hoped to deduce conclusions which contradicted at least one of the remaining axioms. In particular the two alternative axioms were investigated: (1) there is no such parallel, and (2) there are at least two such parallels. Although these mathematicians worked diligently and imaginatively, they were frustrated in that they found no such contradictions. It is reported that Gauss was the first to have arrived at this awkward impasse and that he considered the possibility that alternatives to the parallel axiom were logically possible. So great was the authority of Euclid that he felt it unwise to publish his findings. Later others such as Lobachevski and Bolyai came to similar conclusions, and gradually the secret was shared with the community of mathematicians. The astounding conclusion was that there are three equally acceptable geometries which appear to be satisfactory models of nature. Even today there are no compelling reasons for choosing among them.

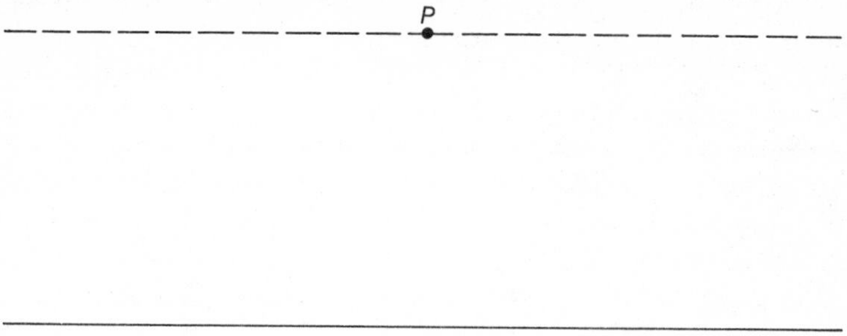

Figure 3. Euclid's parallel axiom.

It required another fifty years for the major impact of this discovery to transform the character of mathematics, but now we are so deeply imbued with the new spirit that young mathematicians cannot understand why anyone ever thought differently. The new philosophy is that abstract systems of undefined words, axioms, etc. (which we previously called mathematical models), need have nothing whatever to do with nature. They are no longer models of anything, but are merely structures built by mathematicians because they are thought to be worth investigating. Since these abstract mathematical systems did not spring from nature, there is no obligation for their advocates to apply the related theorems back to nature, and consequently we have a mathematics which exists purely of and for itself. A large part of contemporary mathematics is of this kind.

You may wonder how one goes about thinking of such an abstract system, and the process is as difficult to describe as are most creative acts. At the initial stages the abstract systems may be called *mutations* of earlier models of nature. For example, geometry has been extended from three dimensions to an arbitrarily large finite number of dimensions, and finally to an infinite number of dimensions. In algebra we are accustomed to assume that $3 \times 4 = 4 \times 3$ and more generally that $a \times b = b \times a$. In one of the newer algebras the rule is that $a \times b = -b \times a$. Abstract spaces are considered in which the notion of distance between two points has been replaced by a much more general concept of *nearness*. And so on. At each step the new abstraction becomes so familiar to the mathematician that he regards it as concrete and makes it serve as the basis for further abstractions. The length of a mathematical generation is about ten years, and each generation regards with dismay the attitude of the following generation, which treats the marvelous abstractions of their predecessors as trivial or narrow.

Another source of abstraction is the unification of two older theories into a single more general one. The two theories may well have sprung from two different mathematical models of nature without any regard for each other. Their combination into a single abstract theory often illuminates each of the parent theories, and always produces a great economy of thought. The growth of mathematical knowledge is so rapid that without such amalgamations no one could find his way through the morass.

Although the appearance of these modern theories suggests that they have no connection at all with nature, I cannot think of a single one which does not owe its existence to a remote mathematical model of nature out of which it has grown by the processes of mutation and generalization. Perhaps the invention of a theory with no remote roots in nature is beyond the powers of the mind, but more probably such a construction will occur before long as the next major breakthrough in the development of mathematics.

Arithmetic in Historical Perspective

Ben A. Sueltz

The contemplation of arithmetic began when primitive man became conscious of differing numbers of things and of differences of size and shape.

Whether we call arithmetic "the science of numbers" or "a study of the quantitative in our experience," the basic structure is the same. But the approach in these two ideas may be very different. It is this difference of "science" versus "experience" that has persisted for several thousand years. The study of prime numbers, of perfect numbers, of arithmetic and geometric progressions, of ways to perform operations such as division and square root, and of arithmetic solutions which are the counterpart of an algebraic equation were characteristics of the arithmetic of the ancient Babylonians, Greeks, and even, to some degree, of the Egyptians. These scholars were not concerned with what we call the "bread and butter" values of the study of arithmetic, but rather were interested in the science of numbers. On the other hand, such peoples as the Phoenicians and some Greeks, Romans, and Egyptians were concerned with calculations applied to surveying, astronomy, measurement, barter, and trade. This, then, was what we call the practical applications of arithmetic.

Throughout history, we find that each of these groups, working from a different challenge, advanced our knowledge of arithmetic. It is easy to see that these two groups still characterize our thinking. The one would teach arithmetic as a science and art which might later be applied to the problems of society, while the other group argues that arithmetic has meaning and

Reprinted from *The National Elementary Principal*, Vol. 39, No. 2 (October 1959), 12–16, by permission of the publisher. Copyright 1959, Department of Elementary School Principals, National Education Association. All rights reserved.

importance only as it is useful to the individual in his daily living. A happy combination of both views is now advocated by our better thinkers in the field.

THE ROLE OF NUMBER SYSTEMS

Consider the following as a fair representation of the way certain ancient groups probably would have written 1959 at a stage in their development of numeration.

$$\text{CD C CD } \downarrow \text{ I X} \qquad \text{Roman}$$

$$X \ulcorner HHH \ulcorner \Delta \ulcorner^{a\imath} IIII \qquad \text{Greek}$$

$$\text{Egyptian}$$

$$\text{Babylonian}$$

Obviously, it would be impossible to perform calculations of multiplication and division in a form corresponding to our modern methods with such number systems. Hence, most of these groups developed some kind of computing frame such as the abacus, or they used other indirect methods such as finger reckoning. No doubt, those who had to compute a great deal learned a number of short cuts such as those now employed by the Japanese in the deft manipulation of the beads on their counting frame. But arithmetic as a science and as an instrument for calculation of commerce could not develop to a high level with the restriction of these cumbersome number systems.

It is worth noting that each of the above systems, except the Babylonian, had some idea of sequence by tens and this probably had its origin in the ten fingers which were commonly used as counters. An examination of old treatises dealing with computation on an abacus or counting frame shows that both ancient and medieval groups made advances within the limits of their number systems and the companion modes of reckoning.

The antecedents of our modern Hindu-Arabic number system were inscribed in a cave on Nana Ghat Hill near Poona, India, at about the third century B.C. While most of the symbols have undergone considerable change, the following are reasonable suggestions of our current notation.

$$- = \mp 6 \, 7 \, ? \qquad \text{``Nana Ghat''}$$

$$I \; \rho \; \varepsilon \; 7 \; V \; 9 \qquad \text{Arabic}$$

$$1 \; 2 \; 4 \; 6 \; 7 \; 9 \qquad \text{Modern}$$

From this it is apparent that we do not use Arabic numerals in this country. At one time, our number system was credited to the Arabs because the prior origin had not been established. The name Hindu-Arabic came from the Hindu origin plus the probable transmission to Europe by Arabs.

The distinguishing characteristic of this system is that each number value, one through nine, has a separate symbol and that these symbols when repeated take different values depending upon their position in relation to other symbols. That is, we have "place value" so that 777 means 7 hundreds, + 7 tens, + 7 ones. The system has no limit. A difficulty arose in the writing of a number such as "two thousand twenty" in which there are no hundreds and no ones. To separate the essential digits several devices were used but finally the zero was adopted and we write the number as 2020.

The invention of the Hindu-Arabic number system with these ten symbols (0, 1, 2, . . . 9) to represent different values and with the principle of place value has been called by scholars the most important invention of the human mind. Certainly, our whole modern structure of mathematics and science would have been impossible without such a system. The sciences and the arts tend to become exact as they are founded upon mathematics and, as Gauss expressed it, "Mathematics is queen of the sciences and arithmetic is the queen of mathematics." The modern electronic computer uses a base of two and, hence, needs only two symbols, 0 and 1. Many experts in the field of arithmetic believe that a full understanding of our number system is most important because this enables one to understand the meaning and nature of operations of arithmetic.

The Hindu-Arabic system, complete with the role of zero, was well understood from A.D. 1000 to 1200, but did not come into common use in Europe for another 500 years. Out of the system all our modern modes of computation have developed. The counting frame has been replaced by paper and pencil and by the electronic computer.

PRINTING LED TO STANDARDIZATION

With the invention of the printing press, interchange of ideas was greatly facilitated and, hence, agreement on symbols finally was established. Robert Record's equality sign (=), the Teutonic plus and minus (+ and −) and the final agreement to use × and ÷ were widely circulated in printed texts. A similar standardization came to weights and measures through commercial interchange and the need for agreement. Many teachers know that *pint* originally meant *small* just as we refer to "pint size," and, of course, the quart is a quarter of a gallon. Many do not understand why the Canadian gallon is different from ours or how the symbol "d" became the sign for penny and for nail size. Much of arithmetic would be enriched if teachers were conversant with the historical development of the subject.

Many older teachers will remember setting down a division exercise as 28) 364 (13. Several hundred years ago the exercise would have appeared:

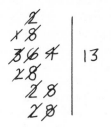

This older "scratch method" is actually easier to perform and with many people more accurate. It probably was dropped because some adults found it less elegant in appearance and to an adult mind probably more difficult to rationalize than our current algorism. For the past three hundred years, the operations of arithmetic have become more refined and more suited to adult business needs.

Printing has become a high art and modern textbooks in many languages are widely circulated. In colonial America, one might find an arithmetic that was a verbatim copy of an English book. Now one finds less apparent similarity but basically the signs, symbols, and operations are the same. Thus, arithmetic has been standardized with the great aid of the printing press.

The limitations of printing also had an effect on the development of arithmetic. For example, the Roman *thousand* was represented by M, the initial letter for milia (1000), but on many Roman inscriptions this appears as C|Ɔ and 500 might appear as either C| or |Ɔ . The letter D is close to the latter form of 500 and hence was adopted in printing. Likewise, the Roman 50 appears as ⅃ or ⊥ or ∟ and the capital L comes close to the third form.

"Scratch" multiplication and division are not easy to set in type and to explain in a text and that may be one reason for dropping it in favor of a method in which many steps are mental and the written record is more attractive and easier to set in type. Actually many current methods of operation with numbers are more difficult than their earlier counterparts but that issue will not be argued here. Suffice it to say that change is slow and that each of us tends to hold dear a method that he learned as a child.

ARITHMETIC AS A SCHOOL SUBJECT

Arithmetic is taught in elementary schools throughout the world. Not only is it useful to the individual in his pursuit of a livelihood and his cultural happiness, but also it is the common language of trade. All peoples that use the Hindu-Arabic number system immediately recognize that $6 \times 7 = 42$. Reading, writing, and arithmetic have long served as the common core of elementary education. In 1636, the Dutch who settled New Amsterdam, now New York, gave this instruction to their colonial schoolmasters: "He is to instruct the youth—in reading, writing, cyphering, and arithmetic." The New England schools taught arithmetic, and the colleges required it for entrance as early as 1745.

Textbooks in the early nineteenth century show clearly that the authors were aware of the social and commercial life about them. However, many of the exercises and problems were unreal and fanciful but were useful in the development and practice of principles. For example, no one would actually want to know how many cucumbers each 5½ inches long would be needed to make a mile of cucumbers but the principle is very important. At this time, teachers and writers were not yet disturbed by the principles of psychology which were formulated a century later.

For the past century, the argument between arithmetic as a science of numbers and arithmetic as a tool in trade has shifted from one position to another with the "reformers" persistently demanding that no principle or process be developed unless it has a direct usefulness in society and the extremists saying that such a use must be immediate and at the age-level of the pupil. Our schools would be sad indeed if such an argument were applied to all areas of instruction. Fortunately, out of the shifting discussions a middle-road position usually results and another generation of pupils is spared the deficiencies that would result from well intentioned but often poorly informed reformers.

During most of the nineteenth century, arithmetic occupied at least 25 percent of the total school time. In 1928, this had been reduced to 11.6 percent as shown in a study of how schools use their time by Carlton H. Mann. In a study published in *The Arithmetic Teacher*, November 1958, G. H. Miller presents this data:

Time Allotment for Arithmetic

Grade	Median Minutes per Day	
	Large Cities	Small Cities
1	23	30
2	32	35
3	40	42
4	45	47
5	45	47
6	45	47

Of course, the time allotment is not as important as what is done during this time. Schools generally set aside a separate period for learning arithmetic because they realize that here is a body of related and sequential materials that requires study and practice and that this cannot be achieved by casual and incidental experience. Arithmetic is not now regarded as merely a tool subject to be learned and kept in a pocket for ready reference when some mathematical situation is encountered.

It is interesting to note the trends in textbook authorship for the past two centuries. Earlier books were written by scholars who made a study of the processes of arithmetic. In our Colonial era, most books were written by physicians and clerics. Later, mathematicians prepared texts. Then school teachers, state school officers, and administrators became popular as authors. More recently, teacher-scholars have tended to serve as leading authors with the assistance of elementary school teachers at the various grade levels.

APPROACHING THE MODERN ERA

Educational philosophy and educational psychology, whether directly expressed or implied, have had an influence on the content, the method, and the placement of arithmetic. It is never possible to note a sharp demarcation between one era and the next because school practice varies considerably and one section of the country may be honoring methods and materials that have already been discarded in another. However, it is worthwhile showing trends and developments during the past century.

During the period 1850 to 1890, educational thinking was dominated by a "faculty psychology" which extolled "training the mind" in such aspects as memory and reasoning. It was generally considered that one who learned to reason in arithmetic would be a good reasoner in other areas. One textbook served grades one through eight. These books did not break a process into sub-parts. Long division was presented as a whole unit operation. Exercises were not restricted to simple easy numbers and problems which may have had a close bearing on the contemporary scene were frequently unreal. This was the era of the cistern problem: If pipe A can fill a cistern in 3 hours and pipe B can fill it in 5 hours and if pipe C will drain the cistern in 6 hours, how long will it take to fill the cistern if all three pipes are operating to capacity?

In the late nineteen hundreds, educational psychology became important to school people and by 1920 principles of learning were established. Such terms as motivation, readiness, exercise, effect, threshold of learning, and overlearning entered into discussion. Two or three textbooks for the first eight grades became standard, drill exercises were greatly multiplied, and the more fanciful problems were dropped. Processes were developed in steps but the stage of minute step mastery came later.

In the interim, roughly 1920 to 1935, the psychology of "readiness-exercise-effect" was supreme and educational practice featured drill. Processes were analyzed into many subskills to be memorized, several researchers found the relative difficulty of subskills such as addition combinations, and then textbook writers used these studies to provide practice exercises in quantity to match the difficulty of the skills. "Transfer" was denied. To accommodate the necessary drill, one book was provided for each grade. Long division could be learned if the thirteen substeps were mastered. Column addition required 1090 skills. Teachers drilled and drilled their pupils and still they couldn't remember arithmetic. Learning was mechanical memorization and forgetting was rapid. Understanding was not a prime goal of the arithmetic of the period. The psychologists and researchers of the era did much to lower the esteem of thoughtful teachers for psychology and research. Many schools found it necessary to use workbooks to supplement the textbooks.

In the 1930 period, one heard of "progressive education" and psychology was replaced by child development. The terminology of the period included "satisfyingness," "peer group," and "educate the whole child." In arithmetic, the concept of social utility was revered. What arithmetic do children and adults actually use? Why teach something that no one will normally encounter? There were researches which showed that no one ever used a decimal fraction of more than three figures and that common fractions of halves, fourths, and eighths were about the only ones necessary to learn. During this period, a committee published many articles showing the mental age necessary to learn a process such as division. Thoughtful people at that time made such remarks as "the halt leading the blind," and "you can't hit it if you can't see it." The dominant method of learning was still drill and memorization and forgetting was a concern. But during this period, a few people began to insist that pupils should understand what they were learning and should see the sense of it and of its usefulness in society.

Topics such as fractions were spread over a range of several school years with the easier concepts and operations coming early and the mastery stage of more difficult computations delayed one or two years beyond former practice. In general, the mastery stage was reached from one half to one year later than in the early 1920's.

The child development concept persists to the present time. Promotions are made annually. Grade five has come to mean the year after grade four. Each grade has a very wide range of ability and achievement. The "happiness" and "avoid frustrations" cults are in the descendency.

In the 1950 period, "action research" has been replacing "scientific research." It is hoped that the future will yield a research that can be genuinely useful to schools in organizing learning and in the selection of method. Certainly, researchers are more cognizant of the variables and know a little more about the human mind and how it functions. Arithmetic books still continue one book per grade. They are attractive, the mathematical developments are well presented, and the concept of subskills is placed in better perspective. Textbooks claim to feature meaning and understanding and the accompanying teachers' manuals often suggest doing things that cannot be done in a textbook. More recently, writers have been using the term "discovery" to indicate a pupil's active role in learning. Instead of mere excellence in computation and problem-solving, pupils are expected to think, to see relationships and patterns, and to discover. From such a procedure should come the beginnings of mathematical insight.

More and more, teachers realize that a textbook is not the best tool for learning all arithmetic. They are using multisensory approaches where such enhance learning. They are looking at the norms of standardized tests more intelligently. There is a tendency toward flexible grouping of pupils within a grade and the adjustment of goals in terms of the abilities of the pupils.

In recent years, the Russian *sputnik* has had an awakening effect upon school people. The public has been asking questions. Schools have been wondering if they are doing as well as they could and should be doing. Mathematicians are becoming concerned about arithmetic in the elementary school. Teachers are seeking more background knowledge. National and state sponsored institutes provide opportunities hitherto unknown. Arithmetic has become important again. In fact, our national welfare depends upon it.

Let us hope that schools will not revert to the mistakes of a generation ago. Now is the time for "quality control" in education but this must be a control that looks not for uniformity or standardization but rather at the honest abilities and needs of the several levels in our society.

THE TEACHER OF ARITHMETIC

At the beginning of the twentieth century, many elementary school teachers had no training beyond the elementary school. A few had finished high school and had a course or two in "didactics" and school management. Later, the one-year programs in normal schools were extended to two and three years. Now it is gratifying to note that most states are requiring four years of college training for elementary school teachers. It is disheartening to note that many states require no substantial amount of work in arithmetic or mathematics for these teachers. The doctrine of a generation ago which held that one could teach (almost anything) if he had 18 semester hours of work in education still dominates some areas. It is not uncommon to find teachers who cannot explain why the divisor is inverted in the division of fractions, or who have never been sufficiently curious about "lb." as the abbreviation for pound to look for it in the dictionary.

Textbooks, courses of study, beautiful school buildings, and a wealth of school supplies are important, but all of these together cannot equal the worth of a good teacher. In a real sense, he is the better textbook, the better course of study, and the better resource. The role of the teacher is so important that he should have a wealth and depth of background in the areas he teaches. This should be possible in a four- or five-year program of education. Probably more significant than the mere possession of a wealth of background is a quality of mind that is curious and seeks to experiment and to learn.

Arithmetic will advance as teachers develop an insight into the subject matter and its significance and as they learn more and more about the boys and girls they teach and how the human minds, bodies, and emotions combine in the behavioral learning situation.

A New Look at the Old Mathematics

Veryl Schult

When you were in the fourth grade and the teacher showed you how to do long multiplication, did you wonder why each partial product had to be "moved over" one place? And did you wonder why, when there was a zero in the multiplier, the partial product "moved over" two places?

I did. In fact, I wondered why, for variety, the partial product didn't "move over" to the right occasionally. It wasn't until years later in an algebra class, while studying so-called digit problems, that I learned what "moving over" was all about.

Today, children do not have to wait until they study algebra to learn why they "move over," "bring down," "carry," and "borrow." Indeed, because the processes are understood instead of parroted, such expressions are no longer necessary. Multiplication is taught without mysteries, and pupils know the reason for each step. For instance:

The *learning* way		The *final* way
323		323
× 132	(2 + 30 + 100)	× 132
646	(2 × 323)	646
9,690	(30 × 323)	969
32,300	(100 × 323)	323
42,636		42,636

Although you may think the "final" way is the same as the old way you learned multiplication, the difference is that now pupils understand the process. As a result, they can remember it better, and even the slower students are getting a better grounding in mathematics.

Reprinted from *NEA Journal*, Vol. 54, No. 4 (April 1964), 12–15, by permission of the author and the National Education Association.

Recently, I visited an algebra class in which the teacher was preparing the class for division of polynomials by explaining the meaning behind long division in arithmetic. Her explanation involved no vague "zero difficulties," no "bringing down." For instance, in dividing 2,639 by 13, she said, the question is how many 13's can be subtracted from 2,639. First, she subtracted 200 of them, thus leaving the number 39. Next, she subtracted three 13's from 39, so there are 203 thirteens in the number 2,639.

$$
\begin{array}{r}
3 \\
200 \\
13\overline{)2,639} \\
2,600 \\
\hline
39 \\
39 \\
\hline
\end{array}
$$

The boy sitting next to me turned and, in an indignant tone, said, "Why didn't they tell us this before?"

What is happening to school mathematics that is exciting youngsters, challenging their teachers—and baffling their parents?

Many people are not aware of the fact that mathematics is an active, growing subject. Probably more new mathematics has been developed since 1900 than in all of history up to this century. This new mathematics has made possible many of the wonders of the space age.

Because mathematics is finding uses in more and more fields, the kinds of mathematics being used necessarily change. For instance, suppose a missile is being launched. Can you picture mathematicians with paper and pencil using logarithms, which was the fast method of computing a century ago, to make the computations using the data being sent back from the missile concerning its movements each fraction of a second during the few critical minutes that it is rising from the launching pad? Such a procedure would be unthinkable. In directing the path of a missile, mathematicians use automatic computers which can do the necessary computations in mere millionths of a second.

The use of electronic computers has greatly influenced present-day living. They are being used to handle data of all kinds, to control machinery, to aid in research, to translate languages, to compose music, and even to design new computers. They are affecting the jobs of countless workers in many fields.

Recently, a mother who worked in an office using a UNIVAC computer took a day of her precious annual leave to visit her daughter's seventh grade class where the youngsters were studying the binary system of numeration. The mother said that she knew her work would be more interesting if she understood the mathematical principles on which the UNIVAC computer is based.

Nothing is wrong with traditional mathematics, however. Old theorems are still valid, but many have become obsolete as new and more useful ones have taken their place. The question is not whether a thing is new or old, but whether it does the job properly.

The ability to do computations accurately is still an important objective in teaching mathematics. Nonetheless, an understanding of the rationale of computation cuts down on much of the time that used to be spent on reteaching. This stress on understanding is one important way in which the new mathematics differs from the old.

In what other ways do the new curriculums differ from the old ones?

The change in terminology from "arithmetic" to "elementary school mathematics" is one important indication of what is taking place. Research is showing that students at all grade levels can learn with enjoyment more real mathematics than used to be taught. Just as arithmetic used to be a college subject before it moved down into the elementary school, so a good many of the fundamental principles and concepts of mathematics which used to be met for the first time in college or high school are now making the early years of mathematics instruction more meaningful.

The former practice of teaching many separate facts and processes is giving way to teaching the unifying mathematical ideas which youngsters meet from year to year and greet as old friends. For instance, the fundamental mathematical idea of *grouping* is the same in all of the following problems.

$$
\begin{array}{cccc}
22 & 2\frac{1}{2} & 5.6 & 2 \text{ ft. } 1 \text{ in.} \\
-9 & -\frac{3}{4} & -.8 & -6 \text{ in.} \\
\hline
13 & 1\frac{3}{4} & 4.8 & 1 \text{ ft. } 7 \text{ in.} \\
\end{array}
$$

(One teacher has commented that the choice is between *grouping* and *groping*.)

The solution to these problems depends on a most important fact which is stressed in the new programs: *Any number may be expressed by countless different numerals.* For example, the number 22 might be expressed as **XXII** or $4\frac{4}{2}$ or $20 + 2$ or $10 + 12$. The last expression is the most convenient way of thinking about 22 in order to do the problem $22 - 9$.

$$
\begin{array}{rl}
22 = & 10 + 12 \\
-9 = & -9 \\
\hline
13 = & 10 + 3 \\
\end{array}
$$

Another characteristic of the new mathematics is its more precise vocabulary. Distinction is made between a number (which is an *idea*) and a numeral (which is a written *symbol* for an idea). For instance, in the problem $5 - \frac{1}{4}$, children now think of 5 as $4 + \frac{4}{4}$, and thus it is easy for them to subtract $\frac{1}{4}$ and get $4 + \frac{3}{4}$. This last numeral used to be written as $4\frac{3}{4}$, but it is more meaningful if the plus sign is retained, as it is in several of the new textbooks.

(The need for acquiring a better vocabulary in geometry is also apparent from the following story. A teacher who was riding on a bus from Washington, D.C., to Virginia was passing the Pentagon Building when she heard a gentleman in the seat behind her comment on the seemingly odd name of the building. His companion remarked that he thought it was named after some famous general!)

The concept of sets is a fundamental idea in mathematics that is being emphasized in the new courses. When children learn to count, they make a one-to-one correspondence between the elements of a set of objects to be counted and the set of counting numbers, starting with one:

★	★	★	★	★	(a set of stars to be counted)
↕	↕	↕	↕	↕	
1	2	3	4	5	(the set of counting numbers)

Pupils soon learn that other sets of numbers are necessary, such as fractions when parts of things are needed, or negative numbers when numbers "below zero" are needed. Therefore, the number line is being widely used in illustrating numbers:

$$\overset{\longleftarrow}{\underset{-4 \quad -3 \quad -2 \quad -1 \quad 0 \quad +1 \quad +2 \quad +3 \quad +4}{\rule{0pt}{0pt}}}\overset{\longrightarrow}{\rule{0pt}{0pt}}$$

Pupils can see that a number line goes on and on in both directions, that some numbers are to the right of zero, some to the left. They can also see that fractions are needed to identify many points on the number line between those shown above. Later they learn that no matter what fraction they may choose, there are many points on the number line such as $\sqrt{2}$ and $\sqrt{5}$ which cannot be expressed as common fractions.

Most of the new courses include a study of the operations with numbers and the general principles which apply in the use of them. One of these principles is the commutative principle which states that the order in which factors are combined does not change the product. That is, $4 \times 6 = 6 \times 4$. When this principle is learned, the traditional 100 multiplication facts are practically cut in half.

Equations and inequalities are also appearing early in the grades—in fact as early as relationships on the number line are observed. Equations are especially useful devices in helping pupils solve problems.

Because many more things in this world are unequal than equal, symbols that express inequalities are useful. Thus, "5 is greater than 3" becomes "$5 > 3$"; "8 is less than 20" becomes "$8 < 20$". These symbols are used throughout mathematics. In fact, one of the most important features of the new mathematics programs is that correct ideas are established from the beginning and *un*learning is not necessary.

Pupils are also enjoying an early introduction to elementary number theory and are speculating about interesting number facts. For example, why are 3, 6, 10 . . . called "triangular numbers"?

Is the sum of two even numbers always an even number? Yes. Is the sum of two odd numbers ever an odd number? No. Why?

Another topic which appears in most modern programs is a study of systems of numeration other than our base-ten system. In our most familiar system 13 means $10 + 3$ because we have agreed to use ten as a base.

However, there is nothing sacred about ten (although a child once asked if we use ten for a base because of the Ten Commandments). We could use any base, just so we have as many digits as the base. Because we agree to use ten as a base, a number such as 324 means $3(10 \times 10) + 2(10) + 4$. But if we used five as a base, 324 would mean $3(5 \times 5) + 2(5) + 4$.

In designing modern computers, the binary system using base-two is the most convenient because it consists of only two digits, zero and one, which can easily be expressed by a machine. For instance, if computations are expressed on a machine tape, a punched hole means one and a blank space means zero.

Two reasons for teaching other systems of numeration are (1) to help pupils distinguish between the number idea and the way it is expressed on paper, and (2) to help them understand better their own system with its place value based on tens. The difficulty of teaching the idea of place value was brought home to a seventh grade teacher, who asked one young boy why in Roman times ||| meant three whereas today it means one hundred eleven. The boy paused a moment, then replied philosophically, "Well, times have changed."

Times *have* changed, and with them teaching methods. More and more teachers are doing what the best teachers used to do—encouraging children to think, to discover relationships, and to understand rather than memorize. As some psychologists have pointed out, learning is thinking, and the new mathematics courses reflect this concept.

Standardized tests are also reflecting this emphasis on thinking. It takes thinking rather than computation to answer a question such as, "Which is the largest: $\frac{1}{4}$, $\frac{1}{10}$, $\frac{1}{3}$, $\frac{1}{9}$, $\frac{1}{5}$?" (The story is told about a certain congregation which was urged to tithe to the church, but if the members couldn't afford a tenth of their income, then a ninth, an eighth, or even a fourth would do!)

Teachers as well as children are discovering that mathematics is not a bag of tricks but an exciting system of knowledge, full of interesting facts, ideas, and patterns. Indeed, someone has described modern mathematics as a search for patterns.

In one class, after the children had discovered many interesting and exciting patterns in the multiplication table, the teacher wrote the following facts on the chalkboard:

$$8 = 3 + 5 \qquad 14 = 3 + 11 \qquad 28 = 5 + 23$$
$$10 = 3 + 7 \qquad 16 = 3 + 13 \qquad 56 = 3 + 53$$
$$12 = 5 + 7 \qquad 18 = 5 + 13 \qquad 90 = 17 + 73$$

When the pupils were asked if they observed anything interesting about these statements, they pointed out that each number on the left was an even number and that each one seemed to be the sum of two prime numbers (numbers which are divisible only by themselves and by one).

"Do you suppose," said the teacher, "that *any* even number can be expressed as the sum of two primes?" The pupils set to work eagerly looking for an exception (and getting much practice in addition). On they went: $20 = 3 + 17$; $22 = 3 + 19$; $24 = 7 + 17$ . . . $32 = 3 + 29$. Then to larger numbers: $120 = 59 + 61$ . . . $186 = 89 + 97$. They could find no exception.

The teacher told them that the mathematician Goldbach many years ago made the same conjecture about every even number being expressible as the sum of two primes and that mathematicians to this day have not been able to prove whether it is true or false. She told them that most mathematical facts are at first conjectures; later, either an exception is found or an attempt is made to prove that they are always true. Then the teacher said, "Maybe one of you will prove Goldbach's conjecture some day!" She said of fifty famous unsolved problems listed by mathematicians in 1900, forty-seven have now been solved.

The changes in mathematics curriculums are not the result of some experimenters' whims but represent a sincere and thoughtful effort to prepare today's students for the demands that will be made of tomorrow's workers and citizens.

In the new mathematics programs, teachers and students are making exciting discoveries together, so much so that teachers report a new desire among many students to read and work ahead on their own. Can a teacher give a student any greater gift than the stimulation to pursue worthwhile intellectual activity?

Today's Mathematics—and You

Herbert F. Spitzer

The "new mathematics," a term that will be used here to refer to the many new and often radically different proposals for teaching arithmetic (mathematics), and the extensive criticisms of old content and methods made by some advocates of the new, are causing some good teachers to become doubtful of their ability to teach arithmetic. For good teachers to lose confidence in their ability to instruct is not only undesirable for teacher morale but is almost certain to impair their instructional efficiency.

While admitting that the new thinking about mathematics (perhaps "intense recent interest" would be more appropriate) has created some problems for the elementary school teacher, it is the opinion of the writer that the benefits from the new will far outweigh the difficulties created.

Proper consideration of the topic questions requires a look at some of the major characteristics of the situation. To facilitate the presentation of these selected characteristics, numbers are used.

1. The current interest in mathematics teaching is very extensive and deep-rooted, and therefore not likely to be another of the flash-in-the-pan type of reforms to which teaching often seems to be addicted. The significance of this interest is in part shown by the large sums of money invested in the various new projects by foundations, research organizations and our federal government, and although the money and publicity involved are unmeasurable influences, the number of mathematicians involved in the projects to improve mathematics teaching is truly impressive. Never before in history has the subject of mathematics in the elementary school received so much help and attention. The results should be beneficial.

2. It seems to be a characteristic of all new movements in educational procedure for the proponents of the new to assume extreme positions, to claim much more for their proposals than evidence warrants and to denounce older procedures as inferior. The new movement in mathematics education has many of these characteristics. An illustration is the ascribing of the mathematical deficiencies of some students of today to the old system of teaching, but failing to credit the old system for the many mathematically proficient students (including most of the advocates of the new), who obviously got their start under the old system. The extravagant claims by advocates of the new are a normal phenomenon and warrant only extra careful consideration of new proposals—not blanket rejection of them.

3. The new mathematics as described by most of its proponents has as its primary aim the development of mathematicians or, as often stated, of stu-

Reprinted from *Grade Teacher* (April 1962), 49, 90, 92, by permission of the author.

dents who think mathematically and not just computationally (as old ways of teaching seem, by implication, to have done). All students of education should recognize that such an aim is at variance with the facts as far as the curriculum for elementary schools is concerned. Arithmetic would be taught even if no other mathematics were to be studied. This is true, first, because arithmetic gives to the person who masters it immediately recognizable intellectual power and, second, it gives to pupils a skill of recognized value. Arithmetic is not, then, in the curriculum solely to aid in producing mathematicians. Fortunately, as the writer sees it, there need be no conflict between the aims as seen by traditional students of arithmetic and the aim to produce mathematicians.

4. There are many prophets of the new whose viewpoints differ markedly. For example, some advocates of the new emphasize discovery, with the variety of suggestions and procedures that accompany such. These advocates minimize showing and telling. Other advocates of the new use a very narrow or one-way approach with practically every step explained. In this plan there is then much showing and telling, and a minimum of discovery. Some other advocates of the new make use of set terminology as low as first grade, while still others do not even mention set language. This divergence of views regarding the new mathematics is a fairly clear indication that *the one and only way* to teach mathematics in the elementary school has not yet been found and that the adoption of any one plan and the rejection of all others, including the old, may not then be wise.

5. That the current interest in mathematics teaching, of which the "new mathematics" is a part, has already resulted in the introduction of some marked changes in arithmetic teaching is a fact which all teachers should recognize. Other changes will undoubtedly be introduced in the near future. Three of what the writer considers examples of highly beneficial changes are listed below.

a. There has been a reversal of the trend to upgrade arithmetic topics. As a result, some new pupil textbooks now include ideas and procedures that would have been considered too difficult ten years ago.

b. The field of mathematics, and not social usage alone, is becoming the major source of arithmetical content, with the result that pupils now have an opportunity to study content that was considered inappropriate a few years ago.

c. Questions and assignments which require and promote original thinking about arithmetical facts and operations by the learners are being included in arithmetic instruction. Where such procedures are used, study of arithmetic becomes as challenging, as interesting and as satisfying as does the study of such other subjects as science or history.

The five factors of the current scene in elementary-school mathematics teaching listed above provide the basis for one answer to the question,

"Where do you, the modern teacher, relate to this new thinking about mathematics?" The intense current interest in mathematics, the claims for the new and the criticisms of the old, the narrow, almost erroneous, notion of the role of arithmetic in the curriculum held by most advocates of the new, the fact that there are many prophets of the new, and the fact that some marked changes in content and teaching have already been introduced, warrant that if you, the modern teacher of arithmetic, are to continue to deserve that title, you must become acquainted with and begin to participate in the tryout and refinement of the new.

That your help is needed in the tryout and refinement of the new becomes very evident upon examination of some of the instructional materials prepared by or under the direction of the mathematicians. Most of these people are almost as naive and uninformed about classroom teaching of children as you are about mathematics. Then, before the new materials can assume the role in instruction they seem to warrant, much refinement, in which teachers by the nature of their work can contribute, is in order.

You are then to continue to be a student of the content and method of teaching. The only changes from what you have been doing to keep professionally up to date will be in the specific attention that you give to the mathematical aspects of the subject.

The preceding discussion relative to teacher study of new and old has indicated a partial answer to the question, "How do you determine where we are going?" Further careful consideration of this question in light of some of the facts presented indicates possible principles for determining where we are going. Since it is true that the "old arithmetic" has been and is effective in giving intellectual power and utilitarian tools, it does not seem wise, until the new content and teaching methods have been proven to be superior, to abandon completely those of the old. A first guide principle then is to recognize that much of the content and perhaps some of the methodology of the old will be used in the arithmetic that you will teach in the years ahead. The so-called "new" mathematics will then be looked upon first as a modification of and an addition to our current program.

The question, "Does this concept or procedure give my pupils any immediately recognizable knowledge or skill of value?" may also be a guide. This applies to both old and new arithmetic and will do much to prevent the introduction of material that might well be postponed until needed in later study of mathematics.

Another question, "Does the procedure used make for mastery of basic facts and procedures at a level that is satisfactory for further exploration and discovery in the subject?" might serve as a guide in charting the course of elementary mathematics. This question indicates the importance of a high level of computational competence to understanding the major features of mathematics.

The most practical answer to the question, "How do you get under way in the right direction?" is "Try out some of the new procedures in your classroom." If a plan for tryout and study of new materials is followed, the modern teacher will have little difficulty in keeping abreast of the times. Such a plan will at the same time give pupils an opportunity to get acquainted with some of the procedures and content of the new mathematics.

2

Teaching Elementary School Mathematics

During the past decade, we have witnessed a number of revolutions. Perhaps among the most important revolutions was the one called "modern mathematics." This revolution in mathematics education was and continues to warrant attention in order to understand its impact and potential. We have yet to see the wide application of the modern mathematics programs, and it is here that its revolutionary impact and possibilities are greatest. New insights about learning, a restructure of the discipline, new techniques for directing learning, and many other considerations are all having their impact on the children who are attending the elementary schools of today. There is evidence to suggest that these and other considerations which are soon to evolve will serve to unify the mathematical and pedagogical ideas which undergird the contemporary mathematical programs found in our elementary schools.

The considerations which raise important issues and which guide the direction of curriculum development in the elementary schools are the following: a distinction between education and training, the nature of children, the goals of elementary education, the objectives of a modern elementary mathematics program, and how children learn mathematical concepts as well as other distinctive issues that revolve around organizational features.

How are these considerations interwoven as a teacher goes about developing daily programs? In what ways are the assertions presented in this section compatible with knowledge about children, mathematics, and learning theory? Utilizing the insights presented here, how would you go about developing a mathematics program for the elementary school that is unlike contemporary programs? What other considerations are necessary for building a mathematics program for contemporary elementary school children? What precautions are necessary in developing changes for elementary-school mathematics programs? What characteristics are common to the development of programs for elementary school children? Can you expect continued changes? Why will elementary school mathematics programs continue to change?

Modern Goals of Elementary Education

John F. Travers

Today, as never before, society is making demands of the elementary school that tax its utmost capacity. Education at this level is expected to form products that are intellectually capable, socially acceptable, physically strong, emotionally stable, morally aware of the difference between good and evil, vocationally efficient, prepared for worthy home membership. Such a list could be extended through numerous other categories.

In addition to educating for the above, experimentation continues. At what grade level should foreign language study be initiated? How much more science and math can be included in the elementary curriculum? What are the possibilities of expanding guidance services at the elementary level?

These are but a few of the many questions to be answered by our educational leaders. In order to clarify these issues there must be a frame of reference to which they may be referred. This frame of reference should take the form of fixed and determined goals that are comprehended and realized as attainable by all in the school system.

With this in mind, the Educational Policies Commission in 1948 identified three major goals for the elementary school:

1. A good elementary school seeks to develop basic skills and adequate independence and initiative to enable our citizens to attack the problems that face them and to press forward ever-improving solutions.
2. A good elementary school strives for the discovery and full development of all the humane and constructive talents of each individual.
3. A good elementary school emphasizes social responsibility and the cooperative skills necessary for the progressive improvement of social institutions.

GOALS TOO VAGUE

Goals such as the above are admirable and worthwhile; they serve as a starting point in any identification of objectives. But, they must be clarified

Reprinted from *Education* (Indianapolis: The Bobbs-Merrill Company, January 1966), 263–267, by permission of the publisher.

and stated in more precise language for a particular school system. From beginnings such as these three goals, the individual school system and the writers in the field of elementary education may spell out in detail particular objectives for the elementary school to attain.

One of the outstanding spokesmen for elementary education today, Henry Otto, in detailing major objectives and subdivisions, writes:

Among the objectives of self-realization one finds such items as these: "the educated person can speak the mother tongue clearly"; "the educated person reads and writes the mother tongue effectively"; and "the educated person appreciates beauty." All of these are items of school concern from kindergarten or primary grades through high school (1).

This brief quotation illustrates what is meant by drawing specific, concrete objectives from general goals. It is not enough for the individual school system, or the textbook writer in the elementary area, to accept and repeat generalities. Each generality must be tailored to a particular situation in order to acquire meaningfulness. Otherwise, it becomes a meaningless fact.

Perhaps the chief cause of uncertainty in the expression of aims is that the attempts to outline specific objectives have originated mainly within the twentieth century. These objectives have been projected in an effort to satisfy educational needs in our modern, complex society.

In establishing desirable goals we need to select a comprehensive definition of education and delineate the major areas of a pupil's personality. So, we may define education in terms of the harmonious development of all the powers and capacities of the individual. If we interpret these powers and capacities to mean the social, moral, physical, emotional, and intellectual forms of development, we have a starting point for forming objectives.

In molding educational objectives it may be well to follow the suggestions of Ralph Tyler. In his excellent syllabus, *Basic Principles of Curriculum and Instruction* (2), he points out that, in the final analysis, objectives are a matter of choice. Therefore, he outlines a mechanical procedure by which objectives may be formulated according to any philosophy of education, and regardless of any theory of learning.

This procedure involves obtaining inferences concerning society in general, and also, the particular city or town for which objectives are being developed; obtaining inferences concerning life in its general and specific aspects (it is here that the general goals of education mentioned earlier are applied and used as a basis); and inferences concerning the subjects to be taught. These are then passed through a "screen" reflecting the particular philosophy of education and psychology of learning practiced by the school system. This gives us the objectives desired by the schools.

The utilization of a rationale such as Tyler's is certainly recommended, but a key factor in this procedure is the proper fashioning of the general goals of education. This brings us to the manner of shaping these far-reaching aims in a more precise and determined style.

THE GENERAL GOALS OF EDUCATION

For the purposes of this paper, it may be stated that the over-all purpose of the elementary school is the wholesome, well-rounded growth and development of the child, in all phases of his personality. These phases of personality are social, moral, physical, emotional, and intellectual. Thus, the elementary school is devoted to the development of each of these phases.

The statement of these goals is ideal from a theoretical standpoint, but we may ask how may they be expressed and applied in the classroom? What do they mean to the teacher? Do they differ at the different levels of education?

The goals do *not* differ at different levels; nor is their meaning substantially altered for the teacher at different levels. Rather, what does differ is the curriculum, the methods, and the organization.

Growth in the five aforementioned areas becomes the goal of the elementary school, but this growth must be accomplished according to the particular, unique function of the elementary school. Let us now turn to a discussion of how these areas of development may be attained in the classroom.

SOCIAL GROWTH

The child's social growth must be carefully nurtured in order that the individual become capable of mingling with the group, or other individuals, on a normal, acceptable basis. He must develop attitudes of respect for authority, courtesy, politeness, civic responsibility, tolerance, etc. These attitudes will prepare him to mix with all types of persons with no feelings of uneasiness or anxiety, and make possible a better adjustment in all phases of personality.

It is in this area that the function of the elementary school teacher assumes maximum importance, because of the delinquencies and complexity of our society. The child at the elementary school level is extremely impressionable and imitative, and the attitudes and ideals of the teacher are often adopted by the child as his own. A youngster may often learn in spite of a teacher, but seldom does he acquire proper social attitudes and ideals unless they are presented to him in the form of good example.

Our teacher colleges and schools of education can well afford to spend more time and energy in research concerning the most effective way of inculcating desirable attitudes and ideals in order that their future teachers might bring such practices into the public schools.

PHYSICAL GROWTH

The physical growth of the elementary school child is tremendous, and there must be an outlet for this great source of energy and vitality. This outlet of energy should occur through proper games and exercises conducted on a regularly prescribed routine and of such a nature, that they carry over into extracurricular activities.

The widespread acceptance of the familiar quotation, "a sound mind in a sound body," implies that any neglect of bodily health may affect mental health and, as a result, lessen intellectual efficiency and social competence. Malnutrition and poor personal hygiene have an adverse effect on the pupil's physical development that extends into the area of general education and emphasizes that physical education has values quite apart from health.

The American Association of School Administrators has summed up the importance of this phase of education as follows:

Health teaching in the elementary school will center around the formation and extension of desirable practices, attitudes, and understandings associated with (a) nutrition and growth, (b) relaxation, rest, and sleep, (c) activity, (d) fresh air and sunshine, (e) elimination, (f) cleanliness, and care of teeth, body, and clothing, (g) importance and means of securing medical and dental attention, (h) control of infection, (i) care of eyes and ears, (j) posture, (k) safety, (l) emotional and social development (3).

One more factor must be considered—the best evaluation of physical attitudes toward health education is by observation of pupil behavior.

EMOTIONAL GROWTH

Feelings and emotions influence the thought and action of the individual, and often furnish the motivation which causes the pupil to adopt and maintain worthwhile practices. Children of elementary school age form nervous habits as a consequence of fears, superstitions, and inhibitions which must be recognized and eliminated.

The cultivation of self-control should be desired by the school with the constant reminder that legitimate emotional expression is necessary for the child. Anyone who has seen youngsters enter the first grade cannot but be impressed by the emotional immaturity and lack of self-control manifested.

By proper emotional development, by allowing freedom of expression when and where needed, and by insisting on restraint when needed, the school will go a long way toward solving disciplinary problems.

MORAL GROWTH

Should the moral development of youth be the concern of the school? Today, there seems to be little dispute concerning an affirmative answer, since home life and home relations have a steadily decreasing influence upon the child. It then becomes the duty of the school to strengthen moral values and to aid in the recognition of the fundamental concepts of right and wrong.

How can this be accomplished? The schools are now operating released-time programs and attempting to offer limited, general discussion concerning religion and God. This is all to the good since separation of church and state certainly does not imply a rejection of religion. Education without acceptance of moral value can scarcely be termed education at all.

There is an abundance of material that the schools utilize every day without fully comprehending the penetrating uses to which it may be applied —for example, discussion of songs such as "America," "God Bless America," inscription on coins, "In God We Trust," the Declaration of Independence, the Constitution, and many others. While no attempt is being made to outline minute details of content and method, nevertheless, such examples are necessary if we are to eliminate the vagueness around such phrases as "moral development."

INTELLECTUAL GROWTH

If education is a social as well as an individual process, then the child must be equipped with the indispensable subject matter that makes possible a person's satisfactory adjustment to self and society. The ability to read and write fluently, to carry on a conversation in proper English, are all properties to be attained through a thorough orientation in the language arts.

The social studies program must leave the pupil adequately acquainted with the historical and geographical knowledge essential for an awareness and interpretation of current events. Science and math must be present in such a manner that they represent both quantity and quality.

In other words, what we are concerned with here is the acquisition of the basic intellectual tools that will enable the youth of this age to go on to a successful secondary education, and at the same time to have obtained the foundation for intelligent and orderly personal accommodation to life.

CONCLUSIONS

This represents an attempt to inject a note of clarity into the literature concerning the objectives of the elementary school. The underlying concern of all interested in elementary education is to give it proper direction, but let us now turn our attention to structuring these objectives in such a way as to insure complete comprehension and consumption in all phases of the American community.

REFERENCES

1. OTTO, HENRY J., *Elementary School Organization and Administration* (New York: Appleton-Century-Crofts, Inc., 1954).
2. TYLER, RALPH, *Basic Principles of Curriculum and Instruction* (Chicago: University of Chicago Press, 1950).
3. AMERICAN ASSOCIATION OF SCHOOL ADMINISTRATORS, N. E. A. *Health in Schools* (Washington: The Association, 1952).

Developments in Human Behavior

Ira J. Gordon

It seems to me that we have reached a place in the behavioral sciences where it has become important to stop and take a look at the progress that has been made in the development of basic concepts, and to see what suggestions might grow out of this for educational practice and research.

This paper will attempt, therefore, to discuss some of the emerging concepts about human behavior that lie behind the descriptive data and that might be somewhat fundamental in any discussion of the directions for education.

I have selected, or rather ordered or organized, seven concepts for such a discussion. These all overlap to some degree; they are not nice discrete entities—at least they are not in my thinking. Why are there seven rather than another number? Perhaps it is because of the strong Hebraic concern with the magic of the number—seven days for a week, every seventh year a sabbatical one, and so forth—perhaps it's because I gave out of ideas at this point. Whatever the case, here they are:

1. The concept of "process."
2. The concept of "the open energy system."
3. The concept of "organization" and "order."
4. The concept of "self."
5. The concept of "growth."
6. The concept of "individual variability."
7. The concept of "multiple causation."

Reprinted from *Educational Theory,* Vol. 8, No. 4 (October 1958), 259–268, 274, by permission of the author and publisher.

Each of these will be discussed in turn including some definition, some discussion of its meaning, and some guesses as to its use in education.

1. PROCESS

We have been so used to thinking of "things" and "entities" that it is fairly difficult for us to think or feel in terms of ongoingness. We can visualize something in the process of changing continuously through time, but this is not what I mean. It seems to me that the individual is not something "in the process of" but the individual *is* a process or rather a series of interrelated processes.

I should like to explore this notion in terms of one particular facet that I feel is of tremendous importance in the field of human development. This particular notion is that of the inter-relatedness of structure and function. It used to be that we saw these as two discrete "entities" with the notion that structure determined function. We moved in biology, physiology, and other behavioral sciences to a recognition of the "inter-relatedness" of these two—a recognition that not only could structure determine function, but that function in turn could effect structure. It seems to me that we are now reaching the point of seeing structure and function simply as two different approaches to the same thing. It might be said almost that structure *is* the organization of function at a particular moment in space-time.

This is not only in terms of bodily processes where we might say that bone, muscle, etc., are structures, and the behaviors of the person are functions, but this way of seeing structure-function is also to be conceived of in terms of psychological and cultural processes.

For example, in the case of the differentiation of cells so that an animal or a worm differentiates out along a pole from head-to-tail, research has clearly shown that the development of structure is related to location in the field of the animal rather than to a "given" within the cell that is different than the "given" in a cell alongside it or ten cells down the line. As Gerard states: "Clearly there was nothing in the cell itself to determine which of these different paths (i.e. becoming a head or a tail cell) it would follow but only its position relative to the other cells" [1] so that "the head end gets the bumps and the bumps make the head end." [2]

Where does such a notion or principle of circularity lead us? First, let me say that this "principle of circularity" is based not only on biological research but also research in the field of perception [3] and in the field of self-regulating

---

[1] R. W. Gerard, *Unresting Cells* (New York: Harper and Brothers, 1949), pp. 359–360.
[2] *Ibid.*, p. 357.
[3] F. Allport, *Theories of Perception and the Concept of Structure* (New York: John Wiley, 1955).

and servo-mechanisms in engineering.[4] We can, if we wish to extend this, see that the physicist's definition of the atom is also in terms of process. Even though he uses the word "particles" as though they were actually entities, he *operates* with a recognition that they are not.

Let us now look at the meaning of this for us. First of all, by conceiving of the individual as an organization of processes all reciprocally related, it becomes easier to break down any mind-body dichotomy. It provides a background for understanding psychosomatic dynamics. It frees us, to some degree, from dealing with "givens" as though they were insurmountable barriers—for example, "native intelligence" becomes virtually meaningless as a "given." It makes more understandable several other concepts we will discuss, such as the extremely fascinating, implication-wise, generally accepted in lip service, notion of individual variability.

It helps us to get away from some limits that are perhaps self-imposed as to the growth potential of the human being. For example, we are finding that, in relation to developmental norms in the United States, "the norms are in the process of changing . . . there is evidence that growth and rate of development in the present generation of North American infants has significantly advanced over the norms established on the Gesell, Cattell and Viennese infant development scales." [5]

In education, it may mean that seeing a child as constantly "becoming" gives a new impetus to seeing the teacher's role as being concerned with the processes of experiencing, particularly as they are perceived by the child, rather than being concerned with an end-product defined in terms of containment of so much knowledge, so much skill, thus-and-such an attitude, as though both the culture and the child were static or at best dynamic entities in constant contact with each other.

2. THE OPEN ENERGY SYSTEM

All living organisms can be defined as open energy systems or at least semi-closed systems. A system is an organized "something" that has a direction to it and some degree of internal unity. An organism as a system is partly continuous with its environment. In an open system such as an organism "there is a continuous input from the environment and a continuous output of products of the system's action." [6]

The system is greatly affected by the environment, and is not to be considered or understood apart from the situation in which it is. We cannot look

[4] N. Weiner, *The Human Use of Human Beings* (New York: Doubleday, 1954).
[5] E. Jackson, "Child Development Patterns in the United States," in K. Soddy (Editor), *Mental Health and Infant Development* (New York: Basic Books, 1956), pp. 87–88.
[6] Allport, *op. cit.*, p. 471.

at the system in isolation; we cannot understand the individual apart from the culture which has influenced and is continuing to influence him.

There are several characteristics of such a system: it maintains a "steady state," that is, it attempts to maintain its own integrity and balance of forces within the system. It does not reach "equilibrium"—this is death. It is constantly and continuously active, indeed this is its most outstanding characteristic.

In addition, the notion of ceaseless activity does not mean uncontrolled activity. The system has "built-in" regulators which we will look at in the next section. In this maintenance of a "steady state," the organism is not merely responding to the external environment but also to the "milieu interieur." Cannon's concept of "homeostasis" fits here.

Activity is ever present—even activity in the conceptual nervous system (CNS) is continuous. This CNS activity is self-sustained and does not rely on input of nervous energy from without. These circuits reverberate and are circular. To some degree, these circuits are sub-systems maintaining their own order and integrity. In terms of motivation, this has many implications, some of which we will look at at the end of the section on "self." These circular causal processes lead us to our third concept, which is perhaps the central concept or keystone of this paper and that is the notion of "organization" or "order" or "control."

3. ORGANIZATION

We have said that a system by definition has an organization. We said of structure that it is momentary organization. An organism by definition is an organization.

An open energy system has a particular kind of organization or order. It is not like a building—the organization of the individual is organizing, ordering activity. A characteristic of such a system is direction—it can only go forward; it can't reverse itself as a closed system can. This order or organization, then, is a *directional* one—as seen in such activities as growth, learning, goal-setting, etc. It maintains its organization through activity, but it organizes this activity in a systematic way. ". . . living things do not just blindly explode their energy stores in response to environmental vicissitudes; they also direct them. The organism must maintain its complex integrity against the hostile forces of confusion, it must fend the "slings and arrows of outrageous fortune" and so counter or adjust to the surrounding environmental whirl that it remains itself and yields as little as may be necessary. The more it changes the more it remains the same. True, over longer times, covering the evolution of the race or even the development of the individual, progressive change is a vital part of the life picture, and again along regular rather than random lines. But from moment to moment the individual acts to preserve itself in its current state. To environmental changes, or stimuli, living things respond adaptively, they make such changes in their behavior as most effectively preserve the status quo." [7]

How does the organism control its activity? What determines its direction of energy? At this stage, we are able only to theorize and hypothesize about these questions. But there are clues which come to us from biology, from cybernetics, from perceptual psychology.

For example, from cybernetics we have the notion of "negative feedback" and the notion mentioned earlier of "built-in regulators." The basic homeostatic processes controlling the physical and chemical properties of the blood stream are examples of the operation of negative feed backs.

This control is accomplished through the sending of information from tissues to the CNS which then sends out impulses to bring the system back to a steady state. While control seems to reside in the CNS, any sub-system or tissue system can be the instigator of new activity. The CNS itself, since it is always active, can instigate organized activity.

The concept of "order" needs to be examined here. We have the idea that the universe is running down, that while we cannot reduce the amount of energy in the universe, the amount of useful energy is constantly being dissipated. The world, in effect, is becoming more disordered and disorganized. This concept of movement toward complete randomness is known as entropy. In seeming contradiction to this, the organism, when viewed as a system, is becoming more ordered, more organized, and is using its energy more efficiently. Organisms are characterized by their ability to wrench order from disorder or by negative entropy. We can look at this in the following fashion. The food we take in is free energy; we convert it into tissue; we store it as fat; we burn it up in behavior. We burn some of it up in the process of converting it into tissue and fat as well, so it is lost. But the remarkable thing is that we *can* convert and store it for future use. There is another kind of "energy" we take in—this is stimulus energy, or information. This can come either from outside the system or from within. In either case information serves to bring order out of chaos, to organize the system. Information is the reciprocal of entropy. Food energy provides the wherewithal; information provides the direction, the order, the organization.

All of this may seem very removed from education at the classroom level. Are there any meanings we can draw from this?

First, we are saying that the individual is always active, is in constant transaction with the environment, is always moving in the direction of increased complexity, and acts to order himself and his environment. We are imputing *direction* to him, and, in addition, we are saying the direction choice is within the system. As Freeman states: "We are justified in taking this egocentric view, which says in effect that man conceives his world; for

[7] Gerard, *op. cit.*, pp. 211–212.

in the interests of preserving internal constancies, the exterofective system develops and maintains optimal external constancies. By means of overt reaction to specific external stimuli, the human organism stabilizes and betters its surroundings, eliminates potential dangers . . . From our point of view, these self-constituted surroundings ARE the organism, and the behavioral processes by which they are maintained are homeostatic-regulatory. That is to say that a slander is just as much a threat to a man's good name —built up by a series of elaborate exterofective behaviors—as is a change in oxygen supply a threat to essential life processes. The organism will react to both displacements with behavior calculated to restore balance and equilibrium. The only difference in the two examples is that the 'good name' constancy is not nearly as stable and universal as is the oxygen requirement." [8]

It must be remembered, however, that the system includes the environment through the internalization of past experiences and the present field of forces.

Furthermore, this concept of organization presents another focus for us. This drive for order pervades the individual organism and the society. Order and predictability are security-giving. The Gestalt concept of "closure" is an example of this. We perceive order, we *create* order where the field is such that there is a semblance of completeness. We attempt to see things as closed when they are not, because the closed system is more satisfying.

We are not only trying constantly to organize our world, we then get caught, so to speak, in our organization. It requires too much energy to change an organization. We maintain it even when, like the appendix, it may have outlived its usefulness. The organization becomes an end in itself. It becomes a dynamic. We tend to treat it not as our creation, but as a "given." We surrender to it some of our power. For example, social institutions, clubs, committees, etc., become self-perpetuating. Nobody questions their existence; or, if someone does, he's reminded that "we've done it this way for 87 years . . ."

Our drive for order and organization, then, is what makes us, to some degree, human—it helps to explain our behavior as individuals because we strive to grow and perpetuate our organization. It helps explain individual resistance to change as well as cultural lags and the perceptions of social institutions as sacred and having an existence of their own apart from people.

In classroom operation, it means that pupils' needs for order need to be satisfied. I'm not talking about "discipline," but their need to see that the class or course has some system, some direction to it, whatever the particular organization may be. For example, introduction of newer teaching methods reflecting research in group processes or psychotherapy can be threatening

[8] G. L. Freeman, *The Energetics of Human Behavior* (Ithaca, New York: Cornell University Press, 1948), pp. 146–7.

to pupils when they perceive these approaches either as lacking any organization or as violating their already developed concepts of what a classroom situation "should be."

4. THE CONCEPT OF "SELF"

One way of seeing and labelling these organizing processes of the individual by which he attempts to structure his world is by using the concept of "the self." This permits us at one and the same time to talk about the consistency of an individual's organization and its ongoingness. Self here is defined as the processes by which an individual organizes the organism pole of the constantly fluid organism-environment field. The self-system might be defined as "what is" organized at a given moment.[9] As a part of one's self-system are those highly differentiated, integral, fairly persistent aspects which are one's concepts of himself. As Snygg and Combs say, "the self-concept includes those parts of the phenomenal field which the individual has differentiated as definite and fairly stable characteristics of himself." [10] This self-system fits the criteria for definition of an open-energy system—it attempts to maintain a "steady state"; it has direction to it; it has some degree of internal consistency; it is in continuous transaction with its environment. While its atomistic ingredients change—cells die and are replaced, behaviors, too, die and are replaced—the system goes on and has a recognizable identity. This recognizable identity, behavior wise, is a function of the self-system and to a great degree of its self-concepts. By analogy, today's members of the First Division still wear the fourragère awarded to the division by the French in World War I. I would guess that nobody in the present division was there at the time, but the identity of the Big Red One is continuous. Stretching it a bit, while we cannot predict the behavior of an individual soldier in the division, we might predict that the unit as a whole would maintain its organization, its traditions, etc., in battle. We might predict the future performance of the organization by knowing its present identity—its present self-system, and its concept of itself as visually displayed on the shoulders of its members.

The self-system, then, is at one and the same time a resultant of all the previous organism-environment transactions and it is one of the transactees. It is acting and being acted upon. We said the self has direction—it is going somewhere. This direction is not only in terms of time's arrow, but also in terms of purposes or goals. We can only understand the behavior of a person when we have some understanding of what he is striving *toward*.

[9] I. J. Gordon, *The Teacher as a Guidance Worker* (New York: Harper and Brothers, 1956), p. 168.

[10] Snygg and Combs, *Individual Behavior* (New York: Harper and Brothers, 1949), p. 112.

The whole organism is goal-oriented. Understanding of self, then, means becoming aware of not where a person has been so much as becoming aware of *where he is going*. For education this has many implications. Education is concerned with present and future; the self-system is concerned with present and future. The past, of course, is embodied in the present and future. Both are goal-directed. The first task of the teacher is the clarification of goals—his own and his pupils'. This requires that he have a knowledge of the goals of man—the nature of the beast, so to speak, and then an understanding, as best he can, of the self-systems of his individual students. What are the goals of man?

5. THE CONCEPT OF "GROWTH"

Growth may be seen as the ability and activity of the organism to preserve its steady state independent of its original conditions. For our purposes here growth may also be defined as the entire series of anatomic and physiologic changes thus combining growth and maturation. Both increase in size and increase in complexity are growth processes. Growth itself is a "goal" of organisms. As a way of maintaining organization in a fluid environment, the organism reaches out into it, incorporates it both physically and psychologically, "feeds" on it (remembering our earlier statement about information being the reciprocal of entropy) and grows. While growth as increase in size stops, growth as increase in organization and complexity continues throughout the life cycle. At the risk of being teleological, the organism has growth as a goal or purpose. Growth is a means for maintaining organization and is also a directional process of organization.

Thus, a basic goal of man is continuous growth. This means a reaching out for experience, a curiosity, a need for coming to grips with his environment, a terrific urge to learn. As one of my undergraduates put it, a "ravishing appetite for knowledge." Cantril states: "the outstanding quality of man's motivation . . . appears to be a desire to bring forth and experience the value aspects latent in every concrete behavior." [11] He further says: "man is constantly making his environment more 'human' by extending his understanding of the significances of events or happenings." [12] Man hunts for significance, for meaning in his world. He orders this world in terms of meaningfulness.

Man grows as he organizes. His goal is the development of a whole person, enhancement of the experiencing organism. As Sinnott puts it, "the goal of the organizing process is a single, whole individual." [13]

[11] Hadley Cantril, "The Qualities of Being Human," *American Quarterly,* Vol. VI, No. 1, Spring, 1954, p. 8.
[12] *Ibid.*
[13] Sinnott, Edmund, "The Biology of Purpose," *The American Journal of Orthopsychiatry,* Vol. XXII, No. 3, July, 1952, p. 466.

Individual development can be seen, then, as the processes by which a person, from the moment of birth on, works toward self-actualization, fulfillment, completeness, or, to use the term we have been dealing with throughout, maximum organization and integration. This development can be studied, for example, from the observer's viewpoint by gathering data about those aspects of growth that are measurable or observable physically —height, weight, the appearance of secondary sex characteristics, etc. This development, however, needs to be seen in another way—in terms of how the person himself continuously organizes and re-organizes his world as he goes through progressive stages of development. It becomes necessary to not only observe that this child has reached his pre-adolescent growth spurt, but also to observe and infer from observations the *meaning* this has to the child—to discover as best we can what *he* is experiencing.

Let us now take a look at these last few concepts—organization, self, and growth, and explore some of their implications for education.

First, we have said that information is essential to the system. It takes information to maintain organization. There must be input. While some input is from the internal environment, much or most must come from outside the organism. The meaning of the input, the value of it, is determined by the system, not by the objective cue itself. It becomes information when it adds to the already developed pattern or structure. Nevertheless, growth cannot take place without information on which to feed. This means that the primary function of the school must be as a place where cues are readily available. Subject matter *is important*. It becomes information to the person when he sees it as assisting him in enhancing his self-system. He wants it—he needs it—and he seeks for it. There can be no such thing as process in the abstract— the concrete cues must be there for him to use. While it is true that he will fashion these to suit his particular organization, this does not relieve us of the responsibility for providing them. While his organization of them will differ from ours, we cannot escape our responsibility for providing a rich variety of resources.

This has many implications for administration and curriculum development. Research is needed in the areas of thought and concept formation to aid us to plan the timing of experiences as well as the nature of the learning situations we wish to provide. Bruner's work [14] in this direction needs to be expanded so that we may understand how these strategies used in concept formation are acquired or developed as the child grows up. We have virtually no data on this crucial problem of how the child utilizes and organizes data to form concepts which become integrating forces in his self-system.

Allied with this is our notion that the individual is striving to learn, to grow, to have experiences and to symbolize or interpret these experiences.

[14] J. S. Bruner, J. J. Goodnow and G. A. Austin, *A Study of Thinking* (New York: John Wiley and Sons, 1956).

The child, or youth in school is active, thirsty (and not just for the many drinks of water he takes throughout the day), and inquisitive. We don't have to make him want to learn those things he perceives as meaningful. The older notion of motivation—that you could "motivate" another—makes little sense in this framework. Motivation is ever present, continuous, and internal. What the teacher can do is enable the child to see relationships between where he is going and the skills, attitudes, behaviors, the school as an agent of society is attempting to convey. The teacher is an active agent in the process; he can serve as a guide and resource person. His task is not so much to arouse interests and curiosity, but to take those that are already there and extend the youngster's horizon, show him opportunities, offer data that he can then use as information. The task of the teacher is in no way diminished by recognizing that children basically want to learn. In some ways, the teacher's job becomes more complex, because he is dealing with a whole child constantly relating to his environment, whose needs for knowledge and experience may transcend the teacher's resources, or whose needs may differ from those of the teacher.

Third, knowledge of growth processes leads us to the recognition that one's presently developed self-system, including, of course, one's physical organism, sets limits on what will be perceived, experienced, turned into information, and therefore "learned." While we have said that structure-function may be seen as two approaches to process, it also must be recognized that external expectations must be related to the present system, and can only be utilized when the system has arrived at a particular point in space-time. For example, it is a cliché to say you can't teach a child to walk until he is ready. We are saying here you can't present any learning situation with hope of success to the individual until his total self-system is "ready." This means teachers need to know about the process of total development—physically and psychologically since in behavior these two aspects are "all of a piece."

6. INDIVIDUAL VARIABILITY

Perhaps the concept most widely accepted in human development is that of individual differences. If there is one "law" about people, it is that no two are alike. We know this—yet so often we act as though we wish this were not so. Let me give you an example from my undergraduates again—a committee, in discussing the needs of children said, "the parent should realize that there are individual differences and that this is not necessarily bad."

We are constantly attempting to use both a nomothetic and an ideographic approach. We have this need for "order" ourselves, and it disturbs us when the concept of individual variability looks to us like chaos. If we could re-organize our thinking to see that the concept is lawful rather than chaotic, we may learn how to see it as the most promising idea for the future rather than one we'd like to do without.

In this search for order we've done another peculiar thing to the notion of individual differences. We say, "yes, they exist, but they exist in an ordered fashion—the normal curve." It would be so comforting if this were so—but unfortunately, it isn't. We have a nice normal curve on intelligence tests, but this is the result of the way we constructed the tests and is not necessarily the result of what exists in nature.

It seems to me at a time in education where we are talking so much about enhancing the individual, developing potentialities and all our other pet phrases that we must come to grips with the meanings of individual variability in our efforts to construct curricula, to develop sequences of experiences, to administer a program still designed—as for example, grade levels—much as the Procrustean bed. In practice, individual differences has often meant lopping off the feet or stretching the body to fit the pre-determined size of the bed. We are faced with the task of re-designing the bed.

Perhaps the first place where a new design must emerge is in our philosophic approach. Do we see differences as a problem to be overcome, or as a challenge to create?

Research is needed here to increase our understanding of individual learning in the group setting. Certainly research is needed about what happens to the *total* development of the child who is at either of the ends of the "normal" curve and who is grouped accordingly. We need further to examine the kind of teacher education which is necessary to provide teachers with skills to enhance the individual development of individuals who must be met in a large group setting.

7. MULTIPLE CAUSATION

Historically, this concept has meant the recognition that behavior not only is caused but also that the causes are some sort of amalgamation of external and internal factors. For example, to explain why a boy might prefer to go to the library rather than go on the playground with his junior high school peers, we might hypothesize that this is due to: (a) he is a late maturer, and (b) he lacks skills in games, and (c) he has low energy output, and (d) his parents encourage him to read, and (e) his teacher has found some special books for him, etc. While this all may be so, the number of variables and the combination of variables are so many that one who wishes to explain behavior is faced with the virtually insurmountable task of gathering historical as well as contemporary data.

It is certainly important to recognize the many experiences that have been organized by the person into his self-system and his Weltanschauung—his view of the world. It reduces our task of understanding and predicting behavior if we attempt to gather and order our data in terms of his self-system. If we do this, it no longer is important to know that his baby sister was born when he was two. It is only important to know what place his sister holds in his present view of life.

What does this do to the concept of multiple causation? It moves the multiplicity *within* the individual. While his present behavior is certainly a resultant of all he has experienced, we may now say that his present behavior is a function of his self-system, which is his unique organization of his past experiences including physiological processes as experiences.

Another way we can look at this is to recognize that man is integrating rather than integrated. This means that the self-system, while it attempts to maintain a steady state, is always to some degree in disequilibrium. Tensions may arise from any part of the system, or from the interplay among the various sub-systems. Multiple causation may then be perceived of as the behavior resulting from the disharmony existing among the sub-systems of the self-system. "Motives are not abstracts out in space that one dangles or creates to inspire learning; they are forever in operation in terms of tension distribution and development." [15] Any part of the system thus may be an instigator of behavior. The direction of the behavior is determined by the *total* system.

Behavior is always a function of the total system operating in a situational field. To understand behavior we need to understand the self-system and the complex interactions of its sub-systems in the present situation.

This means that research needs to be done in helping teachers to find ways to analyze the situations in which they place children, and to infer from behavior the meanings these situations hold for children.

In summary we need to: (1) increase our knowledge of the conceptual and perceptual development of children, (2) develop skills which can be taught to teachers so that they may infer about the self-system of children with a high degree of accuracy, (3) build up our understandings of the role of situation in behavior, since we have repeatedly stated that this is a transactional process, (4) increase our knowledge of how and what individuals learn in group settings, (5) examine more fully the processes of concept formation and the various ways in which concepts are developed, (6) explore the role of "order" in the learning situation. How ambiguous can or should a situation be to be effective? What is the range of individual variation in the need for "order?" (7) raise our sights in terms of goals and free ourselves from setting what may be too low ceilings on the potentials for individual development, (8) clarify and increase our understandings of the process of changing goals and changing the self-system. Since organization

[15] Gordon, *op. cit.*, p. 40.

seems to be an important force, and changes in organization are resisted, just how is change accomplished? How open to change is the self-system? Are there epochs (i.e. the adolescent period) where the system is more open to change? What kinds of environments produce change? And, for social scientists charged with responsibility, we cannot avoid exploring the question of what direction we set up as the one along which the developing child should move. We cannot avoid the choice-making process, but we may be able to make wiser choices as we increase our understandings of the development of human behavior in the cultural milieu.

BIBLIOGRAPHY

1. ALLPORT, F., *Theories of Perception and the Concept of Structure* (New York: John Wiley, 1955).
2. ANDERSON, and ANDERSON, "Social Development" in L. Carmichael (ed.). *Manual of Child Psychol.* 2nd edition (New York: John Wiley, 1954), ch. 19, pp. 1162–1215.
3. BRUNER, J. S., GOODNOW, J. J., and AUSTIN, G. A., *A Study of Thinking* (New York: John Wiley & Sons, 1956).
4. CANTRIL, HADLEY, "The Qualities of Being Human" *American Quarterly* Vol. VI, No. 1, Spring 1954.
5. COURTIS, S. A., "Personalized Statistics in Education." Michigan Academy of Science, Arts and Letters, Univ. of Michigan, March 27, 1954.
6. FREEMAN, G. L., *The Energetics of Human Behavior* (Ithaca, New York: Cornell University Press, 1948).
7. GERARD, R. W., *Unresting Cells* (New York: Harper & Bros., 1949).
8. GOLDSTEIN, KURT, "On Emotions: Considerations from the Organismic Point of View" *The Journal of Psychology*, 1951, 31:37–49.
9. GORDON, I. J., *The Teacher as a Guidance Worker* (New York: Harper & Bros., 1956).
10. HOPKINS, L. T., *The Emerging Self* (New York: Harper & Bros., 1954), pp. 4–13.
11. ITTELSON, WILLIAM H., and HADLEY CANTRIL, *Perception: A Transactional Approach* Doubleday Papers in Psychology, 1954.
12. JACKSON, E., "Child Development Patterns in the United States" in K. Soddy (ed.) *Mental Health and Infant Development* (New York: Basic Books, 1956).
13. MARTIN, WILLIAM W., "Some Basic Implications of a Concept of Organism for Psychology" *Psychological Review*, Vol. 52, No. 6, November 1945, pp. 333–343.
14. MILLER, JAMES G., "Toward a General Theory for the Behavioral Sciences" *The American Psychologist*, Vol. 10 No. 9, 1955, pp. 513–531.
15. SINNOTT, EDMUND W., "The Biology of Purpose" *The American Journal of Orthopsychiatry*, Vol. XXII, No. 3, July, 1952, pp. 457–468.
16. SNYGG, DONALD, "Scientific Method in Psychology" *The Journal of General Psychology*, 1955, 52:189–196.
17. SNYGG & COMBS, *Individual Behavior* (New York: Harper & Bros., 1949).

18. SOLLEY, C. and R. SOMMER, "Perceptual Autism in Children" *J. General Psychol.,* 56(1) Jan. 1957, pp. 3–12.
19. VON FOERSTER, HEINZ (Editor), *Cybernetics* (Josiah Macy, Jr. Foundation).
20. WEINER, N. *The Human Use of Human Beings* (New York: Doubleday, 1954).

Education or Training?

Edgar Dale

To secure a far-reaching fundamental reform in our schools and colleges we must shift from training as the major method of instruction to that of education. Let us note first the essential differences between training and education. Training emphasizes imitation of an available model or the memorization of what the book, or teacher, or the professor said. It is oriented toward things as they are. The textbook, the podium, and the workbook are its symbols.

Education, on the other hand, emphasizes creative interaction. The symbol of education is a man thinking critically: listening or speaking, reading or writing, visualizing or observing. Judgment, not memory, becomes central. Training asks only "how." Education asks "how" and "why."

Training emphasizes short-range, limited, inflexible goals with fixed ceilings. The learning task is predictable; the route to be traveled is clearly and neatly mapped. Education, however, emphasizes long-range, broad goals with flexible ceilings, unlimited horizons. The compass becomes more important than the foot rule. Education emphasizes changing ends and changing means. Education has bifocal vision and links the present to the future.

Training favors one-way communication—from teacher to taught. The textbook and lecture are usually memorized, rarely criticized. There is limited sharing of ideas and feelings in a mood of mutuality. Education, however, thrives on criticism, judgment, evaluation. It favors and requires feedback, the unlimited sharing of ideas and feelings. Whitehead has said that "Education is the art of talking back."

The "trained" person sees the learning task from the background of unexamined habits and unexamined values. He is at home with the familiar situation but ill-at-ease and disorganized when the fixed habit does not work. The educated person, however, is at home in the atmosphere of un-

Reprinted from *The News Letter,* Vol. 31, No. 1 (October 1965), 1–4, by permission of the author.

certainty. He welcomes the challenge to fixed habits which the "trained" man fears and avoids. William James once said, "Genius, in truth, means little more than the faculty of perceiving in an unhabitual way." This demands education, not training.

A fundamental criticism of training lies in the fact that the articulate exponents of training often believe that one group, the élite, is wise enough to set learning standards for "the masses" and plan their curriculum for them. The élite group may tolerate but rarely love or respect those whom they classify as undeserving of education, capable only of being trained. This attitude is well expressed by Ortega y Gasset, a modern Spanish philosopher, who says in *The Revolt of the Masses:*

As one advances in life, one realizes more and more that the majority of men— and of women—are incapable of any other effort than that strictly imposed on them as a reaction to external compulsion.

Ortega contrasts these persons with the "select men, the nobles, the only ones who are active and not merely reactive."

The philosophy of élitism is by no means dead in the United States. When the suburban cities of the United States prevent Negroes from purchasing home in these suburbs, they espouse the philosophy of superior and inferior classes. Further, it follows that if you don't respect a person, you don't respect his mind and his capacity for education. Therefore, training for docile acceptance will be proffered as the method of teaching the "lower classes."

But the great majority of teachers are democratic, not élitist in their outlook. They emphasize training because this is how they learned and were taught. They accept the proffered curriculum without critical examination, without asking "why." Do you know why you invert and multiply when you divide by a fraction? Most high school graduates and many teachers do not. They learned *how* to get the answer but they didn't learn *why*. They received training in mathematics, not education. The new mathematics emphasizes meaningfulness, learning by discovery.

Do you understand why we have winter in the northern hemisphere when the sun is closer to the earth than it is in our summer? Or why the farther north you go in summertime, the longer the hours of sunshine? Can you go out on a clear night and figure out how many miles you are from the equator? If these answers come easily to you, I suggest that you are geographically educated, not trained.

But what evidence can be presented which discloses that schools emphasize training as contrasted with education? I suggest the following:

First, examine a random sample of the final examination questions in any field—history, arithmetic, literature, medicine, teacher education. Do you discover that judgment is often called for—that the powers of inferring and deducing are rigorously examined, that examinations test the power of critical analysis?

You will find, I believe, that the examination questions which determine success or failure are chiefly those for which answers can be memorized. Hence they test training, not thinking. This is why cheating is possible. Cheating occurs rarely or not at all when judgment, thinking, creativity are the ends in view. There are no set, predictable answers to be memorized.

Do we now educate readers or train them? Certainly many high school and college graduates cannot read critically, analytically, judgmentally. But why should we expect them to? Where in school or college do guidance and practice in critical reading, listening, or viewing occur? Where are they found in the syllabus? Those who are studying the teaching of critical reading report that it is not now a basic part of the curriculum either in school or college. Can you recall experiencing rigorous discipline in the art of critical reading, listening, or observing?

But isn't there a place for training as a part of education? Indeed there is a place for some "training" that includes imitative reaction. That is how all of us first learned to speak, to write, to ride a bicycle, or operate a motion picture camera. What is recommended here, however, is a thoughtful attitude toward all experiences, both imitative and creative. Great artists such as Van Gogh and others have, at some point in their careers, imitated the paintings of earlier great artists. But their aim was not to duplicate the paintings but rather to understand how these masters got the effects they did, to experiment with challenging materials and techniques.

Training can be fruitful if it is developed in an atmosphere of education. Learning to type skillfully is an important ability for one who is learning to educate himself. It is a skill which anyone wishing to succeed in college and graduate school should master. It is a trained skill, and we should make it as self-instructional as possible. But we still need the able teacher who guides, coordinates, inspires and motivates the learner, helps him see the valuable role that skills can play in getting an education.

The "trained" person depends on other persons for his instructions. The maturing, independent learner is on the road to self-education. He is learning to put handles on his own experiences. The great goal of the school and college is to produce the independent learner—who has learned how to learn and loves learning.

Education means independence in learning; training means continued dependence. "My son is coming to do without me," wrote Emerson in his *Journal*, "and I am coming to do without Plato." The test of great teachers is whether they have helped their students to independence, to doing without them. It is likely that Emerson never learned to do without Plato. But what Plato did for him was so inextricably a part of Emerson that he no longer recognized the role that his "teacher" was playing.

An underlying weakness of training is that in the long run—and sometimes in the short run—it bores many students. It does not fire the imagination, it rings few bells. Few shout "Eureka!" during a training session. Jung once said: "Man cannot stand a meaningless life." And training often becomes a drab, unevocative routine. The trainer tells everything. The great writers leave "blank spaces" for the reader to fill in. The educator leaves part of the discovery to the learner. He implies, suggests, infers. What is intentionally *unsaid* forces the student to do independent thinking, to learn what he knows and doesn't know. Ambrose Bierce in the *Devil's Dictionary* defines education as: "That which discloses to the wise and disguises from the foolish their lack of understanding."

What then shall we do about training? I suggest that we maximize its values and minimize its weaknesses by linking it with education. Years ago I visited a refinery in Bayonne, New Jersey, for material on a film I was producing. There I talked with a worker who, I discovered, had taken many of the chemistry courses offered by the company. When I asked him why he did it he said: "When I turn knobs and open and shut valves, I want to know what I am doing and why I'm doing it."

The other day I read a biography of Emerson and was startled to discover that he was not at the top of his college class but in the middle. He did not make Phi Beta Kappa. He was named class poet only after seven others had refused it. But instead of memorizing what the professors and the books said, Emerson was looking at life freshly, creatively. He was becoming a scholar—a person whom he defined as "a man thinking."

The trained man cannot make his way in this complex, unpredictable world. Even though he may have the facts, he lacks the cross-references which change inert knowledge to working knowledge. Dependence on training as the chief approach to learning leads to an acceptance of the idea that repetition and dogged practice are the key methods of learning. Actually they often bore and stultify. Training unenlivened by an atmosphere of education dulls the imagination and kills creativity, does not provide a daily renewal of the human spirit.

Wisdom and insight flow from a thoughtful daily encounter with the problems of life. They are the products of a continuing education. When William James, the psychologist, and Henry James, the novelist, asked their father (a man of independent means) what they should tell people who asked what he did, he replied: "Say I'm a philosopher, say I'm a seeker for truth, say I'm a lover of my kind, say I'm an author of books, if you like; or best of all, just say I'm a student."

Basic Objectives of the Program

E. Glenadine Gibb

Knowledge of what is meant by "New Mathematics" and acquaintance with experimental programs that have given leadership for the improvement of mathematics programs provide a basis for the potential redirection of the mathematics program in the elementary school. One must keep in mind, however, that the purpose of experimentation has been to make a serious attempt to see what can be taught. Successful results of these explorations do not necessarily imply that a given body of content should be taught in a given school setting. For the most part, projects have given attention to better understanding of mathematical ideas. A few critics have asserted that such experimentation has been focused too much on mathematics. However, reforms must proceed slowly. The first step is to define mathematical content and to determine whether it can be taught. Getting some direction for the ways that mathematical ideas can be developed and what ideas can be developed will enable groups who have undertaken projects and future groups of similar nature to give us further guidance in selecting ways of helping children to get a better understanding of the nature and uses of mathematics.

The basic objectives of a good mathematics program in the elementary school are founded on the fundamental function of the elementary school in education—a function not intended to produce mathematicians, scientists, teachers, engineers, or technical specialists but educated people.

BACKGROUND

In the past the general objective of mathematics in the school curriculum has been twofold: (1) to serve a functional need to prepare children for the life they are to live as adults and to enable them as children to use mathematics in the everyday world about them; (2) to develop, at least for some children, mathematical literacy. For the most part, this twofold objective was implemented by having children learn rules of computation in arithmetic. Later, efforts to bring meaning to rules for computing sums, differences, products, and quotients made it possible not just to have "little computers" but to have little computers whose computations made sense to them.

"Basic Objectives of the Program," by E. Glenadine Gibb, 1965 Membership Service Bulletin 16-A, *New Directions in Mathematics*, pp. 17–21. Reprinted by permission of E. Glenadine Gibb and the Association for Childhood Education International, 3615 Wisconsin Avenue, N.W., Washington, D.C. Copyright © 1965 by the Association.

In this era of science, technology, and automation, the educational needs in mathematics for all children have changed. Every citizen of our complex society must understand mathematics if he is to communicate effectively with those who live about him and work with him and if he is to comprehend the operation of government and the materials he reads in newspapers. Without mathematics many possible careers—even careers that are unknown today— may be closed to him. In fact, the twofold objective of the past has become a single one, for today our society places demands on education and on mathematics in particular to the extent that computational "know-how" of arithmetic is not enough. Other areas of the mathematical sciences beyond number systems which must have their beginnings in the elementary school now include ideas of geometry and probability.

BASIC OBJECTIVES

If we are to meet the challenge of teaching mathematics in the elementary school, so as to implement today's objectives, we must—

1. *Develop Mathematical Ideas.* Basic mathematical ideas which have their beginnings in the elementary school include concepts of sets, number, operation, relation, function, proof and some basic concepts of geometry. Opportunities to gain an understanding of these ideas should be provided in a way that will help children develop an intuitive feeling for the structure of mathematics. These intuitive ideas are much more important than the formal statement of rules and properties.

Ideas develop slowly. It is important that we consider the specific level of development at each particular grade. An early introduction to concepts and the style of thinking in mathematics can then hasten the day when students can push forward the frontier of mathematical knowledge and make applications of their knowledge, not only to physics, statistics and engineering but to biology, psychology and economics. A continuous development instead of a familiar learn-unlearn pattern can accelerate the arrival of that day.

This objective necessitates a program different in intent from past programs. For example, instead of developing skill in using counting to identify the number associated with a set of objects, the child first develops an idea of what it is that he is naming. Before being asked to learn basic facts, the child should have the opportunity to develop some intuitive understanding of addition, subtraction, multiplication and division.

2. *Develop Ability to Solve Problems.* Reflect on the emphasis of the past when children were asked to identify a means of solving a problem by seeking out certain "cue words" which might be hidden in the problem. There is little wonder that they were unable to decide whether to add, subtract, multiply or divide when they had little or no understanding of the nature of these operations. In the new programs children use their understanding of

mathematics to recognize problems that can be approached by mathematics. They can describe a physical situation by associating with it an appropriate mathematical sentence which expresses the quantitative relation that exists. Having made this association, they can proceed to use their techniques of computation to solve the mathematical problem, identify the result and use this result in answering the question asked in the physical situation.

3. *Develop Techniques of Computation.* The primary objective of the elementary school mathematics program in the past has been to develop techniques and skill in computing sums, differences, products and quotients for pairs of natural numbers and pairs of fractional numbers.

Any apprehension one might have that the new program has discarded this aspect of our traditional study, a study of computing as we have known it, is without grounds. Certainly the mathematics programs of today do not and should not disregard the importance of computation. Techniques and skills must still be developed. One finds that computation is still a large part of the elementary school mathematics program. However, when children use their understanding of numbers, operations and the decimal system of numeration, they come to see different techniques for computing— not just "the way" imposed by their text or teacher. Just as many skills are individualized, the development of techniques of computation are primarily an individual matter.

Let us consider a specific example. Suppose a child is learning a technique for finding the product of two numbers when at least one of the numbers is greater than ten. For purposes of illustration, he wishes to find the product of 4 and 17. He might well proceed in the following way. Using his understanding of multiplication, he associates the pair of numbers with a physical model. For example:

$$
\begin{matrix}
\cdot & \cdot & \cdot & \cdot & \cdot & \cdot & \cdot & \cdot & \cdot & \cdot & \cdot & \cdot & \cdot & \cdot & \cdot & \cdot & \cdot \\
\cdot & \cdot & \cdot & \cdot & \cdot & \cdot & \cdot & \cdot & \cdot & \cdot & \cdot & \cdot & \cdot & \cdot & \cdot & \cdot & \cdot \\
\cdot & \cdot & \cdot & \cdot & \cdot & \cdot & \cdot & \cdot & \cdot & \cdot & \cdot & \cdot & \cdot & \cdot & \cdot & \cdot & \cdot \\
\cdot & \cdot & \cdot & \cdot & \cdot & \cdot & \cdot & \cdot & \cdot & \cdot & \cdot & \cdot & \cdot & \cdot & \cdot & \cdot & \cdot
\end{matrix}
$$

Using his understanding of numeration he thinks of 17 as $10 + 7$ and separates the arrangement of dots as pictured below

$$
\begin{matrix}
\cdot & \cdot & \cdot & \cdot & \cdot & \cdot & \cdot & \cdot & \cdot & \cdot & & \cdot & \cdot & \cdot & \cdot & \cdot & \cdot & \cdot \\
\cdot & \cdot & \cdot & \cdot & \cdot & \cdot & \cdot & \cdot & \cdot & \cdot & & \cdot & \cdot & \cdot & \cdot & \cdot & \cdot & \cdot \\
\cdot & \cdot & \cdot & \cdot & \cdot & \cdot & \cdot & \cdot & \cdot & \cdot & & \cdot & \cdot & \cdot & \cdot & \cdot & \cdot & \cdot \\
\cdot & \cdot & \cdot & \cdot & \cdot & \cdot & \cdot & \cdot & \cdot & \cdot & & \cdot & \cdot & \cdot & \cdot & \cdot & \cdot & \cdot
\end{matrix}
$$

$$(4 \times 10) \qquad\qquad\qquad (4 \times 7)$$

He now has two arrays and associates two products with them; namely, (4×10) and (4×7). Again, using his understanding of numeration and basic facts, he expresses the product as the sum of 40 and 28. This sum, 40 + 28, or 68, names the product of 4 and 17 using not only the numbers 4 and 17 but also the standard name for this number.

Contrast this with an approach where a child is told first to write 17 and then to multiply 7 by 4, carry a 2 (tens), multiply 1 by 4 and add 2 to 4. His record appears then as

$$\begin{array}{r} 2 \\ 17 \\ \times 4 \\ \hline 68 \end{array}$$

Needless to say, as he develops skill he undoubtedly would advance to algorithms such as 17 or 17 and finally to 17.

$$\begin{array}{r} \times 4 \\ \hline 40 \\ 28 \\ \hline 68 \end{array} \qquad \begin{array}{r} \times 4 \\ \hline 28 \\ 40 \\ \hline 68 \end{array} \qquad \begin{array}{r} \times 4 \\ \hline 68 \end{array}$$

Yet in the new programs these shortcuts are those he is encouraged to make when he can—not those imposed on him by rules in a text or by his teacher.

4. *Develop a Child's Creative Ability.* In the past teachers gave excessive attention to drill, repetition, memorization and rote learning. They put themselves in the role of being "fuel pipes" standing in the front of the room, from which position they explained processes giving very careful explanations, so that boys and girls would understand and use mathematics. But there is a difference in understanding what is said and knowing what it means. In the new programs the role of the teacher has changed. Instead of being a "fuel-pipe" pouring in knowledge, the teacher becomes a "spark plug" encouraging children to think for themselves—a change from "teacher-telling" to "pupil-discovering." Memorizing what others tell us, what we may not fully understand, puts us in the position of being slaves to the person imparting the knowledge. In discovering something for oneself, a sense of freedom and conquest is experienced. Should there be forgetting, a child is more readily able to rediscover what he forgot. It is difficult to go back and rediscover ideas if you have never had the experience of discovering them in the first place.

Thus, in fulfilling this objective, it is important to encourage children to ask questions, to explore, to use their ingenuity and to think in the language of mathematics. Children come to view mathematics as an imaginative, creative study of structure and patterns involving abstraction and generalization.

5. *Challenge Each Individual in the Classroom.* Does each teacher differentiate the curriculum for each child in his classroom? In the past, common goals were held for all children at a particular grade level, without

regard to ability. Slow learners were placed in a position of having to memorize, for it was thought that memorizing was easier than understanding. Quite the contrary is true. It is common knowledge that memorization without understanding is a very difficult task. Slow children who have opportunity to understand mathematics can achieve success where they would otherwise have failed.

Thus, under memoriter learning, the bright child who should have been encouraged to be more analytical in his thinking becomes bored and disinterested because he had not been motivated to use the ability he had. He becomes disgusted with mathematics taught with little appeal to intelligence or imagination or creativity, finally becoming disinterested in the subject altogether. Had he been challenged to use his abilities he might have made a vital contribution in mathematics.

Implementing this objective in terms of providing a differentiated curriculum for individual children carries with it the responsibility of making appropriate selections of materials and teaching methods suitable not only for different age levels but also for different maturity levels at the same age. We must learn to pace our lessons differently for children at different levels in their development of a particular concept.

SUMMARY

The five objectives for a good mathematics program in the elementary school discussed in this article are to develop:

1. an understanding of mathematical ideas
2. the ability to solve problems
3. techniques and skills in computation
4. an atmosphere for creative thinking
5. a differentiated program for individual differences.

There may not be common agreement among authorities in the field about the specific objectives and ways of implementing these objectives. In teaching mathematics, however, each elementary teacher must accept the responsibility for attaining the general objective if his children are to have opportunity to become educated in mathematics. No level of mathematics is more important to people than that which they learn in the elementary school.

Some Perspectives in Education

Vincent J. Glennon

WHAT IS A BALANCED PROGRAM?

One of the educator's easiest tasks is to *change* the curriculum; one of his most difficult tasks is to *improve* the curriculum. Change requires little professional training in educational philosophy, educational psychology, or in the subject matter to be taught. Improvement, however, demands a high degree of each. Change is concerned only with answering the question: "*Can* the child learn a given topic?" Improvement is concerned with the infinitely more profound question: "*Ought* the child learn a particular topic?" Change can be implemented through a monolithic, authoritarian decision; improvement must call upon the combined judgment of the best minds in the several disciplines that impinge upon the school curriculum.

At the outset let it be agreed that the mathematics program which is good, appropriate, and necessary for all children is also, and by that fact, equally good, appropriate, and necessary for the talented. The program for the talented should, in general terms, be a set of well selected and well ordered learning experiences that go beyond, yet are continuous with, those for the average child. For this reason it is of primary importance to first ask the question: "What mathematics is most appropriate, of most worth, *for the average child?*" Having answered this question, we can then know the nature of the foundation upon which we are to build the superstructure for the talented child.

Informed curriculum theorists are in general agreement that the primary criterion for determining the school curriculum in general and of the mathematics curriculum in particular for the average child is that of *balance*. They are also in agreement that balance in the curriculum is difficult to define, obtain, and maintain. This is especially true during periods of rapid social change such as the one in which we are now living.

Herbert Spencer's question of one hundred years ago, "What knowledge is of most worth?," is still the phoenix of today. Evidence of the recurring nature of the problem is the fact that the 1961 Yearbook of the Association for Supervision and Curriculum Development, *Balance in the Curriculum*, is addressed to this problem. Foshay (1:iii) [1] discusses the magnitude of the problem this way:

Reprinted from *Enrichment Mathematics for the Grades:* 27th Yearbook of the National Council of Teachers of Mathematics (Washington, D.C.: National Council of Teachers of Mathematics, 1963), 19–24, by permission of the publisher.

[1] The first number indicates the reference in the bibliography at the end of this article, the second number indicates the page.

A conception of what balance means in the curriculum is a necessity in any time. In these days of upheaval in education, however, such a conception is an urgent necessity. It is possible that the new curriculum patterns, when they have emerged, will prove to be in better balance than anything we have known. However, taken as a whole, it could be that the new curriculum will imply a distorted version of our culture, or our ideals as a people, even what we want an American to be. This has happened in the past, at those times when it has become apparent that the existing curriculum no longer fits the times. The changes have not always proved to be improvements; sometimes, despite the best efforts of wise men, the result has been only to substitute one distortion for another.

In a word then, the search for balance in the curriculum is an unending one and is very much with us today.

The Problem of Balance in Elementary School Mathematics

If we assume some 15 to 30 minutes of arithmetic instruction time per day in the primary grades and some 40 to 50 minutes in the upper elementary grades, which amounts to the rather few clock hours per year of 45 to 90 and of 120 to 150 respectively (with 180 school days per year), our problem becomes: what content is of sufficient importance to merit part of these very few hours out of each whole year in the life of a child? Viewed thus, society can hardly afford the luxury of assuming that all knowledge is of equal worth, and that consequently it matters not *what* one teaches young children.

As has so often happened in the past, when the need for change has been recognized the tendency has been to overcompensate. A recent case in point was the shift away from the mental discipline point of view and toward a narrow interpretation of the social utility point of view. This happened in the 1920's, 30's and 40's. It required the Herculean efforts of such men as Brownell, Clark, Judd, and many others to counteract narrow utilitarianism and restore balance to the program.

Today's problem of balance, of what we *ought* to teach, is not new; it is many hundreds of years old. It is one that each society has had to solve for itself. Yesterday's solution does not fit today's problem. The need for thoughtful, mature, systematic, and unbiased efforts in maintaining balance in all of our school programs (here specifically in the elementary school mathematics program through evolutionary curriculum adjustments) is unending. It is our purpose to aid this effort by presenting next a discussion of balance as a function of the interrelationship of theories of curriculum organization.

THE THREE THEORIES OF CURRICULUM ORGANIZATION

Many educators have presented the problem of balance as that of finding a middle ground between two curriculum theories: the mathematical and the social utility (the pure and the applied) with the mathematical at one end of a line segment and the social utility at the other end. There are in fact *three* curriculum theories—the third one being the psychological theory. Hence the interrelationships among the three theories are more accurately represented by a triangle. All three theories when viewed together constitute a curriculum model for assessing and evaluating the worth of new proposals.

Each is commonly known by other names. The psychological theory is known as the needs-of-the-individual theory, the theory of felt-needs, and the expressed-needs theory. The social theory is known as the needs-of-society theory, the sociological theory, the social-utility theory, and instrumentalism. The theory which stresses the structure of the subject is known generally as the needs-of-the-subject theory, or the logical organization theory; and in mathematics in particular it is known as the pure-game or structural, or meaning, theory of arithmetic. In this discussion we will refer to these theories as the needs-of-the-individual theory, the needs-of-society theory, and the needs-of-the-subject theory.

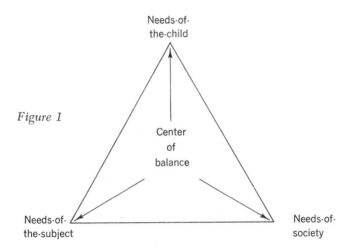

Figure 1

As part of all three theories, those concerned with elementary school mathematics will continue to expect computational competence and problem solving ability; hence, both of these socially desirable learnings are presupposed in this discussion. When all three theories are influencing the program in *appropriate but perhaps not equal amounts* we say the program is a balanced one. Each theory has merits until it becomes the *only* theory.

We can use the triangle in Figure 1 to represent the three theories of curriculum organization which have influenced the elementary school mathematics program in this century. When the effect of any one of the theories exerts a pull or a force that is either disproportionately or inappropriately greater than the other two, the balance is disturbed, distorted, or destroyed.

During this century, these three theories have influenced in varying amounts the content of the elementary school mathematics program. In some schools the effect of the newly created knowledge in mental health, in clinical psychology, and in developmental psychology resulted in arithmetic being taught only when the children expressed a need for it. This approach tended to distort balance in some such manner as shown in Figure 2. The new center of balance has shifted from the region near point A to the region near point X.

In other schools, a rigorous application of the theory of social utility caused certain topics to be deferred to later grades, and other topics to be discarded. The effect on balance is shown in Figure 3, with the new center of balance in the region near point Y.

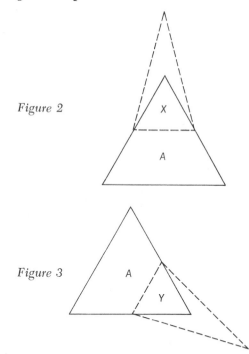

Figure 2

Figure 3

From the mid-1920's to the mid-1950's many mathematics educators directed their efforts toward correcting the excesses of these two trends by emphasizing the meaning (needs-of-the-subject) theory. And since the mid-1950's, this trend has received new impetus from individuals and groups, committees and commissions, foundations and the federal government. From this new activity have come several projects and programs which vary from the moderate—such as suggesting better ways to teach the present program

—to the extreme such as advocating content which has traditionally been a part of the high school algebra and geometry programs. Somewhere between the moderate and the extreme would be that program which not only proposes better ways to teach the present program but also includes that part of the new mathematics that is appropriate to the elementary school level.

An extreme application of the needs-of-the-subject theory would cause the center of balance to shift in some such manner as shown in Figure 4. Little regard would be given to either the ability of the child to learn the mathematics or to the usefulness of the content. Such a shift would be unfortunate.

Just as unfortunate as *too great* a shift in the balance of the program would be a reactionary effort which would cause the program to be frozen to the *status quo* position. Over the past few years several individuals and groups have expressed their concern about both the possibility of too much change and of too much rigidity—but particularly about the former; see Brownell (2:44), Fehr (3:34), and Jones (4:65).

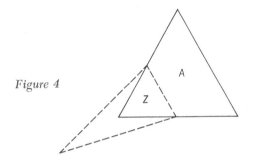

Figure 4

Perhaps the most significant statement on the need for progress, but *balanced* progress, is the recent one endorsed by some 65 mathematicians and mathematics educators (5:191). They readily admit that: "the teaching of mathematics in the elementary and secondary schools lags far behind present-day requirements and highly needs essential improvement." But they also expressed this caution against too rapid a shift: "Mathematicians, reacting to the dominance of education by professional educators who may have stressed pedagogy at the expense of content, may now stress content at the expense of pedagogy and be equally ineffective."

The Newly Emerging Concept of Balance

There is little question among the majority of mathematics educators that reform is needed in the elementary school mathematics program. Further, there is little question but that out of the efforts of the many who are working on the problem, and whose efforts are to be applauded, a new concept of balance will emerge. However, it is very unlikely that the new program will include *for all children* in the primary grades, say, the construction of perpendicular bisectors to given line segments; and for those in the middle grades quadratic equations, even though these topics *can* be taught and some sort of learning does take place. The fact that a given topic can be taught and learned is in itself no logical argument that it *ought* to be learned. Determining "oughtness" requires as Clark stated (6:388) "the combined judgment of teachers, psychologists, mathematicians and educational philosophers."

The newly emerging concept of balance can be illustrated by the triangle in Figure 5 in which the shaded area indicates that (a) more new socially useful content will be skillfully integrated into the present program, and (b) all will be taught with greater emphasis on the mathematical nature of the content, by (c) teachers who have an increased understanding of the teaching-learning process.

Figure 5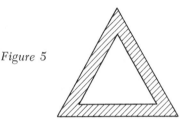

REFERENCES

1. FOSHAY, ARTHUR W. "From the Association." *Balance in the Curriculum.* Yearbook 1961. Washington, D.C.: Association for Supervision and Curriculum Development, a department of the National Education Association, 1961. pp. iii–iv.

2. BROWNELL, WILLIAM A. "Arithmetic . . . in 1970." *The National Elementary Principal* 39: 42–45; October 1959.

3. FEHR, HOWARD F. "Trends in the Teaching of Arithmetic." *Frontiers of Elementary Education VII* (Vincent J. Glennon, editor). Proceedings of a Conference on Elementary Education. Syracuse: Syracuse University Press, 1960. Chapter III, pp. 29–37.

4. JONES, PHILIP S. "The Mathematics Teacher's Dilemma." *The University of Michigan School of Education Bulletin.* Ann Arbor: University of Michigan, School of Education 30: 65–72; January 1959.

5. NATIONAL COUNCIL OF TEACHERS OF MATHEMATICS, a department of the National Education Association. "On the Mathematics Curriculum of the High School." *Mathematics Teacher* 55: 191–95; March 1962.

6. CLARK, JOHN R. "Looking Ahead at Instruction in Arithmetic." *Arithmetic Teacher* 8: 388–94; December 1961.

A Brief Historical Overview of Arithmetic Methodology

Paul C. Burns

The history of arithmetic methodology in the United States is a topic which has received little attention by students of arithmetic. This article attempts to picture arithmetic instruction during the period from about 1900 through 1925 as reflected in a number of professional arithmetic books written during that time.

Early professional books devoted a good deal of attention to the development of the subject of arithmetic. The unfolding of number concept; the contributions of early man and later of the Greeks and the Romans; the evolution of arithmetic algorisms; the influence of persons as Pestalozzi, Tillich, Kranckes, Grube and others; treatises on yet earlier arithmetic in the public schools of the United States—these are topics frequently touched upon in such books (18:1–19).

Issues relative to a satisfactory arithmetic course of study were prominent in a number of professional books. A comparison of American and European courses, the grade distribution of topics, and time allotments were widely discussed (18:20–38). The consensus was that the placement of topics in the United States schools was generally about one year behind the comparable grade level in the foreign schools. There was some early research to indicate the grade distribution of topics and time allotment for the subject of arithmetic at that time, yet no evidence as to what should be the practice:

The forty-five combinations are completed by a majority of schools in the second grade. About ten per cent complete these in the third grade and only four per cent in the first grade. The multiplication tables are generally completed in the third grade, though there is greater variation in this particular than in the completion of the forty-five combinations. The fourth grade is the grade of long division. About twenty per cent of the schools teach the topic in the third grade and three per cent in the fifth. Formal fractions are taught in the fifth grade by the majority of schools. Twenty-eight schools teach addition and subtraction of fractions and multiplication and division of fractions in different grades. In nineteen of these cases the first two processes are taught in the fourth grade and the latter in the fifth. Decimal fractions likewise are taught in grades five, six, and seven, yet the fifth grade is predominantly the grade in which decimal fractions are taught. Although percentage appears in the sixth, seventh, and eighth grades, and in some cases as low as the fifth, yet the sixth grade is the most frequent grade in which percentage is taught (10:37).

Reprinted from *School Science and Mathematics* (June 1961), 461–466, by permission of the publisher.

. . . About 13% of the total school time is devoted to arithmetic. This does not tell us whether this is too much or too little. But if the cities in the lower quartile get satisfactory results with only 9% of their total time given to arithmetic, then it is reasonable to suppose that all cities might reduce the time at least as far as the median (10:64).

Other problems with which the writers of the first quarter of the twentieth century were wrestling may also sound familiar: What provisions should be made for individual differences? (The pros and cons of minimum, general, and maximum goals were frequently presented (11:18–25). Is the spiral or the topical approach more effective? (A combination seemed most acceptable, but professional books generally followed the topical approach rather than year-by-year approach in their presentation.) How much oral work is justified as compared with written work? (A frequent statement was that one-third of the recitation time should be devoted to oral work (17:21). When should arithmetic texts be introduced to pupils? (Many writers felt that the third grade was the best grade for introducing the pupil's textbook (25:151). How can arithmetic texts be best selected and used?

Teachers were advised that "adequate scientific standards for judging textbooks have not been determined" (10:134). As to the use of a textbook, teachers were counseled that they should not make the mistake of feeling that everything in it should be undertaken by the class. "One of the distinguishing features of the work in best European schools is the freedom with which the teacher omits matter from textbook and supplies problems of local significance" (25:36–37).

Relative to two or three other questions, further consensus would appear to indicate that writers favored a definite program of arithmetic in the first grade as opposed to an incidental pattern (27:34); that many topics should be eliminated from the courses of study and textbooks: the greatest common divisor; involved processes with fractions (and why not if the example cited in one source (24:6) was typical: "Divide $1\frac{9}{24}$ of $2\frac{8}{33}$ of $1\frac{1}{14}$ of $7\frac{1}{9}$ by $2\frac{3}{35}$ of $\frac{5}{8}$ of $1\frac{6}{23}$ of $\frac{8}{35}$ of $24\frac{5}{12}$!"); least common multiple; obsolete tables; problems of longitude and time (example: "If the distance between two places is $46° 18' 20''$, what is the difference in time?"); measurement of lumber, roofing, flooring, plastering, painting, papering; square and cube root; and many business forms (16;26:1–22).

Issues usually left unresolved included such questions as: Should addition and subtraction facts be presented together or separately? What is the best method of teaching subtraction? Should the zero facts be taught? Should long division be taught before short division? What place has the metric system? By what sequence should the multiplication facts be attacked, regular or mixed (23:115–116)? These were considered as debatable issues and, generally speaking, no conclusive recommendations were made.

An effort seemed to be made in the early professional books to be quite explicit in other areas of the instructional program. For example, the unit skills, required in the fundamental operation of various processes, such as common fractions, were broken down into rather minute parts. Depending upon the author's pattern, the result was a certain number of types of examples. For example, if common fractions were broken into three patterns —in terms of denominator, addend, and answer—the result was 46 addition types; 65 subtraction types; 70 multiplication types; and 80 division types or a total of 261 types (22:21). Furthermore, extreme care in the gradation of presentation was generally advised. The following might represent a typical proposal of gradation in the treatment of addition of common fractions:

1. Denominators alike
2. Largest denominator the lowest common denominator
3. Same as (1) and (2) except there are three or more addends arranged in column form
4. Column addition, the lowest common denominator larger than any given denominator
5. Mixed numbers, no carrying from fractions to units
6. Mixed numbers, with carrying (21:188–189).

Care was advised in the modes of expression and algorisms that should be presented to children (16:370–372). A list of preferred and unpreferred expressions often included such as the following:

Recommended	*Not Recommended*
Nineteen hundred twenty	Nineteen hundred and twenty
$6\frac{2}{3} = 6\frac{8}{12}$	$6\frac{2}{3} = \frac{8}{12}$
8 is 2 times as great as 4	8 is 2 times greater than 4
2×3 sq. ft. = 6 sq. ft.	2 ft. $\times$ 3 ft. = 6 sq. ft.
1×3 is 3	1×3 are 3
12 divided by 4	4 goes into 12

$$\$8$$
$$6\times$$
$$\overline{}$$

$$\$8$$
$$\times6$$
$$\overline{}$$

$$2\overline{)40}$$

$$2\overline{)40}$$

$1\frac{1}{2}$	2
$2\frac{3}{4}$	3
$4\frac{1}{4}$	$\frac{5}{4}$

1	$\frac{1}{2} = \frac{2}{4}$
$+2$	$\frac{3}{4} = \frac{3}{4}$
3	$+\frac{5}{4} = 4\frac{1}{4}$

Generally speaking, the inductive type of lesson was recommended over the deductive lesson (16:27–38; 26:191–205). No little space was devoted to presentation of samples of inductive teaching. While some of the lessons seem formal and lacking in color (8:40–43), others appear to be rich in teaching potential (15:148–179; 19:49–135). At least one or two writers recommended the discovery approach as a general overall procedure.

This method (of discovery) has many advantages. . . . In the first place it secures thinking on the part of the pupils because it presents the proper situation to cause thinking—that is, a problem situation. None of the other methods do this as they all start by giving the information. In this method, the pupils are confronted with a problem. In the illustration used before, the problem is to discover an easy way to multiply by ten. In order to solve this problem, the pupils must review what they already know about multiplying by ten, compare, draw their conclusion and verify. This method has the further advantage that it encourages the pupils to use what they already know to meet new situations; it trains them to acquire knowledge for themselves; to verify their first conclusions; and not to depend entirely on their teacher and textbook. Finally it is more interesting, simply because of the natural pleasure of discovery and of doing things (19:52–53).

An interesting issue was the question of children's analyses of their work (27:60–68). Some writers felt that if pupils could rationalize their work it was simply "memorized rigmarole." Others defended it on the ground that it helped make clear to the teacher what the pupil understood. The defenders of analyses asked not for blind recitation of formal statements of every example and problem but felt that to neglect it entirely would be quite as serious an error as to go to the other extreme (25:67–71). They felt it was reasonable to achieve understanding from a pupil to the point where he could take the example ½ of ¾ and analyze the work as follows:

1. By drawing horizontal lines the rectangle is divided into four parts, of which 3 parts are considered.
2. By means of the vertical line one-half of 3 parts or ½ of ¾ is determined. This gives the 3 smaller or shaded parts.
3. By continuing the vertical line with dotted line the size of the part is determined by showing that 8 of the parts are required to make a whole. Hence each part is an eighth. This gives the answer: ⅜ (16:92).

This type of analysis was considered "overelaboration" by those who equated habituation and arithmetic instruction—if these two quotations are typical:

It makes little if any difference whether or not he knows why we carry. The important thing is that he has proper habits of carrying. These acts are taught as memory or habit, inasmuch as they are best performed by the method forever after (26:5).

The child constantly performs operations which he does not understand; he delights to perform them, and grows strong mentally and physically by performing them. In language, he masters a vocabulary of hundreds of words, holds them in memory and recalls them without an effort; but why a spade is called a spade has never occurred to him. Walking, whistling, swimming, are mastered long before the laws of equilibrium, of sound, and of hydrostatics are understood. He learns that b-o-y spells boy; he memorizes the fact; he uses this knowledge as a tool to express thought. Let him also learn that nine times six are fifty-four; let him memorize the fact; let him use this knowledge as a tool in computation. And unless some pedagog should ask him why eight sevens are fifty-six, he will probably never have occasion to inquire (5:34).

Whenever drill was recommended by the professional books, individual drill procedures generally were rated more efficient than class drill procedures. The value of speed was widely stressed (19:161–174). Checks, proofs, and short cuts were generally approved, particularly those dealing with casting out nine. So, too, were the following: approximation; cancellation; different methods of solution; multiplication and division by powers of ten; and multiplication of aliquot parts (1:185–193; 16:345–364). Objective instruction was generally encouraged, particularly diagrams in the area of fractions. Some writers warned that indiscriminate use of objects was a danger to be aware of and that objective instruction should taper off at more advanced grade levels (27:42–59). Some of the recreational arithmetic called for attention to mathematical curiosities and the like (19:180). Russian multiplication, requiring the ability to add and to multiply and divide by 2, is one example. Pupils were taught that to multiply 85 × 94, they placed the numerals as below, and halved and doubled them as shown. The numerals in the odd columns (checked) are added for the product.

$$
\begin{array}{rl}
85 \times & 94 \ \checkmark \\
42 - & 188 \\
21 - & 376 \ \checkmark \\
10 - & 752 \\
5 - & 1504 \ \checkmark \\
2 - & 3008 \\
1 - & \underline{6016} \ \checkmark \\
& 7990
\end{array}
$$

Races, games, and puzzles were sometimes encouraged. "Crossing the river" was a popular game (16:377). A number question for Friday's games might have been: "A hare starts 50 leaps before a greyhound, and takes 4 leaps to the hound's 3; but 2 of the hound's leaps are equal to 3 of the hares. How many leaps must the hound make to overtake the hare?" (19:190).

The aims of instruction appeared to be evolutionary rather than static. During this particular period, arithmetic seemed to have come from a scientific, formal discipline. It appeared to have advanced toward an extreme business utility, but was striving to arrive at a broader interpretation of social utility (27:9–20). At least two new influences were bearing upon arithmetic instruction, the project method (12:69–117) and standardized tests. Regarding the project method one author wrote:

We shall not expect too much of the project method. Long years of scientific investigation will be necessary. In all reforms a sensible compromise is best, retaining the good of the old and adapting the most usable of the new (16:397).

The new standardized tests, such as Rice's, Stone's, Courtis', and Woody's, were being examined for their uses and samples of their content were sometimes included in the books for teacher acquaintance and study (16:9–20; 18:299–318; 26:221–257).

In conclusion, it might be pertinent to point up the fairly universal pleas for teacher competence of the materials which he is to teach if he would rise above the level of barren formalism (6:1–25). It was often stated that the teacher's knowledge of the subject must be greater than the academic knowledge which he obtained as a pupil. An old Scotch adage has it, "He who teaches all he knows, teaches more than he knows." As the source of a water supply for a fountain must be higher than the fountain's spray, so the sources of a teacher's information on a subject need be greater than his output. Writers urged teachers to know something of the historical development of the subject area and an understanding of the logical development of the subject insofar as this might lead to an appreciation, recognition, and understanding of more recent methodology (3; 4; 7; 9; 13; 14; 20). They further felt that this might give teachers a new zeal for the subject; an assurance in the value of what he presents to his pupils (21:Preface).

If this article has indicated somewhat that the thinking done a few years ago on some of the issues of arithmetic instruction is worthy of consideration as a background for today's problems, it will have served its purpose.

BIBLIOGRAPHY

1. BROWN, JOSEPH, *How to Teach Arithmetic*, Chicago: Row, Peterson and Co., 1914.
2. CLARK, JOHN R.; OTIS, ARTHUR; and HATTON, CAROLINE, *First Steps in Teaching Numbers*, Yonkers-on-Hudson: World Book Co., 1929.
3. DRUMMOND, MARGARET, *The Psychology and Teaching of Numbers*, Yonkers-on-Hudson: World Book Co., 1922.
4. DUNTON, LARKIN, *Methods of Teaching Arithmetic in Primary Schools*, N. Y.: Silver, 1891.
5. GILLAN, S. Y., *Arithmetic in Common School*, Milwaukee: Gillian, 1898.
6. HALSTED, G. B., *On the Foundation and Technic of Arithmetic*, Chicago: Open Court Publ. Co., 1912.
7. HAMM, FRANKLIN, *Outline and Suggestive Methods and Devices in Teaching Elementary Arithmetic*, Philadelphia: Lippincott Co., 1916.
8. HARWOOD, S. E., *Notes on Method in Arithmetic*, Terre Haute: The Inland Publ. Co., 1897.
9. HOWELL, HENRY BUDD, *A Foundational Study in Pedagogy of Arithmetic*, N. Y.: Macmillan Co., 1914.
10. JESSUP, WALTER A., *The Supervision of Arithmetic*, N. Y.: Macmillan Co., 1917.
11. KLAPPER, PAUL, *The Teaching of Arithmetic*, N. Y.: D. Appleton Century and Co., 1916.
12. LENNES, NELS, *Teaching of Arithmetic*, N. Y.: Macmillan, 1923.
13. McLAUGHLIN, K. L., *Number Projects for Beginners*, Philadelphia: J. B. Lippincott Co., 1923.

14. McLellan, James A. and Dewey, John, *The Psychology of Number and Its Application to Methods of Teaching Arithmetic*, N. Y.: D. Appleton Century and Co., 1895.

15. McMurry, Charles A., *Special Method in Arithmetic*, N. Y.: Macmillan Co., 1916.

16. McNair, G. H., *Methods of Teaching Modern Day Arithmetic*, Boston, Badger, 1923.

17. New Jersey Dept. of Public Instruction, *Teaching of Elementary Arithmetic*, 1912.

18. Newcomb, Ralph S., *Modern Methods of Teaching Arithmetic*, N. Y.: Houghton-Mifflin Co., 1926.

19. Overman, James R., *Principles and Methods of Teaching Arithmetic*, Chicago: Lyons and Carnahan, 1920.

20. Ritter, Carlton M., *Pedagogics Applied to Arithmetic*, Stockton, California: Atwood, 1891.

21. Roantree, William, Taylor, Mary S., *An Arithmetic for Teachers*, N. Y.: Henry Holt and Co., 1925.

22. Ruch, Guy, Knight, F. B., Olander, E. A., Russell, G. E., *Analysis of Drill in Fractions*, University of Iowa Studies in Education, Vol. 10, No. 2, 1936.

23. Schorling, Raleigh, Overman, J. R., Shriner, Walter, *Contemporary Guide in Teaching of Arithmetic*, Ann Arbor, Michigan: Edwards Bros. Inc.

24. Smith, David E., *The Progress of Arithmetic in Last Quarter of a Century*, N. Y.: Ginn and Co., 1923.

25. Smith, David Eugene, *The Teaching of Arithmetic*, Boston: Ginn and Co., 1913.

26. Stone, John C., *The Teaching of Arithmetic*, Chicago: Sanborn and Co., 1918.

27. Suzzalo, Henry, *Teaching of Primary Arithmetic*, Boston: Houghton Mifflin, 1911.

28. Thorndike, Edward Lee, *The New Methods in Arithmetic*, Chicago: Rand McNally, 1921.

Why the New Mathematics?

Mary Folsom

Elementary school teachers in all parts of the world have a relatively new common bond. Whether they are teaching in the United States, Japan, or Uganda, all are beginning to feel the impact of the change in mathematics—a change so far-reaching that the term "revolution" is often applied.

Since changes in curricula are usually evolved over long periods of time

Reprinted from *The Instructor* (December 1963), 6-7, by permission of F. A. Owen Publishing Company.

(one well-known estimate is fifty years), the rapid movement in mathematics in the last five years has tempted some teachers to go to extremes. On the one hand is Jane Doe who buries her head in the sand like the ostrich, hoping that the situation will not last, and at the other extreme is John Smith who hops on the bandwagon without any clear understanding of the basic philosophy or mathematics involved. Either position is an untenable one. Although it is true that there is more of the old than of the new in the new mathematics, the fact is slowly emerging that changes in content and approaches to content can neither be ignored nor be accepted blindly as the solution to our problems.

The change is an expression of the needs of our society in an age of technology, with its demands for more mathematicians, more technicians, and a more mathematically aware citizenry. While these reasons may very well be valid ones, they are so far removed from the classroom that they have little impact on elementary school teachers. Since the success or failure of any new movement in education is eventually decided by the degree to which teachers understand and accept it, it is essential that they have an understanding of the rationale of the new mathematics.

Behind the new mathematics there is the drive to prepare children by giving them an opportunity, at all stages of their development, to learn the fundamental facts, ideas, and methods of mathematics. It is essential to develop attitudes which will enable them to learn any additional mathematics they may need in the future in a rapidly changing society. Moreover, there is a very real desire not only to teach more mathematics and require more mathematical sophistication but also to have youngsters know what mathematics really is. And to know mathematics is to struggle with it intimately, to discover, to come to grips with the big ideas, the structure, the language. Children need to learn at an early age that mathematics is stimulating, exciting, and if you will excuse the term—FUN.

In the elementary school it is desirable to secure mastery of that part of arithmetic which must be committed to memory—the basic facts. But mastery of the big ideas is not secured by memorization. It develops slowly and is completely dependent on understanding. The early introduction of nonmetric geometry and coordinates is a reflection of this philosophy. In geometry, for example, children are not expected to master such elusive ideas as point, line, plane, space, angle, and simple closed curve. They will meet all such ideas again and again, building more understanding as they study some of the representations of these in the things they see about them. It is recognized that time is a dimension in children's learning such concepts as charity and justice. The analogy holds in mathematics. Give the youngsters time to develop some of the fundamental concepts before they are forced to sink or swim in a course in high school geometry.

At the core of modern mathematics is set theory. Set theory is NOT taught in the elementary school because for the most part it is too advanced even for high school students. But the idea of set, which is so fundamental that you cannot understand modern mathematics without it, is so simple that even a first-grade child can understand it.

By the time the child comes to school, he has had many experiences with sets or collections of objects. However, since most children are saying number names (with or without meaning) before they enter school, there has been, in the past, a tendency to move relatively quickly to the writing and use of numerals to represent the numbers. The activity of matching one-to-one objects in sets may seem quite simple, but the importance of the concept involved must not be underestimated.

The child must understand that two sets, as in A, may contain entirely different objects and still have a common property. The property common to the two sets is that the objects or elements in them can be paired. If the objects in two sets can be paired or put into one-to-one correspondence, then they are matching sets. The property common to matching sets is called a number. If the sets have the same number, a name and a symbol are assigned to point to that particular number or property that is common to a whole collection of such sets. If the sets, as in B, do not match, they do not have this property in common and therefore do not have the same number.

As you can see, this is the reverse of the traditional approach, which gave the names and symbols to the child, and then attempted to have him associate these names and symbols with sets of objects.

In many programs today, the meaning of operations on numbers is based on operations on sets. Addition and subtraction are used here as examples.

Given two sets: (☐ △ ☆ and ☐ ◇ ,

the union, or result of joining these two sets, is a new set as shown:

(☐ △ ☆ ☐ ◇

The mathematical sentence is $4 + 2 = 6$, since the addition of the numbers of members in disjoint sets (sets which have no members in common) results in the number of members in the union.

Given the set

⚲ ☐ ☆ ▽ ⊘ ℓ

the separation of this set into two subsets　　　🧍 □ ☆ ▽ ⟨ O ∫

and the removal of subset　　　　　　　　　　　O ∫

leaves the remainder set　　　　　　　　　　🧍 □ ☆ ▽

The mathematical sentence is written $6 - 2 = 4$.

The distinction between operating on sets and operating on numbers becomes apparent. You join sets, or partition a set into subsets, but you add or subtract numbers. All of this ties together the very fundamental idea that number is a property of a set.

The terminology of the new mathematics has made many teachers feel they are learning a new language. And indeed they are. The policy is to call an idea by its actual mathematical name, since it is known that children can learn any language that has meaning to them, and which they have an opportunity to use. It is always a handicap not to be able to speak succinctly and precisely about any subject, and mathematics is no exception.

Most teachers were not exposed to this terminology in their own school days. One reason is that some of these terms are new. Since new words are constantly being added to our vocabulary in other facets of our lives, is it not to be expected that mathematics, which is not a static, dead subject (popular opinion to the contrary), will also require new words to express new ideas? Our grandfathers did not have such terms as *astronaut*, *plutonium*, and *guided missile* in their vocabularies, but no one raises a fuss that these terms have been made part of our language.

The term *set* is an example of this. Teachers often ask why *set* is used instead of *group*. It is because, in mathematics, *group* has a different connotation. It is a set which has certain specified properties.

Again, some changes in language have been made in order to avoid ambiguity. The distinction between *number* and *numeral* is an example of this. Just as the word *red* is the printed symbol for the concept or idea of redness, but is not actually red as printed on this page, so 9 is the symbol or numeral which represents a *number*. A number is a concept, and therefore not amenable to physical manipulation.

This distinction opens many avenues. For example: $4 + 8 = 12$, $3 \times 4 = 12$, $25 - 13 = 12$ and $60 \div 5 = 12$. All of these are true mathematical sentences, because $4 + 8$, 3×4, $25 - 13$, and $60 \div 5$ are other names for, or other symbols which represent, 12. The old, incorrect idea that when you add or multiply, you get more, or when you subtract or divide you get less, should die a quick and painful death. The operations of addition, subtraction, multiplication, and division are regrouping processes, and the equal-sign tells you that what is on one side of it is simply another name for that which is on the other side. Such mathematical atrocities as $7 \times 3 = 21 + 14 = 35$ must disappear when real understanding of equality is present.

Some changes in language have resulted from a desire to make statements more precise. One book published in 1958 says, "Two angles are equal if one can be made to fit exactly over the other." This sentence cannot be true if the equal-sign means what we have shown it to mean. In the drawing below, the

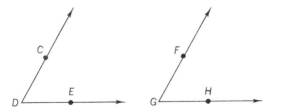

angles can be assumed to be *congruent;* that is, one can be made to fit exactly over the other. It may be true that the measure of one angle is equal to the measure of the other; it is obvious that the angles themselves are not equal, for angle CDE is not another name for angle FGH (that is, not the same set of points). It is almost appalling to note the ease with which some children handle such ideas, and the appreciation they have for such preciseness of language!

Since arithmetic is a system of thought, a structure, which man has devised in order to deal with the quantitative situations he faces in the world in which he lives, to look upon it as a hodgepodge of accepted facts is largely wasted effort. Mathematics is a search for patterns, and a group of naturally connected ideas, within the structure of mathematics, forms a pattern. The recognition of a pattern, and the relation of the pattern to the total structure, makes it easier to understand the ideas connected. A knowledge of the properties of the set of whole numbers enables the child to master the basic facts with greater ease. It makes it easier for him to deal with other sets of numbers, of similar structure, even though they possess additional properties.

While *meaning* was the watchword of the previous decade, the password today is DISCOVERY. The assumption is that discovery by the child himself will shorten learning time and lengthen retention time, over and above the results attained by a meaningful presentation of the material by the teacher. All the meaningful presentation of place-value, or regrouping, via the abacus and the place-value chart, cannot overbalance the inherent advantages of having the child discover the conventional and time-saving way of grouping by tens and powers of ten, as a result of learning that he can regroup in many ways. As a matter of fact, if the child does not understand this freedom, does he really understand place-value and regrouping?

The introduction of equations in elementary school came as a consequence of the search to provide for individual differences. Aimed first at the bright child, experimentation with children of lesser abilities has shown that the topic is appropriate for nearly all children in elementary grades. It is not algebra, but it does familiarize the child with the use of a frame ($6 + \square =$

10), or a letter $(24 - n = 12)$, as a variable, and practically guarantees that if the child can write the equation, he can solve the problem correctly.

Some topics, such as greatest common factor, least common multiple, and factoring, have been reintroduced because they involve fundamental properties of the number system, and the student who takes algebra will be better prepared if he first learns them in arithmetic.

This follows a well-known teaching principle. If you are going to introduce a new topic, do it at the lowest level of difficulty. The use of the distributive property of multiplication is typical of this point of view. Why wait till the student encounters

$$4m\,[-2x + (-3y)] = [4m \times (-2x)] + [4m \times (-3y)]?$$

The child will use this property every time he multiplies a number larger than ten by a number greater than one but less than ten.

$$
\begin{array}{r}
25 = 20 + 5 \\
\times 3 \quad \times 3 \\
\hline
60 + 15 = 70 + 5 = 75
\end{array}
$$

Or in the horizontal form:

$$3 \times 25 = 3 \times (20 + 5) = (3 \times 20) + (3 \times 5) = 60 + 15 = 75$$

The material presented in this discussion is, of course, only part of the changes in content and approaches to content typical of the new mathematics curricula advocated for the elementary school. The main objective of all new programs is to present good solid doses of mathematics which are teachable to youngsters. Since the mathematics presented is not trivial, it does require study. The programs have been developed, however, with confidence that the material is worthwhile, that the elementary school teacher can teach it, and that when understanding is present and enthusiasm is kindled, the elementary school teacher will be able to distinguish that which is important. It IS quite a challenge they have given us!

Some Psychological Principles Underlying Mathematics Instruction

Henry Van Engen

A study of the history of the mathematics curriculum in the U.S. will reveal that the mathematics of the schools has been influenced by (1) shifts in the philosophic position of educators and lay groups, (2) changes in sociological

Reprinted from *School Science and Mathematics* (April 1961), 242–250, by permission of the publisher.

conditions, (3) the demands of industry and a rapidly expanding technology, and (4) the basic principles of a psychology of learning commonly held by those who create climates of opinion. At present we are in a period in which the technological changes that are occurring in our Land are forcing the schools to take a long hard look at mathematics and science courses. The mathematics of yesterday is not the mathematics for today. For some, it is hard to realize that the spirit and content of school mathematics must change if the schools are to serve our twentieth century America.

As the work progresses in revising the curriculum, it is apparent that the psychological positions of thirty to fifty years ago are just as inadequate as the mathematics of this period. The old faculty psychology that held the center of the stage from Plato's time to the beginning of the twentieth century has been thoroughly discredited. The Thorndikian psychology of the twenties and the thirties still holds some of our schools in its rigid stimulus-response grasp. If this were not so, how else could one explain the atomization of the arithmetic and algebra as they occur, all too frequently, in the schools? For example, in the algebra classes of years ago the solution of equations was taught by types with little thought for a basic pattern of thought. In arithmetic, long division was taught, and, all too frequently, still is taught, in some thirty to forty lessons, scattered throughout the fourth, fifth, and sixth grades, without once developing a central idea and a basic mathematical principle. In the light of what is known today, these positions are untenable. The stimulus response principles of thirty years ago must be used with great care, in constructing a learnable sequence of ideas for the schools.

What then are some basic psychologically oriented principles that can serve to develop readily learnable sequences of mathematical ideas for the schools? This paper will discuss and illustrate the uses of only a few such ideas. A more complete discussion can be found in the literature pertaining to the teaching of mathematics.[1]

The first of the fundamental principles that must be kept in mind by all who profess to work with human beings, and in particular school children, is the tendency of the human mind to think in terms of physical things and events. The mathematician recognizes this fact when he illustrates his lecture in advanced mathematics by means of a picture on the board. A good illustration of this technique is the excellent film by E. J. McShane on Limits. The visual aids used in this film were not necessary for the mathematics but they were essential for illustrating the meaning or pattern of symbols. The things of this world, if properly used, are the source of many ideas of interest to mathematicians.

Psychologists recognize that children and adults learn by abstracting from

---

[1] *The Learning of Mathematics: Its Theory and Practice,* Twenty-first Yearbook of the National Council of Teachers of Mathematics. Washington, D.C.: The National Council of Teachers of Mathematics, 1953.

the physical world. We need give only two quotations from the many that can be found in the literature. "So that everything we have said in this work is to show that the thought of the child is less conscious than ours has *ipso facto* led us to the conclusion that childish thought is devoid of logical necessity and genuine implication; it is nearer to action than ours, and consists simply of mentally pictured manual operations, which, like the vagaries of movement, follow each other without any necessary succession.

"These movements and operation are a preparation for conscious reasoning insofar as they reproduce and prepare anew the manual operations of which thought is a continuation." [2]

Werner says,

"The child's concepts always have a concrete content. Image and concept are an indivisible unity. The conceiving and the describing of a thing are not distinctly separated activities. As is true of primitive man, the child's need of adjustment to adult language creates conceptual forms which arise out of concrete perception, which are indeed both perception and conception, which appear to be metaphors and yet really are not. . . . To conceive and define things in terms of concrete activity is in complete accordance with the world-of-action characteristic of the child." [3]

Almost any observing teacher of young children, or an observing parent, will recall experiences which verify the generalizations given in these quotations. Teachers know that to a child a ball is "Something you throw," and a knife is "Something you cut with." The reliance on physical things to produce a feeling of oneness in the world of symbolism is illustrated by the ninth grader who was somewhat doubtful about 8 being the correct answer for $6 - (-2)$. He said, "Show me that it works in dollars and cents and I'll believe it." In other words, this ninth grader felt better about the difference being greater than either the minuend or subtrahend if he could think of concrete things. He was abstracting from the physical world, and he was trying to verify that the abstraction was a valid one.

Furthermore, what teacher would dream of teaching geometry without drawing pictures of lines, triangles, and points on the chalkboard? All this in spite of the fact that the pictures of lines and points on the board are not the lines and points in the mathematical system. Here the appeal to physical things enables the student to take a first step in his study of mathematical systems.

Let us make the generalization that is inherent in the above remarks. It is a fundamental problem of curriculum construction to so plan the child's experiences with the things of this world that he can arrive at the study of mathematics—a mathematics without reference to the things of this world.

[2] Piaget, Jean, *Judgment and Reasoning in the Child*. New York: Harcourt, Brace and Co., 1928, p. 145.

[3] Werner, Heinz, *Comparative Psychology of Mental Development*. New York: Harper and Brothers, 1940, pp. 271–72.

In other words, it is a fundamental problem of curriculum construction to plan the pupil's experiences so as to enable him to divorce his thinking from physical things and to transfer his thought patterns to mathematical entities. The child must be lead from physics to mathematics. This means that the teacher must select a model of the mathematical system to be taught and lead the child to abstract from the model to the system.

This position has many important implications for instruction. Just a few of these implications will be discussed briefly.

1. A cardinal number is a number associated with a set of objects. As such it has nothing to do with the color of the objects or the length of a stick formed by gluing together several blocks, or the shape the group of objects may have taken when viewed as a set. Hence, those methods of instruction that use color recognition, or length, or volume as a primary ingredient in the first experiences for developing the concept of number are false leads. They are "pools of quicksand" in the path of easy concept development. Experiences based on physical properties, such as recognizing three because the blocks are red, cannot serve as the model for the mathematical concept of cardinal number.

Neither should the first experiences with number be based upon hazy mathematical ideas such as the property of a set of sets of objects. A set of sets may have no property or it may have many properties. Hence, to teach a child that a number expresses a property of a set of sets is not good mathematics, and it is much worse than "not good" as a psychological foundation for number ideas. In this case, the model obstructs teaching because, in addition to its not being mathematically defensible, the property cannot be made evident to the five year old.

It is a sad comment on the depth of thinking exhibited by some research mathematicians interested in educational problems who give smiling approval to proposals for elementary instruction that do not "fit" good mathematics. "Colored" number is one illustration. Teaching that two is the property of the set of all sets of couples is still another.

On the other hand, recent literature on teaching mathematics contains proposals that are mathematically sound but for which adequate models are not available from which the child can sense the mathematical structure. As examples of proposals showing a woeful lack of psychological insight one can cite those who advocate the use in the third grade of the cross-product of two sets as the definition for multiplication and the use of the elementary ideas of analytical geometry to teach the multiplication facts in the elementary school.

2. The first steps children are asked to take to form a concept of a mathematical operation is not easily discernible in many elementary programs. For example, those experiences needed to serve as a model of the mathematical idea of an operation are too frequently absent or not clearly pointed out in instruction. The mathematical idea, in this instance, is based on the union

of two disjoint sets. The child must learn that the number associated with the union of a set of 5 objects and a set of 8 objects is symbolized by $5 + 8$. He must learn that this same symbol is associated with the union of these two sets regardless of the kinds of objects in the sets. Thus, the number associated with the union of a set of 5 cats and 8 chickens is also symbolized by $5 + 8$. Another name for $5 + 8$ is 13. It is the standard name for the set which results from the union under consideration. Such experiences enable the child to take the first step in recognizing what the operation of addition is. As he progresses through the years of schooling, he learns that this operation has several properties and, in particular, he learns that addition is a function. In this instance, the model fits the mathematical idea. The path from physics to mathematics is clear and straight.

Consider the implications this position holds for curriculum construction. Not too long ago, teachers always taught the basic addition combinations before they undertook to teach the problem solving. Too frequently, this is still the case. Consider this problem. John has four apples. His mother gave him two more apples. How many apples does John have now? If the point of view advocated in this paper is taken, teachers must use this problem as an instance in which the child must recognize the union of two sets. The child learns that the number associated with this union is symbolized by $4 + 2$ and that all other unions of a set of 4 with a set of 2 are also symbolized by $4 + 2$. Furthermore, he learns that the standard name of $4 + 2$ is 6, and that this combination occurs so frequently that he must memorize it. Briefly, we are saying that certain well selected problem situations form the basis for developing the concept of addition. After having taken the first steps toward understanding addition the child learns to memorize the number combinations. This is just the reverse of the sequence of events as arithmetic was taught some years ago.

Consider a few ideas from the more advanced mathematics in the schools. Let us go to first year algebra for our illustration.

3. Efforts to revise the mathematics curriculum are well under way at present. It is known that some mathematicians reject the placeholder idea as a valid basis on which to develop the idea of a variable. This is a mistake. There is a certain "earthiness"—a closeness to action—about the placeholder idea. The pupil thinks of "taking" a number from the universe and replacing the variable by that number. He then reacts to see if he has a true statement. These are first experiences with letters to hold places for numerals. These experiences are close to action—it is something a child can do with letters and numerals to reach a decision. Psychologically, the placeholder idea forms a sound basis for the first steps to take in grasping the use of letters in mathematics. To substitute the definition which says that a variable is the name of some unspecified member of a given set can only make the first steps harder to comprehend. The placeholder idea can be attained in the late elementary grades. This cannot be done with the "unspecified name for a member of a

given set" definition of a variable. This lesson has not been learned by many who are at present writing for the elementary and junior high school.

Failure to provide an "action type" experience is all too common in materials that are now appearing for our schools. Witness the attempts to formulate a generalization about number in the junior high school before having said anything about how letters are used in mathematics.

As a good example of such mystical writing, one need only cite recent fourth grade materials in which the letters A, B, and C are used as the names for numbers and a generalized form for subtraction written down without developing a psychologically sound background for such language. The generalization, in this instance, was attained within the space of one line of printed words.

It is essential that teachers become aware of at least one of the "Dangers of Our Times." It is very difficult to make some mathematicians understand that what is important to a learner as a learner may not be important to a mathematician as a mathematician. This statement is true also about mathematicians who are sincerely interested in improving school mathematics. Mathematical structures, mathematical language, mathematical idioms, and mathematical patterns of thought are not necessarily structured so as to be easily learned by adolescents. They are structured so as to be useful to the mathematician as a mathematician. For example, the statement that, for all a, b, and c, $a(b+c) = ab + ac$ is simple and straightforward to a mathematician but to a first-year algebra student it can easily become a series of hieroglyphics to be memorized if not properly taught. Furthermore, such statements will remain a series of meaningless hieroglyphics for most algebra students unless the proper foundation is laid for just such mathematical idioms. For a mathematician with strong intuitions about mathematical entities (and these intuitions must be strong if he is a good mathematician) it is difficult to comprehend what must be done to make this a meaningful statement to a fourteen-year-old boy or girl. It is difficult to make some mathematicians comprehend that the distributive law can cause trouble at the very outset of the study of first-year algebra.

Those teachers interested in the learning problem in secondary mathematics must make it known that what is important to a mathematician must be important to the budding young mathematician in our schools, but the converse of this theorem is not true. What is important to the learning of mathematics frequently is of little importance to the mathematician. And herein resides one of the "Dangers of Our Times."

We come now to the second psychological principle to be discussed in this paper.

Continuity is a basic principle of curriculum construction. By continuity is meant the smooth flow of ideas from paragraph to paragraph, chapter to chapter, and year to year. The principle of continuity implies that the ideas in the curriculum are structured, that is, that the basic ideas of the subject are so related that they seem to be placed "on top of the other." Furthermore, this system of ideas is complete. There are no holes and no big gaps in the structure.

It is of more than passing interest that curriculum specialists, psychologists, and mathematicians have made considerable use of the term structure. Each group uses the term in a somewhat different sense, but there is a vast amount of similarity in the use of the term by the psychologist, the mathematician, and the curriculum specialist. There are also differences. The mathematician can exhibit an instance of structure somewhat more readily than the curriculum specialist. The psychologist has more difficulty than almost anyone else if requested to give a good illustration of his concept of structure. Yet, for the psychologist structure is there, and its characteristics are much like the structure of the mathematician. In each case, it is a fitting together of parts to make a well defined whole.

This interest in structure in the various fields of education is no mere coincidence. Its use indicates how basic structure is to the educational process. Bruner, a psychologist, in his recent book, *The Process of Education*, takes structure as one of his central themes. He claims, "(1) Understanding fundamentals makes a subject comprehensible, (2) memory requires a structured pattern, (3) understanding general or fundamental principles is the main road to the transfer of training, and (4) constant re-examination of material, as it is taught in the elementary and secondary school for fundamental character, narrows the gap between advanced knowledge and elementary knowledge."

Major efforts to reform the curriculum have been centered around the central idea of a mathematical structure. Most certainly, as was pointed out in the first section of this paper, mathematical structure must play a central role in curriculum reform. Schools cannot teach contemporary mathematics unless the curriculum reflects the things that contemporary mathematicians are interested in. However, once having decided upon the mathematical structure that seems the most appropriate for the schools, there remains the very difficult problem of structuring the sequence of ideas from grade K through 12 so as to make the mathematical structure easily understood. The mathematician with his strong intuitions about mathematics and the secondary school teacher with weak intuitions about the certain psychological problems involved in learning mathematics do not always form a good team. As a result, some recent materials for use in the schools are more difficult than they need be and in some instances the goals are unattainable. Consider just a few examples.

1. It is standard practice in mathematics to define a rational number as the quotient of two integers. This definition requires a considerable degree of mathematical sophistication if it is to be understood. This definition requires more mathematical sophistication than a junior high school mathematics pupil possesses if he is to reach psychological closure. Before this

definition can be understood, the junior high school pupil must know that the algebra of quotients is the same as the algebra of rational numbers. In fact, the quotients of integers and the rationals are isomorphic. If the junior high school pupil is to understand this, the proper foundations must be laid. This is very seldom done. In the recent efforts to improve the mathematics curriculum, too little attention has been paid to just this type of problem. Mathematics cannot be easily learned unless its ideas are structured and unless the sequence of learning experiences are structured.

2. As has been said before, the schools must give particular attention to the structure of mathematics. In fact, some contend that the overriding objective of the schools is to give the high school student some concept of a mathematical structure before he graduates. However, to achieve this objective the high school student must be taught the techniques of a mathematical argument. Within the body of the proof of any theorem there are three or four standard techniques of logic that every high school student should be well acquainted with. These techniques have a structure, just as much as mathematics has a structure. These structures are similar, yet different. But this is not the main point. I have quoted from Bruner, to the effect that learning requires a structured pattern. Hence, if a student is to learn how to prove a theorem he should understand the strategies used most frequently in the proof of a theorem. This fact has been thoroughly neglected by most groups; the most notable exception being the University of Illinois group (USICSM).

It is well known that in a mathematical system the first few theorems are usually proved by means of an indirect proof. In the SMSG materials, the first theorems in both first-year algebra and geometry require indirect proofs or are uniqueness proofs. It is hard to convince students that an indirect proof is a proof at all. There is something mysterious about it. For this reason, it is questionable whether the student should encounter indirect proofs as his first experience with proof. It is also questionable whether students should be "just pushed into proofs" without an adequate study of such things as rules of inference, how to deny a theorem, and contrapositives. If, as some psychologists claim, structured learning is the most fruitful learning, then present practices with respect to strategies of proof cannot be condoned.

3. As our third and last illustration, we invite you to consider the larger problem of structuring a curriculum from the kindergarten to the college. Up to the present day, this problem has not been attacked by any national group. True, the curriculum has been studied chapter by chapter and grade by grade by various subsets of the mathematical world, but a detailed study which tries to visualize a continuous sequence of ideas for the schools has not been undertaken.[4] This situation should not continue to exist. Some of the larger and more important learning problems are obscured by a local

[4] The Commission on Mathematics of the College Entrance Examination Board concerned itself with the gross structure of the curriculum.

study, that is, a grade by grade study by different committees, such as is now being attempted. Examples of such problems are: (1) What do we do about the real number system in the first twelve years of school? (2) How do we develop the idea of a mathematical structure in the schools? Should it be first taught in the tenth grade? The sixth grade? (3) Should we have a one-track program for all or a multiple track program for segments of the school population? (4) What mathematics can *and should* be taught at the various age levels? These problems, and a multitude of other problems, cannot be solved by committees whose sole responsibility is to develop a course for a particular grade. The schools of America need a comprehensive study made by a committee composed of the best of the various talents that are available in America. The money is available, but it would seem that our imagination has not been sufficiently developed. Or is it that the mathematical community does not really understand the larger problems which confront it when constructing a curriculum for the schools of America? If not, it is up to the school people to impress upon those whose influence is dominant that the problems of mathematics are not solved piecemeal. We need a structured attack on school problems just as badly as we need a structured mathematics in the schools. Let us hope that the time will not be long before we see a comprehensive attack on the broader problems of mathematics instruction.

Beginning Ideas About Numbers and Numerals

Betty Kiser Plunkett

The child beginning elementary school has almost certainly had some experience with numbers and with numerals. He therefore has some ideas based on these experiences. The following discussion, then, will attempt to summarize the ideas or concepts that children in the primary grades are likely to have concerning (a) numbers and (b) names for numbers. The purpose of such a discussion is to provide information relative to these questions: "What does the primary school child know about number?" "Can he use numerals to communicate number ideas?" "Does he recognize the essential difference between number and numeral?" and finally, "What is the appropriate amount of emphasis to place on the 'correct' use of the words *number* and *numeral?*".

Printed by permission of the author.

A consideration of the young child's ideas about number leads one directly to the works of Jean Piaget and his colleagues. His systematic study and published materials offer extensive information to those of us interested in the teaching of elementary school arithmetic. Of particular interest, at this point, is his volume, *The Child's Conception of Number* (9).* In this volume Piaget identifies three stages of development for the ideas of the young child concerning number.

At the first stage the child bases his evaluation on perceptual relationships. For example, he would say that a small glass full of marbles contained more than a larger glass only partially filled with marbles, even though he observed (or participated in) the filling of the glasses with the same number of marbles. At this stage he may be able to count to a certain number, but counting for him is verbal, not operational. That is, he may count the six marbles in each glass and observe the one-to-one correspondence and yet make the judgment that the full small glass has more. The child's judgment as to the equivalence of two sets is based on perceptual comparison. (Note: Two sets are equivalent if they have the same number of elements. The elements in one set can be matched or paired with the elements in the other set, and it is said that a one-to-one correspondence exists between the two sets. Thus, one element in a set is matched with exactly one element in the other set and vice versa, and both sets have the same number associated with them.)

As may be expected, the second stage is between the first and third stages. The child here makes conflicting judgments. He does not rely completely on perception. Neither has he progressed to the point where he can consistently judge two sets to be equivalent on the basis of a one-to-one correspondence between the sets. The child would maintain that there was the same amount of marbles in each glass if he saw the marbles dropped in, one at a time. Then, on finally looking at the two glasses with different shapes, he would insist that the small full glass contained more marbles than the larger, partially filled glass. Most of these children can say the number names (count) at least up to ten, but counting is not fully operational yet. They can make the one-to-one correspondence, thus demonstrating the equivalence of two sets, but they will not agree that the equivalence will withstand rearrangement of the elements, and so they revert back to perceptual judgment.

The child who has reached the third stage is not in conflict over perceived differences. He can justify his judgments operationally. He knows that the number of elements in a set will not change even though the elements are rearranged. He can make the one-to-one correspondence between two equivalent sets and will maintain that the equivalence lasts. For this child, counting is operational and serves to demonstrate the one-to-one correspond-

* The numerals in parentheses refer to the references at the end of this article.

ence between sets. He has solved the problem posed by perceptual differences by construction of a correspondence with lasting equivalence. This third stage is attained by approximately ages six to seven and one-half. Thus, one can expect the beginning elementary school child to have attained some of these ideas.

As mentioned previously, the works of Piaget are quite extensive and informative. The preceding discussion concerns only a few of the basic ideas that the young child may have about number and number names. For further reference it is hoped that the reader will check some of the sources at the end of this article (3, 5).

Many studies concerning arithmetic concepts possessed by the beginning school child have been conducted. The findings generally are consistent with the findings of Piaget and his collaborators. Results from the three studies described below serve to illustrate this point.

Bjonerud (1) administered both oral and written tests to 127 kindergarten children to secure information about specific number concepts possessed by the preschool child. He found that every child tested displayed some facility in counting. The mean for the group was approximately nineteen. A few of them could count as high as one hundred. In a situation where flashcards with pictured items were used and the children were asked questions concerning the number associated with the sets of items, Bjonerud found that ninety-three per cent of the students tested could recognize *two* items and that this percentage declined with the increase in number of items. When a set of eight items was flashed, only twenty-one per cent could respond correctly.

Another study concerning the preschool child's concept of number is reported by Brace and Nelson (2). They tested 124 children ranging in age from five years four months to six years five months. The test purported to measure the underlying concepts of number as distinct from the ability to remember number names and was administered individually to these children. The fifty-five items were organized into six subtests concerning rational counting, comparisons, conservation of number, the cardinal property of number, the ordinal property of number, and place value. The performance of the children in this study indicated the large majority of them could count beyond twenty. About eighty per cent of them tended to confuse the number of objects in a group with the spatial arrangement of the objects, thus basing their judgment of "how many" on perception. Brace and Nelson concluded that the preschool child's ability to count is not necessarily indicative of the child's development of the concept of number. In fact, the preschool child, although perhaps able to count, has a very limited knowledge of the nature of cardinal number. Their research indicated that age is an important factor in the preschool child's concept of number. Those children age six and above performed much better than those below six years. Finally, they concluded that the assumption that a preschool child has developed the basic ideas underlying the concept of number is an invalid one and that attention to the development of number concepts *should* precede any experiences involving the manipulations of number symbols.

Holmes (7) tested 220 first-grade students in order to determine their knowledge of equality and inequality, understanding concerning the subsets which comprise a set, and number properties of sets. Approximately fifty per cent of the items concerning number property of sets were answered correctly. The per cent of items concerning knowledge of subsets that were answered correctly was less than fifty on all three subtests. The items concerning equality concepts were analyzed in two groups. The first group of items required matching of two sets which had the same number of elements and fifty-eight per cent of these items were answered correctly. The second group of items presented the student with two sets, asking him to mark a subset of the second set which had the same number of elements as the first set, and only twenty-two per cent of these items were answered correctly. Based on these results, Holmes suggests that first-grade teachers *need* to give serious attention to aiding in the development of concepts related to equality and number property of sets.

Now that we know the general stages through which a beginning child progresses and we have some information concerning what knowledge he is likely to have about number, the question to be considered involves what can be done to use this information. First of all, it appears desirable to provide the student with many experiences with sets of objects. He must be able to see and touch and manipulate these objects. Thus, he could be led to perceive the collection as a set or as a unity. The concept of a set as a grouping together of some diverse elements can be fortified by many experiences of this type. Intuitive notions of equality, equivalence, greater-than and less-than can be developed and fostered through these initial experiences. The student can progress along the continuum of concrete to abstract experiences by participating in activities involving pictures of sets of objects, such as workbook materials or pictures from magazines, and so on. At this point, ideas about equivalence of sets and inequivalence along with equality and inequality of numbers can be developed and strengthened. The student needs many chances to apply and test the hypotheses he has formulated or been guided to formulate. These experiences can lead to development of the ability to abstract and generalize.

The young child can see two big brothers, their two bicycles, their two beds, their two plates, and so on, and by matching elements, setting up a one-to-one correspondence, he associates the number two with each of these sets. Then, to communicate this idea he needs to use words or symbols, so he selects an appropriate symbol that appears to be understandable to the ones with whom he wishes to communicate (i.e., "deux," "zwei," "two"). The beginning student needs experiences with sets so that he can abstract the "how-manyness"; realize that this number is associated with all sets that match; and assign appropriate numerals to the number in order to talk about the number property of sets. Research has indicated that he can say number names without having the knowledge of number. Thus, appropriate experiences for the beginning student would be those leading to knowledge of the number property of sets. Quite literally, we want the child to know what he's talking about.

Some of the elementary mathematics programs have interpreted this to mean that it is necessary to distinguish between use of the words *number* and *numeral* in their textbooks. Others have not. There is, then, varying emphasis placed on the distinction between numerals and numbers by elementary mathematics programs. Some textbook authors dismiss it with two or three sentences with an accompanying phrase such as "should be clear from the context." Other authors devote pages to explaining the distinction and relating its basic and necessary quality. That there is some disagreement concerning this distinction is made evident by the following three excerpts taken from elementary mathematics books:

> The distinction between ideas and their symbols is in accord with the teachings of semantics. There is educational merit in recognizing that "Words are not ideas." However, since the terms "number" and "numeral" are commonly used as synonyms in general conversation and are so identified in current standard dictionaries, the educational value of rigorously differentiating between them is questionable. Until there is convincing evidence that such practices make substantial contributions to mathematical understanding and to educational development, they should be used sparingly or not at all. Clearly distinguishing between a number idea and the symbols referring to it is important. But, pedantic stressing of arbitrary distinctions between equally representative symbols leads only to confusion and frustration. (12, p. 42)

> In textbooks for elementary grades, the name of a number is sometimes called a numeral. When no confusion can result, we will sometimes ignore this distinction. (4, p. 16)

> In mathematics, as elsewhere, it is often very important to be sure whether (a) we are talking about the thing to which a word or symbol refers, or whether (b) we are talking about the word or symbol being used to designate that thing. This matter is not a trivial one. An easy way to make sure whether we mean the thing itself or merely its symbol is to use quotation marks. For example:
> 1. Helen is a girl. "Helen" is a girl's name.
> 2. Trees have leaves. "Trees" has five letters.
> 3. If you put poison on your tongue, you will be sorry.
>   If you put "poison" on the label, you will be safe.
> Remember also that the name given to a thing is not necessarily a property of the thing.
> When the thing we are talking about is a number, the symbol that stands for the number is called a numeral. Thus the numeral "5" stands for the number 5. Remember that a number is an idea—an abstract concept. We said you couldn't see a number. The numeral "5" which you can see, stands for the number 5. The number 5 means "fiveness"—something which does not belong to any particular set of objects, but which is characteristic of all the sets of objects which can be

matched with the fingers of one hand. Any particular number may be represented by several different symbols—whether words or marks.

We are not quibbling when we distinguish between a numeral and a number. (11, pp. 151–152)

Attention to this distinction has caused some controversy. One finds such questions being asked as: "Are fractions numerals or numbers?" or "Are exponents numbers or numerals?" If fractions are numbers, then how can one talk about top terms (numerators) and bottom terms (denominators) since "top" and "bottom" refer to positional properties of numerals? If fractions are numerals, then how can one talk about adding or multiplying, and so on? Similarly, if exponents are numerals, can we add and subtract them? Or can exponents be numbers if they are exponents because of their position, a numeral property? Francis J. Mueller in "On the Fraction as a Numeral" somewhat facetiously suggests that we extend number properties to numerals and therefore we can "add," "subtract," "multiply," and "divide" to compute answers. His point is quite clearly stated:

There was a great deal of this thing a few years ago when our attention was first directed toward the numeral-number distinction, but we have tended to outgrow it and let the usually obvious context take care of the distinction. (8, p. 234)

The controversial nature of the distinction between use of "number" and "numeral" led the writer (10) to examine the understanding that exists among a group of elementary school students concerning the distinction between symbols and referents, and more specifically, numerals and numbers. Evidence was obtained which indicates that the ability to distinguish between a symbol and its referent is related to the general ability of the student. With particular attention to the numeral-number distinction, students who had had four years of instruction from an arithmetic textbook series which emphasizes the distinction performed no better than the students who had had four years of instruction from an arithmetic textbook series which doesn't even make the distinction. These two groups of students were given a test utilizing a tape-recorded interview situation. The test contained twenty-two items, and each item called upon the student to distinguish between a symbol and its referent (for example, the name of a thing and the thing being named). Three-fourths of the students answered at least one-half of the items in a satisfactory manner.

This information leads one to question the amount of emphasis being given to the distinction between numerals and numbers in the textbook materials for elementary arithmetic students. From the results of this research, the emphasis does not lead to greater understanding of the distinction between symbols and referents for these students.

It is possible that emphasis on the distinction between numeral and number may have some detrimental effects on elementary school students in their study of arithmetic. An examination of some of the exercises from a textbook series emphasizing the numeral-number distinction indicates that precision of language has made these exercises more difficult to understand, rather than more lucid. For example, consider the following exercise:

This is a number puzzle. One figure is missing in each numeral. Can you think of some figure to use so that each numeral will mean a greater number than the numeral before it does? __1, 2__, 2__, __3. (6, p. 109)

If the object of the authors was to be precise, then they have succeeded. However, if their object was to measure the students' knowledge of place value, or of numbers greater than other numbers, their success is questionable.

If the distinction between numerals and numbers is a desirable one, it would appear that the distinction between nouns and their referents is equally desirable. Yet, one finds such examples as the following:

For each problem on this page draw the coins that you would use in making change. Under each coin write the numeral you would say as you make the change. (6, p. 58)

For these authors it is important to insist that the student does not write numbers, but writes names for numbers. It seems that it would be equally important to insist that he does not draw coins, but draws pictures of coins. Just as there are no numbers on the page, there are no coins on the page. And the student knows this.

We have looked at some of the ideas that the beginning elementary school child may have concerning numbers and names for numbers. The experiences which he encounters through the arithmetic program must be well chosen in order to be consistent with the developmental sequence of the child's number concepts. Thereby, appropriate concepts can be introduced, fostered, and strengthened. Each new concept should build on previous ones to promote arithmetical understanding for the elementary school child.

REFERENCES

1. BJONERUD, CORWIN E. "Arithmetic Concepts Possessed by the Preschool Child," *The Arithmetic Teacher*. November 1960, pp. 347–350.
2. BRACE, ALEC and L. DOYAL NELSON. "The Preschool Child's Concept of Number," *The Arithmetic Teacher*. February 1965, pp. 126–133.
3. COXFORD, ARTHUR F., JR. "Piaget: Number and Measurement," *The Arithmetic Teacher*. November 1963, pp. 419–427.
4. CROUCH, RALPH and GEORGE BALDWIN. *Mathematics for Elementary Teachers*. John Wiley & Sons, Inc., New York, 1964.
5. DUCKWORTH, ELEANOR. "Piaget Rediscovered," *The Arithmetic Teacher*. November 1964, pp. 496–499.

6. HARTUNG, MAURICE L., HENRY VAN ENGEN, LOIS KNOWLES, and CATHARINE MAHONEY. *Seeing Through Arithmetic 3.* Scott, Foresman and Company, Chicago, 1963.
7. HOLMES, EMMA E. "First Graders' Number Concepts," *The Arithmetic Teacher.* April 1963, pp. 195–196.
8. MUELLER, FRANCIS J. "On the Fraction as a Numeral," *The Arithmetic Teacher.* May 1961, pp. 234–238.
9. PIAGET, JEAN. *The Child's Conception of Number.* W. W. Norton & Company, Inc., New York, 1965.
10. PLUNKETT, BETTY K. "Symbol-Referent Discrimination by Fourth Grade Students." University of Illinois. Unpublished doctoral dissertation, 1967.
11. SCHAAF, WILLIAM L. *Basic Concepts of Elementary Mathematics.* John Wiley & Sons, Inc., New York, 1965.
12. SPENCER, PETER L. and MARGUERITE BRYDEGAARD. *Building Mathematical Competence in the Elementary School.* Holt, Rinehart and Winston, Inc., New York, 1966.

Adjusting Instruction in Arithmetic to Varied Ability Groups

John R. Clark and Don R. Eberhart

A problem of continuing concern in the teaching profession is that of adjusting instruction to the varied abilities of pupils in the average classroom. We have come to realize that we are not fully meeting the needs of pupils of exceptionally high ability or of the very slow learner. For the pupil of above average ability, subject matter is often too easy and lacking in challenge. Consequently, the pace at which he works is too slow for him to put forth his maximum effort. The pupil of below average ability, on the other hand, is continually frustrated by a too rapid pace and by material too difficult for him to master.

Adjusting instruction to individual needs is of particular concern to arithmetic teachers, for the pupil's ultimate achievement in mathematics often depends on his success in the arithmetic of the early grades. The following statement from *The New York Times* indicates that this problem is widely recognized.

Attitudes of frustration build up because of insufficient challenge or because of too difficult work in the elementary grades. The students of today's classroom represent widely different capacities and interests which cannot be satisfied through

Reprinted from *Notes for the Arithmetic Teacher,* No. 25, by John R. Clark and Don R. Eberhart (New York: Harcourt, Brace & World, 1961), by permission of the publisher.

uniform content and method. . . . The future of many American scientists and mathematicians depends on how they feel about mathematics in the early grades: *

Differences in arithmetical ability are relatively easy to identify. Even casual observation reveals the pupil who cannot multiply, for example. Preparing a program that will remedy the situation, however, is not so easy. As Rolland R. Smith has pointed out, "we know more about the existence of individual differences than we do about the manner of dealing with them." In many ways, providing for individual differences in arithmetic seems more difficult than providing for them in other areas of the curriculum. Learning in arithmetic should be orderly and sequential, proceeding rapidly from the concrete and simple to the abstract and complex. Each individual must progress from one level to the next, and provision must be made for him to succeed at each task if he is to learn at a rate commensurate with his ability.

The ideal arithmetic program for most pupils is one which guarantees an optimum degree of success. There must be a differentiation in depth or in rate of learning so that each pupil, whether quick, average, or slow, is successful three or four times out of five. Experience has shown that the pupil who never succeeds is soon frustrated. Failure and fear destroy his initiative and he loses his essential motivation to try to do better. In contrast, the pupil who *never* fails often becomes bored by lack of challenge and indifferent about his work.

In addition to providing each pupil with the opportunity to succeed, a differentiated arithmetic program must be such that it can be used under prevailing methods of school organization and with instructional materials that are readily available. In general we have two procedures that will meet these qualifications: varying the pace of instruction, and varying the difficulty. In a program of varied pace, the course is sequential, and approximately the same material is covered by each pupil. The differentiation is in the rate of learning, bright pupils advancing through the program more rapidly than pupils of lesser ability. In a program of varied difficulty, pupils move from topic to topic at the same rate, but provision is made for them to work at different levels of difficulty.

VARYING THE PACE

A program that is differentiated by varying the pace moves forward on an irregular front. The more able pupils progress to advanced topics while those of average ability cover the regular program. Less able pupils continue to work on basic understandings for a long enough time to insure a thorough foundation before moving on. Examples of this kind of program may be found in both heterogeneous classes and in classes grouped on the basis of

* "Feel for Science Develops in Youth," *The New York Times*, February 18, 1957.

ability. When used with the latter, we generally provide three "tracks" of instruction: an accelerated program, a conventionally paced program, and a slower moving program. Since each class progresses through its own program topic by topic, the tasks of lesson planning, record keeping, and selection of material are greatly simplified. In fact, many feel that a variation of pace can be achieved only through some form of ability grouping. Recently, however, experience with a new procedure of instruction, team learning, has opened the way for use of a varied pace in the heterogeneous classroom.

The principle of team learning is based on the natural human need for mutual aid. It provides a way for pupils to work together, to share ideas, and clarify thinking. They are challenged by what may be called the "cooperative-competitive" nature of team work.

Usually two pupils of approximately equal ability make up the learning team and work as partners. Sometimes three pupils make an effective team. Occasionally, but rarely, a very rapid learner may work alone. The pupils of each team study new topics together. Sometimes pupils are directed to work alone for purposes of testing or special practice. At other times the teacher may bring several pupils together for group work.

Each team works from a series of assignments, or "job" sheets. Each job sheet is a kind of contract assignment; successful completion of it leads the team to the next one, and so on. Periodic testing prevents pupils from advancing without understanding or mastery. The job sheets are specifically planned to encourage sequential advance through textbooks for the elementary grades at varying rates of progress.

Reports from schools where team learning has been in operation for an extended period of time indicate that the procedure is excellent for above-average and average pupils. Able pupils, stimulated by "competitive cooperation" with their equally able teammates, make excellent progress, often moving as much as a year ahead of the normal achievement in arithmetic. Pupils of average ability find that the flexibility of the program enables them to stay longer with complex topics and to move rapidly through topics that are less complex. Above-average and average pupils generally show better than normal achievement under a program of team learning. However, we are not yet sure how effective these procedures are for pupils of less than average ability. Results from experimenting schools are inconclusive and are less clear cut. At the present time, it appears that slower learners will profit most under a program which offers each of these children more individual attention from the teacher.

VARYING THE DEPTH

The procedure of varying the *difficulty* or depth of the arithmetic program is based upon the fact that there are a variety of approaches to the learning of a topic. Smith described the concept as "levels of learning." "The concept," he said, ". . . recognizes the fact that children of various degrees of ability or maturity can learn to do the same thing on several different levels from the simple concrete to the more complex abstract." This method, in contrast to varying the pace of instruction, carries learning forward on a regular front. The entire class moves from topic to topic together, with some pupils using concrete materials, some exploring the relationships between manipulative materials and the algorisms, and a third group, the more able, working independently as they apply the new learning.

Teaching by levels of learning is made easier by grouping, but the grouping is of a far different sort from the conventional "fast" and "slow" groups. Grouping is varied and flexible. Pupils will group themselves differently for different topics. A difficult topic may result in a relatively small "fast" group, while an easier topic may find a large group ready in a short time for independent work. For some topics the entire class may work together. Children are stimulated by the opportunity to approach each topic through a variety of ways, and since groups are constantly changing, less able children escape the stigma of being irrevocably assigned to the "slow" group.

Whether we attempt to differentiate the arithmetic program through varying the pace or varying the difficulty, the type and quality of materials used are of the utmost importance. Textbooks and supplemental study materials should be flexible. For each topic covered, there should be a variety of approaches so that each pupil may be assured of success at his own level of ability. The sequence of topics must be carefully planned, and adequate practice must be provided. Of greatest importance, the materials used should offer a variety of challenges. Optional material should be provided for the more able learner, and special exercises that supply fun, interest, and enrichment should be included, as well as exercises in "mental" computation.

In summary, it is important that we continue to explore methods of differentiating arithmetic instruction, always keeping in mind the relationship of success to learning. Well earned success—success after honest effort—is the best motivation to continued learning. In our democracy, dedicated to the rights of the individual, each child has the right to achieve to the limit of his capacity.

REFERENCES

JONES, P. S., AND PINGRY, R. E. "Individual Differences," *Instruction in Arithmetic* (Twenty-fifth Yearbook). Washington, D.C.: The National Council of Teachers of Mathematics (1960), pp. 121–148.

JUNGE, CHARLOTTE. "The Gifted Ones—How Shall We Know Them?" *Notes for the Arithmetic Teacher, Number 17*. Tarrytown, New York: World Book Company.

McHUGH, WALTER J. "Team Learning in Skills Subjects in Intermediate Grades," *Journal of Education,* Vol. 142 (December 1959), pp. 22–51.

McMEEN, GEORGE H. "Differentiating Arithmetic Instruction," *The Arithmetic Teacher*, Vol. VI (April 1959), pp. 113–120.

MOSER, HAROLD E. "Levels of Learning," *Notes for the Arithmetic Teacher, Number 16*. Tarrytown, New York: World Book Company.

SAUBLE, IRENE, AND THIELE, C. LOUIS. "Guidance and Counseling," *Instruction in Arithmetic* (Twenty-fifth Yearbook). Washington, D.C.: The National Council of Teachers of Mathematics (1960), pp. 148–178.

SMITH, ROLLAND R. "Provisions for Individual Differences," *The Learning of Mathematics, Its Theory and Practice* (Twenty-first Yearbook). Washington, D.C.: The National Council of Teachers of Mathematics (1953), pp. 271–302.

WEAVER, J. F., AND BRAWLEY, C. F. "Enriching the Elementary School Mathematics Program for More Capable Children," *Journal of Education*, Vol. 142 (October 1959), pp. 1–40.

Articulation Between the Primary Grades and the Junior High Mathematics Program

Thomas C. Gibney

We are experiencing in mathematics education a program that contains sound mathematics and is built on a psychology of learning where understanding of mathematical ideas is regarded as the most important goal. The great progress in the past few years has produced revised or new textbook series from practically all the textbook companies plus several experimental curriculums from colleges and groups. Old topics are being introduced effectively at earlier grade levels, and many new topics and new procedures are being suggested and taught at all levels.

With the many changes that are taking place in the elementary mathematics curriculum there is a definite need for an effective articulateness between the primary and junior high school teachers. Listed below are several illustrations where better articulation is needed in the elementary school.

PREPARATION OF TEACHERS

If all teachers of elementary school mathematics would make effective use of the teachers manuals we would experience a large improvement in rate, depth, and amount of learning by students. Too many teachers skip the pages devoted to understanding the *why* of algorisms and omit ex-

Reprinted from *School Science and Mathematics* (February 1965), 125–131, by permission of the publisher.

periences designed to develop concepts and discussion of mathematical ideas. The typical junior high teacher has not known the whys behind much of the content he teaches but he can lead his students through algorisms and the students learn by imitation. We now find algebraic concepts being introduced earlier in the elementary school and the "whys" of these concepts are being questioned by the teachers in the primary and intermediate grades because they have not had the sufficient background in mathematics to lead their students through the algorisms and they are attempting to teach the whys. This shift of content in the elementary school will lead teachers to the manuals for help. This is a good trend and should result in better instruction of algebraic concepts than we are now receiving from junior high teachers. If a teacher needs help in effectively using the teachers manual this help might come from an inservice workshop conducted by a mathematics coordinator who is familiar with the textbook being used.

CONTENT NEEDED BY ELEMENTARY TEACHERS

It appears evident from current articles and research that teachers are not adequately prepared for teaching mathematics in the elementary school. Teachers can increase their knowledge of mathematics during their teaching provided they follow a systematic plan. Inservice workshops can greatly help all teachers in the elementary school if all teachers contribute actively to the workshop. The eighth grade mathematics teacher or the mathematics consultant may and probably should be placed in charge of the workshop but the instruction for the sessions should be provided by all the participants of the workshop.

There is little or no general agreement upon what content should be included in mathematics courses to be required of all elementary teachers. From conferences with beginning teachers during the past three years this writer found some who had just finished undergraduate methods and content courses in mathematics where the terms "modern mathematics" and "contemporary mathematics" received minor emphasis. The only reference made was when the college professor stated there was nothing new in the "modern mathematics" and that *he* had been using it all his life. The other extreme was told by some experienced teachers who stated they had been enrolled in graduate elementary mathematics courses where they had spent five weeks of a six week summer session working on bases other than ten and that now they felt well qualified to teach modern mathematics. We can not look to the content or methods courses now offered in colleges to determine what mathematics an elementary teacher should know. There is no evidence that the typical background course in college mathematics actually contributes to superior teaching of arithmetic. The sensible answer to the question—"What mathematics content is needed by elementary teachers?"—

seems to be to examine the textbook or course of study within a given district and identify those content areas where inservice training will benefit the faculty, and then have the workshop prepared and taught by the complete faculty.

NUMERAL CONSTRUCTION

The concern in this area is with the overlapping and similarities in teaching mathematics and language arts. Three examples follow to demonstrate this problem:

1. Several second grade students placed arithmetic examples on the blackboard. When the students were finished the remaining class members were asked by their teacher to spot the errors. There were sixteen comments from the students, all of which related to grammatical errors. No one found the three glaring computational errors.

2. During a third grade mathematics class the teacher held up Nancy's paper for discussion. The teacher asked the class for suggestions for helping Nancy improve her paper. At the close of the discussion the teacher stated, "Next time, Nancy, we suggest you do such and such—." The rest of the papers were handled in a similar manner. From timing this activity for five consecutive days it was determined that seventy-five minutes of the two hundred minutes devoted to mathematics were spent in discussing the format of the arithmetic paper and this was done during the latter part of the second semester.

3. Should third grade students be required to always answer in complete sentences? Must their zeros always be closed? Must they always make their numerals the same size? Many times an important contribution is about to emerge from a third grade student at the blackboard, but the teacher interrupts with statements as: "Bill, answer only in a complete sentence." "Thomas, close the zeros in your numeral 200.", or "Sara!, erase your numerals and write them over so that they are all the same size." Many students caught in this dilemma simply give up and return to their seats with the result that their contribution is lost. It does not take many occurrences of this situation before these students become reluctant to participate in mathematical classroom activities and soon their interest in mathematics has turned to a dislike for the subject.

These examples were not for the purpose of criticizing the usefulness of the teacher's suggestions but rather to illustrate the large amount of time during mathematics classes that is devoted to the instruction of Language Arts, and also what this emphasis upon format might do to the student's interest in mathematics in the primary grades.

We can quickly move from the primary grades to the junior high school where the teachers hesitate giving an essay test in mathematics because they could not read the answers or where the teachers allow the students to do their work on scratch paper not to be handed in because it would be too messy for the teachers to examine. Students in the upper grades often correct their own papers because neither their peers nor teachers can read them. The problem of numeral construction is an area where suggestions must circulate in the elementary school so that all teachers can work together to edit a common form to follow as a guide and pursue effective use of school time in the construction of numerals and other symbols used in mathematics.

STUDENT EVALUATION

We are going to need more direct evaluation of our mathematics programs in the elementary school than we currently practice. The teacher of the self-contained classroom as well as the departmentalized teacher has a need for objective evaluative procedures from grades kindergarten through eight. The era of the missing or sparsely filled-in grade book supplemented with the teacher's judgment of what the student can do will not satisfy the parents today who are looking at Modern Mathematics through the work and experiences of their children. Some of the textbook series offer chapter and semester tests. These tests are good starting places for a continual evaluation program progressing up through the grade school. We must examine the tests included with the textbooks to see if they are not too easy and do not encourage rote learning. Those items that can be used with an open book test are probably satisfactory and with a few added items from a teacher can form a good test. Records of individual student performance on the major tests should be recorded each year and included in the student's cumulative folder. By computing class means each year it will be easier to identify and make allowances for unusually strong or weak classes. The test items used for each semester should be available for all teachers to examine and should have stood the test of an item-analysis or at least agreement by the majority of the mathematics teachers within a grade. Constructing good test items takes a great amount of teacher planning time, therefore, a pooling of good items certainly proves advantageous to all teachers involved. If you were teaching in a building where three teachers of sixth grade mathematics were employed you might prepare the tests for units one, four, seven, etc., or you might prepare items on percent and measurement while the other two teachers prepared items on other areas of mathematics. After this works effectively within a grade you are ready to work with teachers in other grades and finally arrive at an articulated evaluation program for grades kindergarten through eighth.

HOW TO TEACH SUCCESS

There is a definite need for articulation between the junior high teachers and the primary teachers in how the student should experience success in working mathematics. We must encourage primary teachers to allow their students to experience failure as well as successful learning. Much time is wasted in the primary grades preparing the students for a worksheet which often takes only ten minutes to complete. If the worksheet is so far out of sequence that three days are needed for preparation, it would be better to omit or postpone until later. We need to motivate our students in creating a desire to learn and we need to confront them at all grade levels with new experiences to determine their capabilities to learn. If we explain and structure every new thing for the students during the primary grades we cannot expect them to carry anything to the junior high level except a few rote memory tables. It does little good to fill the students with facts unless we can give them experiences where they must structure these facts in a new situation and either arrive at a successful or an unsuccessful solution to the problem.

A teacher does not need to occupy the front center seat or desk throughout the year. When a teacher's desk remains prominent in the front of the room, it often places a premium on instruction rather than pupil activity. When the desk is pushed off to the side or back of the room one cannot help but think the teacher is probably an instructor who allows her students to learn and discover for themselves. The accessibility of the blackboard is further visual evidence of opportunity for student participation. When five of six panels of the blackboard are covered with bulletin board displays of pupil achievements one cannot help but believe that this teacher has not allowed her students the privilege of making mistakes in working mathematics at the blackboard. The blackboard is by far the most misused and underused tool in the elementary school. Articulation is needed so that more classtime is devoted to blackboard experiences in the lower grades and less in the upper grades where the student can listen for a longer span of time. We have now too much blackboard drill in the junior high school where this type of activity will settle the discipline and content planning for the day while there is too little use of the blackboard in the primary grades because the blackboard space has been used for other purposes.

SELECTING A TEXTBOOK

The largest criticism this writer has of junior high mathematics teachers must be directed at those who maintain they do not need or want a basic textbook from which to teach. In lieu of a textbook they want to take the best content from several programs and build a "super" content structure for their students. When we closely examine this "super" content structure, we usually find a teacher who used a unit on numeration from one series, five pages on successive subtraction or ordered pairs from another series, a few terms and exercises from The School Mathematics Study Group Materials, a chapter on the language of sets from another series, and a week's enrichment unit on Modular Arithmetic from another series, thus leaving approximately one-hundred forty of the one-hundred sixty lesson plans to come from textbook series that the teacher has used for many years. A few teachers can offer a satisfactorily fused course of this nature without serious gaps but most junior high teachers will finish the year with discouraged students, many serious gaps, and omissions in the content and about all that can be said for the year's effort is that the teacher had fun at the expense of the students. This type of arrangement produces apprehension in the primary teacher because she does not have the time or desire to arrange this "super" content structure. Junior high teachers are foolish to think that they can look at three to six modern mathematics programs and select the best content from each, rather they should select a basic textbook series along with the primary teachers and then supplement the textbook in the areas where it is weak. This should be done jointly in the primary and intermediate grades as well as the junior high school.

METHODS CAN BE LEARNED FROM EACH OTHER

Outstanding classroom procedures can be found in all grades of the elementary school. Four observed classroom experiences are reported below.

1. A third-grade teacher used immediate feedback by having each student raise his or her hand when they disagreed with a student who was either reading an example to the class or working an example at the board. When a student made a mistake he was immediately confronted with fifteen to twenty-five "quiet" hands extended in the air. The teacher also used this procedure of raising her hand quietly when she disagreed with a student, although her hand was never observed as being the first to be raised. When the student observed the raised hands he quickly and quietly attempted to find his error, if any, and then either changed his answer to the favor of his peers or defended the answer he believed to be correct. This immediate type of reinforcement seemed more beneficial to the student than the usual type that is followed in grades seven and eight where the teacher interrupts the student and tells him he is wrong and corrects him or where several other students yell that the student is wrong and give him the correct answer before he has a chance to discover it for himself.

2. Another area where all teachers could benefit from sharing ideas is in working with the slow-learner in mathematics. Far too often the following facts are evident: John cannot attend second grade mathematics class because his English or Social Studies work is not completed. Bill is not in mathematics class today because he was rude during Science class and he must sit out in the hall. Ellen is taking her band lesson during mathematics class because she can make up the mathematics assignment easier than her other assignments. Tom and Dan are working on the stage crew for the class play during mathematics class because they are poor in mathematics and pounding a hammer is something they like. The point is that throughout the elementary school teachers neglect a small group of students by allowing these typical excuses to temporarily rid them of the students who cause

concern during mathematics classes. Teachers need to be more stern throughout the elementary school by keeping the slow learners in regular attendance and helping them to do the work that is expected of them. By identifying these students a faculty can quickly see that several teachers have been responsible for the injustice that many slow-learners in mathematics have received from the school. The identification of the students who regularly miss mathematics classes will also show that several of these students may come from the same family and that the teachers have been treating Billy's younger brothers and sisters the way they treated Billy without giving them a chance. It has not been uncommon for this writer to observe two or more children from the same family missing mathematics classes in different grades the same day for various reasons.

3. The following homework assignment was given to a low-ability third grade class which consisted of seventeen boys and two girls. Add nine to the even numerals two through twenty. The next day the teacher asked the class what they learned by adding these numerals. Among their comments were the following three:

(1) The answers kept getting larger.
(2) The even numbers were skipped in the answers.
(3) The ones column in the answer is one less than the ones number on top of the problem.

This activity occurred after a junior high teacher suggested this type of assignment to a third grade teacher. The suggestion was followed and appreciated by the third grade teacher. This teacher was an outstanding instructor in the area of Language Arts but had no expressed desire for mathematics. After following this suggestion and others by the junior high teacher she stated that she had never had a low-ability group in mathematics as enthused and interested as her present class and that she was even receiving pleasure from teaching mathematics that she had never enjoyed before. This suggestion was small indeed but it gave impetus and confidence to an experienced teacher to try new methods in her classroom. Getting a faculty together in a given district to share methods and ideas seems far more important as a starting place in updating the mathematics curriculum than to bring in an expert for a workshop or adopting a new modern mathematics series.

4. The following exercises were observed in a fourth grade class that was starting on long division after they had completed work with short division. Four students were sent to the blackboard and asked to work the following exercises and fill in the bottom of the problem. All students placed the answers on top first and then filled in the bottom with these results. All answers were correct yet each example had one or more errors in the algorism. If the fourth grade teacher in your district brought this problem to your junior high teacher could he help her? Would the fourth grade teacher in your district feel comfortable in presenting this type of problem to the junior high teacher? If "no" is an answer to either of these questions then you are in need of better articulation between the junior high and primary teachers within your district.

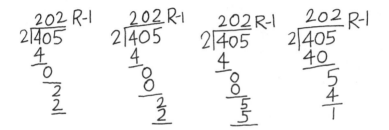

Relating Arithmetic to Everyday Life

Frances Flournoy

It is generally agreed that there are two major mutually related and inter-dependent purposes for arithmetic instruction: a social purpose and a mathematical purpose. The mathematical purpose gives arithmetic its principal content—the concepts to be gained, computational procedures to be learned, relationships to be realized, and principles to be understood. The social purpose has to do with the application of arithmetic to the practical affairs of daily life. Through this latter purpose, we intend to assist the learner in solving quantitative problems of daily living both now and in the future, and to appreciate how quantitative ideas are needed and used by the society in which we live.

Through the mathematical aim, arithmetic is *understood* and its learning becomes *meaningful*. Through the social aim, arithmetic has *usefulness* and its learning becomes *significant*. The two aims complement each other. The learner must understand arithmetic in order to apply it most effectively in the quantitative situations of life. It is also essential that a social situation be used as a springboard in the sequence of steps taken to develop mathematical understanding. The learner must be able to relate the mathematical skills and understandings he is learning to significant social situations in everyday life in order to make the most effective application of the arithmetic skills.

How may children be made aware of the important role of mathematics in daily life, be guided in exploring the mathematical aspects of daily living, and be given encouragement and opportunity to use arithmetic effectively? A variety of procedures which may be helpful to teachers and principals faced with this important responsibility are suggested here. Others may be developed through cooperative planning.

RELATING SOCIAL EXPERIENCES TO ARITHMETIC

Added significance may be given to arithmetic if the textbook program is supplemented with fresh, quantitative situations which the pupils help to identify and explore.

Introduce new skills in a social situation using a problem of immediate

Reprinted from *The National Elementary Principal*, Vol. 39, No. 2 (October 1959), 29–32, by permission of the publisher. Copyright 1959, Department of Elementary School Principals, National Education Association. All rights reserved.

importance when such a problem is available. One third-grade class was planning a field trip. The problem chosen to introduce division was: "We have 30 children in our class. If 5 children can ride in each car on the field trip, how many cars will be needed in all?"

Ask children to think of situations in life in which a selected arithmetic skill is used. The list of needs for multiplying skills compiled by one fourth-grade class included finding how much money can be saved in four weeks by saving 15¢ each week; how much five 4¢ stamps will cost for use in the class letter exchange program with another school; how many points would be earned for selling 6 magazine subscriptions at 15 points for each; and how many children can play a certain new game with three groups and four children in each group.

Pupils should be given experience in constructing true-to-life problem situations which will require the use of each new arithmetic skill that is taught. This procedure should also effectively contribute to the improvement of problem-solving ability.

Encourage children to tell of real number experiences which they have had that are similar to quantitative problem situations described in the text-book.

Guide children in analyzing social situations to note the arithmetic skills needed. These should be situations in which members of the class participate or with which they are familiar. A fourth-grade class analyzed the following social situations to note arithmetic skills needed: buying lunch in the cafeteria, taking a vacation trip by car, delivering and collecting for newspapers, making cookies, marking off a softball diamond on the playground.

Plan with the class for keeping a record of how class members use arithmetic during a one-week period. Primary pupils might report orally to the teacher each day during the week. Intermediate grade pupils could be encouraged to keep a written record. The class should discuss these uses for arithmetic and identify the arithmetic skills needed in each situation. The teacher might also make dittoed copies of these problem situations for practice materials to be used by the children.

Provide pupils with numerous opportunities to solve without the aid of paper and pencil simple word problems read aloud. This experience is of great importance to the pupil since the majority of arithmetic problems which he meets in everyday life will have to be solved without paper and pencil.

Plan dramatizations or actually act out social situations requiring arithmetic skills. Examples for the primary grades are: dialing the telephone, serving cookies, buying postage stamps, buying valentines, making lemonade, selling groceries, and buying a train ticket. Examples for the intermediate grades are: paying bills for parents, borrowing money, buying paint for classroom walls, making a deposit at the bank, buying on an installment plan, planning ball courts for the playground, and buying a rug for a bedroom. A very suitable assembly program could be planned around the dramatization of situations in which arithmetic is used.

Keep a class scrapbook of arithmetic usages found in magazines and newspapers. Individuals in the class can contribute to the scrapbook. Each usage is discussed to identify the arithmetic involved.

Put up bulletin boards to show how arithmetic is used. These could be in the classroom or, if the school has hallway display space, in the corridors. Interesting and effective bulletin boards can be centered around such topics as: How We Use Counting, How We Use Adding, Uses for Common Fractions, Uses for Linear Measures, How Graphs Are Used.

Display materials of social usage related to arithmetic skills taught. An important aspect of this procedure is to encourage active and voluntary participation by students in collecting display materials. Examples of effective materials are: a thermometer, a barometer, an automobile speedometer, a rain gauge, a weather map, measuring instruments, box or can containers labeled to show amount of contents, recipes, house floor plans, graphs, road maps, time tables, advertisements, sales slips, bills for utilities, transportation tickets, bank deposit slips, a savings book, a check book, cancelled checks, receipts for money paid, and pamphlets [1] on occupations that require facility in mathematics, such as engineering, navigation, architecture, accounting, merchandising, and banking.

SOCIAL ARITHMETIC UNITS

Most arithmetic textbook units are organized around subject-matter units. The logical sequence aspect of arithmetic generally necessitates a subject-matter unit organization. It usually remains, then, for the teacher to organize one or more arithmetic units each year around social usage of arithmetic. Faculty groups might plan a sequence of social arithmetic units with perhaps two units planned as appropriate for each grade level. These should prove to be of considerable value in giving children an opportunity to explore social uses of arithmetic and to practice a variety of arithmetic skills.

The usual unit procedure can be followed during the regular arithmetic period: motivate the pupils for study of the unit; plan with the pupils problems for study and ways of studying; guide pupils in gathering data; guide pupils as a class in sharing and considering findings and reaching conclusions.

Examples of unit topics are: [2]

---

[1] Kidd, Kenneth P., Brown, Kenneth E. *Teaching Materials for Mathematics Classes.* U.S. Department of Health, Education, and Welfare, Office of Education, Circular No. 399. Washington, D.C.: Superintendent of Documents, Government Printing Office, pp. 1–12.

[2] Brueckner, Leo J., and Grossnickle, Foster E. *Making Arithmetic Meaningful.* Philadelphia: John C. Winston Company, 1953, pp. 137–161.

Grade 1: How are numbers used in our favorite games?
Grade 2: How much does it cost to keep a dog?
Grade 3: In what quantities are foods packaged for selling?
Grade 4: How much does a vacation trip by car cost?
Grade 5: What is included in the cost of advertising?
Grade 6: How is a classroom planned and furnished?

RELATING ARITHMETIC TO OTHER AREAS OF THE PROGRAM

The importance of arithmetic in other areas of the school program can receive additional emphasis if several arithmetic projects and problems related to social studies and science units are planned and carried out each year. These may be activities during the social studies or science period, or may be part of an enrichment activity during the arithmetic period. Individuals or small groups might carry out the projects as enrichment activities and share them with the whole class.

Examples of such projects are: [3]

Grade 1: Keeping a weather record by days (cloudy, sunshine, rain) with summary reports by weeks.
Grade 2: Reading and keeping daily records of temperatures and indicating them daily on a model ribbon thermometer.
Grade 3: Planning and mapping a garden.
Grade 4: Figuring distance from hive of bees to source of nectar.
Grade 5: Constructing a date line.
Grade 6: Figuring yield per acre by use of a sampling technique.

In addition, it is possible to take advantage of incidental opportunities to use arithmetic in other areas of the school program. Numbers are a part of children's reading, listening, speaking, writing, playing, drawing, singing, and constructing. Only a few examples can be given here; the teacher will recognize other incidental opportunities to use arithmetic as it relates to other areas of the school program.

Examples of such incidental opportunities are: finding page numbers in a book, placing the date on paper for written exercises, counting how many beats a musical note gets, timing a race, keeping game scores, keeping a record of batting averages, reading a map scale, printing letters, lining charts, reading and interpreting numbers as these appear in social studies and science content. Quantitative terms and statements appear with high frequency in social studies and science reading materials. Children need experience in setting up tables of reference measures,[4] selecting a suitable reference measure, and comparing an unfamiliar quantity with a familiar quantity.[5]

[3] Spitzer, Herbert F. *The Teaching of Arithmetic.* Boston: Houghton Mifflin Co. 1954. pp. 196–199.
[4] Spitzer, Herbert F. *ibid.* Pp. 286–291.
[5] Flournoy, Frances. 'Interpreting Definite Quantitative Statements Occurring in Reading Reference Materials," *Elementary School Journal* 58: 208–211; January 1958.

ARITHMETIC IN CLASSROOM LIVING

Certain of the activities which are carried on as a part of the social living of a classroom, but which are not strictly a part of the curriculum, involve the use of numbers. The alert teacher will take advantage of these situations as a rich means of emphasizing the social usefulness of arithmetic and encourage pupil application of arithmetic skills in real life problem situations. These experiences will prove to be valuable in developing greater competence in the use of arithmetic.

The following are examples of typical classroom situations involving some use of numbers and number processes: passing out books, paper, pencils; filling out attendance slips; collecting money for morning milk or lunch money; daily reading of the calendar; weighing and measuring heights of pupils; planning a time schedule for the day's activities; collecting and keeping a record of funds for the Junior Red Cross; and planning and preparing refreshments for a class party.

USING COMMUNITY RESOURCES

Resource persons and places can be used effectively to develop an awareness of the important role of arithmetic in community life. Pupils can conduct interviews, speakers can be invited to the classroom, and field trips can be taken as part of this project.

The farmer, grocer, milkman, postman, department store clerk, policeman, weatherman, gas station attendant, engineer, accountant, and banker are some of the people living in the community who could be asked to share interesting number experiences with children. Each could be invited to talk about "How I Use Arithmetic in My Work" and might be asked to bring a variety of illustrative materials with him into the classroom to supplement his talk.

Teachers might also plan with pupils to interview their own parents, both the mother and father, as to how they use arithmetic. Pupils could share the ways their parents use arithmetic and might also write story problems about these for the class to solve.

The drug store, department store, grocery store, bank, post office, shipping room, depot, airport, and building or construction sites are but a few examples of places where children may observe arithmetic being used. Field trips taken in connection with social studies and science units could include a study of the importance of arithmetic in the social or scientific problems being studied. Faculty groups might well work together in preparing a whole school plan regarding resource persons and places in a particular community which might be used at each grade level in developing an awareness of how arithmetic is used in many different ways by people in the community.

Further and excellent suggestions regarding the utilization of community resources in teaching mathematics may be found in the United States Office of Education publication which was cited earlier.

ENRICHING ARITHMETIC

A deep and broad investigation of social applications of arithmetic is one excellent means of enriching the field of mathematics for the learner. While arithmetic may be enriched for all children through attention to its interesting applications, the teacher should provide the encouragement and opportunity for the child who is able to "dig deeper" to investigate a greater number and also more complex social applications of arithmetic. The able learner can independently carry on a variety of activities and investigations of social situations as suggested in preceding paragraphs. Through such projects he can greatly deepen his knowledge, appreciation, and insight into the role of arithmetic in the daily affairs of life.

Arithmetic in Action is an interesting pamphlet which emphasizes the role of arithmetic in life insurance.[6] It presents a variety of quantitative problems to be solved and could be used independently for enrichment purposes by pupils in grades five and six.

A FINAL WORD

In this article, a number of suggestions have been given for procedures which may be used in guiding children in exploring the mathematical aspects of everyday life and in applying arithmetic skills they are learning. Faculty groups might work together quite effectively to assure whole school planning of certain aspects of a program for emphasizing the social usefulness of arithmetic.

A variety of activities may be used during the regular arithmetic period which help relate the skills being learned to social uses for these skills. In addition, it is most important that children be encouraged to note the role of arithmetic in all the activities of the school day and in life outside of school. Let us not be so hurried in our teaching that we fail to take advantage of valuable and interesting opportunities to relate arithmetic to the mathematical aspects of everyday life and to enrich the learning of arithmetic through active investigation of its social applications.

[6] Institute of Life Insurance. *Arithmetic in Action.* Educational Division. Institute of Life Insurance, 488 Madison Avenue, New York 22, New York.

The Problem of Reading Instruction in Mathematics

John R. Clark

While on an automobile tour not long ago, I went into a stationery store one evening to do some shopping. The only persons in the store were three boys, in the rear, doing, or attempting to do, their homework in mathematics. One of the boys, evidently the son of the proprietor, came forward with a polite "Sir, may I help you?" After completing my purchases, I said, "What are you boys doing?" One replied, "Our math problems, sir. We're stuck. Could you help us?"

I expressed my interest and accompanied them to the rear. One of the boys handed me the textbook (of which I was an author) and said, "We're having trouble with problem four."

"Will you read it aloud to me?" I asked. The boy pronounced the words unusually well, but with such obvious lack of comprehension of the nature of the problem that I commented: "Your reading doesn't help me to understand the problem." I pointed to another boy. "Will you read it?" His reading revealed no better interpretation than did that of the first boy. The third boy then volunteered to read it aloud. His reading indicated quite clear comprehension of the thought and meaning of the problem, and brought forth from the other boys an "Oh! I see. I get the point."

I took leave of the trio with the remark, "Boys who read well, who interpret the ideas in their problems, have very little trouble with mathematics. Reading isn't just saying words. It's seeing the ideas behind them. Reading is very much like thinking."

Many junior high school boys and girls do have difficulty in reading their textbooks in mathematics. This paper proposes procedures for teaching reading which the author has found effective with most pupils, excluding only those whose mental, emotional, or physical conditions render them "clinical cases."

LEVELS OF READING ABILITY

We know that junior high school pupils in mathematics classes vary greatly in their ability to read the explanations and problems in their textbooks. For some pupils, reading at best consists of mere saying of words, with little or no comprehension. They dislike reading. Obviously they require

Reprinted from *Improving Reading in the Junior High School,* Bulletin 1957, No. 10, U.S. Department of Health, Education and Welfare.

more of the oral developmental, experiential type of instruction which is currently so effectively employed in many elementary schools.

At the other end of the scale are those pupils who, independently, are able through reading to modify old concepts or to acquire new ones. They are capable of reading for a degree in depth, difficulty, and range greater than that of the average mathematics text. Unless challenged by reading content appropriate to their capacity, they are likely to lose interest in the subject. If effectively challenged, they will be able to become outstanding thinkers. In this group we are most likely to find our future leaders in science and mathematics.

Then there is the large middle group of readers at whose level most of us direct much of our teaching and our writing. In this group we find various kinds of reading disabilities—mental, physical, and emotional. Specialists in reading have made significant contributions to classroom techniques, looking toward correction and prevention of such disabilities.

The purpose of this paper is to suggest instructional procedures to benefit, in varying degrees, learners at all levels of ability and achievement, both in mathematics and in reading.

OBJECTIVES OF MATHEMATICS EDUCATION

Before considering further the place of reading in our mathematics classrooms, we must have a large measure of agreement concerning the major objectives of mathematics education.

For our purposes here we shall assume, not argue, these major objectives. Stated very briefly, they are (1) learning to reason, to think one's way through a problem situation (quantitative, of course) to find a response that has not previously been learned, and (2) learning to compute and to estimate, once the reasoning has disclosed the operations required to bring forth the wanted results.

But reasoning requires ideas, concepts, meanings. Reasoning is rearranging or relating the ideas in the problem situation so that the "what is wanted" is seen as a consequence of the "what is known." Thus, reasoning presupposes knowledge of the concepts. Hence, we have as an *instrumental objective* the teaching of the fundamental concepts inherent in the number system. (Recently we have been calling these ideas or concepts the *meanings* of mathematics.)

We may say, then, that we are greatly concerned with instruction in the concepts of our field, in order that the learners may be able to "think about," to "reason about" significant problems in their experience.

Experience has taught us that in the initial stages of instruction in each new concept we should rely upon *oral* rather than *written* communication. We *explore, say, hear, discuss, talk about* the problem. We experiment, discover, explain, listen, use illustrations, and develop. We build new meanings and modify old ones; we generalize and particularize. We introduce new symbols, and new words in context. All the while, the teacher records these new words and symbols on the chalkboard and calls attention to their spelling and formation. The learners use them in sentences and enter them in their "New words" or "New symbols" lists.

These symbols and words, such as *circle, diameter, circumference, ratio,* and π (*pi*), illustrate the technical vocabulary of mathematics. This technical vocabulary is unique and indispensable. Meanings and interrelationships are more effectively learned at the outset through oral discussion, experimentation, and informal verbalization than through reading. But there comes a time when it is to the learner's advantage to be able to supplement, if not replace, the oral expression. He must be able to read, to comprehend thought communicated through written or printed sentences. Reading, of course, helps the pupil to establish and clarify concepts which he has acquired through more direct experience.

MAKING AND READING MATHEMATICAL GENERALIZATIONS

Let us continue our discussion of the concepts of *circle, circumference, diameter, ratio,* and *pi.* As a result of the informal, developmental, discussion type of teaching, the pupil will have participated in the making of such generalizations as:

1. The circumference of a circle is a little more than three times its diameter.
2. When we divided the length of the circumference of a circle by the length of its diameter, we got a quotient of about 3.
3. We called the "quotient of the circumference divided by the diameter" the *ratio* of the circumference to the diameter. Ratio means quotient.
4. We agreed to call the ratio or quotient *pi.* It's the same for all circles.
5. We also found that the diameter is about one-third of the circumference.

These, and other observations about the concepts of *circumference, diameter, ratio of circumference to diameter,* and *pi,* are prerequisites for reading. They constitute a kind of mathematical reading readiness. The teacher prepares learners *for* reading!

After this careful preparation, most learners may be expected to be able to read and respond successfully to such written questions and statements as the following (presumably found in the textbook or supplied in other written form):

1. The circumference of a circle is about how many times as long as its diameter?
2. Jack measured the diameter of a circle, and decided that it was 12.2 inches. He wanted to find its circumference. To do so, would he have to measure it? Why not?

3. Is *ratio* a sum, a difference, a product, or a quotient?

4. To find the ratio of circumference to diameter (when both are known), would you divide the diameter by the circumference, or divide the circumference by the diameter?

5. Make a sentence using the words *circumference, diameter,* and *pi.* What is the subject of your sentence?

6. Complete the sentence: To find the circumference when the diameter is known, ...

7. Complete the sentence: To find the diameter when the circumference is known, ...

PROBLEM ANALYSIS LEADING TO READING AND SOLUTION OF PROBLEMS

In the circle-circumference-ratio-pi illustration, we have been concerned with learning that prepares the pupil to read generalizations with comprehension. We shall now consider the analysis of the so-called verbal problem, leading to its reading and solution.

"Find the rate of discount on a six-dollar pair of skates that sold for four dollars." To solve the problem, the learner (the reader) must bring to the problem a galaxy of previous learnings. These include:

1. *Marked price, selling price, discount,* and *rate of discount.* Without these concepts, there can be no real reading, even though the words may be pronounceable and spellable.

2. Understanding by the reader of the *relationship* between (*a*) the concepts of marked price, selling price, and discount, and (*b*) the rate of discount, discount, and marked price.

Obviously the particular data in the above problem (six dollars, etc.), are relatively unimportant in comprehending the problem; they are necessary only for computing the numerical answer.

Thus, as we said previously, before the learner can be expected to read with comprehension the above problem, before he is ready to read it, he must realize that discount means "marked price minus selling price," and that *rate of discount* means the ratio of discount to the marked price, or "*discount compared with marked price by division.*"

Guidance or help in the reading of the problem is almost, if not wholly, equivalent to guidance in the reasoning required in solving the problem. This may be facilitated by such questions as:

1. What is the problem? (Finding rate of discount.)

2. What do you have to know and do to find rate of discount? (Know discount and marked price; and then divide discount by marked price.)

3. Does the problem tell you the discounts? (No.)

4. What must you know and do to find the discount? (Know marked price and selling price; and then subtract selling price from the marked price.)

5. Does the problem tell you the marked price and the selling price? (Yes, six dollars and four dollars; so the discount is two dollars.)

6. Now that you know the discount and the marked price, what did you say you must do to find the rate of discount? (Divide the discount by the marked price.)

The reader must be in possession of the concepts of marked price, selling price, discount, and rate of discount. He must be prepared to read, i.e., to sense the ideas denoted by the words and phrases of the verbal statement. With this preparation, the reading (getting the thought) is possible.

To emphasize the ideas or concepts in reading a verbal problem, we often have the problem read and paraphrased, naming only the big ideas. Thus, in our rate of discount problem the pupil might paraphrase as follows: I paid so much for an article which regularly sold for so much; I got a discount of so much; I have to find the rate of the discount.

We are insisting that reading in mathematics, whether of generalizations or problems, implies analysis, recognition of ideas and the relationships among them. In a sense, reading is thinking, relating what is wanted to what is given. The ability or inability of the pupil to *read* mathematics exposition and problems with comprehension and discernment is determined to a great degree by the clarity, depth, and range of his mathematical concepts. Good readers are those who have the conceptual equipment necessary to recognize the mathematical ideas connoted by mathematical words, phrases, and symbols. Poor readers are those who are deficient in this conceptual equipment. Remedial reading is closely equivalent to relearning or improved learning of the ideas.

The pupil whose understandings are relatively immature will of necessity be a relatively poor reader. We improve his reading by clarifying his understandings, by reteaching, by moving him at a slower pace, by providing more experiences with ideas.

Now let us consider what reading difficulties may be encountered in a group of verbal problems. What opportunities for growth in reading may be provided?

1. Meaningless technical words or phrases may appear in one or more of the problems. If so, they, the problems, should be omitted from the assignment. In this case the teacher or textbook will have violated the accepted principle that verbal problems should apply *previously learned concepts*.

2. The non-technical vocabulary may be inappropriate or above the reading level of the class, or some members of the class. In this case the problem should be read aloud by one or more good readers, after which the word or phrase may be modified, or replaced.

3. The sentences may be too long. Here the teacher may have the pupils suggest ways of revising them to make them more readable.

4. The problem may contain insufficient data for its solution. If so, this fact should be recognized by the class, with a resulting agreement as to what action should be taken to supply the missing needed data.

5. A problem may contain irrelevant or unneeded information. In fact, some problems of this type are desirable. Identification of such information makes for purposeful reading.

CHARACTERISTICS OF MATHEMATICAL READING

Reading in mathematics is distinctive in three important respects:

1. The vocabulary of mathematical reading is probably more limited and more exacting than that of any other subject area. Its words and symbols are characterized by a high degree of precision of meaning. Its sentences are succinct. The flow of thought is sequential. Such words and phrases as *since, therefore, consequently, put-together, take-apart, compare, by definition, by assumption,* and the like, call for keen discernment. The learner's reading rate is necessarily slow. There is no such thing as "skimming." Every word, phrase, and symbol must be digested. The reader becomes disposed to ask himself, "What does this mean? How are the ideas related? In which direction do I go now? Is the statement always true?" In this reading-thinking process, explanations and problems may need to be read several times for full comprehension.

2. The symbolic or shorthand language of mathematics cannot be read intelligently until the symbols have meaning. This symbolic language can have meaning only by skillful association with less symbolic and more meaningful language.

For example, to read with insight such symbolic expressions as $a \div b$, $b \overline{\smash{)}a}$, the pupil must have the concepts of partition and comparison division. Interpreted as partition, the verbalization of each algorism is: "Some number a is to be separated into some number b of equal parts." Interpreted as comparison division, the verbalization of each is: "How many b's are there in a?" or (when b is larger than a) "a is what part of b?"

Effective reading of such expressions as $y = 2x + 3$ presupposes the concepts of *variable, equality, multiplication,* and *addition.* The expression states that "two numbers are so related that one of them is always 3 more than twice the other."

Thus, as in the reading of word symbols, the reading of mathematical symbols demands of the reader the possession of concepts and understanding of the relationships among them.

3. Reading improves and extends language usage and builds mathematical understanding. Textbooks are generally written in terse, concise, and correct statements. Pupils must be taught to appreciate the various and equally correct ways in which mathematical thought is expressed. For example:

(1) The commission at the rate of 5% on sales of $1600 is (a) 5% of $1600, or (b) .05 × $1600, or (c) $1600 multiplied by .05, or (d) the product of .05 and $1600, etc.

(2) The number of yards in a mile (5280 feet) is (a) the quotient of 5280 feet divided by 3 feet, or (b) equal to the number of times 3 feet is contained in 5280 feet, or (c) may be computed by dividing 5280 feet by 3 feet, etc.

(3) The area of a rectangle 4 feet wide and 6 feet long is (*a*) 4×6 square feet, and (*b*) 6×4 square feet, or (*c*) $4 \times 6 \times 1$ square feet, or (*d*) the product of its dimensions (in feet), etc.

The stating and reading (with comprehension) of such varied, equivalent, and equally correct ways of thinking and expression deepen insight. Practice in re-casting, in other equivalent language, statements found in the text is rewarding.

HIGH-LEVEL MATURITY IN READING

It will be apparent that up to this point we have proceeded upon the assumption that the teacher has played the major role in the instruction. She has employed reading, to be sure, but chiefly as a follow-up, as a continuation, extension, and enrichment of the oral, developmental instruction. She has prepared the pupil for reading by making sure that he has the conceptual background prerequisite to the reading. However, the teacher believes that the pupil should become increasingly able to learn through his reading, and become less and less dependent upon her. Eventually the pupil should be able, through his reading, to sense and clarify the ideas, get new ideas, and see the relationships among them. Through critical study of what he reads, he can be his own teacher. At this mature level, reading will have become the open sesame to mathematical insight.

A colleague of mine ingeniously and effectively promotes this kind of teaching. One of his pupils reads (and reports to the class) textbook A's treatment of a topic, such as *area*. Another pupil reads and reports on textbook B's treatment of the same topic, and so on for several other texts. On other topics, other pupils read and report. The teacher's assumption is that pupils *can read*, and that they derive profit and pleasure from the reading and from the sharing and comparing of their learning experiences.

CONCLUSION

1. In order to be able or ready to read mathematics, most pupils require an oral, exploratory, experimental, developmental, discussion type of teaching designed to build and enlarge the concepts and generalizations. During this period the essential oral and written vocabulary becomes familiar and meaningful.

2. Following the above procedure, pupils having no special disabilities are able to read with comprehension statements and questions about the topics just developed. Emphasis is upon the recognition of ideas and the relationships among them.

3. After verbal problems have been read, they should be paraphrased or restated so that the mathematical ideas appear in bold relief. This facilitates the reasoning leading to their solution, and at the same time aids the poor reader.

4. Mathematical reading is highly specialized. The person best equipped to guide the reader is the mathematics teacher, who conceives of the teaching of reading of mathematical ideas as an integral part of the learning in his field. Mathematics teachers, however, need the guidance of "reading specialists" in the prevention and correction of deep-seated reading disabilities.

Meaning and Skill—Maintaining the Balance

William A. Brownell

The subject given me poses a question. It is no academic question arising out of purely theoretical considerations. It is assumed that both meaning and computational competence are proper ends of instruction in arithmetic. It is implied that somehow or other both ends are not always achieved and that there is evidence that this is so.

Indeed there is such evidence. More than one school system has embarked upon a program of so-called meaningful arithmetic, only to discover that on standardized tests of computation and "problem solving" pupils do none too well. In such schools officials and teachers are likely to believe that they have made a bad bargain; and school patrons are likely to support them vehemently in this belief.

We may try to convince all concerned that the instruments used to evaluate learning are inappropriate, or at least imperfect and incomplete. True, standardized tests rarely if ever provide means to assess understanding of arithmetical ideas and procedures. Hence, the program of meaningful instruction, even if well managed, has no chance to reveal directly and explicitly its contribution to this aspect of learning. On the other hand, can we deny that the learning outcomes that *are* measured are of no significance? To do so is to say in effect that computational skill is of negligible importance, and we can hardly justify this position.

Why is there now the necessity to talk about establishing and maintaining the desirable kind of balance between meaning on the one hand and computational competence on the other?

Reprinted from *The Arithmetic Teacher*, Vol. III, No. 4 (October 1956), 129–136, by permission of the author and publisher.

SOURCES OF THE DILEMMA

1. INCOMPLETE EXPOSITION OF "MEANINGFUL ARITHMETIC"

Perhaps those of us who have advocated meaningful learning in arithmetic are at fault. In objecting to the drill conception of the subject prevalent not so long ago, we may have failed to point out that practice for proficiency in skills has its place, too. It is questionable whether any who have spoken for meaningful instruction ever proposed that children be allowed to leave our schools unable to compute accurately, quickly, and confidently. I am sure that all, if asked, would have rejected this notion completely. But we may not have *said* so, or said so often enough or vigorously enough. Our comparative silence on this score may easily have been misconstrued to imply indifference about proficiency in computation.

If this has actually happened, we can scarcely blame classroom teachers if they have neglected computational skill as a learning outcome. It is characteristic of educational movements to behave pendulum-wise. When we correct, we tend to over-correct. Just this sort of thing seems to have happened in the teaching of arithmetic. In fleeing from over-reliance on one kind of practice, we may have fled too far. It is a curious state of affairs that those of us who deplored the limitations of this kind of practice must now speak out in its behalf and stress its positive usefulness.

2. MISUNDERSTOOD LEARNING THEORY

A second possible explanation for our dilemma may be found, as is frequently the case in the practical business of education, in misinterpretations or misapplications of psychological theories of learning. Over-simplification of certain generalizations in learning theories as widely apart as are those of conditioning and of field theory could lead, and may have led, to the lessening of emphasis on practice in arithmetic.

a. Conditioning theory. According to the learning theory of one influential exponent of conditioning, once a response has been made to a stimulus a connection has been established. Thus, the child who says "Seven" in replying to the question, "How many are two and five?", sets up a connection between 2 and 5 as stimulus and 7 as response. If this is so—if the connection is actually formed by the one response—then at first glance practice might seem to be utterly purposeless.

But this inference is quite unfounded, as the psychologist in question makes abundantly clear. In saying that a connection is "established" he means no more than that a new neuromuscular pattern is available. He does *not* mean that our hypothetical child after the one experience will always, only, and instantly respond with "seven" when asked the sum of 2 and 5. If the response "seven" is to be the invariable one, moreover if the response is to be made in situations differing ever so slightly from the original one, then practice is required. In this theory of learning as conditioning, therefore, there is no comfort for those who would abandon practice as a means to promote the learning of arithmetical facts and skills.

b. Field theory. No more comfort is to be found in field theory of learning. It is often said that one experience of "insight" or "hindsight"—before, during, or after success—is enough; but enough for *what?* It may be all that is needed to understand a situation and the method of dealing with it. Yet, it is one thing to know the general rationale for solving a complicated mechanical puzzle but quite another thing to be able to manipulate the parts correctly with facility, ease, and speed.

So in arithmetic it is one thing to comprehend the mathematical principles governing decomposition in subtraction—something that can come from a single insightful experience—but another thing to be able to subtract quickly and correctly. Indeed if in examples like $73 - 47$ and $52 - 19$ a child who possesses this understanding always thinks through the complete logical explanation, his performance will be impaired, at least from the standpoint of speed. Understanding and skill are not identical. A single instance of insight may lead to understanding but will hardly produce skill. For skill, practice is necessary.

3. Influence of General Educational Theory

A third explanation for failure to stress computational competence is to be found in the recent history of educational theory. It must be remembered that the place of meaning and understanding in arithmetic has been generally recognized for not more than fifteen or twenty years. In 1935 we were still under the influence of somewhat sentimental and unrealistic notions both about children and about the course of their development. In extreme form these notions led to a kind of teaching that was anything but systematic. Indeed, what children learned, when they learned it, and how they learned it was left pretty much to the children themselves. Attempts to guide and direct learning and to organize learning experiences were frowned upon as "violating child nature" and as almost certainly productive of serious derangements of child personality. To those who held these views practice was anathema.

In the public schools, as contrasted with college departments of Education, this conception of the processes of learning and teaching did not gain much of a foothold. Nevertheless, it was in this climate of thought that stress on meaning in arithmetic put in its appearance. Those who were committed to the educational theory I have mentioned welcomed the new emphasis as confirming both what they did and what they did not do. If, deliberately or unwittingly, they accepted only the part of the emerging view most congenial to them, they committed an error that is very common and that is altogether human. Be that as it may, the consequences were none too good. True, these teachers may have been largely responsible for the quick and general endorsement of one aspect of meaningful arithmetic—learning with understanding. On the other hand, they could not themselves absorb the whole of it, and they remained hostile to practice in learning. Pupils taught by such teachers cannot be expected to make high scores on standardized arithmetic tests of skill in computation and "problem solving."

4. INADEQUATE INSTRUCTION ON MEANINGS

I have suggested three hypotheses as explaining why we may not be obtaining balance between understanding and computational competence in arithmetic, on the assumption that our shortcomings relate to the latter (computational competence) rather than to the former. These three are: the possible failure of advocates of meaningful arithmetic to emphasize sufficiently the importance of practice in acquiring arithmetical skills; misinterpretations of psychological theories of learning which have had the effect of minimizing the place of practice; and the unwillingness of some teachers, who believe completely that arithmetic must be made intelligible to children, to provide the practice necessary for computational proficiency. May I add a fourth? It is that we may not as yet be doing a very good job in teaching arithmetical meanings as they should be taught.

There is ample evidence in psychological research on learning that the effects of understanding are cumulative. There is also ample evidence, if not in arithmetic, then in other types of learning, that the greater the degree of understanding, the less the amount of practice necessary to promote and to fix learning. If these truths are sound—and I think they are—then they should hold in the field of arithmetical learning. It follows that computational skills among school children would be greater than they are if we *really* taught them to understand what they learn.

Again I remind you that meaningful arithmetic, as this phrase is commonly used, is a newcomer in educational thought. Many teachers, trained in instructional procedures suitable, say, to a view of arithmetic as a tool or a drill subject, find it difficult to comprehend fully what meaningful arithmetic is and what it implies for the direction of learning. Others than myself, I am sure, have, in conferences with teachers, been somewhat surprised to note that some of them are unfamiliar with major ideas in this conception and with methods of instruction adapted thereto.

Perhaps the commonest instructional error is, in a different context, the same one that has always distorted learning in arithmetic, namely, the acceptance of memorized responses in place of insistence upon understanding. Mathematical relationships, principles, and generalizations are couched in language. For example, the relationship between a given set of addends and their sum is expressed verbally in some such way as: "The order of the numbers to be added does not change the sum." It is about as easy for a child to master this statement by rote memorization as to master the number fact, $8 - 7 = 1$, and the temptation is to be satisfied when children can repeat the words of the generalization *verbatim*. Similarly, the rationale of computation in examples such as: $33 + 48$ and $71 - 16$, makes use of concepts deriving from our number system and our notions of place value. But many a child glibly uses the language of "tens" and "ones" with no real comprehension of what he is saying. Such learning is a waste of time. To use an Irish bull, the meanings have no meaning.

I intend no criticism of teachers. Until recently there have been few professional books of high quality to set forth the mathematics of arithmetic and to describe the kind of instruction needed. Moreover, many teachers have had no access to these few books. Again, until recently not many courses of study and teachers' manuals for textbook series have been of much help. It is not strange, therefore, that though meaningful arithmetic is adopted in a given school system, not all members of the teaching staff are well equipped to teach it. As a result, their pupils, denied a full and intelligent treatment of arithmetic as a body of rational ideas and procedures, have been unable to bring to computation all the aid that could come through understanding.

TOWARD A SOLUTION

So much for possible explanations—explanations of a general character—for our failure to keep meaning and skill in balance. I have no way of knowing the reality of any of the four hypotheses suggested or of the extent of its validity, to say nothing of the degree to which, taken together, the four account adequately for the situation. The fact remains that something needs to be done. What is the remedy?

Certainly we shall not get very far as long as we think of understanding and practice in absolute terms. I have deliberately done this so far in order to examine the issue in simple terms. Actually, it is erroneous to conceive of understanding as if it were either totally present or totally absent. Instead, there are degrees or levels of understanding. Likewise, not all forms of practice are alike. Rather, there are different types, and they have varying effects in learning.

LEVELS OF UNDERSTANDING

Consider the example $26 + 7$. The child who first lays out twenty-six separate objects, next seven more objects, and then determines the total by counting the objects one by one has a meaning for the operation. So has the child who counts silently, starting with 26. So has the child who breaks the computation into two steps, $26 + 4 = 30$ and $30 + 3 = 33$. So has the child who employs the principle of adding by endings,$-6 + 7 = 13$, so $26 + 7 = 33$. So has the child who, capable of all these types of procedure, nevertheless recognizes 33 at once as the sum of 26 and 7. All these children "understand," but their understandings may be said to represent different points in the learning curve. The counter is at the bottom, and the child who through understanding has habituated his response "thirty-three" so that it comes automatically is at the top of a series of progressively higher levels of performance.

All these levels of performance or of understanding are good, depending upon the stage of learning when they are used. For instance, finding the sum of 26 and 7 by counting objects is a perfectly proper way of meeting the demand at first; but it is not the kind of performance we want of a child in grade 4. At some time in that grade, or earlier, he should arrive at the stage when he can announce the sum correctly, quickly, and confidently, with a maximum of understanding.

It is a mistake to believe that this last stage can be achieved at once, by command as it were. When a child is required to perform at a level higher than he has achieved, he can do only one of three things. (a) He can refuse to learn, and his refusal may take the form; "I won't," or "I can't," or "I don't care," the last named signifying frustration and indifference which we should seek to prevent at all costs. (b) Or, he can acquire such proficiency at the level he *has* attained that he will be credited for thinking at the level desired. Many children develop such expertness in silent counting that, in the absence of close observation and questioning, they are believed to have procedures much beyond those they do have. (c) Or, third, he may try to do what the teacher seems to want. If an immediate answer is apparently expected, he will supply one, by guessing or by recalling a memorized answer devoid of meaning. If he guesses, obviously he makes no progress at all in learning. If he memorizes, only unremitting practice will keep the association alive; and if he forgets, he is helpless or must drop back to a very immature level of performance such as counting objects or marks by 1's.

For the stage of performance we should aim for ultimately, as in the case of the simple number facts, higher-decade facts, and computational skills, we have no standard term. We may use the word "memorization" to refer to what a child does when he learns to say "Four and two are six" without understanding much about the numbers involved, about the process of addition, or about the idea of equivalence. If we employ "memorization" in this sense, then that word is inappropriate for the last step in the kind of learning we should foster. Hence for myself I have adopted the phrase "meaningful habituation." "Habituation" describes the almost automatic way in which the required response is invariably made; "meaningful" implies that the seemingly simple behavior has a firm basis in understanding. The particular word or phrase for this last step in meaningful learning is unimportant; but the *idea,* and its difference from "memorization," *are* important.

Teaching meaningfully consists in directing learning in such a way that children ascend, as it were, a stairway of levels of thinking arithmetically to the level of meaningful habituation in those aspects of arithmetic which should be thoroughly mastered, among them the basic computational skills. Too many pupils, even some supposedly taught through understanding, do not reach this last stage. Instead, they stop short thereof; and even if they are intelligent about what they do when they compute, they acquire little real proficiency. In instances of this kind both learning and teaching have been incomplete.

How are teachers to know the status of their pupils with respect to progress toward meaningful habituation? Little accurate information is to be had from their written work, for both correct and incorrect answers can be obtained in many ways, and inference is dangerous. Insightful observation and pupils' oral reports volunteered or elicited through questioning are more fruitful sources of authentic data. Since children differ so much in their thought procedures, a good deal of this probing must be done individually. One of the most fruitful devices I can suggest for this probing consists in noting what children do in the presence of error.

I recall a conversation with a fourth grade girl whom I knew very well and who was having difficulty in learning—in her case, in memorizing—the multiplication facts. I asked her—her name was June—"How many are five times nine?" (This form of expression was used in her school instead of the better "How many are five nines?") Immediately she responded, "Forty-five." When I shook my head and said, "No, forty-six," she was clearly upset. Her reply, after some hesitation, was, "No, it's forty-five." When I insisted that the correct product is 46, June said, "Well, that isn't the way I learned it." I suggested that perhaps she had learned the wrong answer. Her next statement was, "Well, that's what my teacher told me." This time I told her that she may have misunderstood her teacher or that her teacher was wrong. June was obviously puzzled; then she resorted to whispering the table, "One times nine is nine; two times nine is eighteen," and so on, until she reached "five times nine is forty-five." Again I shook my head and said, "Forty-six." When she was unable to reconcile my product with what she had become accustomed to say, I asked her, "June, have you no way of finding out whether forty-five or forty-six is the correct answer?" Her response was, "No, I just learned it as forty-five." Of course I did not leave her in her state of confusion; but the point of the illustration is, I hope, quite apparent: Her inability to deal with error was convincing evidence of the superficiality of her "learning" and of its worthlessness.

Compare my conversation with June with that I had with Anne, another fourth grade girl whom also I knew well and who, like the first girl, was learning the multiplication facts. When I asked Anne, "How many are five times nine?", the correct answer came at once, just as in June's case; but from here on, mark the difference. I introduced the error, saying that the product is 46, not 45. Anne looked at me in disgust and said, "Are you kidding?" I maintained my position that $5 \times 9 = 46$. Immediately she said, "Do you want me to prove it's forty-five?" I told her to go ahead if she thought she could. She answered, "Well, I can. Go to the blackboard." There I was instructed to write a column of five 9's and, not taking any chances with me, Anne told me to *count* the 9's to make sure I had 5. Next came the command, "Add them." When I deliberately made mistakes in addition, she corrected me, each time saying, "Do you want me to prove that, too?" Obviously, I had to arrive at a total of 45. Having done so, I said, "Oh, that's just a trick," to which she replied, "Do you want me to prove it another way?" Exposure to error held no terrors for this child; she did not become confused or fall back upon repetition of the multiplication table; nor did she cite her teacher as an authority. Instead, Anne had useful resources in the form of understandings that were quite lacking in the case of June whose discomfiture I have described.

Probing for understanding need not depend wholly on opportunities to work with individual children. On the contrary, there are possibilities also under conditions of group instruction when questions beginning with "How" and "Why" supplement the commoner questions starting with "What." The worth of valid knowledge concerning level of understanding is inestimable for the guidance of learning. The demands upon time are not inconsiderable, but no one should expect to get full knowledge concerning every pupil. The prospects are not hopeless if ingenuity is exercised and if the goal is set, not at 100% of knowledge, but more realistically at perhaps 20% more than is now ordinarily obtained.

TYPES OF PRACTICE

In crude terms, practice consists in doing the same thing over and over again. Actually, an individual never does the same thing twice, nor does he face the same situation twice, for the first reaction to a given situation alters both the organism and the situation. A changed being responds the second and the third time, and the situation is modified accordingly.

We must concede the truth of these facts. At the same time, for our purposes we may violate them a bit. Let us conceive of practice of whatever kind as falling somewhere along a continuum. At the one end of the continuum is practice in which the learner tries as best he can to repeat just what he has been doing. At the other end is practice in which the learner modifies his attack in dealing with what is objectively the same situation (or what to him are similar situations). We may call these extremes "repetitive practice" and "varied practice," respectively.

An instance of repetitive practice is memorizing the serial order of number names by rote or applying the series in the enumeration of groups of objects. An instance of varied practice is the attempt, by trying different approaches, to find steadily better ways of computing in such examples as $43 + 39$, $75 - 38$, $136 \div 4$, and 32×48. Between the two extreme types of practice are innumerable others, differing by degree in the extent to which either repetition or variation is employed. But again, for our purposes, we may disregard all the intervening sorts of practice: we could not possibly name them all, or describe them, or show their special contributions of learning.

Both repetitive and varied practice affect learning, but in quite unlike ways. For illustration we may choose an instance of learning outside of arithmetic, for example, the motor activity of swimming. Suppose the beginner engages in repetitive practice: What does he do, and what will happen? Well, he will continue to use as nearly as he can exactly the movements he employed the first time he was in deep water, and the result will be that he may become highly proficient in making just those movements. He will hardly become an expert swimmer, but he will become an expert in doing what he does, whether it be swimming or not.

On the other hand, suppose that the beginner engages in varied practice. In this case he will seek to *avoid* doing precisely what he did at the outset. He will discard uneconomical movements; he will try out other movements, select those that are most promising, and seek a final coordination that makes him a good swimmer. Then what will he do? He will change to repetitive practice, for, having the effective combination of movements he wants, he will seek to perfect it in order to become more proficient in it.

The differences between repetitive practice and varied practice, both in what the learner does and in what his practice produces, are clearly discernible when we think of motor activities. They are less easily identified when we think of ideational learning tasks like the number facts and computational skills. But the differences are there none the less. The child who counts and only counts in dealing with examples like $36 + 37$ and $24 + 69$ is employing repetitive practice. The more he counts, the more expert he becomes in counting; but the counting will not, and cannot, move him to a higher level of understanding and of performance. In contrast is the child who, through self-discovery or through instruction, tries different ways to add in such examples. Under guidance he can be led to adopt higher and higher levels of procedures until he is ready for meaningful habituation. If then he does not himself fix his automatic method of adding, he can be led to do so through repetitive practice. In any case it is safer to provide the repetitive practice in order to increase proficiency and make it permanent.

The distinction between repetitive and varied practice, in their nature and in their consequence, is not always recognized in teaching. If repetitive practice is introduced too soon, before understanding has been achieved, the result, for one thing, may be blind effort and frustration on the part of the learner. Or, it may fix his performance at a low level, the level he has attained. No new and better procedure can emerge from repetitive practice though it may appear under conditions of drill when a child, tired of repetition or disappointed in its result, abandons it in search of something new.

There may be an instructional error of another kind, one already alluded to. This error is to insist, to quote some, that "there is no place for drill in the modern conception of teaching." True, there is no place for unmotivated drill on ill-understood skills; but the statement goes too far in saying that there is no place at all for repetitive practice. How else, one may ask, is the final step of meaningful habituation to be made permanent; how else is real proficiency at this level of learning to be assured?

The kind of practice most beneficial at any time, then, is the kind best adapted to accomplish a given end. For illustration, let us return to June and Anne and their learning of the multiplication facts.

June was trying to master these facts by repetitive practice, by saying over and over and over again the special grouping of words for each separate fact. Her level of understanding of the numbers and relationships involved was close to zero. Unless engaged in almost ceaselessly, her repetition of verbalizations could give her little more than temporary control, and control, be it noted, of the verbalizations alone. Lapses of memory would be nearly fatal and would subject her to the hazards of guessing. In no way could her memorization of senseless phrases contribute much to sound learning of the facts themselves, not to mention the deficiencies of its results for more advanced forms of computation and functional use. What June needed was not repetitive, but varied practice. By contrast, Anne, who was able to "prove" her announced products and who thereby demonstrated her full understanding of the relationship of the numbers, no longer needed varied practice and could safely and properly be encouraged to engage in repetitive practice.

We employ varied practice, then, if we wish the child to move upward from where he is toward meaningful habituation, and repetitive practice if we are endeavoring to produce true competence, economy, and permanence in this last stage of learning (or at any earlier stage which represents a type of performance of worth in itself). Practice has to be designed to fit the learner's needs, a fact which brings us back again to the individual and to the critical importance of accurate knowledge concerning his learning status.

IN CONCLUSION

To sum up, the balance between meaning and skill has been upset, if indeed it ever was properly established. The reasons are many, some of them relating to educational theory in general, others to misconceptions of psychological theories of learning, others to failure to teach arithmetical meanings thoroughly, and still others to carry learning in the case of computation to the level I have denoted meaningful habituation, and then to fix learning at that level. I have discussed these matters at length, perhaps at unwarranted extent in view of the fact that the remedy for the situation can be stated briefly. The remedy I propose is as follows:

1. Accord to competence in computation its rightful place among the outcomes to be achieved through arithmetic;

2. Continue to teach essential arithmetical meanings, but make sure that these meanings are just that and that they contribute as they should to greater computational skill;

3. Base instruction on as complete data as are reasonably possible concerning the status of children as they progress toward meaningful habituation;

4. Hold repetitive practice to a minimum until this ultimate stage has been achieved; then provide it in sufficient amount to assure real mastery of skills, real competence in computing accurately, quickly, and confidently.

3

Cognitive and Affective Development in Elementary School Mathematics

In an educational program, all activities are directed by the expectations of certain outcomes. It has been said frequently that the main purpose of education is to change individuals in some way: to develop certain skills, to develop understandings or concepts, to develop an appreciation, or to add to a person's knowledge. The statements of these expected or desired outcomes can be codified under psychomotor, cognitive and/or affective characteristics.

Teaching children to think is most difficult. We know that education does not take place without thought and without encouraging further thought. We also know that further thought about any topic will exist only to the degree that one possesses a favorable disposition toward that topic, idea, or subject.

It is, therefore, necessary to study those aspects of behavior which are inclusive of the aims of an elementary-school mathematics program. What is more important, what a child knows or how he feels about what he knows?

There seems to be a large segment of the population whose attitude toward mathematics is negative. While their abilities might be considered marginal or better, their attitudes are less favorable. How do we go about developing favorable attitudes toward mathematics? Surely many alert minds have had Procrustean experiences with mathematics, only to depart from these experiences, resenting the time spent and carrying the scars of aversion; or do value considerations enter? What can we do to make mathematics more appealing? How can we more fully develop the affective domain?

We would all agree that the receptive mind is more apt to develop higher cognitive facilities. How does early external stimulation develop mathematical thinking? What major changes in thinking about number, quantity, and measurement does Piaget present? Does the Piaget model consider cognitive as well as affective insights? What are the alternatives? Where shall we place the emphasis?

As you contrast past programs with contemporary programs and their emphasis, what factors seem to be more inclusive? How do contemporary programs provide for the development of these aspects? What dangers may be inherent in contemporary programs? Can you justify why a teacher needs to be alerted to the ideas treated in this section?

On Learning Mathematics

Jerome S. Bruner

I am challenged and honored to be asked to speak before a group of teachers of mathematics on the nature of learning and thinking—particularly mathematical learning and thinking. Let me introduce you to my intentions by citing a remark of the English philosopher, Weldon. He noted that one could discriminate between difficulties, puzzles, and problems. A difficulty is a trouble with minimum definition. It is a state in which we know that we want to get from here to there, both points defined rather rawly, and with not much of an idea how to bridge the gap. A puzzle, on the other hand, is a game in which there is a set of givens and a set of procedural constraints, all precisely stated. A puzzle also requires that we get from here to there, and there is at least one admissible route by which we can do so, but the choice of route is governed by definite rules that must not be violated. A typical puzzle is that of the Three Cannibals and Three Missionaries, in which you must get three missionaries and three cannibals across a river in a boat that carries no more than two passengers. You can never have more cannibals than missionaries on one side at a time. Only one cannibal can row; all three missionaries can. Another puzzle, one in which the terminus has not yet been achieved, is the so-called Twin Primes Conjecture. Now, Weldon proposes that a problem is a difficulty upon which we attempt to impose a puzzle form. A young man, trying to win the favor of a young lady—a difficulty—decides to try out successively and with benefit of correction by

Reprinted from *The Mathematics Teacher* (December 1960), 610–619, by permission of the author and publisher.

experience, a strategy of flattery—an iterative procedure, and a classic puzzle —and thus converts his difficulty into a problem. I rather expect that most young men do all this deciding at the unconscious level; I hope so for the sake of my daughters! But the point of mentioning it is not my fatherly jealousy, but to emphasize that the conversion of difficulties into problems by the imposition of puzzle forms is often not always done with cool awareness, and that part of the task of the mathematician is to work toward an increase in such awareness. But this gets me ahead of my exposition.

Let me urge that the pure mathematician is above all a close student of puzzle forms—puzzles involving the ordering of sets of elements in a manner to fulfill specifications. The puzzles, once grasped, are obvious, so obvious that it is astounding that anybody has difficulty with mathematics at all, as Bertrand Russell once said in exasperation. "Why, the rowing cannibal takes over another cannibal and returns. Then he takes over the other cannibal and returns. Then two missionaries go over, and one of them brings back a nonrowing cannibal. Then a missionary takes the rowing cannibal over and brings back a nonrowing cannibal. Then two missionaries go over and stay, while the rowing cannibal travels back and forth, bringing the remaining cannibals over one at a time. And there are never more cannibals than missionaries on either side of the river." It is simple. If you say that my statement of the solution is clumsy and lacking in generality, even though correct, you are quite right. But now we are talking mathematics.

For the mathematician's job is not pure puzzle-mongering. It is to find the deepest properties of puzzles so that he may recognize that a particular puzzle is an exemplar—trivial, degenerate, or important, as the case may be—of a family of puzzles. He is also a student of the kinship that exists between families of puzzles. So, for example, he sets forth such structural ideas as the commutative, associative, and distributive laws to show the manner in which a whole set of seemingly diverse problems all have a common puzzle form imposed on them.

It is probably the case that there are two ways in which one goes about both learning mathematics and teaching it. One of them is through a technique that I want to call unmasking: discovering the abstracted ordering properties that lie behind certain empirical problem solutions in the manner in which the triangulation techniques used for reconstructing land boundaries in the Nile valley eventually developed into the abstractions of plane geometry, having first been more like surveying than mathematics. Applied mathematics, I would think, is still somewhat similar in spirit, although I do not wish to become embroiled in the prideful conflict over the distinction between pure and applied. The more usual way in which one learns and teaches is to work directly on the nature of puzzles themselves—on mathematics *per se*.

I should like to devote my discussion to four topics related to the teaching or learning of mathematics. The first has to do with the role of *discovery*, wherein it is important or not that the learner discover things for himself. I have been both puzzled (or I should say "difficultied") and intrigued hearing some of you discuss this interesting matter. The second topic is *intuition,* the class of nonrigorous ways by which mathematicians speed toward solutions or cul-de-sacs. The third is mathematics as an analytic language, and I should like to concentrate on the problem of the *translation* of intuitive ideas into mathematics. I hope you will permit me to assume that anything that can be said in mathematical form can also be said in ordinary language, though it may take a tediously long time to say it and there will always be the danger of imprecision of expression. The fourth and final problem is the matter of *readiness:* when is a child "ready" for geometry or topology or a discussion of truth tables? I shall try to argue that readiness is factorable into several more familiar issues.

DISCOVERY

I think it can be said now, after a decade of experimentation, that any average teacher of mathematics can do much to aid his or her pupils to the discovery of mathematical ideas for themselves. Probably we do violence to the subtlety of such technique by labelling it simply the "method of discovery," for it is certainly more than one method, and each teacher has his own tricks and approach to stimulating discovery by the student. These may include the use of a Socratic method, the devising of particularly apt computation problems that permit a student to find regularities, the act of stimulating the student to short cuts by which he discovers for himself certain interesting algorisms, even the projection of an attitude of interest, daring, and excitement. Indeed, I am struck by the fact that certain ideas in teaching mathematics that take a student away from the banal manipulation of natural numbers have the effect of freshing his eye to the possibility of discovery. I interpret such trends as the use of set theory in the early grades partly in this light—so too the Cuisenaire rods, the use of modular arithmetic, and other comparable devices.

I know it is difficult to say when a child has discovered something for himself. How big a leap must he take before we will grant that a discovery has been made? Perhaps it is a vain pursuit to try to define a discovery in terms of what has been discovered by whom. Which is more of a discovery—that $3 + 4 = 7$, that $3x + 4x = 7x$, or that 7 shares with certain other sets the feature that it cannot be arranged in rectangular ranks? Let me propose instead that discovery is better defined not as a product discovered but as a process of working, and that the so-called method of discovery has as its principal virtue the encouragement of such a process of working or, if I may use the term, such an attitude. I must digress for a moment to describe what I mean by an attitude of discovery, and then I shall return to the question of why such an attitude may be desirable not only in mathematics but as an approach to learning generally.

In studying problem solving in children between the ages of 11 and 14, we have been struck by two approaches that are almost polar opposites. Partly as an analogy, but only partly, we have likened them, respectively, to the approach of a listener and the approach of a speaker toward language. There are several interesting differences between the two. The listener's approach is to take the information he receives in the order in which it comes; he is bound in the context of the flow of speech he is receiving, and his effort is to discern a pattern in what comes to him. Perforce, he lags a bit behind the front edge of the message, trying to put the elements of a moment ago together with those that are coming up right now. The listener is forced into a somewhat passive position since he does not have control of the direction of the message or of its terminus. It is interesting that listeners sometimes fall asleep. It is rare for a speaker to fall asleep. For the speaker is far more active. He, rather than lagging behind the front edge of the message he is emitting, is well out ahead of it so that the words he is speaking lag behind his thoughts. He decides upon sequence and organization.

Now a wise expositor knows that to be effective in holding his auditor he must share some of his role with him, must give him a part in the construction game by avoiding monologue and adopting an interrogative mode when possible. If he does not, the listener either becomes bored or goes off on his own internal speaking tour.

Some children approach problems as a listener, expecting to find an answer or at least some message there. At their best they are receptive, intelligent, orderly, and notably empirical in approach. Others approach problem solving as a speaker. They wish to determine the order of information received and the terminus of their activity and to march ahead of the events they are observing. It is not only children. As a friend of mine put it, a very perceptive psychologist indeed, some men are more interested in their own ideas, others are more interested in nature. The fortunate ones care about the fit between the two. Piaget, for example, speaks of the two processes of accommodation and assimilation, the former being a process of accepting what is presented and changing with it, the latter being the act of converting what one encounters into the already existing categories of one's thought. Each attitude has its excesses. The approach of the listener can become passive and without direction. The approach of the speaker can become assimilative to the point of autistic thinking. As Piaget points out in his brilliant studies of thinking in early childhood, some sort of balance between the two is essential for effective cognitive functioning.

It is in the interest of maintaining this balance that, I would propose, the approach of discovery is centrally important. The overly passive approach to learning, the attitude of the listener, creates a situation in which the person expects order to come from outside, to be in the material that is presented.

Mathematical manipulation requires reordering, unmasking, simplification, and other activities akin to the activity of a speaker.

There is one other thing that I would emphasize about discovery: its relation to reward and punishment. I have observed a fair amount of teaching in the classroom: not much, but enough to know that a great deal of the daily activity of the student is not rewarding in its own right. He has few opportunities to carry a cycle of working or thinking to a conclusion, so that he may feel a sense of mastery or of a job well done. At least when he makes a paper airplane, he can complete the cycle almost immediately and know whether or not the thing flies. It is not surprising then that it is necessary to introduce a series of extrinsic rewards and punishments into school activity —competition, gold stars, etc.—and that, in spite of these, there are still problems of discipline and inattention. Discovery, with the understanding and mastery it implies, becomes its own reward, a reward that is intrinsic to the activity of working. I have observed and even taught classes in which the object was to stimulate discovery, and I have seen masterful teachers accomplish it. I am impressed by the fact that, although competitive advantage is still strong in such a classroom atmosphere, it is nonetheless the case that the experience of discovering something, even if it be a simple short cut in computation, puts reward into the child's own hands.

I need not tell you that there are practical difficulties. One cannot wait forever for discovery. One cannot leave the curriculum entirely open and let discovery flourish willy-nilly wherever it may occur. What kinds of discoveries to encourage? Some students are troubled and left out and have a sense of failure. These are important questions, but they should be treated as technical and not as substantive ones. If emphasis upon discovery has the effect of producing a more active approach to learning and thinking, the technical problems are worth the trouble.

INTUITION

It is particularly when I see a child going through the mechanical process of manipulating numbers without any intuitive sense of what it is all about that I recall the lines of Lewis Carroll: "Reeling and Writhing, of course, to begin with . . . and then the different branches of Arithmetic—Ambition, Distraction, Uglification, and Derision." Or as Max Beberman puts it, much more gently, "Somewhat related to the notion of discovery in teaching is our insistence that the student become aware of a concept before a name has been assigned to the concept." [1] I am quite aware that the issue of intuitive understanding is a very live one among teachers of mathematics and even a

---

[1] Max Beberman, *An Emerging Program of Secondary School Mathematics* (Cambridge, Massachusetts: Harvard University Press, 1958), p. 33.

casual reading of the Twenty-fourth Yearbook [2] of your Council makes it clear that you are also very mindful of the gap that exists between proclaiming the importance of such understanding and actually producing it in the classroom.

Intuition implies the act of grasping the meaning or significance or structure of a problem without explicit reliance on the analytic apparatus of one's craft. It is the intuitive mode that yields hypotheses quickly, that produces interesting combinations of ideas before their worth is known. It precedes proof; indeed, it is what the techniques of analysis and proof are designed to test and check. It is founded on a kind of combinatorial playfulness that is only possible when the consequences of error are not overpowering or sinful. Above all, it is a form of activity that depends upon confidence in the worthwhileness of the process of mathematical activity rather than upon the importance of right answers at all times.

I should like to examine briefly what intuition might be from a psychological point of view and to consider what we can possibly do about stimulating it among our students. Perhaps the first thing that can be said about intuition when applied to mathematics is that it involves the embodiment or concretization of an idea, not yet stated, in the form of some sort of operation or example. I watched a ten-year-old playing with snail shells he had gathered, putting them into rectangular arrays. He discovered that there were certain quantities that could not be put into such a rectangular compass, that however arranged there was always "one left out." This of course intrigued him. He also found that two such odd-man-out arrays put together produced an array that was rectangular, that "the left out ones could make a new corner." I am not sure it is fair to say this child was learning a lot about prime numbers. But he most certainly was gaining the intuitive sense that would make it possible for him later to grasp what a prime number is and, indeed, what is the structure of a multiplication table.

I am inclined to think of mental development as involving the construction of a model of the world in the child's head, an internalized set of structures for representing the world around us. These structures are organized in terms of perfectly definite grammars or rules of their own, and in the course of development the structures change and the grammar that governs them also changes in certain systematic ways. The way in which we gain lead time for anticipating what will happen next and what to do about it is to spin our internal models just a bit faster than the world goes.

Now the child whose behavior I was just describing had a model of quantities and order that was implicitly governed by all sorts of seemingly subtle mathematical principles, many of them newly acquired and some of

---

[2] *The Growth of Mathematical Ideas, Grades K–12*, Twenty-fourth Yearbook of the National Council of Teachers of Mathematics (Washington, D.C.: The National Council, 1959).

them rather strikingly original. He may not have been able to talk about them, but he was able to do all sorts of things on the basis of them. For example, he had "mastered" the very interesting idea of conservation of quantity across transformations in arrangement or, as you would say, the associative law. Thus, the quantity 6 can be stated as $2 + 2 + 2$, $3 + 3$, and by various "irregular" arrangements, as $2 + 4$, $4 + 2$, $2 + (3 + 1)$, $(2 + 3) + 1$, etc. Inherent in what he was doing was the concept of reversibility, as Piaget calls it, the idea of an operation and its inverse. The child was able to put two sets together and to take them apart; by putting together two prime number arrays, he discovers that they are no longer prime (using our terms now) but can be made so again by separation. He was also capable of mapping one set uniquely on another, as in the construction of two identical sets, etc. This is a formidable amount of highbrow mathematics.

Now what do we do with this rather bright child when he gets to school? Well, in our own way we communicate to him that mathematics is a logical discipline and that it has certain rules, and we often proceed to teach him algorisms that make it seem that what he is doing in arithmetic has no bearing on the way in which one would proceed by nonrigorous means. I am not, mind you, objecting to "social arithmetic" with its interest rates and baseball averages. I am objecting to something far worse, the premature use of the language of mathematics, its end-product formalism, that makes it seem that mathematics is something new rather than something the child already knows. It is forcing the child into the inverse plight of the character in *Le Bourgeois Gentilhomme* who comes to the blazing insight that he has been speaking prose all his life. By interposing formalism, we prevent the child from realizing that he has been thinking mathematics all along. What we do, in essence, is to remove his confidence in his ability to perform the processes of mathematics. At our worst, we offer formal proof (which is necessary for checking) in place of direct intuition. It is good that a student know how to check the conjecture that $8x$ is equivalent to the expression $3x + 5x$ by such a rigorous statement as the following: "By the commutative principle for multiplication, for every x, $3x + 5x = x3 + x5$. By the distributive principle, for every x, $x3 + x5 = x(3 + 5)$. Again by the commutative principle, for every x, $x(3 + 5) = (3 + 5)x$ or $8x$. So, for every x, $3x + 5x = 8x$." But it is hopeless if the student gets the idea that this and this only is *really* arithmetic or algebra or "math" and that other ways of proceeding are really for nonmathematical slobs. Therefore, "mathematics is not for me."

I would suggest, then, that it is important to allow the child to use his natural and intuitive ways of thinking, indeed to encourage him to do so, and to honor him when he does well. I cannot believe that he has to be taught to do so. Rather, we would do well to end our habit of inhibiting the expression of intuitive thinking and then to provide means for helping the child to improve in it. To this subject I turn next.

TRANSLATION

David Page wrote me last year: "When I tell mathematicians that fourth grade students can go a long way into 'set theory,' a few of them reply, 'Of course.' Most of them are startled. The latter ones are completely wrong in assuming that set theory is intrinsically difficult. Of course, it may be that nothing is intrinsically difficult—we just have to wait the centuries until the proper point of view and corresponding language is revealed!" How can we state things in such a way that ideas can be understood and converted into mathematical expression?

It seems to me there are three problems here. Let me label them the *problem of structure*, the *problem of sequence*, and the *problem of embodiment*. When we try to get a child to understand a concept, leaving aside now the question of whether he can "say" it, the first and most important problem, obviously, is that we as expositors understand it ourselves. I apologize for making such a banal point, but I must do so, for I think that its implications are not well understood. To understand something well is to sense wherein it is simple, wherein it is an instance of a simpler, general case. I know that there are instances in the development of knowledge in which this may not prove to be the case, as in physics before Mendeleev's table or in contemporary physics where particle theory is for the moment seemingly moving toward divergence rather than convergence of principles. In the main, however, to understand something is to sense the simpler structure that underlies a range of instances, and this is notably true in mathematics.

In seeking to transmit our understanding of such structure to another person—be he a student or someone else—there is the problem of finding the language and ideas that the other person would be able to use if he were attempting to explain the same thing. If we are lucky, it may turn out that the language we would use would be within the grasp of the person we are teaching. This is not, alas, always the case. We may then be faced with the problem of finding a homologue that will contain our own idea moderately well and get it across to the auditor without too much loss of precision, or at least in a form that will permit us to communicate further at a later time.

Let me provide an example. We wish to get across to the first-grade student that much of what we speak of as knowledge in science is indirect, that we talk about such things as pressure or chemical bonds or neural inhibition although we never encounter them directly. They are inferences we draw from certain regularities in our observations. This is all very familiar to us. It is an idea with a simple structure but with complicated implications. To a young student who is used to thinking of things that either exist or do not exist, it is hard to tell the truth in answer to his question of whether pressure "really" exists. We wish to transmit the idea that there are observables that have regularities and constructs that are used for conserving and representing these regularities, that both, in different senses, "exist," and the constructs are not fantasies like gremlins or fairies. That is the structure.

Now there is a sequence. How do we get the child to progress from his present two-value logic of things that exist and things that do not exist to a more subtle grasp of the matter? Take an example from the work of Inhelder and Piaget. They find that there are necessary sequences or steps in the mastery of a concept. In order for a child to understand the idea of serial ordering, he must first have a firm grasp on the idea of comparison—that one thing includes another or is larger than another. Or, in order for a child to grasp the idea that the angle of incidence is equal to the angle of reflection, he must first grasp the idea that for any angle at which a ball approaches a wall, there is a corresponding unique angle by which it departs. Until he grasps this idea, there is no point in talking about the two angles being equal or bearing any particular relationship to each other, just as it is a waste to try to explain transitivity to a child who does not yet have a firm grasp on serial ordering.

The problem of embodiment then arises: how to embody illustratively the middle possibility of something that does not quite exist as a clear and observable datum? Well, one group of chemists working on a new curriculum proposed as a transitional step in the sequence that the child be given a taped box containing an unidentified object. He may do anything he likes to the box: shake it, run wires through it, boil it, anything but open it. What does he make of it? I have no idea whether this gadget will indeed get the child to the point where he can then more easily make the distinction between constructs and data. But the attempt is illustrative and interesting. It is a nice illustration of how one seeks to translate a concept (in this instance the chemical bond) into a simpler homologue, an invisible object whose existence depended upon indirect information, by the use of an embodiment. From there one can go on.

The discussion leads me immediately to two practical points about teaching and curriculum design. The first has to do with the sequence of a curriculum, the second with gadgetry. I noted with pleasure in the introductory essay of the Twenty-fourth Yearbook of the National Council of Teachers of Mathematics that great emphasis was placed upon continuity of understanding: "Theorem 2. Teachers in all grades should view their task in the light of the idea that the understanding of mathematics is a continuum. . . . This theorem implies immediately the corollaries that: (1) Teachers should find what ideas have been presented earlier and deliberately use them as much as possible for the teaching of new ideas. (2) Teachers should look to the future and teach some concepts and understandings even if complete mastery cannot be expected." Alas, it has been a rarity to find such a structure in the curriculum, although the situation is likely to be remedied in a much shorter time than might have been expected through the work of such organizations as the School Mathematics Study Group. More frequently fragments are found here and there: a brilliant idea about teaching co-ordinate systems and graphing, or what not. I have had occasion to look at the list of teaching projects submitted to the National Science Foundation. There is everything from a demonstrational wind tunnel to little Van de Graaff generators, virtually all divorced from any sequence. Our impulse is toward gadgetry. The need instead is for something approximating a spiral curriculum, in which ideas are presented in homologue form, returned to later with more precision and power, and further developed and expanded until, in the end, the student has a sense of mastery over at least some body of knowledge.

There is one part of the picture in the building of mathematical curriculum now in progress where I see a virtual blank. It has to do with the investigation of the language and concepts that children of various ages use in attempting intuitively to grasp different concepts and sequences in mathematics. This is the language into which mathematics will have to be translated while the child is en route to more precise mastery. The psychologist can help in all this, it seems to me, as a handmaiden to the curriculum builder, by devising ways of bridging the gap between ideas in mathematics and the students' ways of understanding such ideas. His rewards will be rich, for he not only will be helping education toward greater effectiveness, but also will be learning afresh about learning. If I have said little to you today about the formal psychology of learning as it now exists in many of our university centers, it is because most of what exists has little bearing on the complex and ordered learning that you deal with in your teaching.

READINESS

One of the conclusions of the Woods Hole Conference of the National Academy of Sciences on curriculum in science was that any subject can be taught to anybody at any age in some form that is honest.[3] It is a brave assertion, and the evidence on the whole is all on its side. At least there is no evidence to contradict it. I hope that what I have had to say about intuition and translation is also in support of the proposition.

Readiness, I would argue, is a function not so much of maturation—which is not to say that maturation is not important—but rather of our intentions and our skill at translation of ideas into the language and concepts of the age we are teaching. But let it be clear to us that our intentions must be plain before we can start deciding what can be taught to children of what age, for life is short and art is long and there is much art yet to be created in the transmission of knowledge. So let me say a word about our intentions as educators.

[3] Jerome S. Bruner, *The Process of Education* (Cambridge, Massachusetts: Harvard University Press, 1960).

When one sits down to the task of trying to write a textbook or to prepare a lesson plan, it soon becomes apparent—at whatever level one is teaching —that there is an antinomy between two ideals: coverage and depth. Perhaps this is less of a problem in mathematics than in the field of history or literature, but not by any means is it negligible. In content, positive knowledge is increasing at a rate that, from the point of view of what portion of it one man can know in his lifetime, is, to some, alarming. But at the same time that knowledge increases in its amount, the degree to which it is structured also increases. In Robert Oppenheimer's picturesque phrase, it appears that we live in a "multi-bonded pluriverse" in which, if everything is not related to everything else, at least everything is related to something. The only possible way in which individual knowledge can keep proportional pace with the surge of available knowledge is through a grasp of the relatedness of knowledge. We may well ask of any item of information that is taught or that we lead a child to discover for himself whether it is worth knowing. I can only think of two good criteria and one middling one for deciding such an issue: whether the knowledge gives a sense of delight and whether it bestows the gift of intellectual travel beyond the information given, in the sense of containing within it the basis of generalization. The middling criterion is whether the knowledge is useful. It turns out, on the whole, as Charles Sanders Peirce commented, that useful knowledge looks after itself. So I would urge that we as school men let it do so and concentrate on the first two criteria. Delight and travel, then.

It seems to me that the implications of this conclusion are that we opt for depth and continuity in our teaching rather than coverage, and that we reexamine afresh what it is that bestows a sense of intellectual delight upon a person who is learning. To do the first of these, we must ask what it is that we wish the man in our times to know, what sort of minimum. What do we mean by an educated man? There is obviously not time now to examine this question in the detail it deserves. But I think we would all agree that, at the very least, an educated man should have a sense of what knowledge is like in some field of inquiry, to know it in its connectedness and with a feeling for how the knowledge is gained. An educated man must not be dazzled by the myth that advanced knowledge is the result of wizardry. The way to battle this myth is in the direct experience of the learner—to give him the experience of going from a primitive and weak grasp of some subject to a stage in which he has a more refined and powerful grasp of it. I do not mean that each man should be carried to the frontiers of knowledge, but I do mean that it is possible to take him far enough so that he himself can see how far he has come and by what means.

If I may take a simple example, let me use the principles of conservation in physics: the conservation of energy, mass, and momentum. Indeed, I would add to the list the idea of invariance across transformation in order to include mathematics more directly. The child is told, by virtue of living in our particular society and speaking our particular language, that he must not waste his energy, fritter it away. In common experience, things disappear, get lost. Bodies "lose" their heat; objects set in motion do not appear to stay in motion as in the pure case of Newton's law. Yet, the most powerful laws of physics and chemistry are based on the conception of conservation. Only the meanest of purists would argue against the effort to teach the conservation principles to a first-grade student on the grounds that it would be "distorted" in the transmission. We know from the work of Piaget and others that, indeed, the child does not easily agree with notions based on conservation. A six-year-old child will often doubt that there is the same amount of fluid in a tall, thin glass jar as there was in a flat, wide one, even though he has seen the fluid pored from the latter into the former. Yet, with time and with the proper embodiment of the idea—as in the film of the Physical Science Study Committee where a power plant is used as an example—the idea can be presented in its simplest and weakest form.

Let the idea be revisited constantly. It is central to the structure of the sciences of nature. In good time, many things can be derived from it that yield tremendous predictive power. Coverage in this sense, that is, showing the range of things that can be related to this particular and powerful something, serves the ends of depth. But what of delight? If you should ask me as a student of the thought processes what produces the most fundamental form of pleasure in man's intellectual life, I think I would reply that it is the reduction of surprise and complexity to predictability and simplicity. Indeed, it is when a person has confidence in his ability to bring off this feat that he comes to enjoy surprise, to enjoy the process of imposing puzzle forms upon difficulties in order to convert them into problems. I think we as educators recognize this idea in our doctrine of the "central subject," the idea of coordinating a year's work around a central theme. But choosing a central theme horizontally, for the year's work, is arbitrary and often artificial. The central themes are longitudinal. The most important central theme is growth in your own sense of mastery, of knowing today that you have more power and control and mastery over a subject than you had last year. If we produce such a sense of growth, I think it produces delight in knowledge as a by-product automatically.

My choice of the conservation theorems as an illustration was not adventitious. I tried to choose one as basic to the natural sciences as one could make it. Similar themes recur and have eventual crescendo value in other fields: the idea of biological continuity whereby giraffes have giraffe babies and not elephant babies, the idea of tragedy in literature, the notion of the unit of measure in mathematics, the idea of chance as a fraction of certainty in statistics, the grammar of truth tables in logic. It would seem to be altogether appropriate to bring about a joining of forces of experienced teachers, our most gifted scholars, and psychologists to see what can be done to structure longitudinal curricula of this order.

When we are clear about what we want to do in this kind of teaching, I feel reasonably sure that we will be able to make rapid strides ahead in dealing with the pseudoproblem of readiness. I urge that we use the unfolding of readiness to our advantage: to give the child a sense of his own growth and his own capacity to leap ahead in mastery. The problem of translating concepts to this or that age level can be solved, the evidence shows, once we decide what it is we want to translate.

I have perhaps sounded optimistic in my remarks. The evidence warrants optimism, and I cannot help but feel that we are on the threshold of a renaissance in education in America. Let me recapitulate my argument briefly. With the active attitude that an emphasis on discovery can stimulate, with greater emphasis (or fewer restraints) on intuition in our students, and with a courteous and ingenious effort to translate organizing ideas into the available thought forms of our students, we are in a position to construct curricula that have continuity and depth and that carry their own reward in giving a sense of increasing mastery over powerful ideas and concepts that are worth knowing, not because they are interesting in a trivial sense but because they give the ultimate delight of making the world more predictable and less complex. It is this perspective that makes me optimistic and leads me to believe that our present flurry is the beginning not of another fad, but of an educational renaissance.

How Children Form Mathematical Concepts

Jean Piaget

It is a great mistake to suppose that a child acquires the notion of number and other mathematical concepts just from teaching. On the contrary, to a remarkable degree he develops them himself, independently and spontaneously. When adults try to impose mathematical concepts on a child prematurely, his learning is merely verbal; true understanding of them comes only with his mental growth.

This can easily be shown by a simple experiment. A child of five or six may readily be taught by his parents to name the numbers from 1 to 10. If 10 stones are laid in a row, he can count them correctly. But if the stones are rearranged in a more complex pattern or piled up, he no longer can count them with consistent accuracy. Although the child knows the names of the numbers, he has not yet grasped the essential idea of number: namely, that the number of objects in a group remains the same, is "conserved," no matter how they are shuffled or arranged.

On the other hand, a child of six and a half or seven often shows that he has spontaneously formed the concept of number even though he may not yet have been taught to count. Given eight red chips and eight blue chips, he will discover by one-to-one matching that the number of red is the same as the number of blue, and he will realize that the two groups remain equal in number regardless of the shape they take.

The experiment with one-to-one correspondence is very useful for investigating children's development of the number concept. Let us lay down a row of eight red chips, equally spaced about an inch apart, and ask our small subjects to take from a box of blue chips as many chips as there are on the table. Their reactions will depend on age, and we can distinguish three stages of development. A child of five or younger, on the average, will lay out blue chips to make a row exactly as long as the red row, but he will put the blue chips close together instead of spacing them. He believes the number is the same if the length of the row is the same. At the age of six, on the average, children arrive at the second stage; these children will lay a blue chip opposite each red chip and obtain the correct number. But they have not necessarily acquired the concept of number itself. If we spread the red chips, spacing out the row more loosely, the six-year-olds will think that the longer row now has more chips, though we have not changed the number. At the age of six and a half to seven, on the average, children achieve the third stage: they know that, though we close up or space out one row of chips, the number is still the same as in the other.

In a similar experiment a child is given two receptacles of identical shape and size and is asked to put beads, one at a time, into both receptacles with both hands simultaneously—a blue bead into one box with his right hand and a red bead into the other with his left hand. When he has more or less filled the two receptacles, he is asked how they compare. He is sure that both have the same number of beads. Then he is requested to pour the blue beads into a receptacle of a different size and shape. Here again we see differences in understanding according to age. The smallest children think that the number has changed: if, for instance, the beads fill the new receptacle to a higher level, they think there are more beads in it than in the original one: if to a lower level, they think there are fewer. But children near the age of seven know that the transfer has not changed the number of beads.

In short, children must grasp the principle of conservation of quantity before they can develop the concept of number. Now conservation of quantity of course is not in itself a numerical notion; rather, it is a logical concept. Thus these experiments in child psychology throw some light on the epistemology of the number concept—a subject which has been examined by many mathematicians and logicians.

The mathematicians Henri Poincaré and L. E. J. Brouwer have held that the number concept is a product of primitive intuition, preceding logical notions. The experiments just described deny this thesis, in our opinion. Bertrand Russell, on the other hand, has supported the view that number is a purely logical concept: that the idea of cardinal number derives from the logical notion of category (a number would be a category made up of equivalent categories) while the notion of ordinal number derives from the logical relationships of order. But Russell's theory does not quite fit the psychological processes as we have observed them in small children. Children at the start make no distinction between cardinal and ordinal number, and besides, the concept of cardinal number itself presupposes an order relationship. For instance, a child can build a one-to-one correspondence only if he neither forgets any of the elements nor uses the same one twice. The only way of distinguishing one unit from another is to consider it either before or after the other in time or in space, that is, in the order of enumeration.

Study of the child's discovery of spatial relationships—what may be called the child's spontaneous geometry—is no less rewarding than the investigation of his number concepts. A child's order of development in geometry seems to reverse the order of historical discovery. Scientific geometry began with the Euclidean system (concerned with figures, angles and so on), developed in the 17th century the so-called projective geometry (dealing with problems of perspective) and finally came in the 19th century to topology (describing spatial relationships in a general qualitative way—for instance, the distinction between open and closed structures, interiority and exteriority, proximity and separation). A child begins with the last: his first geometrical discoveries are topological. At the age of three he readily distinguishes between open and closed figures: if you ask him to copy a square or a triangle, he draws a closed circle; he draws a cross with two separate lines. If you show him a drawing of a large circle with a small circle inside, he is quite capable of reproducing this relationship, and he can also draw a small circle outside or attached to the edge of the large one. All this he can do before he can draw a rectangle or express the Euclidean characteristics (number of sides, angles, etc.) of a figure. Not until a considerable time after he has mastered topological relationships does he begin to develop his notions of Euclidean and projective geometry. Then he builds those simultaneously.

Curiously enough, this psychological order is much closer to modern geometry's order of deductive or axiomatic construction than the historical order of discovery was. It offers another example of the kinship between psychological construction and the logical construction of science itself.

Let us test our young subjects on projective constructions. First we set up two "fence posts" (little sticks stuck in bases of modeling clay) some 15 inches apart and ask the child to place other posts in a straight line between them. The youngest children (under the age of four) proceed to plant one post next to another, forming a more or less wavy line. Their approach is topological: the elements are joined by the simple relationship of proximity rather than by projection of a line as such. At the next stage, beyond the age of four, the child may form a straight fence if the two end posts parallel the edge of the table, or if there is some other straight line to guide him. If the end posts are diagonally across the table, he may start building the line parallel to the table's edge and then change direction and form a curve to reach the second post. Occasionally a youngster may make a straight line, but he does so only by trial-and-error and not by system.

At the age of seven years, on the average, a child can build a straight fence consistently in any direction across the table, and he will check the straightness of the line by shutting one eye and sighting along it, as a gardener lines up bean poles. Here we have the essence of the projective concept; the line is still a topological line, but the child has grasped that the projective relationship depends on the angle of vision, or point of view.

One can proceed to study this with other experiments. For instance, you stand a doll on a table and place before it an object oriented in a certain direction: a pencil lying crosswise, diagonally or lengthwise with respect to the doll's line of vision, or a watch lying flat on the table or standing up. Then you ask the child to draw the doll's view of the object, or, better still, ask him to choose from two or three drawings the one that represents the doll's point of view. Not until the age of about seven or eight can a child deduce correctly the doll's angle of vision.

A similar experiment testing the same point yields the same conclusions. Objects of different shapes are placed in various positions between a light and a screen, and the child is asked to predict the shape of the shadow the object will cast on the screen.

Ability to coordinate different perspectives does not come until the age of 9 or 10. This is illustrated by an experiment I suggested some time ago to my collaborator Dr. Edith Meyer. The experimenter sits at a table opposite the child, and between the child and herself she places a cardboard range of mountains. The two see the range from opposite perspectives. The child is then asked to select from several drawings the ones that picture both his own and the opposite person's views of the mountain range. Naturally the youngest children can pick out only the picture that corresponds to their own view; they imagine that all the points of view are like their own. What is more interesting, if the child changes places with the experimenter and sees the mountains from the other side, he now thinks that his new view is the only correct one; he cannot reconstruct the point of view that was his own just a little while before. This is a clear example of the egocentricity so characteristic of children—the primitive reasoning which prevents them from understanding that there may be more than one point of view.

It takes a considerable evolution for children to come, at around the age of 9 or 10, to the ability to distinguish between and coordinate the different possible perspectives. At this stage they can grasp projective space in its concrete or practical form, but naturally not in its theoretical aspects.

At the same time the child forms the concept of projective space, he also constructs Euclidean space; the two kinds of construction are based upon one another. For example, in lining up a straight row of fence posts he may not only use the sighting method but may line up his hands parallel to each other to give him the direction. That is, he is applying the concept of conservation of direction, which is a Euclidean principle. Here is another illustration of the fact that children form mathematical notions on a qualitative or logical basis.

The conservation principle arises in various forms. There is first the conservation of length. If you place a block on another of the same length and then push one block so that its end projects beyond the other, a child under six will suppose that the two blocks are no longer of equal length. Not until near the age of seven, on the average, does the child understand that what is gained at one end of the block is lost at the other. He arrives at this concept of the conservation of length, be it noted, by a process of logic.

Experiments on a child's discovery of the conservation of distance are especially illuminating. Between two small toy trees standing apart from each other on a table you place a wall formed of a block or a thick piece of cardboard, and you ask the child (in his own language, of course) whether the trees are still the same distance apart. The smallest children think the distance has changed; they are simply unable to add up two parts of a distance to a total distance. Children of five or six believe the distance has been reduced, claiming that the width of the wall does not count as distance; in other words, a filled-up space does not have the same value as an empty space. Only near the age of seven do children come to the realization that intervening objects do not change the distance.

However you test them, you find the same thing true: children do not appreciate the principle of conservation of length or surface until, somewhere around the age of seven, they discover the reversibility that shows the original quantity has remained the same (e.g., the realignment of equal-length blocks, the removal of the wall, and so on). Thus the discovery of logical relationships is a prerequisite to the construction of geometrical concepts, as it is in the formation of the concept of number.

This applies to measurement itself, which is only a derived concept. It is interesting to study how children spontaneously learn to measure. One of my collaborators, Dr. Inhelder, and I have made the following experiment: We show the child a tower of blocks on a table and ask him to build a second tower of the same height on another table (lower or higher than the first) with blocks of a different size. Naturally we provide the child with all the necessary measuring tools. Children's attempts to deal with this problem go through a fascinating evolution. The youngest children build up the second tower to the same visual level as the first, without worrying about the difference in height of the tables. They compare the towers by stepping back and sighting them. At a slightly more advanced stage a child lays a long rod across the tops of the two towers to make sure that they are level. Somewhat later he notices that the base of his tower is not at the same level as the model's. He then wants to place his tower next to the model on the same table to compare them. Reminded that the rules of the game forbid him to move his tower, he begins to look around for a measuring standard. Interestingly enough, the first that comes to his mind is his own body. He puts one hand on top of his tower and the other at its base, and then, trying to keep his hands the same distance apart, he moves over to the other tower to compare it. Children of about the age of six often carry out this work in a most assured manner, as if their hands could not change position on the way! Soon they discover that the method is not reliable, and then they resort to reference points on the body. The child will line up his shoulder with the top of his tower, mark the spot opposite the base on his thigh with his hand and walk over to the model to see whether the distance is the same.

Eventually the idea of an independent measuring tool occurs to the child. His first attempt in this direction is likely to be the building of a third tower next to and the same height as the one he has already erected. Having built it, he moves it over to the first table and matches it against the model; this is allowed by the rules. The child's arrival at this stage presupposes a process of logical reasoning. If we call the model tower A, the second tower C and the movable tower B, the child has reasoned that B = C and B = A, therefore A = C.

Later the child replaces the third tower with a rod, but at first the rod must be just the same length as the height of the tower to be measured. He then conceives the idea of using a longer rod and marking the tower height on it with his finger. Finally, and this is the beginning of true measurement, he realizes that he can use a shorter rod and measure the height of the tower by applying the rod a certain number of times up the side.

The last discovery involves two new operations of logic. The first is the process of division which permits the child to conceive that the whole is composed of a number of parts added together. The second is the displacement, or substitution, which enables him to apply one part upon others and thus to build a system of units. One may therefore say that measurement is a synthesis of division into parts and of substitution, just as number is a synthesis of the inclusion of categories and of serial order. But measurement develops later than the number concept, because it is more difficult to divide a continuous whole into interchangeable units than to enumerate elements which are already separate.

To study measurement in two dimensions, we give the child a large sheet of paper with a pencil dot on it and ask him to put a dot in the same position on another sheet of the same size. He may use rods, strips of paper, strings, rulers or any other measuring tools he needs. The youngest subjects are satisfied to make a visual approximation, using no tools. Later a child applies a measuring tool, but he measures only the distance of the point from the side or bottom edge of the paper and is surprised that this single measurement does not give him the correct position. Then he measures the distance of the point from a corner of the paper, trying to keep the same slant (angle) when he applies the ruler to his own sheet. Finally, at about the age of eight or nine, he discovers that he must break up the measurement into two operations: the horizontal distance from a side edge and the perpendicular distance from the bottom or top edge. Similar experiments with a bead in a box show that a child discovers how to make three-dimensional measurements at about the same age.

Measurement in two or three dimensions brings us to the central idea of Euclidean space, namely the axes of coordinates—a system founded on the horizontality or verticality of physical objects. It may seem that even a baby should grasp these concepts, for after all it can distinguish between the upright and lying-down positions. But actually the representation of vertical and horizontal lines brings up quite another problem from this subjective awareness of postural space. Dr. Inhelder and I have studied it with the following experiments: Using a jar half-filled with colored water, we ask our young subjects to predict what level the water will take when the jar is tipped one way or another. Not until the age of nine, on the average, does a child grasp the idea of horizontality and predict correctly. Similar experiments with a plumb line or a toy sailboat with a tall mast demonstrate that comprehension of verticality comes at about the same time. The child's tardiness in acquiring these concepts is not really surprising, for they require not only a grasp of the internal relationships of an object but also reference to external elements (e.g., a table or the floor or walls of the room).

When a child has discovered how to construct these coordinated axes by reference to natural objects, which he does at about the same time that he conceives the coordination of perspectives, he has completed his conception of how to represent space. By that time he has developed his fundamental mathematical concepts, which spring spontaneously from his own logical operations.

The experiments I have described, simple as they are, have been surprisingly fruitful and have brought to light many unexpected facts. These facts are illuminating from the psychological and pedagogical points of view; more than that, they teach us a number of lessons about human knowledge in general.

Developing Positive Attitudes

Donovan A. Johnson and Gerald R. Rising

It is widely recognized that students need to learn something besides facts and skills. They need to develop desirable attitudes and creativity—goals of the affective domain, which are much more difficult to attain than those of the cognitive domain (concepts, facts, and skills).

An effective way of attaining the affective goals of instruction is an enrichment program that is part of the regular day-to-day instruction. This planned enrichment gives breadth and depth to mathematics learning. This program should capitalize on the varying capacity of each student to visualize, to use intuition, to pursue intellectual curiosities, and to be creative. It should encourage each student to develop his mathematical ability, to consider mathematics as being worth studying, and to extend independently the mathematics known to him. Although this program has special implications for gifted students, it should be appropriate for all levels of mathematical ability. In the following discussion the word enrichment is used in it broad sense, not in the narrow sense of "extra materials" to which it has too often been assigned by the teacher.

Consider the role of enrichment in our own daily lives. We frequently hear the expression "he has lived a rich life" or "her life is drab and routine." What are the experiences which contribute to an enriched life? We would likely agree to include the following:

1. *Success* in our work and day-to-day activities. Since we spend a major portion of our time on the job, the joy and satisfaction of success is one of the greatest factors for an enriched life. This success gives us a feeling of security that is so essential for participation in a variety of activities.

2. A *sense of values* which gives meaning to our lives. A life without a purpose or a goal is an empty existence.

3. A variety of *social activities* at home and elsewhere, such as those we enjoy through travel, conversation, and group organizations.

4. Participation in *cultural activities,* such as music, art, drama, or literature.

5. *Intellectual activities,* such as reading, listening to lectures, and participating in discussions which satisfy our curiosity about life around us.

6. *Recreational activities,* such as hobbies and sports.

7. *Creative activities,* such as craftwork, writing, gardening, and sewing.

Whether or not one can live an enriched life which involves these activities depends upon the ability and resources of the individual and the resources of the community in which he lives. Enrichment of some type is usually desired by all age groups and at all socio-economic levels.

In exactly the same way, the learning of mathematics should involve satisfying experiences which enrich the learning process. Activities are needed to satisfy the learner's need for enriched learning. It is the learner's experiences, not the teaching activities, that satisfy this need. Thus, the enrichment of mathematics instruction should provide the learner with the following experiences, which parallel the enrichment factors of daily living:

1. *Success in learning* the ideas, skills, and structure of mathematics. Success in the understanding and mastery of mathematical concepts is developed through the learner's participation in discovery, discussion, illustration, problem solving, practice, and application. Thus, instruction which builds confidence, independence, and security in this way enriches the learning of mathematics. This means that adequate time must be devoted to the mastery of ideas. Our task as teachers, then, is to "uncover" material rather than "cover" a specific sequence.

2. *A sense of the value* in learning mathematics gives meaning to learning activities. Learning without a goal or purpose is empty activity. Discussions of the role of mathematics in our society, the power of mathematical analysis, the applications of mathematics, and the mathematics needed in different vocations enhance the importance of learning mathematics.

3. *A variety of learning activities* can be planned by the use of teaching aids, historical sidelights, dramatic topics, or excursions. In these learning activities there should be much interaction between students as they discover, discuss, and apply mathematical ideas.

4. *The cultural aspects* of mathematics are made evident, so that the learner can look upon it as a human invention important in itself. Mathematics has aesthetic aspects—for instance, in the properties of symmetry and reflections—comparable to music or art. And, in turn, music and art have mathematical aspects of their own.

5. The relation of *intellectual curiosity* to mathematics is unique and exciting. Mathematics is one of the greatest intellectual inventions of the human mind. Its logic, its abstractness, its paradoxes, its study of patterns, its unsolved problems can satisfy intellectual appetites at many levels.

6. *Recreational activities* involving mathematics are plentiful. These include tricks, puzzles, games, and stunts. Mathematics is a hobby for many people who are not mathematicians. Unusual properties of geometric figures and number operations provide such entertaining interludes.

7. *Creating new mathematics* can be made an intriguing activity. Constructing a model, planning and producing a mathematics assembly program, building a mathematics exhibit—all of these are creative activities. Originality may be nourished by new inventions, an elegant new proof, or a new mathematics structure.

The student's participation in enrichment activities depends upon the ingenuity and background of the teacher, upon the ability and interest of the individual, upon the time available, and upon the resources of the school. When a student's curiosity, concern, and creativeness are aroused, learning becomes automatic.

THE ROLE OF ATTITUDES IN LEARNING MATHEMATICS

Attitudes are fundamental to the dynamics of behavior. They largely determine what students learn. The mathematics student with positive attitudes studies mathematics because he enjoys it, he gets satisfaction from knowing mathematical ideas, and he finds mathematical competency its own reward.

The development of positive attitudes toward mathematics is a fundamental concern of the mathematics teacher for a number of reasons:

1. *No student can be forced to learn mathematics which he doesn't want to learn.* He may superficially satisfy you that he is learning by adhering minimally to your classroom demands and standards, but he will carry away virtually nothing unless he is interested in doing so. In this regard all teachers should consider how deeply involved students—even low achievers—become in their hobbies, whether they be stamp collecting, model building, scouting, or sports. Students would make rapid progress in mathematics if they could equal their knowledge of mathematical principles with their knowledge of baseball rules. Such knowledge, which often includes a vast store of memorized detail, is motivated by strong intrinsic attitudes.

2. *Even if students learn the mathematics of a given text, the primary concern of continuing learning is lost when students do not develop positive attitudes.* The mathematics of tomorrow cannot be taught today; so an abiding interest in mathematics should be instilled to encourage learning in the future.

3. *Vocational choices are largely dependent on attitudes.* Mathematics teachers close doors for students when they allow them to develop poor attitudes toward such an all-pervasive subject as mathematics.

4. *Application of mathematical ideas in large measure depends on a positive attitude.* We tend to remember favorable, pleasant experiences and block out the unpleasant. If this leads to blocking out mathematical concepts, they will not be available when needed.

5. *Many people take pride in professing ignorance of mathematics.* Few adults admit that they are poor history students, but the parents of many pupils announce the fact that they "never did understand math." It is in this negative environment that the teacher must work.

6. Finally, there is a selfish aspect of attitude improvement: *Positive attitudes reflect favorably on the teacher.* They form an excellent basis for a teacher's rating by students, parents, and colleagues. The mathematics teacher who inspires his students and whose students are enthusiastic about his class is the teacher who is in line for salary increases, institute recommendations, and—best of all—the prestige of success.

STUDENT BASIS FOR POSITIVE ATTITUDES

It is very important for the classroom teacher to assess his students in order to determine established attitudes toward mathematics and to assure himself of a sound basis on which to build a program of attitude improvement and motivation. While many individual students will bring to the classroom very specific acceptable and unacceptable interests, there are many attitudes that are common to the major segment of the student population. To become involved in emotional dynamics, the classroom teacher must be aware of these and be sensitive to quantitative differences among students. These basic desires include:

1. Wanting to avoid embarrassment or punishment.
2. Wanting to win approval of teachers and parents.
3. Wanting to gain confidence in his own ability.
4. Wanting to succeed in progress toward goals acceptable to him.
5. Wanting to attain approval of his peers individually and as a group.
6. Wanting to be secure.

Many teachers fail to recognize the difficulty they face in developing real sensitivity to these strong drives within their students. It is not easy to be sensitive to the subtleties of student desires and motives. How often has the remark been passed in the faculty room that a student showed quite unexpected concern for something or someone? The fact that such feeling was quite unexpected means that the teacher did not really know his student and that he had therefore underestimated him.

It should be noted that all the desires listed are basically oriented toward the development of positive attitudes. In the beginning they are working for the teacher. Too soon, however, they can all be misdirected. For example, the desire to avoid embarrassment often turns a bright girl into an underachiever when she is criticized by her friends for being the teacher's pet.

This leads to a special point that should be stressed about attitudes. The mathematics teacher cannot choose to avoid the problem of developing positive attitudes toward mathematics. *Whether the teacher likes it or not, each student responds emotionally to his teachers.* Students react strongly, acquiring or rejecting on the basis of this response the attitudes, values, and appreciations of the teachers.

No matter what topic is being taught, much concomitant learning and changes in attitude are taking place. For example, when being taught how to solve a mathematical problem, a student may be learning:

1. To dodge responsibility or to be cooperative.
2. To maintain his integrity or to cheat.
3. To trust the teacher or to lose respect for him.

Attitudes may not be taught systematically or directly. Teaching is not a mechanical operation. It is not even a science, although science too has its artistic side. Teaching attitudes is more like painting a picture, playing a musical selection, planting a garden, or writing a letter to a friend. The teacher must put all his heart into his instruction. It is human warmth that adds the emotional vector needed in the development of positive attitudes toward mathematics.

DESIRED POSITIVE ATTITUDES TOWARD MATHEMATICS

Most mathematics teachers would accept the following attitudes as being those which characterize an ideal product of their instruction, whether they are teaching new or conventional mathematics:

1. *Appreciation* of the power, elegance, and structure of mathematics.
2. *Curiosity* about mathematical ideas.
3. *Confidence* in mathematics.
4. *Loyalty* to mathematics, the mathematics teacher, and classmates.
5. *Enjoyment and satisfaction* in learning mathematical ideas.
6. *Respect* for excellence in mathematical achievement by himself and others.
7. *Optimism and cheerfulness* about one's progress in mathematics.

In addition to these specific attitudes, teachers must take responsibility for many general attitudes or values like honesty, kindness, respect, and self-reliance.

NEGATIVE STUDENT ATTITUDES TOWARD MATHEMATICS

Whenever mathematics students are questioned concerning attitudes toward mathematics, the five most recurring reasons they give for negative attitudes are:

1. *Lack of understanding of mathematical principles.* This lack of understanding kills curiosity and appreciation no matter what content is being taught.
2. *Lack of application of mathematics to a life situation, leading to a loss of confidence in the importance of mathematics.* This lack of emphasis on the practical aspects of mathematics is even more pronounced in modern programs.
3. *Too many boring problems assigned daily.* The constant emphasis on manipulation and daily homework kills the zest of students for learning mathematics.
4. *Uninspired, impatient, uninteresting teachers.* Poor teaching kills confidence, loyalty, and enjoyment of learning, no matter how good the content may be.
5. *Lack of success, leading to development of feelings of frustration and insecurity.* Failure leads to dislike, dislike to fear, and fear to hatred of a subject.

Being sensitive to these sources of negative reactions should help us avoid further reinforcement of negative attitudes.

WAYS TO BUILD POSITIVE ATTITUDES
TOWARD MATHEMATICS

The teacher's appreciation of mathematics as an important, dynamic, remarkable subject must be real and deep, his attitude toward students must be sympathetic and understanding, his interest in learning must be great, his enthusiasm for teaching sincere. If the teacher's attitudes are less favorable or his motivation the same as that of the student, no transmission of enthusiasm can take place.

Once the teacher has set his own standards high, he must still establish himself as a person who has the respect and esteem of his students. Maintaining the students' esteem in the face of their constant judgmental response is a sobering problem for the teacher. Students are quick to sense the smallest insincerity just as they note the slightest insecurity. It is extremely important that the classroom atmosphere be friendly, accepting, and supportive, even when it is demanding and challenging. A spirit of security, enjoyment, and loyalty should be the basic goal of classroom organization. The teacher should make his students feel that his attitude will still be friendly regardless of the success or failure of the students' efforts. If we want students to think for themselves, we must allow them to try out their own ideas and answers.

Some of the really important ways in which teachers influence their students' attitudes have to do with pleasant communication habits: the teacher's voice inflection, the way he looks at students, his responses, or even his failure to respond. The classroom itself should be attractive. It should contain books, pamphlets, pictures, and displays reflecting an intellectual atmosphere and providing a proper setting for an enriched program.

Here are some specific examples of things to do to build positive attitudes toward mathematics:

1. To develop *appreciation* of the elegance, power, and structure of mathematics we need to:
   a. Emphasize the nature of mathematics and how it is a model of a deductive system. Often, we forget to teach what mathematics *is*.
   b. Illustrate the harmony, symmetry, and beauty of mathematical patterns.
   c. Include current applications of mathematics.
2. To nourish *curiosity* in mathematical ideas we need to:
   a. Give experiences in discovering new ideas.
   b. Make each lesson have significance for the learner.
   c. Include enrichment topics such as computer programming or game theory.
   d. Assign open-ended questions and problems.
3. To build *confidence* in and loyalty to mathematics we need to:
   a. Be the kind of person students accept and are willing to imitate.
   b. Work with students with patience and kindness so that *each day each student* has some success.

    c. Make learning mathematics a *privilege* rather than a punishment.

    d. Be fair in *marking* and in *discipline.*

4. To make learning mathematical ideas a *pleasure* we need to:

    a. Present the material so that it is understood. Be sure that students attain a reasonable level of competence before going on to new topics.

    b. Use a variety of materials and methods that provide student participation in discovery, discussion, or laboratory lessons.

    c. Make reasonable assignments.

5. To nourish *respect* for excellence in achievement we need to:

    a. Stress the things a student does well. Do not humiliate him because of failure.

    b. Show how mathematical achievement relates to the student's goals.

    c. Establish reasonable competition for marks and keep the student informed of his status.

6. To establish an *optimistic* attitude we need to:

    a. Present problems in a way that does not threaten the student's ego.

    b. Assign tasks that are within the range of the student's ability.

    c. Have a repertoire of illustrations, problems, sidelights, and applications that add variety and sparkle to daily lessons.

    d. Be an optimistic, enthusiastic, sincere person.

USING MATHEMATICAL RECREATIONS
TO BUILD POSITIVE ATTITUDES

Many teachers have found the use of mathematical recreations in the classroom the key to attitude development. Of course, learning mathematics is not all play, and no student should bypass the hard work of the subject. But much good mathematics can be learned from enjoyable recreations. In fact, enrichment activities of this type have been the source of much high-quality mathematics. Such outstanding mathematicians as Gauss, Leibnitz, and Euler found in such pastimes sources of new ideas and even new fields of mathematics. Two examples of such mathematical topics growing out of recreation are probability theory and game theory.

Recreations may sometimes be brought into the program as optional activities; for instance, many teachers pose a weekly problem for extra credit. On the other hand, it is quite appropriate to incorporate recreational activities that introduce, underscore, or extend the regularly required program.

The possibilities for worthwhile recreational activities in the mathematics class are very great. Most lessons can be dressed up with a puzzle, trick, paradox, or anecdote. The references and books listed in the Appendix will supply you with a wealth of ideas.

Here are some examples of recreations that stimulate students to participate, be observant, learn rules, work independently or cooperatively, and, most of all, find satisfaction in mathematics:

1. A game like "Battleship," in which teams "shoot" at various-sized ships marked on coordinate grids, provides good practice in locating points on a graph.

Another game that provides this same practice is a form of the Japanese game Go-Moku. To play, the class is divided in half, and each side attempts to locate a row, column, or diagonal of four counters, at the same time preventing the opponents from doing so.

2. Alphametics encourage junior and even senior high students to examine the structure of mathematical operations. In these each different letter represents a distinct digit. Here are some examples:

$$2(HOHOHO) = 9(OHOHOH)$$

```
    HAVE         SANTA        FORTY
  + SOME       - CLAUS          TEN
  -------      -------      +   TEN
   HONEY         XMAS        -------
                             SIXTY
```

$$\frac{SHE}{DID} = .TALK\ TALK\ TALK\ \ldots$$

3. Paradoxes force students to examine more closely the operations they carry out without thinking. For example:

You are as old as I am!

If x represents your age and y mine, then let our average age, $(x + y)/2$, be M. Then $x + y = 2M$. Multiplying by $x - y$ gives $x^2 - y^2 = 2Mx - 2My$, or $x^2 - 2Mx = y^2 - 2My$. Add M^2 to each member and factor:

$$x^2 - 2Mx + M^2 = y^2 - 2My + M^2$$
$$(x - M)^2 = (y - M)^2$$

But this means $x - M = y - M$ or $x = y$. In other words, you are exactly the same age I am.

4. Number tricks often help students to understand the operations of simple algebra and encourage them to explore the field further:

Think of a number between 0 and 10. Multiply it by 5. Add 6 to your answer. Multiply this answer by 2. Add any other number between 0 and 10. Subtract 5 from this result. The answer can be represented as $10x + y + 7$, which quickly identifies the chosen numbers.

Select a number between 100 and 1,000 that has a first digit and a last digit that differ by at least as much as two. Reverse the digits of this numeral. You now have another number represented by a three-digit numeral. Subtract the smaller number from the larger of these two numbers. The difference should be another number between 100 and 1,000. Reverse the digits of this difference. Add the difference and the number represented by its reversed digits. The sum is 1,089.

5. Recreations can show the versatility of logical analysis. The following situation is an example of a problem using indirect reasoning:

A professor wishing to choose an assistant decided to test the mentality of the three top candidates. The professor told the candidates that he would blindfold each one and then mark either a red or blue cross on the forehead of each. He would then remove the blindfold. Each candidate was to raise his hand if he saw a red cross and drop his hand when he figured out the color of his own cross. The professor first blindfolded each candidate and proceeded to mark a red cross on each forehead and then removed the blindfolds. After looking at each other, the prospective assistants all raised their hands. After a short interval of time, one candidate lowered his hand and said, "My cross is red," and gave his reasons. Can you duplicate his reasoning?

6. Recreations may be appropriate "homework." A puzzle, game, or stunt is an excellent way for student and parents to work together at learning mathematics. Since parental attitudes are a key to student attitudes, this joint enjoyment of "doing" mathematics together can be extremely productive. Such assignments also give an answer to the oft-repeated parent question: "How can we help?"

Geometry for Primary Children: Considerations

Nicholas J. Vigilante

Curious circumstances trigger trains of thought. Glancing across a library table recently, I saw this title appearing in *The Arithmetic Teacher:* "Geometry for the Primary Grades." The student reading the article was evidently intrigued by the title, for he seemed to return to the title page on a number of occasions. This caused me to wonder what such notables as Euclid, Poincaré, Euler, Gauss, Moebius, Bolyai, Lobachevski, Riemann, and all of the other great minds, both past and present, would have written under the same title. I began to wonder what would emerge if these immortals were to coauthor this topic with another group that included Piaget, Montessori, Bruner, Suppes, Hawley and others. What unified, harmonious medley of understanding would emerge? This surely had all the overtones of a setting of individuals bent on a course that might bring together the necessary components for a panacean program of geometry in the primary grades—a program that would be organized on a logical and psychological basis that takes into consideration the age of the child. This is the context in which present-day geometry for primary-grade children is being explored—the child, the topic, and the environmental influence of both.

It has been said frequently that professional literature reflects what the readers are ready to accept. As one surveys the number of articles concerning geometry at the primary level that have recently appeared in the professional literature, one notes that they exist in growing numbers. The literature definitely reflects the growing notion that geometry is respectable for primary children. In fact, the Cambridge Conference Report specifically

Reprinted from *The Arithmetic Teacher,* No. 14 (October 1967), 453–459, by permission of the publisher.

recommends that the "twin streams of arithmetic and geometry" be developed in the curriculum of Grades 1–6.[1] As you survey *The Arithmetic Teacher*, for example, you may discover the following statistics: Between the years 1954 and 1960 it contains one article on the topic "elementary school geometry." In contrast, approximately twenty-five such articles appear between the years 1961 and 1966; and approximately half of these articles are directed to the primary grades. Most of these published papers convey the notion that geometry at this level makes its greatest contribution when approached informally, using a theory of instruction that consists of multisensory experiences. A great deal of experimentation with geometry is now taking place at the primary level.

At all levels of our educational hierarchy increasing attention is being paid to issues concerning the learning process. At every stage we hear of the need to find new answers for the present challenge to education. Our educational institutions, as well as our industrial and commercial enterprises, continue to express a need for men with adaptable and open minds—for flexibility within an open system. Inherent in this quest is a need to search continually for fresh approaches that are conducive to allowing viable constructs to emerge and that assist with the ever-growing body of content in any subject area. We need to encourage exploration of geometry at the primary school level. Wouldn't it be interesting to foretell what continued attention to geometry at the elementary school level will reveal?

Primary teachers need to question continually the value of certain forms of geometry for their children. Their anxieties and concern can be relieved as they discover the values to be derived. The statements advanced most frequently to substantiate the inclusion of geometry in the primary grades are the following:

1. Children can see position, shape, and size in space as something they can understand, use, control, and manipulate to explore their environment.

2. Children can develop an appreciation of geometry at this most impressionable age.

3. Children are able to use geometric insights to facilitate and develop creativity and the spirit of inquiry.

4. By exploring vocational and daily applications, children learn how geometry can be useful to mankind.

5. Geometry can be useful in developing other forms of mathematical insights.

THE WORLD OF GEOMETRY

The most important tool available to men in science is mathematics. The science of numbers through the ages has presented attraction and great

[1] Irving Adler, "The Cambridge Conference Report: Blueprint or Fantasy?" *The Arithmetic Teacher*, XIII (March 1966), 179–86.

difficulties to the minds of men. Throughout the long history of mankind enthusiastic mathematical minds have spent an exorbitant amount of time with speculation about, and contemplation of, number properties. As a result, through the efforts of such notables as Gauss, Fibonacci, Leibniz, Cantor, Descartes, the knowledge of mathematics has been and continues to be cumulative and developmental.

With respect to logical symmetry and completeness, arithmetic and algebra differ from geometry. The science of geometry came from the very early works of Greek thinking, in a form that has remained unchanged throughout the ages. Euclid ultimately brought together the great works of geometry by summarizing and systemizing what seemed to give geometry its finality. Therefore, would it not seem appropriate to tie the introduction of geometry in the primary grades to an organization of the content appropriate for children of this age? Concepts would be related to position, shapes, and size. The pedagogical approach would be based upon experiences that children meet daily and that relate or involve the actions of exploring, constructing, describing, and systemizing objects found in their environment. The spirit of inquiry would be stimulated by informal exploration of the children's environment. And, finally, the vocabulary introduced would allow for development of a broad range of conceptual understandings, ranging from marks on paper to geometrical ideas or concepts such as angles.

Geometry is an indispensable way of life; for in its very structure, form, and beauty, every imaginable object is governed by properties of geometry. Without this tool of knowledge our very lives, our needs, and the world about us would be altered beyond any describable form. Yet because of its inherent structure and utility, geometry finds its application in the vocational needs of the most demanding professions: architecture, engineering, navigation, physics, and art, to mention a few. For this reason, many people feel it is too technical a subject for them to understand, and certainly beyond young children. However, in daily life we can identify innumerable instances where geometric insights have been applied to the nearest objects. Geometry has been used to design the form of this page, the pencil used to write this article, the desk on which I am writing, the light bulb that illuminates the room, and the room itself, which is one of many in a building located at a point on this spherical planet.

Too frequently, geometry is introduced under the aegis of a body of content that rests on the rigors of a set of abstractions and basic, organized, deductive "proofs." For one to deal with geometry in a very sophisticated manner, he must be familiar with, and knowledgeable about, the basic elements, definitions, assumptions, axioms, postulates, theorems, and other understandings; and he must have a facility for reasoning by the careful rules of logic. This paper proposes that primary children will approach geometry with greater fervor and livelier interest when we deal with it primarily in its aesthetic sense (appealing to intuitive perception) rather than by a formal treatment. Thus we can come to realize that the geometric curves, surfaces, shapes, sizes, and positions are found in the world of technology and very definitely in the artistic world and in the very existence of nature. These geometric insights can be developed with primary children through experimentation, intuition, sense perception, induction, and simple informal reasoning.

In accordance with Jerome Bruner's enactive-iconic-symbolism paradigm,[2] I should like to take the liberty of making the following assumption: that the technical geometrician deals with geometry on the symbolic level, while the general layman deals with geometry on the enactive level. Further, I shall make the following parallel assumption: early elementary school children deal with geometry on the enactive level, intermediate-grade children deal with geometry on the enactive-iconic level, and high school students deal with geometry on the iconic-symbolic level. This is to say that we can deal more proficiently with geometry after having experiences discerning, describing, and living with geometric reality. It is only after having experiences on the enactive level that an individual can come to generalize on the basis of these experiences, which provide for him the firm foundation necessary to deal with geometry on the symbolic level. As discriminating elementary school teachers you are continually called upon to select, organize, and provide *qualitative* experiences for your children. More especially, as primary teachers you are charged with developing a firm foundation on which future teachers will build by providing your children with experiences that reach more toward the symbolic level. Because of the very nature of the children with whom you deal, success with your children comes more with experiences that are on the concrete, enactive level. Experiences that provide opportunity for children to explore, manipulate, and develop spatial perspectives are desirable. Children at this age need to handle and explore physical models or objects because of their *geometrical* implications. Primary teachers are encouraged to organize experiences for children that deal with real experiences, and to ask children what they have experienced or what they see in their daily travels, continually directing the dialogue to an awareness of geometric form and using appropriate terminology.

GEOMETRIES

To speak of geometry in a singular sense tends to give the term an archaic connotation, which technically was understood and employed by earlier geometricians. Today's point of view is not geometry but the plural—geome-

[2] Jerome Bruner, *Toward a Theory of Instruction* (Cambridge, Mass.: Harvard University Press, 1966).

tries. Aside from the Euclidean metric geometry, which bears the name of the man who assembled all the geometric insights known in his time, our primary-grade children are exposed to programs that are more extensive and that include projective geometry as well as topology. The first response to a query about what geometry is studied in school might be "Plane and solid geometry." This variety is known as Euclidean metric geometry. Plane geometry deals with two-dimensional figures drawn on a flat surface, where length and width are the only dimensions considered. It deals with points, lines, polygons, and circles on a flat surface. A child might explain it as the "skin" of an object. It has been said that a shadow on a flat surface comes the closest to a truly two-dimensional figure. The silhouette of an object gives no indication of its weight, texture, or color. Since its only characteristics are length and width, it is typical of the form studied in plane geometry. Solid geometry deals with points, lines, and planes in space. Solid objects that exist in nature have three dimensions—width, length, and height or thickness. This aspect of Euclidean geometry enables man to explain his physical world. Through solid geometry we can identify the three dimensions for spheres, cylinders, cones, cubes, rectangular objects, and prisms.

Projective geometry is a form of nonmetric geometry. Nonmetric geometry is concerned with that phenomenon of space perception that can be either two- or three-dimensional in nature. Projective geometry studies what happens to shapes when they are distorted. You can see that it is nonmetric if you look at a row of telephone poles strung out over a set distance. Certain distortions seem to be evident. We know the poles are all the same size, yet the farthest one appears much smaller than the closest. A circular plate viewed from certain angles may appear to be elliptical. Things look different or appear to change shape when viewed from varying vantage points. A baseball held close to your eyes will seem larger than a basketball or the moon. From our position on earth the sun appears to be the same size as the moon. Another example is to be found as we look at the length of the shadow of a tree during various times of the day. Toward noon the shadow is shorter than early morning or late afternoon. The measure of the length of the tree, a metric property, is not preserved in the projected shadow of the tree. Artists particularly are faced with the problem of depicting three-dimensional objects on a plane surface. In Euclidean geometry, parallel lines never meet; in projective geometry, they do.

The newest geometry, topology, is that branch of mathematics that decides what is possible with geometric figures. This geometry is the mathematics of distortion. It is more interested in position than in size or shape. In topology the usual query is, Where? (Outside? Inside? Between what?) Distance has no meaning in this form of nonmetric geometry. In Euclidean geometry, objects always remain the same size. Topology is the study of objects that change in size and form when moved—surfaces that can be twisted, bent, stretched, or otherwise deformed, but never torn. For example, what would happen to a circle on a rubber sheet if we were to stretch the sheet? When a child re-forms a ball of clay to the shape of a snake, he has made a change called a topological change or topological transformation. As a child plays with an inflated balloon, he similarly performs topological transformations. The child standing before a fun-house mirror that distorts his reflection provides an example of a topological transformation. Each point on the child has a corresponding point on the mirror. Can the sum of the angles of a triangle be less than 180°? The answer in non-Euclidean geometry is "yes" when dealing with the pseudosphere.

The distinctive development in mathematics in the last one hundred years is the rise of a discipline whose central concept is neither number nor quantity, but structure.

If, indeed, these are the areas of geometry that might be explored with children of the primary grades, we might begin to ask some questions. Which geometry ought to be given preference? Are young children capable of discriminating geometrical ideas of one type prior to another? Which of the geometries outlined above do children deal with realistically? Does the literature reveal insights, through carefully designed experimentation as well as empirical evidence, to substantiate a priority for one geometry in preference to another? What can primary teachers do to facilitate children's understandings of geometrical insights? What knowledge is of most worth? What geometric experience is most worthwhile for primary children? What are the prerequisites?

PERCEPTUAL AWARENESS

One of the problem areas a primary teacher confronts is the area of perception. I presume no one will object to the long-acceptable principle that geometry is the resultant of sense perception and abstract thought. I wonder if, in our desire and our haste to develop the power of abstract thinking, we are forgetting the basic prerequisite—sense perception. I've been impressed with the voluminous research and personal documentations showing that our children can learn just about anything and at a very early age. I'm sure this is an earnest attempt to remind ourselves that children are capable of storing information that can be retrieved upon request. What concerns me is that we recognize the need for perceptual development, yet continue to provide an unbalanced program for our children in the primary grades—a program geared to the symbolic-abstraction type of ability. Perception has surely been recognized as one of the primary psychological functions that governs our behavior. It is the result of all past sensory experiences being called into play when one attempts to resolve or clarify a present experience.

Researchers (Bayley, Carmichael, Piaget [3]) have clearly established the notion that perceptions are among the earliest of the child's learnings that lead to concept formation. As a child meets a variety of related impressions, he organizes them into some unified whole and for convenience attaches a name to them. Perceptions of roundness, mass, probably some color, and solidity in an object, plus hearing his parents say the word "ball"—all these experiences organize themselves into the meaning of ball for the child. In proper geometrical terminology this sphere is an extended awareness of what initially was mentally recorded in terms of a circle. The recognition and integration of stimuli is a higher mental process taking place in the brain, not in the organs of reception such as the eyes. In the perception of the form of a circle, visual awareness takes place in the eye, but the recognition and conceptual recognition of this figure as a ball—more abstractly, a sphere—occur in the brain. Accurate perceptual abilities enable a child to deal with his world of reality in a symbolic form. We have research to prove that inaccurate sensory data prevent the child from recognizing objects and their relationship to each other in space. Distorted perceptual awareness makes children incapable of dealing with the abstracts of point-set geometry when it is presented too early in such forms with undefined terms such as "point," "line," "plane," and "space."

With an awareness of perception and the limitations imposed on very young children because of gradual maturation, it seems clear that the role of geometry in the primary grades is fundamentally on solid ground when it is treated informally, using physical reality, and when it is logically organized to give a meaning for the child that gradually tends toward the more abstract.

As we study the child's discovery of spatial relationships, we notice that the development of insights in geometry seems to be the reverse of the organized evolutionary development of geometry. Historically, scientific geometry began with Euclidean insights developed by the early civilizations; projective geometry as formulated by Poncelet had its origin in the seventeenth century; and finally topology was developed—the nineteenth-century geometry that deals with position (interiority and exteriority) and structures that are either open or closed.

Piaget and Inhelder [4] believe children's first geometrical undertakings develop in the area of topology, as represented by such concepts as nearness, order, separation, continuation, and open or closed figures. It is not until after he has developed and mastered topological relationships that the child

[3] Jean Piaget, "How Children Form Mathematical Concepts," in P. H. Mussen, J. J. Conger, and J. Kagan, *Readings in Child Development and Personality* (New York: Harper & Row, 1965).

[4] Jean Piaget and Bärbel Inhelder, *The Child's Conception of Space* (London: Routledge & Kegan Paul, 1956).

is capable of dealing with projective or Euclidean geometry. If topological insights precede projective and Euclidean relations, it would seem this insight should be utilized when appropriate geometrical experiences are being selected for children in the primary grades. Similarity is a simpler concept than congruence. Convincingly, this notion offers definite direction when one is planning the sequence of geometrical experiences; topological insights developed by the child seem to be the prerequisite for successful experiences in projective or Euclidean geometry. Formal treatment must be preceded by intuitive, informal, exploratory experiences.

Before leaving this section concerning perceptions, it would seem most appropriate to mention a second hypothesis. Children function better when they have tangible, manipulative, or visual materials to stimulate their sensory intake. The implication again seems to be clear. We must give children abundant opportunity to investigate the physical world, which consists of geometrical objects: help them to explore form, position, size, and shape in the reality of physical objects. Howard Fehr stated that

in the elementary school, a formalistic logical study of mathematics does not provide a medium in which this freedom of the mind can be developed. Before any formal structure of mathematics can be understood, there must be a host of experiences of doing mathematics in which concepts, manipulations, and relations are developed and applied. It is only after experiences of this type that mathematics as a study of formal structures makes sense.[5]

The implication presented here indicates that the teacher must be a *discriminating consumer* of materials and ideas that facilitate the perceptual and conceptual development of geometric insight for children at the primary level, ultimately leading to higher levels of cognitive development. The ancients advised their followers to remember simplicity—the obvious—for it is in the obvious that great discoveries are brought to light. Let's encourage observation at the primary-grade level. We also need to encourage inquiry at this very early age. After bisecting an orange, what do we observe? How was it bisected? What happens to the internal geometric design? Help the child to see patterns—symmetry. What is the obvious as we observe a seashell, a leaf, a stone, drifts of sand on the beach, a star, or the structure of any physical object? Only a child can ask the obvious questions.

I'm told that Einstein pondered over the meaning of "simultaneous." A good many primary children know it means "happening at the same time." He pondered over this "at the same time" and later realized it was the key to theories dealing with time, movement, and mass. It appears that great insights are generated when humans are perceptually alerted to the obvious,

[5] Howard F. Fehr, "Sense and Nonsense in a Modern School Mathematics Program," *The Arithmetic Teacher,* XIII (February 1966), 83–91.

to simplicity—the world of physical objects. This is a striking example of the role of the primary-grade teacher in developing geometric insights.

With experimentation on physical objects, the primary-grade teacher is able to develop geometric insights that would expand the child's perceptual awareness as it pertains to both in-school and out-of-school activities. As you experiment with your children, you are developing in them concomitant learnings that tend to develop creative and scientific insights, along with that inner feeling that they are capable of constructing and completing their efforts. This provides an internal gratification stimulating the feelings of pleasure and reward—a positive reinforcement. Favorable attitudes, as well as mathematical insights, are developed with this type of approach when dealing with geometry at the primary level.

SUMMARY

As one surveys the literature concerning geometry in the primary grades, some generalizations can be uncovered.

1. Educational planners need to arrange for a continued dialogue between and among (a) geometricians, (b) psychologists, (c) child development specialists, and (d) primary-grade teachers, when considering geometry for the primary grades.

2. Programs designed to include geometry in the primary grades must be attitude-oriented, developing favorable attitudes among the children.

3. The primary-grade teacher must be a discriminating consumer of educational hardware as well as software (materials and ideas).

4. Experimentation with geometry at the primary level is occurring at an ever-increasing pace; much of it is patterned after the Piaget model. (There are some people who question the advisability of adhering to just one theory of instruction, as in the case of the Piaget model.)

5. Geometries—of the geometries, which is best suited for children of this age? What psychological factors are called into play when children first confront geometric concepts? How do we proceed from this point?

6. The design of a theory of instruction that is undergirded by concern for the child, his learning pattern, the topic, and the environmental influence of all related factors will stimulate and promote higher levels of cognitive development.

The New Arithmetic and "Abstraction": A Critical View

Anita P. Riess

The concept of "set" has become a vital part of the New Arithmetic now being introduced in the primary grades of many American schools. Few people would question that an understanding of the concept is one of the essentials for a mathematical approach to arithmetic. However, the use of pictures of sets to establish the concept of number in kindergarten and first grade is open to serious doubt. Such usage is based on the untested assumption that the child gains his concept of number through a process of abstraction from groups or collections of objects presented to him. This assumption is in keeping neither with "abstraction" as defined by set theory nor with fundamentals recognized by those schools of philosophy which are consistent with the findings of genetic psychology.

The great importance of Georg Cantor's set theory—its vast fertility in the field of mathematics—has led some educators to interpret his idea of number as an abstract property of sets to mean that a specific number *originates* by abstraction from the particular properties of things in a collection. They have taken for granted that abstraction, as we know it from the physical sciences, is the very process that leads the child to the recognition of specific numbers. Some rely also on a theory of abstraction that dominated arithmetic teaching long before the advent of the "New Arithmetic." They speak of "levels of perception" that gradually result in abstraction; of the "concrete, the semi-concrete, the semi-abstract" as forerunners of the abstract. In illustrating these "levels" in their textbooks, they show a series of drawings of objects, each successive drawing omitting one more individual feature of the objects, until they finally present drawings of strokes or dots or crosses to stand for the objects. These "semi-abstract" pictures are understood to be the last jumping-off point to "numbers" conceived of as abstract entities. Other writers, staying closer to the terminology and symbolism of set theory, have prepared illustrative material in their textbooks for kindergarten children which shows three or four concrete elements in brackets to represent a set. To bring children to the next level of abstraction they present the same drawing again, this time preceded by a capital N. *This* drawing, followed by an Arabic numeral, is used for the final level of "abstraction" in this series.

From a mathematical as well as from a psychological point of view, a number of fallacies are involved in these methods of teaching. The writings of Cantor himself offer no support for using perception of objects or sets in

Reprinted from *School Science and Mathematics* (May 1965), 409–415, by permission of the publisher.

the described manner as a starting point for evoking concepts of number in children. Cantor's formalistic mathematical logic was concerned with a *general* concept of number that would apply not only to finite classes, but to infinite classes as well. Instead, reliance on *perception* of number as a property of a set harks back to and revives the empiricist theory of number expounded by John Stuart Mill in *A System of Logic*, published as long ago as 1843. Mill's theory may be exemplified by quoting from this book: "That two and one are equal to three is a truth known to us by early and constant experience: an inductive truth: and such truths are the foundation of the science of Number. The fundamental truths of that science all rest on the evidence of sense. . . . All who wish to carry the child's *mind* along with them in learning arithmetic; all who wish to teach numbers, and not mere ciphers—now teach it through the evidence of the senses." [1]

The main contention in the paragraph, that number can be gained inductively, or "abstracted" from sense experiences, has been refuted by philosophers and mathematicians of all possible persuasions, including no less a man than Einstein. He asserted that the concept of number is a free creation of thought, a self-created tool which simplifies the organizing of certain sensory experiences, but a tool which cannot be inductively gained from sense experiences. From this point of view numbers are no longer considered as "entities inherent in and easily abstracted from denumerable things," but are thought of as relationships established in clearly defined constructive activities.

The mathematician and logician Gottlieb Frege, in his famous *Foundations of Arithmetic*, spoke ironically of Mill's arithmetic: "We are driven to the conclusion that number is neither spatial and physical, like Mill's piles of pebbles and gingersnaps, nor yet subjective, like ideas, but nonsensible and objective. Now objectivity cannot, of course, be based on any sense impression. . . ." [2] "What is it that we are supposed to abstract from, in order to get, for example, from the moon to the number 1? By abstracting we get, indeed, certain concepts, namely the following: satellite of the Earth, satellite of the planet, non-self luminous body, body, object. But in this series 1 is not to be met with; for it is not one of the concepts under which the moon could fall." [3] Similarly, a pictured set embracing as elements a bear, a tiger, a lion and a sheep does not in itself yield the number 4. By abstraction we might get mammals, animals, living beings, objects. But, using Frege's terms, in this series 4 is not one of the concepts under which animals could fall.

Educators also, foremost among them John Dewey, threw their authority

[1] *A System of Logic* (New York: Harper & Brothers, Publishers, 1846), p. 167.
[2] *The Foundations of Arithmetic*, trans. J. L. Austin (New York: Philosophical Library, 1950), p. 38e.
[3] Ibid., p. 57e.

against that of Mill. However, Dewey's warning that "number cannot be taught by the . . . presentation of things, since "number is not a property of the objects which can be realized through the mere use of the senses," [4] remains unheeded. Unfortunately, in spite of the well-founded evidence against it, some current articles on "abstraction" still repeat the outmoded empiricist theory. Perhaps this is because, as Einstein writes, "we have the habit of combining certain concepts and conceptual relations (propositions) so definitely with certain sense-experiences that we do not become conscious of the gulf—logically unbridgeable—which separates the world of sensory experiences from the world of concepts and propositions." [5] The more primitive a concept of everyday life we consider, "the more difficult it becomes amidst the mass of inveterate habits to recognize the concept as an independent creation of thinking. It was thus that the fateful conception—fateful, that is to say, for an understanding of these conditions—could arise, according to which the concepts originate from experience by way of 'abstraction,' i.e. through omission of a part of its content."

Psychological studies in the attainment of concepts have further refuted Mill's theory of abstraction. In her experimental studies, Heidbreder came to the conclusion that "the use of numbers requires a definite departure from the perceptual situation. . . . Some aspect or characteristic of the presented perceptual situation must be correlated with some system of symbols—either counting or some functional equivalent like concrete objects or fingers used as tallies and thus used symbolically. These symbols are *not perceived* in the perceptual situation, but become the means of *organizing* the perception." [6] (Italics are supplied.) It is true that in the new textbooks for children a collection is shown in brackets to make it a "set"; that the capital N before the pictured set is supposed to function as a request to count; the Arabic numeral following it, to function as a request to represent the result of counting by a symbol. However, the authors do not specify the creative activities that take place in counting, but imply that perception of pictorial characteristics suffices for the last stages in abstraction.

Apart from viewing arithmetical exercises in the terminology of sets as "ways to abstraction," some writers claim that it is of supreme importance for children to understand that number is a property possessed by all sets. These writers seem to forget or to be unaware of the fact that child psychologists have shown in a variety of careful investigations that, even at the age of two, children react to the manyness of like objects in ways which leave no doubt that they recognize "number" as a significant aspect of collections.

[4] James A. McLellan and John Dewey, *The Psychology of Number* (New York: D. Appleton and Company, 1895), p. 24.

[5] Albert Einstein, "Remarks on Bertrand Russell's Theory of Knowledge," in *The Philosophy of Bertrand Russell* (Evanston, Ill.: Northwestern University, 1944), p. 287.

[6] Edna Heidbreder, "The Attainment of Concepts," *Journal of General Psychology*, XXXV (1946), pp. 218–220.

Any finite collection or set has a limited number of discrete elements. This characteristic may be called its plurality. Children realize the plurality of a collection of physical objects at a very early age. Before they are able to count and to give a specific number, they respond to the idea of "many." Their reactions to a collection may be successive, as demonstrated by their repetitive use of words such as "one more, one more, one more," or "another one, another one, another one," and the like. Or they may respond to a simultaneous totality, either to that of an indefinite number, as indicated by their use of the word "all," or to a specific—very small—number such as a pair. In the light of these findings it seems rather doubtful that one must develop the idea of plurality of a class or set as late as at age five or six.

In responding to a collection, children certainly do use abstraction in subsuming individual elements under a class concept. "Never," says William Stern, "has one observed that children would summarize or put together anything unlike." However, no further abstraction from concrete properties of the set is involved in the next step. What leads the child from a mere recognition of "many of the same kind" to an appreciation of "enough," "more," or "less," is not abstraction, but another well-defined activity, the establishing of a one-to-one correspondence between two sets. At an early age the child will have and use opportunities to establish through his own activities, without counting, the equivalence or similarity of two sets, as, for instance, when he finds that there are "enough" cookies for "just as many" children. Pairing of members of two collections, with no member of either left over, leads to the concept of "same number," but not yet to the idea of a specific number, the answer to "how many?" There is still a gap between attaining the idea "same number" and using a number word or an Arabic symbol for that number. This gap is filled not by abstraction but by *counting*.

The mathematician Courant said in his book, *What Is Mathematics?*: "Fortunately, the mathematician as such need not be concerned with the philosophical nature of the transition from collections of concrete objects to the abstract number concept." [7] But educators, we may say, do need to be concerned with the origin and development of the abstract concept of number. And they were concerned before set theory captured the imagination of textbook writers and some still are!

The most outspoken position taken in regard to this problem is that of Hans Aebli, a disciple of Piaget, who has applied Piaget's researches in genetic psychology to education. He has investigated the nature of the processes by which the child acquires and assimilates concepts. It is one of the main contentions of their school of thought that operations establishing the concept of number have nothing to do with the process of abstraction as described by psychologists of empiricist persuasion. Aebli says: "Number is

[7] Richard Courant and Herbert Robbins, *What Is Mathematics?* (New York: Oxford University Press, 1941), p. 1.

constituted through mental operations and not through intuitive representation." [8]

Once the child has established equivalence between sets, he must engage in other constructive activities to go beyond the concept of "same number" to a specific numerical value. In order to communicate about "how many" he must pair the elements of a set with a representative set of symbols or numerals, either oral or written. In a generally known symbolic set the elements have a definite sequence—as the fingers of one's hands, the ordered succession of number names or the Arabic numerals. Since the members of each of these representative sets come in a specific order, each member conveys *ordinal* meaning. When the child has learned the order of elements in a representative set and has established a one-to-one correspondence between this set and a collection of objects, he learns to use the last symbol used in pairing as the summary record of counting. This symbol then denotes the *cardinal* number of the collection. Seen from a psychological point of view, the ordinal aspect of the counting numbers thus comes before the cardinal, although the grammatical form of the ordinals, first, second, third, and so on, may be learned much later. As a child once put it, "This," pointing to the last stroke of /////*, "is 5, but this," pointing to all five strokes together, /////, "is also 5."

In mathematics the primacy of cardinal or ordinal number has been a controversial point. There are famous proponents of both theories, although at present the tendency is to follow Cantor and accept the primacy of cardinal number. However, at closer inspection it becomes obvious that Cantor did not intend to give a psychological description of the origin and development of counting. He was concerned with the fact that in the case of infinite sets a reordering of the set leads to different ordinal numbers. Therefore, he put aside intentionally the sequence of elements in a perceived set of objects. He said: "We will call by the name 'power' or 'cardinal number' of M the general concept which, by means of our active faculty of thought, arises from the aggregate M when we make abstraction of the nature of its various elements *m and* of *the order in which they are given.*" [9] That is, in order to define plurality or power as the property of infinite as well as of finite sets, he abstracts from, or disregards the original order of elements in a set of concrete objects. Fraenkel, another writer on set theory, recognized that the successive enumeration of the single elements in a set, first, second, third, and so on, presents the simpler aspect of the concept of numbers, psychologically as well as mathematically. When children are asked to determine the specific numerical value of a given finite set, they must *count*, that is, take the elements in any one of the possible sequences.

[8] *Didactique Psychologique* (Neuchâtel: Delachaux et Niestlé, 1951), p. 21. Trans. A.P.R.

[9] Georg Cantor, *Contributions to the Founding of the Theory of Transfinite Numbers,* trans. Philip E. B. Jourdain (New York: Dover Publications, Inc., n.d.), p. 86.

Whether to regard cardinal or ordinal number as primary thus depends on the point of view. In defining the general concept of number one disregards the order of the elements, but in counting, order is paramount. Therefore—if for no other reason—abstraction as used in the logical foundation of set theory cannot possibly be taken as a model for determining consecutive levels in the child's attainment of his concept of natural numbers.

The successive constructive activities that actually take place in constituting number have been described by genetic psychologists. According to them the child must learn:

1. To pair collections in a one-to-one correspondence;
2. To match the elements of the set to be counted with a representative set of ordered symbols;
3. To use the last symbol of the representative set to denote a specific cardinal number.[10]

It is true that we know from experience that reasoning goes from the concrete to the abstract. As the Swiss psychologist Piaget has shown, mental operations grow out of physical activities that have a definite function in real life. The activities listed above might be viewed as having occurred in the cultural history of number as ways of solving problems that arose in concrete situations. These problems might include taking stock of one's possessions, keeping a record, communicating about quantities. A study of such concrete problems will enable the child to realize the function of one-to-one correspondence and of ordinal and cardinal symbols. Thus the child may recognize the significance of truly symbolic responses.

In conclusion: Philosophers concur with psychologists in the determination that there are no "stages of abstraction from perception of objects leading to the concept of number." The child builds his concept of number through the activities outlined above. The use of sets as an initiation to arithmetic *before* the child has recognized numerals as symbols of operations is apt to weaken rather than to strengthen the effectiveness of the new arithmetic. Cantor's concept of abstraction from sets leads to the *general* idea of plurality, but not to a symbolic representation of specific numbers in the finite domain. This is a critical point often overlooked by educators who believe that beginning instruction can be built on a wrongly assumed process of abstraction evoked by more or less concrete representation of sets. Ignoring the concrete constructive activities of the child which give meaning to numerical symbols, these educators cannot help but fall back on a reliance on rote learning. The proponents of modern teaching methods profess to aim at the building of mathematical concepts through creative insight rather than producing mere computational skill through rote learning. For this very reason they should not lose sight of fundamentals established in various

[10] An application of these points to teaching may be found in *Numbers We See* by Anita Riess et al. (Chicago: Scott, Foresman & Company, 1948).

fields of pertinent research: Basic mathematical concepts, such as the concept of number, are not abstract copies of the concrete world of things, but are constructive symbols of specific operations of thought.

BIBLIOGRAPHY

AEBLI, HANS, *Didactique Psychologique:* Application à la didactique de la psychologie de Jean Piaget. Neuchâtel: Delachaux et Niestlé, 1951.

CANTOR, GEORG, *Contributions to the Founding of the Theory of Transfinite Numbers,* trans. Philip E. B. Jourdain. New York: Dover Publications, Inc.: n.d.

COURANT, RICHARD, and ROBBINS, HERBERT, *What Is Mathematics?* New York: Oxford University Press, 1941.

EINSTEIN, ALBERT, "Remarks on Bertrand Russell's Theory of Knowledge," in *The Philosophy of Bertrand Russell* (The Library of Living Philosophers, Vol. V). Evanston, Ill.: Northwestern University, 1944.

FREGE, GOTTLIEB, *The Foundations of Arithmetic,* trans. J. L. Austin, New York: Philosophical Library, 1950.

HEIDBREDER, EDNA, "The Attainment of Concepts," *Journal of General Psychology,* XXXV (1946), 191–223.

MCLELLAN, JAMES A. and DEWEY, JOHN, *The Psychology of Number.* New York: D. Appleton and Company, 1895.

MILL, JOHN STUART, *A System of Logic.* New York: Harper & Brothers, Publishers, 1846.

RIESS, ANITA *et al., Numbers We See.* Chicago: Scott, Foresman & Company, 1948.

Depth Learning in Arithmetic—What Is It?

Charlotte W. Junge

The acquisition of skills has been consistently recognized as one of the basic aims of education to which the elementary school should contribute. From colonial times to the present, much of the attention of schools and of teachers has been centered on this aspect of education. Furthermore, this preoccupation with the development of skills has been associated largely with the "three R's." Reading, writing, and arithmetic, frequently referred to as tool subjects, have been presumed to encompass all the skills which are of real importance in the education of children.

Although it is true that effective use of language and numbers does require high-level skills of a complex sort, the three R's involve far more than skills. One of the most damaging and limiting conceptions in elementary

Reprinted from *The Arithmetic Teacher,* No. 7 (November 1960), 341–346, by permission of the author and publisher.

education arises from the point of view that developing competence in language and arithmetic is largely a matter of gaining command of specific skills. Curriculums and teaching procedures based on this idea result in rote learning, the memorization of specific facts, and the teaching of "things."

Learning, in its proper sense, is concerned not with "things," but with the "meaning of things." All forms of language and mathematics are essentially concerned with meanings. They represent ways of gaining, interpreting, and transmitting ideas, and explaining relationships. These processes rest for effectiveness on basic skill, but the controlling principle in learning is meaning and relationship.

Efficiency in habit and skill alone is not a satisfying end-point of education, if for no other reason than that life itself is not a simple problem in logistics, a problem for which any good Answer Book has the precise formula worked out to the fourth decimal place!

When learning is at its best, it will provide opportunities for the child to produce original ideas, to be active in his own learning, and to give range to his imagination. Somewhere in our teaching procedure we must provide time for contemplation, for experimentation, and for wondering. Was it not Einstein who said to us, "Those who have ceased to wonder are as good as dead"? Is it possible that in our own failure to wonder we do not see the importance of opportunities for children to wonder? All too often in the pressure for efficiency, in our desire to make the curriculum more "rigorous," and in the crowding of assignments up to the pupil's capacity, we forget to save time for the learner to give free expression to the understandings he is developing: to question, to wonder, and to experiment beyond accepted patterns of operation in arithmetic. Like automatons, children are trained to record, retain, and reproduce larger and larger amounts of material to which someone else has given shape and form. Seldom do they experience the excitement of discovery, never the risk of being wrong, never a moment in which they can say, "Poor though it is, it is my own!" For these children learning in arithmetic has taken on a routine quality. It is a surface thing lacking in meaning and in depth.

It was just a few short years ago that arithmetic was the "red-haired stepchild" in the elementary curriculum. Now we ride the crest—due to public interest and concern as well as interest and concern within the profession. For the first time we have the financial support to bring the changes in the curriculum which are necessary to meet the needs of our times and the capabilities of our students. In our headlong pursuit of excellence we *must not* lose sight of a very basic goal in teaching—the development of the ability to think quantitatively. It would be very easy under present pressures to make *record, retain,* and *reproduce* the three R's of arithmetic!

This is not to say that acquisition of the basic facts and principles of arithmetic is unnecessary and unimportant. It is to say that if real learning is to take place on the part of the student, then one must view knowledge as a means, not as an end, in arithmetic education. The building of accurate, well-organized concepts is, from the point of view of the learner, a creative process in which thinking plays a leading role. All thinking is dependent upon a well-organized body of knowledge, thoroughly understood and pertinent to the problem. As we all know, "Wisdom does not come to those who gape at nature with an empty head." [1]

DEVELOPING DEPTH IN LEARNING

Depth learning in arithmetic is not developed, then, by emphasis upon skills alone. Neither is it developed solely by providing children with "enrichment" activities or with content of a more difficult nature taught at an advanced level. It is developed in quite a different way, that is:

1. by confronting the student with challenging problems—but problems within his power of comprehension,
2. by leading him, from the very beginning, to see the futility of thought without dependable data,
3. by maturing him in those methods of disciplined thought that have been found to facilitate the work of mathematicians,
4. by providing opportunities to discover and to find original solutions, and
5. by steadily encouraging him to new levels of creative thinking.

Depth learning in arithmetic results from a way of teaching which encourages reflective thinking, which permits experimentation and originality, and which holds steadily before the learner the *need for knowing* the facts and principles necessary for clear thought. Given these things, children will move on to concepts of greater difficulty and the development of greater skill in handling quantitative relationships.

Note that I have not spoken here of abstraction, but I have spoken of precision in thinking and meaning. Thought may be precise whether abstract or concrete. Note that I have not spoken of rigor. Concepts correctly understood and precisely expressed at any level will embody a standard of rigor appropriate to the thinker's maturity, and as he grows in knowledge and skill and in his ability to sense relationships, his need for higher standards also will grow.

Not all children in the elementary school are equally able. They do not all have the same ability, and as we try to provide opportunities for them to add depth to their learning, it appears that we may attempt the impossible.

Ambitious goals that we set up will be attained fully by some, to a modest degree by many, and to a limited degree by others. Nevertheless, *it is sound policy* to encourage all children to think as hard as they can and to under-

[1] Morris R. Cohen, *Reason and Nature* (New York: Harcourt Brace & Company, 1931), p. 17.

stand as much as they can. It is better to see through a glass darkly than not to see at all. The opportunity to attain adequate understanding and to add depth to their learning should be open to all children.

The unquestionable evidence of differences in learning ability must be faced squarely by those of us responsible for instruction in arithmetic. This need not lead to a pessimistic or defeatist point of view, but to the establishment of attainable goals and the devising of more effective methods for their accomplishment.

Today, there appears to be common agreement among teachers of arithmetic that there should be little, if any, differentiation of topics in the elementary school to meet individual needs. The differentiation, when made, should be in terms of *depth* and scope of learning. As Roland Smith states, ". . . the amount of concrete background in any topic can be varied. Rates of learning can be varied. The extent of any topic can be varied, and each child can be expected to do work only up to his own capacity to learn." [2]

Providing for differentiation in scope and in depth is made easier by a method of teaching which leads children to think as a mathematician would think. It enables them to solve problems that are not exactly like those solved in the classroom or in the textbook. Furthermore, it enables them to deal precisely with precise ideas, and to work with symbols as an aid to thought, full of meaning and conveying ideas which can be understood.

SELECTED EXPERIENCES

Children are particularly delighted with learning carried on in this way. Recently I watched children in a second grade, who had developed some facility with basic addition and subtraction facts, work through a series of questions in which they were solving for the "missing number." For example:

$$5 + \square = 7 \qquad \triangle + 9 = 10$$
$$2 + \square = 8 \qquad \triangle + 6 = 13$$

Each child was encouraged to tell "how he thought" in finding the missing numbers. Then the children were asked to work independently to find pairs of numbers which would make these equations true:

$$\triangle + \square = 7 \qquad \square + \triangle = 5$$

Class evaluation revealed that several different number pairs could be used in each example. Some of the children who experienced no difficulty here were encouraged to go on to the slightly more difficult situation of:

[2] Roland Smith, "Provisions for Individual Differences," *Twenty-first Yearbook* (Washington, D.C.: NCTM, 1953), p. 273.

A
$6 + 3 + \square = 10$
$4 + \triangle + 3 = 9$
$\square + 2 + 4 = 8$

B
$6 + 2 + \square = 10$
$4 + 2 + \triangle = 9$
$1 + \triangle + 4 = 8$

The children were encouraged to create similar exercises with which to challenge their classmates.

At a fifth or sixth grade level, I watched children, who have had opportunities to do this type of work, extend their thinking with exercises in which they decided whether a number sentence was *true* or *false* depending on the numbers used. For example:

A. $3 + 5 = 8$ (true)
     $2 + 7 = 8$ (false)
B. Is the number sentence, $A + 4 = 9$, true?
     · if $A = 4$
     · if $A = 5$
     · if $A = 6$
C. Is this sentence, $A + B + 6 = 12$, true or false?
     · if $A = 3$ and $B = 4$
     · if $A = 2$ and $B = 4$
     · if $A = 2$ and $B = 3$
     · if $A = 2\frac{1}{2}$ and $B = 3\frac{1}{2}$
     · if $A = 5.2$ and $B = .8$

The children were encouraged to find other pairs of numbers which made the sentence true and to share their thinking with the whole class.

Also, I observed a sixth grade teacher working with a group of children of varying abilities. The children worked as a group to solve the following:

· If $T = 4$; $R = 6$, and $V = 5$, find the number which will make each of the following number sentences true.
· $R + T + V = ?$
· $T \times V \times R = ?$
· $(R - T) + V = ?$
· $T + R \div V = ?$

After solving several exercises like these, the children then developed other similar exercises to share with the class.

As children develop understandings and competence with the basic multiplication facts, they may be given opportunities to stretch their thinking on exercises like this:

$$2 \times 9 = (2 \times 4) + (2 \times 5)$$
$$5 \times 7 = (5 \times 2) + (5 \times 5)$$
$$= (5 \times 3) + (5 \times 4)$$
$$= (5 \times 1) + (5 \times 6)$$

Can you complete the following by finding other ways to express the meaning of $4 \times 6, 5 \times 8, 6 \times 7$?

$$4 \times 6 = \underline{\qquad} \qquad 5 \times 8 = \underline{\qquad} \qquad 6 \times 7 = \underline{\qquad}$$

After instruction on how to multiply without pencil and paper pupils in one fourth grade were using six different ways of arriving at the product of 12×25:

1. $10 \times 25 = 250$
    $2 \times 25 = 50$
    $12 \times 25 = \overline{300}$

2. $4 \times 25 = 100$
    $4 \times 25 = 100$
    $4 \times 25 = 100$
    So $12 \times 25 = \overline{300}$

3. $12 = 4 \times 3$
    $3 \times 25 = 75$
    $4 \times 75 = 300$
    So $12 \times 25 = 300$

4. $12 = 3 \times 4$
    $4 \times 25 = 100$
    $3 \times 100 = 300$
    So $12 \times 25 = 300$

5. 25
    12
    50
    250
    $\overline{300}$

6. $12 = 2 \times 6$
    $6 \times 25 = 150$
    $2 \times 150 = 300$
    So $12 \times 25 = 300$

Children whose written work indicates that they require little additional practice in multiplication and division profit from exercises which develop relational thinking. For example:

Tell how you think to get the answer

1.
32
×16
512

   (a)   32   (b)   32   (c)   64   (d)   16

(a) 32×8 (b) 32×32 (c) 64×16 (d) 16×32

2.
12
18/216

(a) $12/216$ (b) $36/216$ (c) $18/432$ (d) 6 $18/\overline{?}$

Having children tell how they think when finding trial quotients in division is not only helpful to individual children, but it helps all children in the class deepen their thinking. Recently, in a fifth grade, I watched children share their solutions to the following examples.

$29/\overline{89}$ Bob: The answer can't be as much as 4, since 29 is almost 30 and $4 \times 30 = 120$. The answer will be a little more than 3.

$51/\overline{426}$ Sue: There are 2 50's in 100. In 400 there will be at least 4 times as many. I'll try 8 as a quotient figure.

$45\overline{/280}$ ANN: There are 2 45's in 100. In 300 there will be about 6. I'll try 6 as a quotient figure.

Occasionally current happenings can be used to bring depth into children's learning. When Pioneer IV was successfully placed in orbit, a fifth grade child related to his classmates that the *velocity* of the rocket was a little less than 25,000 mph at time of launching, that at $X + 1$ the *speed* was about 11,800 mph, and at $X + 2$ the speed was reduced to about 7,800 mph. Class discussion clarified for the children the difference between velocity and speed. The children noted that the rocket's speed at the end of the first hour was about half that at time of launching, and that at the end of the second hour the speed was reduced to about one-third the original speed. A speed of 25,000 mph had little meaning for the children until a little computation indicated that this was about 400 miles per minute. Knowing that it is about 400 miles across Michigan from north to south, the children began to gain an appreciation of the rocket's speed when they realized it would flash across Michigan in one minute.

Another computation indicated that the rocket traveled more than 6 miles a second and, as one child said, "Oh, we would travel from Detroit to Ann Arbor in about 7 seconds!"

When children have gained an understanding of the decimal number system, scientific notation may be introduced in grade six as a shorter and faster way of working with large numbers. For example, the children have learned that in the decimal number system:

1. $10 = 10 \times 1 \longrightarrow 10 = 10^1$ (10 used as a factor once)
$100 = 10 \times 10 \longrightarrow 100 = 10^2$ (10 used as a factor twice)
$1,000 = 10 \times 10 \times 10 \longrightarrow 1,000 = 10^3$ (10 used as a factor 3 times)
$10,000 = 10 \times 10 \times 10 \times 10 \longrightarrow 10,000 = 10^4$ (10 used as a factor 4 times).

They can extend this to include:

2. $10 \times 100 = $?   or $10 \times 10^2 = $?

3. $100 \times 1000 = $?   or $10^2 \times 10^3 = $?

From exercises like these children can be led to discover that, when multiplying powers of the same base, they can add the exponents.

1. $10^3 \times 10^2 = 10 \times 10 \times 10 \times 10 \times 10 = 10^5 = 100,000$

2. $10^2 \times 10^2 = 10^{2+2} = 10^4 = 10,000$

3. $2^3 \times 2^1 = 2^4 = 2 \times 2 \times 2 \times 2 = 16$

If the teacher thinks it advisable, the use of a dot to indicate multiplication may be introduced at this time, too, and children may be encouraged to write 2×5 as $2 \cdot 5$; 6×7 as $6 \cdot 7$, etc.

In helping children extend their understanding of the use of formulas to express relationships, a teacher of eleven-year-olds placed the following number series on the chalkboard and asked if they could find a quick way to find the sum of all numbers from 1 to 101 without adding:

a. 1 2 3 4 5 = 15

b. 1 2 3 4 5 6 7 8 9 = 45

c. 1 2 3 4 5 6 7 8 9 10 11 = ?

d. 1 2 3 4 5 6 7 8 9 10 11 12 13 = ?

After a little study the children said that the sum in each series was equal to the middle number times the last number in the series. This they expressed as "Sum = $M \times L$." Applying this formula to the original question, they found the sum of all numbers from 1 to 101 to be 51×101 or 5151.

Then the teacher called attention to the fact that the number series with which they had been working all ended with odd numbers. She asked, "Will the formula work with a number series ending with even numbers?"

1 2 3 4 5 6 = 21

1 2 3 4 = 10

1 2 3 4 5 6 7 8 9 10 = 55

It was necessary to develop new formula for these series and the children developed three different ones:

1. (First + Last) × (½ of the Last)
   $(F + L) \times (½ \times L)$
2. (Last + 1) × (½ of the Last)
   $(L + 1) \times (½ \times L)$
3. (Last × Middle) or $L \times M$.

In this latter case the children worked with fractions and in the series "1 2 3 4 5 6" used the formula $L \times M = 6 \times 3½ = 21$.

Recently I observed a fourth grade group working with number sequences. They had started with very simple sequences such as:

2, 4, 6, 8

7, 9, 13, 21

and were asked to write the next four numbers, then they advanced to irregular patterns such as 12, 14, 15, 17 and continued to write "the next four numbers." I watched a small girl place the following sequence on the blackboard and ask her classmates to complete it:

$$32 \quad 30 \quad 26 \quad 20 \quad 22 \quad \text{—} \quad \text{—} \quad \text{—} \quad \text{—}$$

It was this same class who, at an earlier date, had worked successfully with numbers to the base of 7!

IN CONCLUSION

These are but a few illustrations of learning experiences used to add *depth* in meaning for children in arithmetic. The rule which we follow in achieving this kind of learning is a simple one:

Broaden the context and lift the skill to the conceptual level, by teaching so that children understand relationships, extend them to solutions of new problems, and have time to think, to question, to wonder.

To do this the teacher must be concerned with the development of the individual student. Each student builds his own ideas, and it is perfectly clear that in so doing his attempts will be attended by trial and error. It is equally clear that there is no substitute for the teacher either in stimulating the child's thinking or correcting and perfecting the ideas he forms. No administrative device, no amount of instructional equipment, important as it is, can take the teacher's place. Because of the complex nature of learning in mathematics, it is crucially important that teachers have adequate preparation. We, too, must add depth to our learning!

Rate of Progress in Learning Arithmetic

Esther J. Swenson

Let us begin with a statement on which there can be little argument: Children are different. Children are different in their present status and rates of progress in learning arithmetic just as they are different in height and weight and fingerprints. All teachers, I suppose, accept this statement as demonstrated fact.

Many teachers, however—perhaps a majority—make some assumptions

Reprinted from *The Mathematics Teacher* (February 1955), 70–76, by permission of the author and the publisher.

about children's learning differences which are *not* sound and which ignore the facts which are known about individual differences. The first of these is the assumption made by many teachers that the wide range of pupil ability and performance in *his* particular class or classes is "very unusual." "Other classes may have wide spreads of ability and performance, but *mine* is *unusually* large." "Yes, children are different, but not usually *this* different." Few will suggest that their classes are remarkably alike; many will maintain that theirs are more different than usual.

Another assumption which seems to be common among teachers at all school levels is that the prevalent wide range of pupil performance and ability (in arithmetic or reading or any other area of the curriculum) is unnecessary and avoidable. They hold that it should not be true. Often, by implication at least, they indicate that it would not be true if someone else (perhaps the children's earlier teachers) had done a good job of teaching.

Here is Jimmie. He is a "whiz at arithmetic," his teacher says. He breezes through all regular arithmetic assignments. If he is lucky, he is given opportunities to extend his learnings beyond the common assignment for his classmates. In the same room is Sammie. He is "getting along all right," his teacher says. He doesn't "set the woods on fire" with his mathematical brilliance but he doesn't seem to have any difficulty keeping up, either. Also in the same class is Willie. His teacher describes him as "just plain hopeless" so far as arithmetic is concerned.

The teacher asks, "How can I hold the class together? How can I teach Jimmie and Sammie and the others if I have to struggle with children like Willie? His teachers in the lower grades could at least have taught him to add and subtract! What were his earlier teachers doing anyway when they were supposed to be teaching him arithmetic?" The answer to the first question is, of course, that the teacher should *not* "hold the class together" if that expression means giving all the same assignments and instruction.

It is, of course, true that the higher we go in the school system, the greater is the spread of abilities. Is it fair for teachers (or anyone else) to take the position that with adequate instruction we could *reduce* the range of individual differences among children instead of *increasing* it? The children in an eighth-grade class are more different in their arithmetic performance and abilities than they were when they were third-graders.

The answer is no. It can't be done! It should not be done! Children are different not only in their original status but also in their rates of development. Other things being equal, they tend to get more and more different, not more and more alike. Junior high school groups tend to be more different than elementary school groups. Senior high school pupils tend to be more different than junior high school pupils.

We wish they were more alike. It would make teaching so much easier, we think. "If wishing could make it so," we think we'd like to have them more alike. On sober consideration, of course, imagine the monotony of having forty-two Sammies, all "average"! In any event, our wishing is not going to make it so. Children are different in their present knowledge of arithmetic. They are going to stay different, and, as they proceed, they are going to get to be more and more different. We may as well face that fact.

AN AUTOMOBILE ANALOGY

Suppose that we have two automobiles at the starting point. One of them is a refugee from a junk dealer's back lot; but it *runs*—after a fashion. We shall call it Model Z. When it is performing well, it can average 30 miles per hour on the open road.

The other car is a late model in excellent condition. It runs beautifully. It has power to spare. How fast this car could go is a secret, but it is certainly a 3-place number. For our illustration let us limit this car, which we shall call Model A, to an average speed of 60 miles per hour.

A averages 60 miles per hour. Z averages 30 miles per hour. They start out at the same time from a given starting point. They follow the same route of travel. At the end of one hour, how far will A have traveled? (60 miles.) At the end of one hour, how far will Z have traveled? (30 miles.) At the end of one hour, how far is A ahead of Z? (*30 miles.*) At the end of two hours, how far will A have traveled? (120 miles). At the end of two hours, how far will Z have traveled? (60 miles.) At the end of two hours, how far is A ahead of Z? (*60 miles.*) At the end of 3 hours, how far will A have gone? (180 miles.) At the end of 3 hours, how far will Z have gone? (90 miles.) How far apart are they now? (*90 miles.*) And so on. The longer they travel, the greater the distance between them. Model A gets farther and farther ahead. Model Z gets farther and farther behind.

Let us agree that this is an oversimplification of a very complex situation, but proceed anyway to draw the analogy for fast and slow learners in an arithmetic or any other mathematics class. Whether we count progress by the day or week or month or year, it will be true that the fast learner with his high-powered grasp of understandings can learn a great deal more arithmetic in the same length of time than can the slow learner. Even if the slow learner is doing his best (like the Model Z) he still is falling farther and farther behind the fast learner (Model A) who may not be using all the learning power he has. Though it might be hard to find a pair of learners who would maintain a steady 2-to-1 ratio in amount learned as suggested for the two automobiles, it would seem that there is a rough parallel between the Model A–Model Z ratio of distance traveled and the Jimmie-Willie ratio of learning achieved. Individual differences in learning do become greater and greater.

But what if the road is bad? What if the road is full of ruts and holes?

Which car must slow down most to prevent breaking springs and jostling passengers? Model A, of course. What if the road is covered with a fine glaze of ice? Which car's speed should be reduced more? Model A. What if the road is hilly and full of hairpin curves? What if the road is a mire of mud? In every case, Model A, for all its power and speed, is held back proportionately more than Model Z. When traveling on bad roads, Model A and Model Z are both held to less than their proposed speeds, perhaps, but it is Model A which is retarded more. Therefore, on *bad* roads, the differences in progress between slow and fast cars is less than on *good* roads.

THE ROAD OF INSTRUCTION

Now how about the road of instruction? Does a poor instructional road have a comparable effect of reducing the differences in rates of learning arithmetic? Does a good instructional road have a comparable effect of increasing differences in pupil rates of progress? Does the analogy hold? It does.

Some examples have been given of hazards which make a highway "bad" for travel—mud, ice, curves, ruts, holes, hills. This is not a complete list. Neither can we provide here a complete list of those instructional hazards which make us classify a child's road of learning arithmetic as "bad." But we can consider a few such impediments to optimum progress.

Take the amount and variety and quality of teaching and learning aids, including books, workbooks, manipulative devices, films, and others. Certainly these affect the kind of instructional road the learner follows.

Consider the curriculum pattern. If it is characterized by flexibility and integration, the individual child's opportunities for learning arithmetic and for understanding where and how it fits with other experiences are immeasurably extended.

And of course, we must consider the teacher. Does the teacher know arithmetic? Does the teacher understand arithmetic? Does the teacher know how to help children understand arithmetic? Does the teacher see problem-solving in arithmetic as more than getting answers by routine procedures to verbal statements of problems? Is arithmetic to the teacher a series of "this-is-how-you-do-it" procedures or does it include some of "this-is-what-it-means" and "this-is-why-it-works"?

We might consider another factor here which is not really a matter of the condition of the road, but which is certainly a driving or travel condition. When on a long trip, have you ever been routed through the downtown business district of a large city at store and office closing time? In the traffic jam does it make any difference whether your car can "do 90" on the open road? For the time being, you can stand still in a Model A or a Model Z just as well. In overcrowded classrooms we have a similar situation. The traffic problem has a good deal to do with both Jimmie's and Willie's progress. Probably, Jimmy is neglected more than Willie.

This is by no means a complete consideration of the contrasts between good and bad instructional roads which learners must travel. But perhaps we have said enough to throw some light on the question at hand, which is: How does better or poorer instruction in arithmetic influence the differences in learning progress for the learners? Does poor instruction tend to increase or to decrease the variation among the pupils in a class so far as their progress in learning arthimetic is concerned?

When is Jimmie (the Model A learner) apt to get the farthest ahead of Willie (the Model Z learner)? Just as with the automobiles, when the road is good. When the class is small enough that the teacher can give assistance to each as he needs it. When instructional materials are well chosen, when there are enough for all, when they are rich in possibilities for assisting children in discovery and understanding. When the curriculum is flexible enough to permit the children to have experiences in situations where there are real problems involving numbers to be solved; when the curriculum is such that the child is encouraged to relate his learnings in arithmetic and science and the social studies. When the teacher understands arithmetic; when the teacher understands children as individuals and as group members; when the teacher knows how to help children see sense in arithmetic and appreciate its values to them in their everyday uses of number and number relationships. These are the times, these are the situations in which Jimmie will far outstrip Willie in his progress in arithmetic. Jimmie will get farther and farther ahead of Willie, but not because Willie is held back. Not at all! Jimmie will get farther and farther ahead because the road has been cleared of obstructions to progress. Willie will also be traveling at his best "30-mile-per-hour" rate. He will be doing closer to his best too, but his possible rate of progress is slower than Jimmie's. With each learning at a high rate *for him*, the difference between what Jimmie learns about arithmetic and what Willie learns about arithmetic will grow wider and wider.

Now let us look at the opposite situation. When do Jimmie (with his Model A abilities) and Willie (with his Model Z abilities) stay closest together? When the road is poor, just as with the automobiles. When the amount of individual attention received by each is at a minimum; when the assignment is the same for both; when Jimmie is held back to Willie's level or to one somewhere in between which fits Sammie. When everyone in the class uses the same textbook or perhaps a drill book devoid of aids to understanding; when there are few or no other instructional materials. When the curriculum pattern tends to isolate arithmetic experiences within the confines of the arithmetic period and the covers of the drill pad. When the teacher has a narrow conception of arithmetic; when the teacher knows how to get answers but not much beyond that; when the teacher thinks and acts as if all children ought to fit the same mold. These are the times, these are the situations in which Jimmie and Willie are held closest together in their growth in arithmetic learnings—held closer together not because Willie catches up with Jimmie but because they are both held to a low rate of progress.

Which situation will we choose for the children to whom we are supposed to teach arithmetic? Do we want to continue our complaints that children are not alike but *ought* to be more alike and *would* be more alike if only the teachers who preceded us had taught what they should? Or are we going to face the fact that the better our instruction is the greater the range of performance will be?

If we face this fact, we can begin to act accordingly, so let's face it. When you get a group of boys and girls who are far apart in their skills and understanding of arithmetic, don't waste your time trying to explain it away by blaming their last year's teacher. Get to work trying to help each one of those children to achieve what will be *for him* a good rate of progress. This won't make them more alike; it won't bring Willie up to Jimmie's level. But it will give Willie a chance to get the most learning possible for him and will challenge Jimmie to speed up that powerful learning motor of his.

Will recognition of the normality of varying rates of progress make teaching easier? No, probably not. At least there is no guarantee that it will. But it will make teaching more *rewarding*.

SLOW TRAVELERS

What is to be done with the child who travels very slowly on the instructional road of arithmetic? Our Willie can learn arithmetic, but he learns much more slowly and covers much less ground in a given length of time than does Jimmie, the fast learner, or Sammie, the average learner. What shall we do with Willie? Shall we "flunk" him? Shall we say to him, "You will have to go back and do this over again. You will have to travel this road over again."

Is that what we would do with the slower car on the highway? Because it is far from its destination, would we advise that it be sent back to cover the last few miles over again? Is that progress? Hardly! It seems that we should, rather, seek to find some way of speeding up the progress of the slow car *from where it is*. We need to diagnose the situation. Why does Model Z travel so slowly?

Part of the answer has already been indicated. Model Z is Model Z. It is not built for speed. We may accept that fact and still explore the possibilities of getting more progress out of Model Z than is being made at present.

Maybe this car is carrying a heavier load than it can manage without retarding its progress. A Model T Ford was laboring up a steep hill in South Dakota. Two of the three passengers got out and walked so old Wheezie could make the grade. With much groaning and straining and boiling, car and driver got to the top of the hill; but, with the lightened load, they *did* make it.

Maybe Willie needs to have his load lightened. Maybe he is carrying (or supposed to be carrying) common and decimal fractions, ratio, and percentage when he can only plod along when carrying a load of addition, subtraction, multiplication, and division of whole numbers. He can't carry this heavy load, so he chugs and jerks to a full stop and makes no progress at all with any part of the load. Maybe some of that load had better ride with Jimmie or Sammie for a while, so that Willie can at least be getting somewhere with the part of the load he can manage.

When Wheezie, the Model *T* Ford, had conquered the hill out there in South Dakota, and when the passengers had labored up the hill, they got in again and all went along nicely. Postponing some topics of study in arithmetic until the learner can master part of his load does not mean permanent postponement or "soft pedagogy." After Willie has been helped along through some of the rough spots so he feels and is competent with whole numbers, we can add again to his load such other topics and ideas and skills as he needs and can carry. He will make better progress in the long run with a load he *can* carry than he will if completely bogged down with a load he *cannot* carry.

Coming back to the Model Z, let us suppose it starts and falters, spits and chugs its way along—very slowly. We study the situation. We find that the gas line is partially clogged. A little dirt, perhaps, has got into the gas line. It is so small, but it causes *much* trouble. We get it out. Model Z is on its way again, not breaking any speed limits but able to make steady progress.

Could it be that Willie has an obstruction in his inner workings that is impeding his progress in arithmetic? Maybe there was some one little point that he did not understand and it keeps him from understanding many other things. If that is the case, this "little" thing is mighty big and mighty important. Let us find out what it is and get it out of his way. Maybe we went too fast for him one day. He almost had the idea and then his teacher looked at the clock and said, "Time's up. The rule is at the bottom of page 67. Learn it and then do Examples 1–20 on page 68." So close to getting the right idea. So near but so far. And Willie has "dirt in his fuel line." His progress is going to be impeded. And his trouble will get worse and worse until someone finds out what it is and removes it.

Sometimes an obstruction to Willie's learning has nothing whatsoever to do with the specific content of arithmetic. It may be an attitude he has acquired. He hasn't done well in arithmetic. He feels uncomfortable about it. He is a little ashamed of himself for not being able to do what he sees Sammie and Jimmie doing. He wishes he didn't have to do arithmetic and show his ignorance. He decides he can't do arithmetic. And when he gets to that point, he *can't.* His learning is blocked. What does he need? He needs to be helped to see that he *can* do arithmetic. Perhaps he needs to go back over some of the things he can do and which he does understand. He needs reassurance, and he needs to have some success in doing something new in arithmetic that he hasn't done before. He needs to demonstrate to himself that he *can do arithmetic.* This is not a time for punishment, for ten extra examples, for staying after school until he gets today's problems done. This is a time for encouragement, for help on the difficulty at hand, for understanding guidance in drawing upon what Willie does know in order that he may discover ways of working from what he does know to what he does not know.

THE SAME OR DIFFERENT HIGHWAYS

Turning now instead to another question about children who have varying rates of progress in learning arithmetic, we might consider whether or not Jimmie and Sammie and Willie ought to be traveling the same highway. Should they, perhaps, be following different routes? So far we have given the general impression that they all follow the same route, the only differences being in the rate of progress and distance covered. For arithmetic in the elementary school I am going to suggest that Jimmie and Sammie and Willie should travel a common road, but that is not the whole story. Certainly they should all gain some knowledge and as much understanding as is possible for each of the meanings of numbers and the decimal number system, of the basic processes of arithmetic, of ways and means for solving problems which involve numbers and number relationships, of whole numbers and common and decimal fractions, of commonly used measures, and so on. On the other hand, there ought to be some side trips for Jimmie and some stopovers for Willie. Jimmie is making such good time along the road anyway that he can afford to take some time out for exploring interesting and informative side paths. He may wish to visit some of the historical shrines to the history of numbers. He may wish to climb the mountain of square root. These and other excursions will be to his benefit and his enjoyment.

Willie ought to have time for an occasional stopover. Motoring in the Model Z is more strenuous than in the Model A. One needs time to rest up, to consolidate one's plans, to start out afresh. Willie needs occasional stops for seeing where he is, for relating this to that, for building up a well-knit organization of that which he already knows.

POINT DESTINATIONS VS. WHOLE-AREA DESTINATIONS

Sometimes when one takes a trip, one has a particular destination at the end of the trip—Cincinnati or New York or Boston. Sometimes that is not the case at all. One may "tour New England" or "take a trip out West" for pleasure or for business. New England in general or the Pacific Coast States in general is the destination. The learner's destination in this analogy of traveling the instructional road to arithmetic is of the latter type. The child does not travel on and on and on to some future destination of skill and understanding in arithmetic. Rather, he is traveling around within the total content of arithmetic. This is an important distinction. It gives the whole trip added significance. It makes each experience important in and of itself as well as for what it leads to later. The learner's motivation is directed toward the present and the future, toward solving present problems and meeting present needs for arithmetic as well as preparing for future needs and uses and problems to be solved.

Furthermore, two travelers who start out from the same point and who seek the same final destination (a given point) may not necessarily follow the same route to get there, though they are apt to follow certain favored routes. But when the same two travelers set out to see a whole region, they are much more apt to follow different routes while seeing pretty much the same sights. So, when we say that Jimmie and Willie may well follow much of the same road in arithmetic learning, we are not limiting them to following it in exactly the same sequence. One pupil may learn column addition before he learns all the basic addition facts; the other may learn all the basic facts before he learns column addition. If certain important places in the region of arithmetic can be reached by only one route, Jimmie and Willie will both have to follow the same itinerary. The point is that wherever they go within the field of arithmetic, children should be arriving as well as traveling. They should be achieving as well as getting ready to achieve.

SUMMARY

Children learn arithmetic at varying rates.

They never start out at exactly the same point; but even if they did, the fast learner is bound to get farther and farther ahead of the slow learner.

Accordingly, the range of pupil performance in arithmetic grows wider and wider as children progress through the elementary school.

The widening range of abilities and performance is not necessarily due to lack of adequate instruction (although certainly inadequate instruction does exist). Rather, the better the instruction, the instructional materials, and the curriculum in general, the wider will be the range of pupil performance.

For pupils whose rate of progress in learning arithmetic is slower than we think it needs to be, we must study the causes for the delay and remove them, not just pile on a heavier load.

Those who can make rapid progress need to be challenged to make that progress and to extend their knowledge and understanding by as many fruit-ful explorations into arithmetical knowledge as seem desirable.

Finally, as we guide children in their travels through the land of Arith-metic, let us make sure that we have the right country in mind. Let us be wary lest we cause children to wander for another forty years in the wilder-ness of routine drills and mechanical manipulations of numbers and algor-isms. Let us hasten the day when the arithmetical travels of *all* children will take place in a region of understanding and independent reasoning and rich experience with arithmetical content—a veritable arithmetical Land of Canaan!

Are You Giving Proper Emphasis to Concept Development in Arithmetic?

Frank S. Deck

Recent years have brought many changes in the psychological bases for the teaching of arithmetic. Many authorities in the field are placing increased emphasis on the development of the basic concepts of number (as opposed to the manipulation of numerals, classification of skills, etc.). Unfortunately, however, these ideas and methods of developing them are not found in all textbooks. The teacher who can identify the arithmetical concepts and the best methods—based on sound psychological theories of learning—to develop these concepts at any particular level will find it easier to assist his pupils in understanding the vital process of arithmetic.

Many teachers unfamiliar with concept development may not understand its full impact on the learner. Some textbooks have been built upon the idea that we teach what we can test. Perhaps for this reason, perhaps for others, not too much attention has been given to the really basic idea of helping the child understand the "whys" of arithmetic.

Much of our recent literature, and many current publications in the field of arithmetic discuss the so-called "meaning theory." The phrase "meaning must precede practice" has become almost a byword in some of our profes-sional books.

If we can succeed in bringing principles to the child's level, and help him see the relationships of these things to his everyday life, then we have suc-ceeded in teaching the concepts of arithmetic.

Reprinted from *School and Community* (January 1960), 33, 42, by permission of the publisher.

Many of these concepts help form the basis of our number system. They involve such things as the decimal nature of number, place value and grouping by tens.

We shall confine this discussion to the concepts involved in understanding one part of one process, i.e., the division of common fractions.

In our study of common fractions many students (and teachers) fail to realize that we are really teaching a new number system. In fractions there is no place value, and we no longer group by tens. Only the symbols remain the same. By the time the student reaches the latter part of the sixth grade, when division of fractions is normally introduced, he should already have in his background of information about arithmetic, a number of skills and concepts which will help him understand this new process.

These concepts are basic to the understanding of division of fractions: (1) Every number, except zero, has a reciprocal. (2) The product of a fraction and its reciprocal is 1. (3) The dividend and the divisor can be multiplied (or divided) by the same number without changing the quotient. (4) If the divisor is 1, the quotient is equal to the dividend.

For example, we have the problem $8 \div \frac{2}{3}$. This can also be written as $\frac{8}{\frac{2}{3}}$. First we need to get 1 for the divisor. This can be found by multiplying it by $\frac{3}{2}$.

$$\frac{8}{\frac{2}{3} \times \frac{3}{2}}$$

$\frac{2}{3}$ has been multiplied by $\frac{3}{2}$, so we must also multiply 8 by $\frac{3}{2}$.

$$\frac{8 \times \frac{3}{2}}{\frac{2}{3} \times \frac{3}{2}}$$
$$\text{or}$$
$$\frac{8 \times \frac{3}{2}}{1}$$

We do not need to write the divisor when it is 1. So now we can write the algorism in this way:

$$8 \times \frac{3}{2} = \frac{24}{2} = 12.$$

Of course, this is more complicated than simply telling the child to invert the divisor and multiply, but he is capable of understanding the concept, and with a little more effort on the part of the teacher, he will most certainly have a better understanding of what we really do in the division of fractions.

Another method which is sometimes used is the common denominator method. If we use the same example, our thinking now proceeds along these lines: the problem remains $8 \div \frac{2}{3}$. We must first change the problem so that both fractions have the same denominator. It now becomes $\frac{24}{3} \div \frac{2}{3}$. We found

$\dfrac{24}{3}$ by multiplying our original fraction 8 or $\dfrac{8}{1}$ by 1, expressed as $\dfrac{3}{3}$. Now the child can see that $24 \div 2 = 12$, and $3 \div 3 = 1$. The algorism is written:

$$8 \div \frac{2}{3} = \frac{24}{3} \div \frac{2}{3} = \frac{12}{1} = 12.$$

The number line is a device which is being used increasingly in the teaching of arithmetic. The problem might now be stated in this manner. How many pieces of ribbon $\frac{2}{3}$ of a yard long can be made from 8 yards of ribbon? The child can actually show this by a line on his paper to represent the 8 yards of ribbon.

Of course he must understand that the problem, which may be stated as how many $\frac{2}{3}$'s are in 8, is really a problem of division, and that $\frac{2}{3}$ is the

```
0     1     2     3           6     7     8
└─────┴─────┴─────┴ ─ ─ ─ ─ ─ ─┴─────┴─────┘
```
This line can represent the 8 yards of ribbon.

```
0     1     2     3           6     7     8
└─┴─┴─┴─┴─┴─┴─┴─┴─┴ ─ ─ ─ ─ ─ ─┴─┴─┴─┴─┴─┴─┘
```
Each of the 8 units is divided into thirds.

unit of measure as well as the divisor. The next step is to divide each of the eight units into thirds.

Now by the process of counting, the child can discover how many $\frac{2}{3}$'s are in 8. Pupil discovery is another area which many teachers fail to recognize as one of importance.

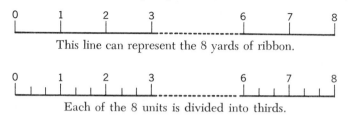

This will help determine how many $\frac{2}{3}$'s are in 8.

There are 12 $\frac{2}{3}$'s in 8. He can get 12 pieces of ribbon.

Finally, in such a difficult process as division of fractions, meaning implies that a student should be able to ascertain whether or not an answer is sensible. In the example $8 \div \frac{2}{3}$, the quotient is 12. The student should know that this answer is sensible because he can reason by a rather simple process. He knows that 8 divided by $\frac{1}{2}$ is 16 and 8 divided by 1 is 8. Since the divisor $\frac{2}{3}$ is larger than $\frac{1}{2}$ but less than 1, the quotient must be less than 16 but greater than 8. The answer 12 is within this range and is thus a reasonable answer.

When a fraction is divided by a fraction the answer can be checked to see if it is sensible by the following three generalizations which upper grade students should be able to understand: (1) When a number is divided by itself the quotient is 1. (2) When a larger number is divided by a smaller number, the quotient is greater than 1. (3) When a smaller number is divided by a larger number, the quotient is less than 1.

These principles can be understood more fully by the student by giving him sufficient background of understanding before introducing the process. This can be demonstrated to the class by developing with them a chart similar to this one:

$$6 \times 4 = 24 \qquad 6 \div 4 = 1\frac{1}{2}$$
$$6 \times 2 = 12 \qquad 6 \div 2 = 3$$
$$6 \times 1 = 6 \qquad 6 \div 1 = 6$$
$$6 \times \frac{1}{2} = 3 \qquad 6 \div \frac{1}{2} = 12$$
$$6 \times \frac{1}{4} = 1\frac{1}{2} \qquad 6 \div \frac{1}{4} = 24$$

Meaning in arithmetic does not imply "all rationalization and no mechanization," but rather that there should be a minimum of mechanical type operations. When a part of a difficult algorism is performed mechanically, such as inverting the divisor and multiplying, a rational check should be applied. After the child has used a mechanical procedure it is important to determine whether or not his answer is sensible. If he understands these basic concepts of the division of fractions (and he will only if his teacher has gone out of her way to discover these things for herself and then impart them to her class) then and only then will he have complete knowledge of the process, but a method of proving why he is right.

Anxiety and the Mathematics Underachiever

Donald Avila and Dwain Small

The problem of underachievement in mathematics is constantly plaguing the mathematics teacher. How can a child do so well in all of his other academic subjects, yet do so poorly in mathematics? Why does a child with an IQ of 125, or so, fail mathematics?

Math teachers are well aware that there are many reasons for these situations, each contributing more or less to any given child's problem of mathematics underachievement. But the results of a recent study have provided some information about the mathematics underachiever that should prove helpful to the mathematics teacher.

The children, thirteen in number, that constituted the sample of subjects

Printed by permission of the authors.

in the study under discussion were selected from grades 4, 5, and 6. They were classified as underachievers because their Stanford Achievement Test nonmathematics scores were equal to or above their grade placement, but their average percentile score in mathematics computation and concepts was two or more deciles below their other scores.

All of the subjects were given a psychological examination which included the following techniques and measuring devices:

1. Behavioral observation by project psychologist
2. Parent interviews
3. California Test of Personality (CPI)
4. Behavior rating scale
5. Wechler Intelligence Scale for Children (WISC)

An analysis of the information collected from these sources led to a description of the study of underachievers as follows:

The underachiever comes from a home that is relatively unstable, in many cases fraught with discord and disharmony. On top of this, these homes are centered around high achievement . . . a great deal of stress is placed upon school grades and college preparation. This home pressure generates a sense of a lack of personal freedom and strong anti-social tendencies, as well as a tremendous amount of anxiety (p. 31).*

By far the most significant factor in the data collected was that of anxiety. A high level of anxiety was discernible throughout most of the various techniques and measures listed above. The subjects particularly manifested a high level of anxiety when they were performing mathematical tasks or tasks which were heavily timed. When the anxiety-producing factors of mathematics performance and time were combined, the negative effect upon their performance was truly dramatic.

The following statement exemplifies the conclusions of the researchers involved in the previously cited study:

The most debilitating result, however, is clearly anxiety. These children are anxious, and it hurts them! The more anxiety-provoking the situation, the more debilitated they become (p. 31).*

Of particular concern to the mathematics teacher is the statement that:

It is a well known phenomenon that in our society both mathematics and time limits are anxiety-provoking factors, even to the most well-adjusted person. The underachiever in the present study seemed to be especially affected by these factors (p. 32).*

* Small, D. E., *et al. The Problems of Underachievement and Low Achievement in Mathematics Education,* U.S.O.E. Project H-307, Final Report, November 1966.

Still more important is the statement made in the same study that "When a child identified as an underachiever in the present study is confronted with high anxiety situations, his performance is lowered considerably, although his basic ability is still present" (p. 32).*

The reason that the subjects in the study were underachievers clearly was not for lack of ability. They were average or above in WISC measured intelligence score (I.Q. range 104 to 138, average score of 125.63), and all of their achievement scores were at or above their grade placement level. Something else, then, was the cause for the fact that the subjects' arithmetic subtest scores on the WAIS were only average and their mathematics achievement scores were below grade placement. The foregoing discussion seems to justify entertaining the hypothesis that at least one major cause is an exceptionally high level of anxiety.

There is reason to believe then that, at least with regards to some underachievers, a much higher level of performance in mathematics could be achieved if some way to reduce their anxiety could be discovered. One way, of course, would be to provide such children with personal counseling. However, this is a costly process which many schools cannot afford to do adequately. Therefore, a more practical approach would be to construct situations right in the classroom that might contribute to anxiety reductions. The authors of the present paper offer the following suggestions as a step in that direction:

1. The underachiever might be placed in a regular class, but with his achievement being measured only at the end of the year rather than constantly throughout the year. This would, at least, decrease the frequency of highly anxiety-provoking experiences with mathematics and offer more opportunity for reinforcement.

2. The underachiever might be placed in a special class in which emphasis is placed upon the *usefulness* and *enjoyment* of mathematics, rather than grades. Again, his achievement could then be measured at the end of a course or year.

3. Allow the underachiever to tutor low achievers in his class, and grade the underachiever either on (a) how well the low achiever improves, or (b) on the basis of the underachiever's own achievement at the end of a course or term. It is likely that this would offer more positive experience to the underachiever in relation to mathematics and enhance the underachiever's self-concept by allowing him to be a "teacher." Such a procedure might improve his academic performance as well as his personal social adjustment.

No one is suggesting that anxiety is the sole cause of mathematics underachievement. Furthermore, it is possible that the problems of the underachievers discussed in this paper cannot be generalized to other underachievers. But the authors believe that the evidence presented is suggestive enough to warrant the implementation of the suggestions listed above, at least on a trial basis.

4

Developing Strategies for Teaching Elementary School Mathematics

No topic receives wider discussion among teachers than organizing for mathematics instruction.

In the not too distant past, there were very few models for teaching. One could enter many classrooms and witness the same strategy being employed: teacher telling, children listening. As we recognize the wide range of individual variations existing among children along with the great variety of learning styles, the role of the teacher becomes more complex. On a visit to a contemporary elementary school, one will notice a variety of teaching styles as well as an abundance of materials and services that help support the educational program.

The topic of developing instructional strategies causes a great deal of anxiety. No topic receives more publicity in the mathematics education literature. It is comforting to know that the strategy is successful to the degree that it is carefully planned. (Consider the factors related to the topics treated in Section 2 of this book.) Few organizational plans can be followed by all teachers with all pupils. Good organization is best accomplished by a dimensional structure geared to the individuals who are to use it. Is there a difference between a strategy directed to an individual and one provided for a group of children?

As instructional leaders plan for the wide range of students, they are confronted with the most difficult task of determining the proper strategy. Realizing a variety of strategies exist offers no consolation to a teacher for she must wrestle with the larger decision of deciding when to employ which strategy. What factors determine the choice of strategy? What are the proper strategies for teaching certain areas of mathematics? Or do all areas of mathematics warrant a similar strategy? A teacher with insight is able to determine which choice of strategy is most appropriate for given settings. She realizes that learning paces

188

and styles vary and therefore is ready to provide compatible strategies.

As you read the articles in this section, what seems to be the common thread which is built in as part of each strategy? Do these strategies utilize the considerations expressed in Section 2? What suggestions do you have for developing strategies that are compatible for today's schools? How do you organize children for learning when you are confronted with the notion that the higher the age level, the wider the range of differences within a classroom; and the better the teaching, the wider the range of individual differences within that classroom? What strategies for teaching are most appropriate for children attending the elementary school?

Strategies and Teaching Elementary Mathematics

Boyd D. Holtan

Every time a teacher plans and teaches a mathematics lesson, some type of strategy is involved. A strategy is a plan of action which serves as the vehicle to achieve the teaching objective. Strategies might be considered broadly, either as classroom strategies, or more narrowly, as concept strategies. Classroom strategies are techniques and methods which characterize the general way the teacher directs the instruction in his classroom. Some examples of classroom strategies are lecture, discussion, laboratory projects, individualized instruction, and programmed instruction.

Concept strategies are a less global way of considering strategies which are related to the teaching of a particular concept. When a teacher chooses to teach a concept, he must also choose the strategy which he will use in teaching it. Johnson and Rising (1967) have described some of these strategies for teaching secondary school mathematics. A very interesting application of the use of logic in developing strategies for discovery sequences has been described by Henderson (1958, 1959, 1967).

Traditionally, the strategy has been implicit in the class textbook, and the teacher merely followed the strategy indicated. Unfortunately, a given

Printed by permission of the author.

strategy is not necessarily successful with all students, and if the teacher blindly follows the textbook lead, he is not making use of his knowledge of the characteristics of individual students in his class. The strategy might be too abstractly presented, based on experiences which the student has not had, or require skills, such as reading, at which the student is not sufficiently proficient. If the teacher has some knowledge of a variety of teaching strategies for the particular concept, a more appropriate selection can be made for the desired concept development.

The teacher must also be able to select alternate strategies when it is found that the student has not gained the necessary understandings after a strategy has been applied. Often, in the past, the plan was to repeat the same strategy even though it had already been found unsuccessful! Therefore, it is crucial that the teacher know, select, and use alternate strategies.

The skill of choosing and using various strategies does not usually come easily to the teacher of elementary mathematics. The purpose of this paper is to present and illustrate four concept strategy types which might be helpful to the teacher in preparing to teach a concept. There are many strategy types, but the teacher could use these four as a nucleus around which he might build a repertoire of usable strategies. The four concept strategy types which I have chosen to illustrate are (1) the number line, (2) applications, (3) mathematical sentences, and (4) diagrams and drawings. Each of these might be used to help the teacher to develop a strategy for teaching a specific concept. In order to illustrate the use of the four concept strategy types, I have chosen two arithmetic concepts and will show how each of the four concept strategy types can be used to develop a strategy to teach the arithmetic concepts. Thus, for each arithmetic concept, there will be shown four strategies to teach it, each based on one of the concept strategy type.

STRATEGIES FOR TEACHING THAT $2\frac{1}{2}$ AND $\frac{5}{2}$ NAME THE SAME NUMBER

Suppose that a teacher wants to teach his students that $2\frac{1}{2}$ and $\frac{5}{2}$ name the same number, that is, the meaning of a mixed fraction. The following illustrations show how the concept strategy types might be used to suggest strategies to teach the concept.

A STRATEGY BASED ON THE NUMBER LINE

The number line can be used to show that $2\frac{1}{2}$ and $\frac{5}{2}$ name the same point on the number line. Write the names for the points 0, $\frac{1}{2}$, $\frac{2}{2}$, $\frac{3}{2}$, $\frac{4}{2}$, $\frac{5}{2}$, $\frac{6}{2}$ at the appropriate positions on the number line (Figure 1). Then write the names for the points 0, $\frac{1}{2}$, 1, $1\frac{1}{2}$, 2, $2\frac{1}{2}$, 3 on the line. The teacher may then call attention to the points which have been named with more than one name, particularly $\frac{5}{2}$ and $2\frac{1}{2}$.

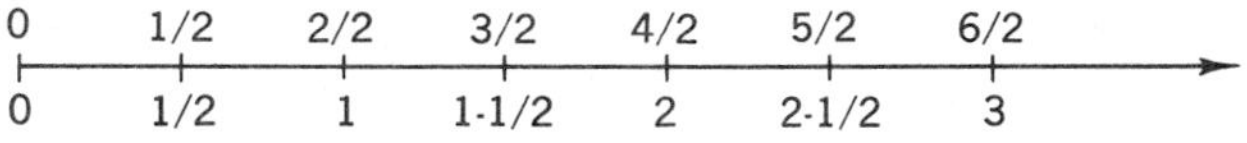
0
1/2
2/2
3/2
4/2
5/2
6/2
0
1/2
1
1-1/2
2
2-1/2
3

Figure 1

A Strategy Based on Applications

Suppose that Mary has $2\frac{1}{2}$ candy bars. She wants to share them with some of her girl friends. So she cuts them into smaller bars, each $\frac{1}{2}$ of the original size. How many of these half-size bars will she have? Notice that the $2\frac{1}{2}$ bars could also be represented as $\frac{5}{2}$.

A Strategy Based on Mathematical Sentences

Complete the frames shown below:

$$1 = \bigcirc \text{ halves or } 1 = \frac{\bigcirc}{2}$$

$$1\tfrac{1}{2} = \bigcirc \text{ halves or } 1\tfrac{1}{2} = \frac{\bigcirc}{2}$$

$$2 = \triangle \text{ halves or } 2 = \frac{\triangle}{2}$$

$$2\tfrac{1}{2} = \square \text{ halves or } 2\tfrac{1}{2} = \frac{\square}{2}$$

From the last sentence, we should conclude that $2\frac{1}{2}$ and $\frac{5}{2}$ name the same number.

A Strategy Based on Diagrams and Drawings

The drawing (Figure 2) shows $2\frac{1}{2}$ circular discs. How many half-discs are there? If $\frac{5}{2}$ describes the discs, then $2\frac{1}{2}$ and $\frac{5}{2}$ both represent the discs in the drawing and are naming the same thing.

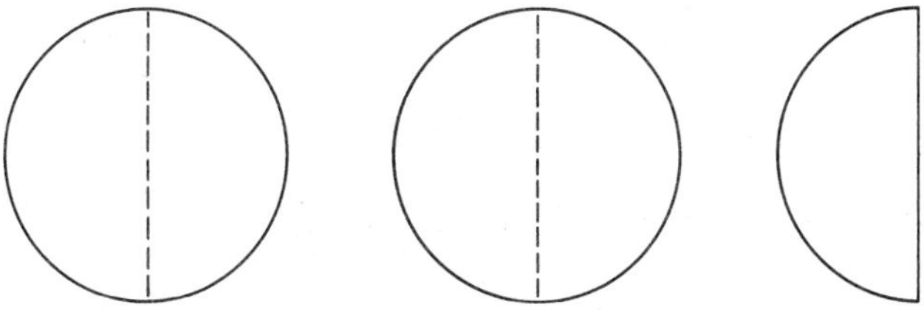

Figure 2

STRATEGIES FOR TEACHING THE COMMUTATIVE MULTIPLICATION PROPERTY

For a second example of an arithmetic concept, assume that a teacher wants to teach or clarify the concept of commutativity for multiplication, or, more specifically, that 2×3 is the same number as 3×2.

A STRATEGY BASED ON THE NUMBER LINE

The number line can be used to illustrate the commutativity principle by showing that two jumps of three units to the right of zero and that three jumps of two units to the right of zero both have the same ending point on the number line (Figure 3). From this we can indicate that $2 \times 3 = 3 \times 2$.

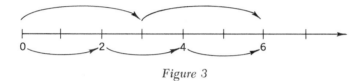

Figure 3

A STRATEGY BASED ON APPLICATIONS

Suppose that Jim planted two flower bulbs in each of three window boxes. John planted three flower bulbs in each of two window boxes. Who planted more? Did they plant the same number of flower bulbs? Here again is an illustration that 2×3 is the same number as 3×2.

A STRATEGY BASED ON MATHEMATICAL SENTENCES

Complete the frames shown below:

$$2 \times 3 = \square \qquad\qquad 3 \times 2 = \square$$

Notice that $\square$ is the same in both sentences, so that 2×3 and 3×2 again name the same number.

A STRATEGY BASED ON DIAGRAMS AND DRAWINGS

The arrays shown (Figure 4) can be used to illustrate that there is the same number of o's if they are arranged into an array of 2 by 3 as if they are arranged into an array of 3 by 2.

An alternate form which uses an array type of strategy is the usual multiplication table. By choosing a pair of numbers, one from the row index and the other from the column index, it can be seen that the product in the body

```
              O  O
  O   O   O   O  O
  O   O   O   O  O
```

Figure 4

of the table is the same as if the column number and the row number were interchanged. A more general concept might be introduced by noticing that the products are symmetric about the diagonal which is the square of each index factor.

Four concept strategy types have been suggested and illustrated with two arithmetic concepts. These concept strategy types may be considered by a teacher when he wants to develop a strategy to teach other concepts. The concept strategy types suggested here are the number line, applications, mathematical sentences, and diagrams and drawings. It would be hoped that each teacher would build his own more inclusive set of strategy types and thereby increase the likelihood that the teaching concept strategy might be appropriate for both the student and the mathematical concept objective.

REFERENCES

HENDERSON, K. B., "Strategies for Teaching by the Discovery Method," *Updating Mathematics,* Vol. 1, No. 3, Section IV, November 1958, and Vol. 1, No. 8, Section IV, April 1959.

———— "A Model for Teaching Mathematical Concepts," *The Mathematics Teacher,* October 1967, pp. 573–577.

JOHNSON, DONOVAN, and GERALD R. RISING. *Guidelines for Teaching Mathematics,* Wadsworth, 1967, Chapter 4.

Developing Mathematical Understanding by Implementing the Strands Report

Janet Briggs Abbott

Modern mathematics is designed to help children develop desirable attitudes and behavior as well as to acquire facts and to develop skills. Its aims are to develop eager, creative children who through firsthand experiences acquire an understanding of mathematics and are stimulated to assume personal

Reprinted from *California Education,* Vol. 3, No. 3 (November 1965), 9–11, by permission of the California State Department of Education.

responsibility for their own learning. These characteristics are difficult to measure, but their presence is indicated by specific changes in the ways that children work. A useful plan for systematic observation of some major changes that are possible through the new mathematics programs is provided by the topics listed for grade two in *Implementing Mathematics Programs in California,* a manual prepared and published in 1964 by the California Association of County Superintendents of Schools.

TOPIC I: SETS

In the past children performed many of the same operations that are part of an understanding of sets, but set terminology was not in use. It is doubtful if pupils saw the operations within the unifying framework which an understanding of sets makes possible. With sets of objects, pupils in the second grade are able to transfer one-to-one matching ideas to one-to-two matching. They use their knowledge of equivalent sets and set union to develop multiplication by joining several sets. They use set partitioning to develop division.

Children freely use braces to enclose set members, capital letters to name sets, and commas to separate members of a set. They begin to develop the concept of infinity through understanding the sets of counting and whole numbers.

TOPICS II AND III: NUMBERS AND NUMERATION SYSTEMS

Formerly, pupils' experiences with whole numbers were often limited to 200. In new programs, most second grade pupils use whole numbers up to 2,000. They develop the concept of the cardinal number through using sets of objects, thus learning rational rather than rote counting. The degree of understanding of the nature of numbers and the ways in which they can be represented vary. In general, these children learn number-numeral distinction easily and quickly; they rename numbers in various ways, selecting names appropriate to their tasks.

Pupils in the second grade demonstrate their ability to rename numbers by using expanded notation, such as the following:

$$25 + 48 = (20 + 5) + (40 + 8) = (20 + 40) + (5 + 8)$$

As pupils practice using these processes, they lay the foundations for algorithms. Thus, pupils do not memorize algorithms; they actually derive them.

As pupils in the second grade use expanded notation, they begin to understand place value. This ability can be observed in their use of such devices as the countingman, place value charts and pockets, counters, hundred boards, and abaci, that are used to demonstrate increased understanding of "what is happening" in the mathematical operations.

The pupils' understanding of fractional numbers and numerals can be observed in their use of equivalent subsets and number lines. Their understanding of odd and even numbers is also seen in their use of the number line.

TOPICS IV, V, AND VI: ADDITION AND SUBTRACTION; MULTIPLICATION AND DIVISION; PROPERTIES OF THE OPERATIONS

Pupils in the second grade readily rename numbers and regroup them to perform addition and subtraction involving three-place numerals. They develop the concepts of multiplication through union of equivalent subsets and division through partitioning a set into equivalent subsets. Many children can perform multiplication and division operations dealing with products through 25. Working first with sets and then with numbers, pupils become aware that multiplication can be seen as repeated addition; furthermore, the pupils also become aware that division can be seen as repeated subtraction.

Pupils in the second grade achieve an understanding of the inverse relationships between addition and subtraction and between multiplication and division through using such devices as number lines, cross number puzzles, addition and multiplication tables (grids), and arrays. They use horizontal forms and the conventional vertical algorithmic form to illustrate commutativity of addition and multiplication. They develop insight into the associative properties of addition and multiplication by working with sets and then with the number line and mathematical sentences.

Second grade pupils reveal much interest in trying things out for themselves. They experiment to see if subtraction and division are communicative or associative. They show real insight into the power of a property if they recognize that it takes only one case (a counter example) in which the property does not hold to prove that the operation does not have that property.

They are able to make pairings of each object in one set with each in another set to illustrate the Cartesian product concept of multiplication (multiplication in rows and columns).

TOPICS VII, VIII, XI: ORDER, RELATIONS, AND MATHEMATICAL SENTENCES; PROBLEM-SOLVING; GRAPHING-STATISTICS

Children show competence in using mathematical sentences to indicate both equalities and inequalities. They enjoy using the relation symbols—

=, ≠, <, > —and the concept of true and false mathematical sentences. They are adept at finding missing addends, sums, factors, products, operational signs, and relation symbols. They display good use of parentheses, both in expanded notation and in showing order of operations in mathematical sentences. Pupils solve equations by giving objects number names, formulating open mathematical sentences, and completing them. They can use their own set objectives to solve problems posed by the teacher or their classmates. They translate these into open sentences and solve them. Solving problems in this way encourages application of mathematics. The interrelationships among mathematical sentences, problem-solving, and life are extremely important. Children need many experiences in using objects to solve real problems. Pupils who are given the opportunity to do this develop great skill and confidence in many techniques essential to later mathematical learnings.

TOPIC IX: MEASUREMENT

Second grade pupils show good understanding in relating equivalent value in units of money (quarters, half dollars, dollars); time (telling time to the nearest five minutes or quarter-hour); and measurement (half-inch, yard; half-gallon, gallon; degrees of temperature). Although children formerly had experiences with most of these measuring units at this grade level, the present approach in unit form makes possible more concentrated experiences. They also do much work in estimating and using pupil-chosen units of measurement.

TOPIC X: GEOMETRY

Teachers who present more material than that included in the textbooks find pupils in the second grade to be very creative in recognizing geometric shapes in the world about them. These children can *see* geometry; they draw conclusions about it intuitively. They are good at exploring ways of drawing lines to form figures and at making geometric designs. They quickly learn the point-set terminology and show excellent comprehension of the ideas of inside and outside, that an "edge" affects the shape, and that the union of the edge and the inside or interior region can be called a distinctive kind of region—for example, a circular region.

Children can discover many ways to measure an area. For example, they use number line segments, or they cut pieces of paper into equivalent shapes and sizes. They are intuitively developing understandings which they will later be able to verify through the deductive reasoning process.

LOGIC

Pupils in the second grade use logic in several ways. They are able to tell if conclusions are probable. They give reasons (principles or justifications) why statements or mathematical sentences are true or false. They recognize that conclusions are established by logical deduction from reasons. Logic is involved each time they generalize or use accepted proved generalizations. Thus, they can use a few key principles to prove that their solutions are correct instead of many isolated, unrelated facts to support their answers.

Second grade pupils, like other children, grow according to their experiences and the insights they accumulate. The new approach to mathematics has revealed that many children possess a much greater store of mathematical insight and intuition than had been assumed. The exact nature of this insight is not known except as children are allowed to have experiences in which they can reveal their insights.

In the new approach to mathematics, the teacher plays a different role than formerly. He sets up a stimulating environment, one highly conducive to learning and, most important, one which allows the child to learn on his own. Curriculum limits are kept free and flexible to permit individual learning rates to develop rather than to have the rates preset.

The Mathematics Laboratory

Harry L. Phillips

Ever since the first customer objected to being short-changed, mathematical skill has been one of the qualifications employers have wanted in their employees. The difference today is that a higher level of skill is required even of the average person. Today's high school graduate steps into a working world that is run by mathematical techniques, a world in which his first paycheck is likely to be a computer-punched card. And experts tell us that further growth of our economy is directly dependent upon the parallel growth of a population with considerable, even formidable, mathematical skills. In short, we must somehow manage to teach more mathematics to more students at all levels of our educational system.

Educators have devised several different kinds of programs in an effort

Reprinted from *American Education* (March 1965), 1–3, U.S. Department of Health, Education, and Welfare.

to help students acquire a better understanding of mathematics. In the elementary school they have devised programs aimed at giving children an early start. The child who in elementary school has been introduced to the "new mathematics"—that is, to the basic mathematical principles and theories—will, educators hope, quickly and easily make the transition to high school and college.

In the high schools, too, new programs are being introduced. Here the purpose is to improve the curriculum, methods, and materials.

The main idea of the "new mathematics" in the elementary school and the revised programs in the high school has been to move away from instruction requiring only slavish learning by rote to instruction enabling the student to discover mathematical ideas—the how and why of mathematics—on his own. In both elementary and secondary grades many school systems are experimenting with something called the mathematics laboratory. The atmosphere and the equipment of the laboratory encourage the teacher to use the discovery method, whether teaching the old mathematics or the new.

The idea of the laboratory in teaching mathematics is not new. For years elementary school classes have used blocks and rods and beads, and the fact that these simple devices are now called visual aids or multi-sensory aids does not make them revolutionary.

What is new about the use of the laboratory is the current upsurge of interest in it as a creative stimulus to math students. The effort to develop and perfect it is also new. Fortunately, many teachers are not waiting for the perfected laboratory, but are using the equipment available to them and defining the term "laboratory" to match the use they are making of it.

The term "mathematics laboratory," as teachers and administrators are using it today, is not easy to define. To some teachers it may mean a cabinet and materials in the corner of the classroom. To others, it may mean a special room supplied with chalkboards, cabinets, desks with graph-ruled tops, and other equipment ranging from a simple protractor to an intricate oscilloscope.

To Mrs. Gladys Thomason, State coordinator of mathematics education, Georgia State Department of Public Instruction, the word "laboratory" means "having sufficient equipment and materials to do a good job of teaching mathematics."

With encouragement from Mrs. Thomason and other State Department officials, Georgia teachers are fast acquiring such labs; to date about half of the State's 196 school districts have them. Last year the department asked teachers what equipment they were finding most useful. Among the items they listed were some that had not until recently been seen in the classroom; others had not been produced commercially until recently.

Teachers of lower elementary grades listed number lines, with which children can learn how to count, add, and subtract; place-value charts, from which children can get a clear picture of the decimal system; and hundreds boards, on which they can learn to count to 100 and to combine the numbers in different ways. Teachers of upper elementary grades listed coordinate charts, percentage charts, spheres, and globes. Teachers of the secondary grades listed geometry models, including cones, pyramids, and prisms; slide rules; and chalkboard geometry sets, including compasses, protractors, and slide rules. Both elementary and secondary teachers listed overhead projectors, films, and filmstrips.

To Mrs. Lore Rasmussen, a Pennsylvania teacher, the laboratory is a means of giving children every possible opportunity to understand each question they are asked about numbers and shapes; in the laboratory they can see the answer illustrated in innumerable ways. It is a room in which the children have the best possible support for solving a problem through handling concrete objects. "It contains a teacher with mathematical competence," Mrs. Rasmussen says, "and a special set of attitudes toward all learners and toward mathematics.

"The mathematics laboratory is not just a room," she goes on to say. "A teacher's pedagogy changes when he uses a laboratory." In the mathematics laboratory, she points out, the teacher can individualize instruction, and get children to work voluntarily on a higher level of accomplishment than they otherwise would. Children can prove to themselves that what they are learning is correct and consequently rely less on authoritarian proof from teachers and textbooks.

Mrs. Rasmussen speaks of mathematics laboratories with enthusiasm and authority, both grown out of her experience in teaching mathematics to elementary children. Currently she is working in Philadelphia: with college students as assistant professor at Temple University; with children through grade 6 in a private school in a middle-class suburb; and with 5- and 6-year-olds in a pilot project in the public school in a congested neighborhood.

All children in the pilot project—there are 400, ranging in ability from the slow to the gifted—are taught in a laboratory specially equipped for language, mathematics, and science classes. The laboratory contains raw materials and carefully selected equipment.

"To the child," Mrs. Rasmussen says, "the mathematics laboratory is a playroom where things can be counted, moved, rearranged, stacked, measured. . . . It is a room with things to be weighed and instruments to weigh them with, machines with buttons and levers and cranks that count, record, and project. A room with books for browsing in . . . books waiting to be written in. A room with objects of interesting shapes and many sizes to be used for building and comparing." The difference between work and play, she says, exists only in the minds of adults.

In their play the children begin to understand the meaning of quantity, length, weight, temperature, shape, and the like. When the children's attention span lengthens, when they begin to concentrate on one form or object, the teachers guide them into individual work. When children indicate by their actions that they are ready to learn about symbols, teachers start them on reading, writing, and arithmetic. The lab is equipped to teach all three. The subject matter is taught simultaneously and interwoven, for, as Mrs. Rasmussen says, the children must begin by learning the names of things.

This is the first year of the project, but already there have been some remarkable results, Mrs. Rasmussen reports. Some of the 6-year-olds are working with fractions and multiplication, and some are making their own math books. Careful records are kept on all pupils, and at the end of the year their progress can be compared with that of pupils who have been in a regular program.

To Mrs. Beatrice Ogren, chairman of the mathematics department, Fridley High School, in a Minneapolis suburb, the mathematics laboratory is an extension of the classroom. "Good teachers have always used lab techniques in teaching mathematics," she says, "but they have not always had the wonderful convenience of having a room where pupils could work on their own, a room that did not have to be cleaned up after every class period. I'm all for having a lab for every mathematics class in the country."

Her school does have labs—one between every two math classrooms, and every lab is used by pupils and teachers, in class and out, Mrs. Ogren's lab is used almost every period of the day, with her encouragement. Three of her students—all boys—spend their vacant periods in the lab nearly every day, making their own models, experimenting with raw materials, or working on their own ideas, going far beyond the lesson assigned. When I talked with her last month, four or five girls were spending their vacant period in the lab experimenting with op art, and a couple of boys were playing chess. The pupils feel that the math lab is their room and they take pride in it, Mrs. Ogren says. She encourages them to prowl about the lab, to experiment with the materials and her students have never abused the privilege.

Laboratory equipment need not be elaborate, Mrs. Ogren says. Her own is not; it has plastic models of all sorts, overhead projectors, calculators, a typewriter with mathematical symbols, and a variety of other materials. Students make transparencies for their own and other classes, and they make many of their own models.

No matter how simple or how complex the equipment is, the aim of the teacher everywhere is always the same—to lead his students to discover mathematical relationships for themselves.

It is, of course, possible to teach such relationships in the classroom with only the chalkboard and textbook as teaching aids, but many students do not grasp abstractions quickly. The laboratory method can reach such students and keep them moving along. "It is a godsend to the slow student," Georgia's Mrs. Thomason says. "The slower the student, the more he needs the concrete aids the lab provides. But the better student needs the lab too."

Mrs. Ogren agrees that the slow students need the lab more, but she finds it more useful with her advanced students because they can work with less supervision. The lab stimulates them and frees them to progress as fast as they can.

In several States schools have purchased mechanized equipment for teaching applied mathematics. In Iowa some schools have purchased enough to provide one machine for every two students in high school math. Such equipment frees the students from the necessity of making arithmetic computations and enables them to concentrate on problems requiring logical reasoning and knowledge of organization. A Philadelphia high school with a data-processing center is giving students a basic course in using electronic computers to help them understand applied mathematics.

So new is the idea of the mechanical mathematics classroom that few manufacturers of instructional materials consider the market large enough to be profitable. In the face of this, both Iowa and Pennsylvania have produced their own textbooks for these classes.

The School Mathematics Study Group, made up of mathematicians and teachers of mathematics and supported in part by the U.S. Government's National Science Foundation (NFS), has produced materials for use in kindergarten through grade 12. Other individuals and groups, some with support from the cooperative research program of the Office of Education, foundations, or professional associations, have also prepared materials. In the meantime some specialists are doing research on comparative methods of instruction.

Some research is now being done to determine whether the teacher using the laboratory gets better results than the teacher who doesn't. But even before the results are known, it seems safe to say that, when the laboratory technique is used by teachers who like it and believe in it, it works.

Very likely the number of such teachers will increase as more efforts are made to train teachers to use the new equipment and to use the discovery method in teaching. Private foundations have joined the NSF to sponsor study groups which have produced new courses of study and have cooperated with institutes for training teachers in the new methods. The programs of these groups have been aimed at providing the better student with an advanced mathematics program and encouraging him to go on to further work in college.

Other groups—State departments of education and regional and local associations of mathematics teachers—are working to improve instruction for all students, the average and the slow as well as the bright. The Georgia State department, for example, demonstrates new equipment at workshops for teachers, in inservice programs, and on statewide educational television.

Even without help, some teachers learn to use a math lab. A teacher may begin by feeling the need for a single model, and as he works with it and finds it more and more useful he recognizes the need for other models or other equipment. The value of a math lab grows on the teacher gradually, Mrs. Ogren says. He soon finds that students have their own ideas about equipment, some of them very sound. Gradually the teacher, with students' help, builds up a laboratory; gradually he acquires skill in using it.

Generally teachers want to do a good job and are eager to learn. Mrs. Rasmussen and others who have conducted workshops report that teachers are enthusiastic about the labs.

There are, of course, exceptions. One teacher turned down her supervisor's invitation to a workshop, saying: "I'll retire in five years. I've learned that book I'm teaching now, and I don't intend to learn another."

Obviously the mathematics laboratory is just another classroom if it is not presided over by a good, knowledgeable teacher. Professor Richard Andree of the University of Oklahoma says:

"Whether or not a mathematical laboratory makes for successful instruction in secondary mathematics depends in large part . . . on the imagination with which this equipment is used by the instructor."

There are reasons to believe that many teachers will acquire skill in using labs: first, teachers colleges are including more instruction in new laboratory techniques in their methods courses; and second, with financial support provided under the National Defense Education Act of 1958 and its amendments, State departments are increasing their staffs of supervisors and raising their demands for high quality in materials and instruction.

Title III of the act makes funds available to the States for their use in providing supervisory services, including inservice education of mathematics teachers. Since 1958 the gain in the number of State mathematics supervisors has been dramatic. Then there were 9 supervisors; now there are 68. Total enrollment in high schools has increased by 28.2 percent and enrollment in high school mathematics courses by 36.7 percent. It seems reasonable to assume that title III has made some contribution to the increase. Title III also makes funds available to the States for equipping mathematics laboratories in the local schools.

As teachers begin to stock their classrooms with long-needed aids, school planners begin to design facilities to house them. In the elementary school the additions have not been ambitious.

As new equipment comes on the market, however, school officials may be encouraged to provide space for it. Both designers and manufacturers of furniture for the elementary school are showing considerable interest in equipment for science and math laboratories.

At the junior high and high school levels, however, some elaborate installations have been designed and built. In some high schools the laboratories are full-scale classrooms. Few of these special rooms have been built, although a number of older classrooms have been converted to use as mathematics laboratories. At the moment there are fewer than 2,000 well-equipped laboratories in the country.

In Baltimore, a city of almost a million, only one laboratory has been built in a junior high school; but two more are planned for high schools now in the blue-print stage.

The situation in Baltimore County is probably typical of the situation in much of the Nation. The county has invested in mathematics equipment but has no plans for special laboratories. "The demand for space in our new schools is so great," a county official explained, "that we cannot afford to build a room which will not have maximum use."

Modernizing the teaching of mathematics is no easy task, even with NDEA and NSF support. There has been a shortage of well-trained high school mathematics teachers for years, and many of the older teachers already in the schools must be retrained to meet the new demands. There are 80,000 mathematics teachers at the high school level alone and there are not enough facilities to retrain those who need retraining.

It is one thing to enlist groups of learned persons to devise texts, courses, and curriculums to benefit all students. It is another matter to tackle the slow, plodding, routine work which must be done if the new ideas and courses are to reach the estimated 7 million high school students in their classes each year—to say nothing of the even larger number of pupils in the elementary schools. Schools are making progress, but there is still much to be done.

Discovery in the Teaching of Mathematics

Robert B. Davis

Whether one thinks of the aeronautical engineer versus the pilot, or of the pure mathematician versus the engineer, or of the economist versus the businessman, virtually every major field of human endeavor is split between a group of theorists and a group of practitioners. It seems to me that it is a sign of health when the two groups are able to communicate, and when they attempt to work closely together. Speaking as one of the clinical people or practitioners, I want to thank the theorists for their efforts at bridging the gap which sometimes seems to separate us.

Reprinted from *Learning by Discovery: A Critical Appraisal*, Lee S. Shulman, Evan R. Keislar, eds. (Chicago: Rand McNally, 1966), 114–128, by permission of the publisher.

My remarks are made from the practitioner's point of view, which is the only one I can legitimately claim. Based on the Madison Project work of the past eight years, I want to cite a few examples and a few ideas related to them.

Specifically, I have three goals: first, I want to give examples of what we have regarded as discovery experience for children, in the hope that some of you will be able to suggest a few of the ways in which these experiences differ from exposition, and even differ from one another. This last remark deserves emphasizing, for it is my present notion that there are many different kinds of discovery experience, and we confuse the issue badly when we treat discovery as a single well-defined kind of experience.

My second goal is to offer a few remarks attempting to interpret or describe some of the things we mean by discovery, and to explain why some of us believe in its importance.

Finally, I shall list a few things that might be called objectives of Madison Project teaching, for this, too, may clarify why we think we believe in 'discovery.'

SOME EXAMPLES AND SOME INTERPRETATIONS

The students in my first example were some low-IQ culturally deprived children in the seventh grade, some of whom were older than normal for grade seven. The topic was the matter of finding pairs of whole numbers that would satisfy linear equations of the form

$$(\Box \times 3) + 2 = \triangle$$

Although we found that $\Box$, $\triangle$ notation useful, and consequently did use it with these children, what I have written above could be translated into traditional x, y notation as

$$y = 3x + 2$$

We passed out graph paper and suggested that suitable pairs of whole numbers be recorded according to the usual Cartesian use of coordinates.

Very nearly all of the students made the obvious discovery that there is a simple linear pattern to the resulting dots. A considerable number of them actually applied this discovery, by extrapolating according to the pattern, then checking to see if their new points gave numbers that satisfied the equation.

It is these students who used the discovery this way whom I wish to discuss. Some of them spent several days working with various linear equations, using the patterns to find points, then checking by substituting into the equation. This was one of the earliest things the project ever did that seemed to fascinate children far beyond their normal degree of involvement with school.

My conjecture is that the important aspect of this was perhaps a combination of achievement in making their own discovery, competitive gratification vis-à-vis those classmates who did not make the discovery, autonomy of having set the task for themselves, some intrinsic esthetic or closure reward, and the existence of a verification that did not depend upon the teacher.

These were culturally deprived children, with a middle-class teacher and a middle-class curriculum. Previous observation had already convinced us that these children were at best *tolerant* of a schoolish learning that was *wrong* in every important respect. The children were always checking up, between school and social realities outside of school, and invariably found the school to be wanting.

The school taught you to speak the language incorrectly—for example, the school taught, 'It is I' in a world where the social reality was, 'It's me'—the school taught personal economics incorrectly, the school taught civics incorrectly, and so on. Nothing ever checked when you tried it out against actual reality. (For example, if a majority of people in the county don't like the sheriff, he won't be reelected—according to what they teach in school. But in reality, perhaps a majority of the people are not even allowed to vote—to use an example that is in our newspapers at the present moment.)

Here, in their own discovery, they had found something that *really worked!* If you tried it out, it checked out perfectly!

In any event, some of the children were captivated, and spent several days on the matter, asking to take graph paper home and so on.

(Incidentally, in the long run—i.e., over the year that we worked with this class—truancy decreased markedly, and parents reported their children taking an unprecedented interest in school—for example, by discussing it at mealtime.)

My second example is perhaps somewhat similar. We wanted to give children in grades 3–9 some experience with *variables* and with *the arithmetic of signed numbers.* It is one of our principles that such experience should always be provided *in a sensible mathematical context,* and (if at all possible) in a form which would permit a student to make one or more interesting discoveries. We believe that this procedure helps get the children in a frame of mind where they are always poking around looking for interesting patterns that may be lurking just beneath the surface.

I should emphasize that the discoveries in question will usually not be part of the basic purpose of the lesson, and it is not essential for a child to discover them. They are primarily a bonus for those who do discover them.

In the present instance, remember, we wanted the children to get some experience using *variables,* and working with the *arithmetic of signed numbers.* We consequently gave them quadratic equations to solve, beginning with

$$(\square \times \square) - (5 \times \square) + 6 = \bigcirc$$

and gradually progressing to harder problems, such as

$$(\square \times \square) - (20 \times \square) + 96 = \bigcirc$$

Now, at first the only method available to the student was, of course, trial and error. If he makes no discoveries, the student continues with this method, and gets full benefit from the basic part of the lesson; that is, he gets a great deal of experience using variables and signed numbers, and in a situation where he does *not* regard this as drill.

But—if the student discovers the so-called coefficient rules for quadratic equations, his use of trial and error can be guided to maximum efficiency. He has discovered a secret—and one which many of his classmates don't know. They may *never* know!

TORPEDOING

In both of the previous examples, we make use of a technique which we call 'torpedoing.' After a student has discovered what he believes is the pattern for linear equations from working with

$$(\square \times 1) + 3 = \triangle$$
$$(\square \times 1) + 5 = \triangle$$
$$(\square \times 1) + 2 = \triangle$$

and so forth—*after* he is confident of his mastery, we unobtrusively slip in a problem like

$$(\square \times 2) + 3 = \triangle$$

He uses his pattern, he checks—and the numbers don't work!
What shall he do?

With a little thought, he discovers there is a pattern here, also—indeed, there is a more general pattern of which he had discovered only a special case.

In a similar way, with the quadratic equations, we begin by using only unequal prime roots, so that one of the two coefficient rules (the product rule) is extremely obvious. Using it alone leads to easy solution of the equations, such as

$$(\square \times \square) - (5 \times \square) + 6 = \bigcirc$$
$$(\square \times \square) - (12 \times \square) + 35 = \bigcirc$$
$$(\square \times \square) - (13 \times \square) + 22 = \bigcirc$$
$$(\square \times \square) - (7 \times \square) + 10 = \bigcirc$$

and so on.

Here also, once the student is really pleased with his discovery, and with the new power it has given him, we confront him—unobtrusively and unexpectedly—with a variant problem which will tend to confound his theory.

In this instance, we slip in a problem having composite roots, instead of the prime roots the student had previously dealt with.

The product rule now seems to indicate more than two roots: for example, with

$$(\Box \times \Box) - (9 \times \Box) + 20 = \bigcirc$$

many students will say the roots are $\{2, 10, 4, 3\}$.

Trial by substitution shows that this is wrong. Again, by persevering, the student finds that there is a broader theory, of which he had found only a narrower part.

WHY DO WE LIKE TORPEDOING?

It may seem that what I have described is simple sadism, or How to Be One Up on Your Students Without Really Teaching. We *feel* that it is not so (although, unfortunately, it *can* be in the hands of a teacher who really *is* a sadist).

Why do we use this technique of torpedoing some of our students' best theories?

It is important to realize that, at the outset, we don't know. We use the technique because, intuitively, it feels right.

But, in the years while we have been using this technique, we have, of course, discussed it often, and even made some analytic attempts at constructing an abstract rationalization for it.

Perhaps we like the technique because:

1. It gives the brightest students something to work on while the others catch up on more basic work;
2. It is a friendly challenge from teacher to student, and students rise to such bait better than fresh-water fish do to flies;
3. Perhaps Piaget's processes of 'assimilation' and 'accommodation' need to be practiced, and this is where you practice them;
4. Or, to put point 3 in less technical language, perhaps the security of a friendly classroom is the best place to gain experience in fixing up theories that used to work, but somehow don't seem to work any more—the classroom is a better place to learn this than, say, the political meetings of anti-integrationists or the radical right;
5. Then, too, it is worth learning that science does not deal in absolute truth. Sufficient unto each day are the theories thereof—and an irreconcilable contradiction may be discovered tomorrow! (Or, for that matter, a better theory!) If your theories work, make the most of them—but keep a wary eye out, just the same.
6. Finally, this is one of the ways that we go about bringing *history* into the classroom. If one wishes to *understand* history, one must have some background of relevant experience. Since the history of mathematics is an unending story of trials,

failures, break-throughs, temporary successes, new points of view, and so on, it is unintelligible to the person who has no background experience in trials, failures, break-throughs, temporary successes, revised points of view, and so on. Torpedoing theories in the classroom provided background experience that parallels important historical phenomena. Can you *realize* what the discovery of irrationals meant to the Greeks if you, yourself, start out with the sophisticated viewpoint of the 20th century?

The "Crisis" Dilemma: Seeking the Unit Matrix

This next example involves a different kind of discovery situation. In the previous examples, the discoveries were merely optional bonuses added to the meat of the lesson; moreover, students discovering any secret patterns kept the secret to themselves, revealing their knowledge only indirectly, by using the secrets to solve difficult problems easily and quickly.

In the present example, all eyes are focussed upon a central problem which we wish to solve, if possible—or to recognize as unsolvable, if a logical argument shows that no solution can exist. If anyone finds an answer, he will announce his discovery at once.

Specifically, we look at the system of 2-by-2 matrices and ask how this new mathematical system compares with the familiar old system of rational numbers. One question is this: is there a 2-by-2 matrix which plays a role analogous to that of the rational number zero? The answer turns out to be that there is, and it is the matrix

$$\begin{pmatrix} O & O \\ O & O \end{pmatrix}$$

So far so good. Now—is there a matrix that plays a role analogous to the rational number *one?* Students invariably—and wisely, on the available evidence—guess

$$\begin{pmatrix} 1 & 1 \\ 1 & 1 \end{pmatrix}$$

but a quick computation shows that this is *not* satisfactory.

Here we have the dilemma: IS there any matrix that behaves like the integer one? Has our failure to find one been a symptom of the impossibility of the task, or have we merely failed due to personal reasons, not reasons of fundamental impossibility? Is it worthwhile trying any longer? If so, how shall we proceed?

This has proved to be a consistently exciting lesson for fifth-graders, or anyone older who doesn't already know the answer.

Going Beyond the Data or the Task

In the filmed lesson entitled, "Graphing an Ellipse," at the end of a lesson on graphing

$$x^2 + ky^2 = 25, \qquad \bigcirc \leq k,$$

a seventh-grade student (Debbie H., according to her nametag) asks: "Why couldn't you use matrices, and make a graph for k less than zero?"

Since these students have previously used matrices to introduce complex numbers, this is an ingenious and appropriate suggestion. The teacher does not immediately respond, but another student (whose nametag reads Lex) answers: "No, you can't, because you won't be able to graph matrices." This answer is essentially correct—but both of these remarks go beyond anything the teacher had planned or anticipated.

The teacher's contribution to this is mainly a genuine appreciation of the students' contributions—but we believe this is important. Children somehow act far cleverer when their cleverness is welcome and appreciated.

Do It Your Own Way: Kye's Arithmetic

Somewhat similar is this example. A third-grade teacher was introducing subtraction, with borrowing and carrying:

$$\begin{array}{r} 64 \\ -28 \\ \hline \end{array}$$

She said: "You can't subtract 8 from 4, so you take 10 from the 60 . . ."

A third-grade boy named Kye interrupted: "Oh, yes you can!

$$4 - 8 = -4$$

$$\begin{array}{r} 64 \\ -28 \\ \hline -4 \end{array}$$

and $60 - 20 = 40$

$$\begin{array}{r} 64 \\ -28 \\ \hline -4 \\ 40 \end{array}$$

and $40 - 4 = 36$

$$\begin{array}{r} 64 \\ -28 \\ \hline -4 \\ 40 \\ \hline 36. \end{array}$$"

The teacher did nothing here to *solicit* originality, but when she was confronted with it, she *listened* to the student, tried to understand, and *welcomed* and appreciated his contribution.

This was an unusual, but actual occurrence. The more common, 'traditional' response would have been to say: "No, Kye, that's not the way you do it. Now watch carefully and I'll show you . . ."

Where does this traditional rejection of his contribution leave Kye? He is given the feeling that mathematics is a stupid subject that never works out the way you'd expect it would . . . Given enough experiences of this sort—and in a traditional situation he will be—Kye will probably transfer his interest and his energy to some other field of endeavor.

This example has always seemed to me to suggest the essence of good 'modern' teaching in mathematics, as opposed to 'traditional' teaching. In a phrase: *listen* to the student, and be prepared for him to suggest a better answer than any you know. The 'modern' teacher *actually learns from his students!*

Kye's algorithm for subtracting was an original contribution of a third-grade boy. It is in many ways the nicest algorithm for subtracting that I have ever seen—and it was invented by a boy in the third grade.

The traditional teacher assumes from the outset that such a thing is impossible. Is it any wonder that the traditional teacher somehow never encounters such clever behavior from students? Like the spirits that move Oui-ja boards, such clever student behavior rarely appears before the eyes of those who don't believe in its existence.

AUTONOMY AND PROLIFERATION

In introducing graphical integration and differentiation to an eighth-grade class, we proceeded as follows: We obtained a print of the PSSC film "Straight Line Kinematics" which is an *expositional* treatment of these topics in relation to velocity and acceleration. The students could view this film whenever they wished—and as often as they wished. They were then given a shoebox full of simple equipment—the PSSC ticker-tape equipment—to take home if they wished, and were asked to devise their own experiments and work up their own data. They later performed their experiments in school, at a session which has been recorded on film.

The effort and ingenuity that some students put into this went far beyond their normal effort for 'schoolwork.'

WHAT QUESTIONS

In one instance, we give physical apparatus to students and ask them *what questions* might be worth studying about this apparatus. The point here is for the student to identify appropriate *questions*. An eminent mathematician, Professor McShane of the University of Virginia, has said that his favorite mathematics problem is stated in a textbook as follows:

A pile of coal catches on fire.

These seven words are the *entire* statement of the problem—in a *mathematics* book!

Now—what *mathematics* questions does this pose?

LEAVING THINGS OPEN-ENDED

Many mathematics problems occur at a stage in the child's life when he is not yet prepared to answer them. An honest use of logic seems to compel us to leave these questions open for the time being. The alternative would be to 'answer' them on the basis of authority—but we believe this would tend to make the child think that mathematics is based upon the pronouncements of authorities. We prefer to leave the question open—after all, aren't most scientific questions open at the present time? Or, perhaps, *always* open?

Example: Is

$$\square \times \bigcirc = \bigcirc$$

an *axiom* or a *theorem*? Ultimately the child will learn that it is a theorem:

$$\square + \bigcirc = \square$$
$$\bigcirc + \bigcirc = \bigcirc$$
$$\square \times (\bigcirc + \bigcirc) = \square \times \bigcirc$$
$$(\square \times \bigcirc) + (\square \times \bigcirc) = \square \times \bigcirc$$
$$\therefore \square \times \bigcirc = \bigcirc$$

This proof, however, involves some subtle and awkward points, so that the child cannot settle the question when it first occurs to him, and we leave the question open. The child knows that if he is ever able to prove the result, he will be able to classify it as a theorem. In the meantime . . . Who knows which it is?

WHERE DOES IT COME FROM?

The Madison Project approach to *logic* is, so far as we know, completely unique and unprecedented. Virtually every existing book on logic *tells* you what *modus ponens* is, *tells* you what the truth table is for 'and,' 'or,' 'if . . . then,' and so on.

But why? Where does all of this come from, anyhow?

Given the transitory nature of scientific knowledge, we can hardly settle for facts which are static pieces torn out of the fabric of time past, time present, and time future.

Where does all of this logic come from? How would we go about making up our own logic if we wished to do so?

In order to answer these questions—at least, according to our own view of the answer—the Madison Project proceeds like this:

First, we ask children (grades 7, 8, 9, or older) to analyze statements of their friends, and to classify them as true or false. They realize that this is a vast oversimplification, for most ordinary statements in the ordinary world are neither true nor false; there's some truth in them, but one still has some possible doubts or reservations.

We then ask the children to focus on actual usages of 'and' and 'or,' and to record *as many different uses of 'and' and 'or' as they can find* by means of truth tables.

Ordinary language has a great many different uses of both words. One of my favorites—we might label it 'and,' in order to distinguish it from *other* uses, which can be labelled 'and$_2$', 'and$_3$' and so forth—is this one:

Keep driving like that and you'll kill somebody.

A somewhat similar use of 'and' occurred prior to the 1964 election, in the radio admonition: Vote, and the choice is yours, Don't vote, and the choice is theirs. If you fail to register, you have no choice. Consider, also, the poem: "Laugh, and the world laughs with you, Weep, and you weep alone." The result of this activity is an extensive truth table with many different columns, headed 'and$_1$', 'and$_2$', 'and$_3$', etc., and 'or$_1$', o'r$_2$', 'or$_3$', and so on. Usually some students insist on moving into a more-than-two-valued logic, in order better to reflect nuances of meaning which seem to them to be present. Once we have collected together this large truth table, we have completed stage one, which might be labelled Observing the Behavior of the Natives.

We move next to the Legislative stage: In order to gain clarity, we agree on one single meaning for the word 'and,' we pick one column in the truth table to define this meaning, and we legislate that 'and' shall henceforth be used in that single sense only.

The study of logic proceeds further: after the Sociological stage, and the Legislative stage, we move on to the Abstract stage, and so forth—but the point is that these children have made up their own systems of logic. As a result, they know where logic comes from. In the same way, you understand Beethoven differently after you, yourself, have written some music of your own composition.

An Active Role, and Focussing Attention. Discovery of another sort is perhaps involved in teaching students (second-graders, say) to plot points on Cartesian coordinates. The teacher plots a few points, but the students learn more by imitation than by following a careful exposition. Learning by imitation of course involves a kind of discovery, since you must figure out how the teacher is doing it.

As David Page has pointed out, the best mathematics students have always learned by discovery—even when listening to a lecture, they are *actively thinking:* asking Why? Why not? How about doing it this way? Now what do you suppose he meant by that? Why can't you do it *this* way? and so on.

Games Using Clues. One of our most successful lessons goes like this:

Three students, working together, make up a rule. For example, Whatever number we tell them, they'll double it and add twenty. They do not tell us their rule; instead we tell them numbers. They apply their rule to each number we tell them, and tell us each answer. It's our job to guess their rule.

There is a great deal of mathematics involved in this lesson—for example, the distinction between formula and function, and such properties of functions as linearity, oddness, evenness, rate of growth, and so on. But perhaps the main *discovery* aspect resembles closely Suchman's (1964) work on inquiry: By choosing wisely the numbers we tell them, we can get *clues* as to the nature of the function they are using. No single clue will usually be decisive, but a suitable combination will be.

A somewhat similar format has been used by David Page in his lessons on Hidden Numbers. A few numbers are written on a piece of paper, and the students are to guess the numbers from a set of clues. To make matters harder, *some of the clues are false,* so that the students must recognize *and make use of the contradictions* which are contained in the set of clues (grades 4, 5, 6, 7, 8, or 9).

TWO THEORETICAL INTERPRETATIONS

An extremely valuable approach to analyzing communications in class has been developed by Professor J. Richard Suchman. The data inside a student's mind at an instant in time can be classified (as an oversimplification, of course) into three categories: facts, unifying mental constructs (roughly, 'theories'), and applications. The possible communications can be diagrammed as follows:

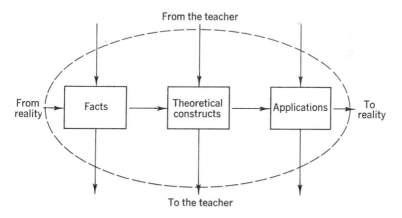

Using this analytical approach in interpreting classroom lessons can be very exciting and gratifying—which, as J. Robert Oppenheimer has remarked, is perhaps the most valid test of a theoretical approach.

Because of limitations of time and space, I shall not attempt to illustrate the use of Suchman's diagrams, beyond remarking that on a Suchman diagram, discovery communications seem to appear as conspicuously horizontal channels, whereas expositional and rote communications appear as conspicuously vertical channels. Particularly in connection with the work of Piaget, Tolman, Lewin, Kohler, White, and Bruner, Suchman diagrams are a powerful analytical tool for the practitioner seeking a rationale for understanding what goes on in the classroom.

Another aspect of discovery experiences is being emphasized in the motivation studies by Richard de Charms (in press) in relation to the analytical dichotomy of the learner's perception of his role, which de Charms polarizes as 'origin' versus 'pawn.'

THE GOALS OF EDUCATION

It is worth remembering that the life of a human being, or the interrelated lives of many human beings, are in reality unified wholes, not separated into pieces in any way whatsoever. When, in order to analyze life abstractly, we break off pieces by invoking *categories,* we do a violence to the reality whole that can impede comprehension as easily as it may, hopefully, facilitate it.

In particular, motivation is not separate *in reality* from perception, personality, learning, social interactions, or communication. Still more specifically, *reality* does not begin with a statement of *explicit goals.* If a teacher begins with an attempted statement of explicit goals, he does so by choice, and may easily do so in error, for his subsequent behavior may not reveal the same goals as his initial words did.

In our own Madison Project teaching, our original conscious goals were general and nonspecific: we wanted to find some of the best experiences with mathematics that children could have. To choose among alternatives we relied upon our intuitive assessments.

From this highly general purpose we spun out a sequence of specific activities in the classroom. In order to *discuss* these experiences, *after they were created,* we have attempted to work out some suitable analytical categories. In particular, we have identified what appear to be some of our probable goals. Here is a tentative list, surely somewhat incomplete:

1. We want to give students *experience in discovering patterns in abstract situations;*
2. We want students to have experience in *recognizing potentially open-ended situations,* and in *extending open-ended situations by original creative work;*
3. We want the students to be familiar with the basic concepts of mathematics, such as *variable, open sentence, truth set, function, Cartesian coordinates, mapping, isomorphism, linearity, matrices, implication, contradiction, axiom,* etc.
4. We want the students to build up, in their own minds, suitable *mental imagery* (in the sense of Lewin, Tolman, Piaget, Leibnitz, Polya, et al.) to permit

them to perform mental manipulations involving the basic ideas of mathematics (such as *function, linearity, isomorphism, mapping,* etc., as mentioned above);

5. We want the students to acquire a modest mastery of the *basic techniques* of mathematics;

6. We want the students to know the basic facts of mathematics, such as $7 + 3 = 10$, $-1 \times -1 = +1$, and so on;

7. We want the students to possess considerable facility *in relating the various parts of mathematics one to another*—for example, using algebra as a tool in studying geometry, or recognizing the structure of the algebra of linear transformations of the plane into itself, and so on;

8. We want the students to possess an easy skill in *relating mathematics to the applications of mathematics* in physics and elsewhere;

9. We want the students *to have a real feeling for the history of mathematics,* derived partly from having been eye-witness observers (or participants) on the occasion of mathematical discoveries.

We regard the preceding nine points as intellectual matters; but they must be accompanied by some emotional or value goals, namely:

10. We want the student to know that mathematics *really and truly is discoverable* (something few people believe);

11. We want each student, as part of the task of knowing himself, to get *a realistic assessment of his own personal ability* in discovering mathematics;

12. We want the students to come *to value 'educated intuition'* in its proper place;

13. We want the students *to value abstract rational analysis* in *its* proper place;

14. We want the students—as much as possible—*to know when to persevere, and when to be flexible;*

15. We want the students to have a feeling that *mathematics is fun or exciting, or worthwhile.*

The preceding goals do not sound like the goals of a traditional arithmetic or algebra program. They are not.

Space and time do not permit us to pursue the matter, but implicit beneath all Madison Project work is the notion that *education* and *training* are different, that education is for people, and training is for electronic machinery (which usually doesn't need it anyhow)—indeed, all repetitious routine tasks are basically nonhuman.

One example of the distinction—a tragic and highly suggestive example— will have to serve where many might be cited:

A few years ago in a hospital nursery in Binghamton, N.Y., the formula for new-born babies was made with salt instead of sugar. By the time the error was discovered, a dozen or so babies had either died or suffered severe and irreparable brain damage.

Now,—who or what was at fault? Many babies—indeed, virtually all of them—*simultaneously* developed feeding problems. Some of the *mothers*— but none of the nurses!—tasted the formula and complained that it was unusually salty.

No nurse heeded either clue. The nurses had been trained to soothe a new mother's anxieties, lest they be passed on to the infant and create feeding problems.

Those of us who have children of our own know how much this episode meant to the parents of the babies involved.

New York State has responded by passing a new law, which, I believe, makes it illegal for a hospital to store salt in a room in which nursery formulas are prepared.

This is a significant step in the wrong direction.

Every time we attempt to by-pass human resourcefulness—by laws, rote training, or otherwise—we move toward, and not away from, the unintelligent behavior of the nurses who were trained but not educated. The response of the *mothers* was more appropriate than that of the nurses, but the non-adaptive blind weight of authority decided the outcome in favor of the 'trained' nurses.

I think it important for every teacher always to remember that *he, the teacher, does not know the right answer or the right response*—he can only hope that, when the time comes, his former students will respond appropriately.

Those theorists who study education are on shaky ground indeed if their analysis assumes that they can separate right answers from wrong answers. If the matter in question is trivial, perhaps they can; but if it is important, they surely cannot.

The present emphasis on creativity and divergent thinking would never have occurred—and should never have occurred—but for the fact that we had gone all too far down the road labelled training, and had, surprisingly, lost sight of education.

Using Pupil Teams in Teaching

Frank W. Lanning

We hear a great deal these days about "grouping for instruction." For the most part, its aim is to better fit our instruction to the individual pupil, and to restrict the inevitable competition between pupils to those of comparable abilities. Although the label we attach to this practice is grouping, our primary concern is still with the individual, and almost forgotten are the potentials of a group operating as a group.

Is there educational merit in having a group, or team, working together to solve arithmetic problems? Can the individual student profit in understand-

Reprinted from *Updating Mathematics* (1964), 65–68, by permission of Croft Educational Service.

ing and increase his personal achievement in arithmetic for having taken part in an arithmetic team effort?

It is the contention here, based on actual experience, that these questions can be answered with an emphatic "yes."

GETTING READY FOR TEAMWORK IN ARITHMETIC

There are two important things to keep in mind as you attempt to group students for arithmetic teamwork. First, the grouping is not merely for classification purposes; its members will be working together as a team. Second, subsequent observations of each group at work will probably suggest adjustments, perhaps even a change in criteria for selecting group members.

One way—or partial way—to choose your groups is to let the pupils decide. Have each pupil list on a piece of paper the names of three or more classmates he would like to work with. Record these choices in a sociograph, like the one shown in the figure. Simply list the names of your pupils in alphabetical order across the top of a sheet of paper and down the left-hand side. Indicate with a mark the names of the persons chosen by each pupil. By counting across you can find the total number of choices each person gave. You will also have a record of those students chosen by each pupil and those who chose each other. The information provided by this sociometric device can be of great assistance to you in identifying pupils who are more likely to work well together.

		A	B	C	D	E	Choices Received
Student Names	A		x	x		x	3
	B	x		x		x	3
	C		x			x	2
	D	x		x		x	3
	E	x			x		2
Choices Given		3	2	3	1	4	

Groups may also be chosen on the basis of ability. Evidence of achievement levels from standardized tests and/or teacher-made tests in arithmetic may be used as the basis for establishing group membership. But remember, even though ability is your criterion for grouping, these groups are formed for the primary purpose of working together on problems in arithmetic.

Often the teacher's observations, his anecdotal records and general personal experience with the pupils in class represent as valid a criterion as any in deciding which pupils should form which groups. Teacher judgment usually correlates rather highly with tests and measures of pupil personality, motivation and achievement.

Very likely you will find there is no one best way to select your groups. Whatever techniques you do employ, you will still need to watch the groups in action and judge whether further adjustments will need to be made.

Finally, a word about the size of the groups. So far, experience with this method has favored groups of five to seven pupils. This seems to be about the optimum size in which all or most of the members of a group can actively participate in teamwork solutions of arithmetic problems.

GETTING TEAMWORK OPERATIONS UNDER WAY

Once you have organized your class in arithmetic "task forces" you have added another valuable means of instruction to your existing methods. You will probably find that teamwork activities are best interspersed throughout the year, either for enrichment activities or as an integral part of your program.

At the intermediate level, for instance, a teamwork project might be initiated by giving a set of story problems to each of the teams, with their goal to solve the problems in as many different ways as possible. At the primary level, the problems would be simpler, with perhaps the goal being to show solutions by means of concrete or semi-concrete materials.

At the outset, all teams would probably work on the same set of problems. As you observe the work, interest and capabilities of the various teams, subsequent problems would tend to differ as you attempt to adapt and make them more challenging to the members of the team.

Many arithmetic problems or projects can be found in other subject areas. From science: Constructing weather instruments such as the vane, barometer, wind-speed indicator, rain gauge, in which dimensions need to be determined and measured, scales drawn, data recorded and averaged. From social studies: Outline maps involving scales, distances between cities, speeds, rates and times.

Although most of the teamwork problems and projects can be planned to be carried out within the normal arithmetic period, some will extend beyond. This is reasonable, for interest within some groups will certainly "spill over," and some enrichment projects are best worked on outside regular class time.

As to procedure, here are seven points that should be considered:

1. *Explain to the members of the groups that they are to arrive at an answer or answers by cooperating with one another.* It will be very important

that pupils in each group understand that they are to work together for a team-solution. Help them to understand that cooperation on the solution of an arithmetic problem does not mean that they are merely to copy from someone else in the group, or that they are to work independently and not share in the process of solution. Explain to them that cooperation *does* mean asking and answering questions of others about the methods used and how to solve the problems. Emphasize that cooperation does mean a direct comparison and challenging of each other's written work, or work done with other materials—blocks, sticks, cutout figures—used in the solution of arithmetic problems.

You may want to designate the chalkboard as a "challenge area." Here members of each team are free to show and explain their methods of working a problem, or perhaps to show why a particular solution is wrong.

2. *Emphasize that all members of a group should be able to explain the procedure for obtaining the solution submitted by the group.* Perhaps it is the ideal situation that would have all members of a given group able to explain how a particular team-problem was solved. Nevertheless, this goal should be set before the members of the group to help insure that each pupil will make some active effort to understand how a particular problem might be solved. Each group should submit a single paper representing what the group has decided as the best solution or solutions; also, work papers of the members of the group should be collected. Through this joint, single paper, stress is given to the fact that the group is engaged in a teamwork effort.

3. *Rotate leadership responsibility among members of the group.* Groupings of this type provide an excellent opportunity for many more pupils to share in the responsibility of being a group leader or chairman. Since the groups are small, rotating the leadership yields several important effects. For one, pupils tend to accept more readily the leadership of another group member because they know that they too, eventually, will be in the role of leader. For another, failure in the leadership role is generally not so critical —also less likely—because only a small part of the class (five to seven) is involved.

4. *The time allotment should be sufficient.* Experience with this kind of teamwork approach suggests that better results occur when the tasks for the groups can be initiated and completed in one block of time. There are exceptions to this, of course. Some very useful arithmetic projects may take several class periods. In either case, be sure to allow sufficient time for the groups to complete their tasks and thus provide for greater "feedback," i.e., immediate knowledge of results and the reinforcement obtained by completing the tasks.

5. *Supervise the groups and be aware that groups have "individual" needs.* Groups as well as individuals need your guidance. You will probably have to help the groups make use of all their members. Through your observations of the groups at work and your knowledge of their members, you will often

be able to anticipate trouble areas or help a group better understand the nature of the problem and the process of sharing in the solutions.

Remember, groups have "individual" problems. Some groups will complete their tasks quickly, while others will be slow or have trouble in working together as a group. The effectiveness of teamwork in large part depends upon how well the teacher can handle these and comparable problems.

6. *Make use of discussion periods so that each group has a chance to tell or show other groups what they have done.* Increasing the amount of discussion and the exchanging of ideas by the pupils within the group is important. To help make the group more effective as a team it is equally important that the small groups have chances to compare, show and discuss their problem solutions with the other groups.

If possible, and whether or not the task is completed, try to have the leader or chairman of each group make a brief progress report before each arithmetic period is over. This serves at least three useful purposes: It allows members of each group to compare their work and progress with that of other groups; it gives you, the teacher, some added opportunities to compare the groups with one another for more effective evaluation; it helps the pupils of each group to identify themselves more strongly as members of a team.

7. *Use a variety of arithmetic problems.* Three general sources of arithmetic problems are well suited for teamwork attack. They are:

a. Stated problems, usually involving two or more steps.

b. Activity projects involving actual measuring and weighing of materials, e.g., map work, scale drawings, construction of a simple star-sighting device (astrolabe) for an astronomy unit.

c. Arithmetic puzzles involving abstract reasoning.

Under these headings many kinds of lesson plans or problems can be developed and used for challenging the groups in a team-search for solutions.

Stated or story problems involving two or more steps help build and reinforce fundamental concepts. The story problem gives each pupil in the group a chance to read and to interpret for his teammates his understanding of the processes involved. Not only can the groups be active in solving story problems, but they can be encouraged to construct their own story problems, complete with solutions, to challenge other groups in their solution.

Arithmetic projects assigned to small groups differ from the usual work with textbook problems in at least two ways. First, there is generally a need for a longer, more comprehensive planning session on the part of the groups, to organize the steps necessary to complete the project. Second, there is more opportunity to distribute leadership responsibility because of the usual variety of tasks needed to arrive at solutions.

For example, let us look at a project that requires each group to plan and construct a bird feeder.

There are questions of design: "What should be the dimensions?" "What kind of shape should it be?" There are questions of materials: "How much wood?" "How much paint?" "What size and how many nails?" "What will it cost?" These questions represent the kind of quantitative planning that the groups will need to do. Not only will completion of the project call for many ideas from all members of the group, there will be also a need for many skills, quantitative and mechanical. A project of this sort should come close to utilizing much of the capacity of the group.

There are many other examples of projects such as map making, scale drawings, compiling data for use in constructing graphs and others that can make demands on both the student's qualitative and quantitative understanding of arithmetic.

The use of arithmetic or mathematical puzzles adds "spice" to problems to be solved by teamwork. There are many such interesting oddities in arithmetic and they are readily found collected in books, in supplemental material to some textbooks, in magazines and by word of mouth from the pupils themselves. Puzzles can help reinforce some of the more intriguing relationships and processes of arithmetic. Be it a magic square, finding an unknown factor or arranging some numbers or blocks to achieve an answer, puzzles are the "dessert" for the often solid "meal" of arithmetic.

EVALUATING TEAMWORK

Evaluation is an important part of the teamwork method. A simple check list can be used while observing or helping the groups, and also at the time of the culminating activity of a group discussion or oral reports.

The following list suggests data of a kind that might be gathered:

1. Time for completion of problems (minutes).
2. Correct answers (number right and number wrong).
3. More than one method discovered and/or used for solution (yes or no).
4. Understanding of arithmetic concepts by the group (low, average, high).
5. Cooperation of group members (low, average, high).
6. Interest and satisfaction with group problem-solving (low, average, high).
7. Effectiveness of leadership (low, average, high).

A check list based on such items provides an objective record of your observations. It also allows for a comparison of observations made at different times. The data you include on your check list should be data that may be used directly in evaluating the work of the groups and, of course, should be consistent with the goals you set for this teamwork approach to arithmetic.

Written work of the groups should be evaluated, too. The group paper usually shows the agreed-upon procedures and solutions. The papers from the individuals are generally in the form of worksheets. These individual papers provide some indication of the extent of understanding and participation in the giving and receiving of aid in arriving at the solutions to the problems. Evaluation of both group and individual papers, then, should determine degree of understanding and suggest directions for additional improvement.

Comparison of the groups will undoubtedly arise. As we have said, groups, like individuals, show different characteristics. Some groups may be effective in teamwork for arithmetic; some may not. You, as a teacher, should be aware of these differences and try to seek answers for such questions as: "Why is Group A doing a superior job?" "Why wasn't Group B able to arrive at a solution?" "Does Group C need more direct help?" "Why did Group D work so well with very little direction?"

Comparing one group with another, seeking some of the reasons "why" and making adjustments when necessary is of crucial importance to your getting the most from the teamwork technique.

In summary the teamwork approach as a method of instruction can give you a chance to supplement individual problem-solving with group problem solving. Despite the laments of some, the fact remains: Increasingly, the mode of attack on the real problems of life are team attacks; more and more our problems are becoming far too complex to yield to the knowledge of the individual alone.

In the arithmetic class, this teamwork approach offers an opportunity for pupils to use their arithmetic vocabulary and understandings in meaningful situations. The method encourages pupils to ask of one another the "how," and especially the "why," of arithmetic. Finally, the technique demonstrates first hand the value of teamwork and the part it can play in the solution of many problems.

Comparative Achievement with Departmentalized and Self-contained Classroom Organization

Edette B. Price, Arthur L. Prescott, and Kenneth D. Hopkins

The most advantageous organizational structure for elementary classrooms has been the subject of much discussion in educational literature. Departmentalization was common practice through the twenties and thirties,

Reprinted from *The Arithmetic Teacher*, No. 14 (March 1967), 212–215, by permission of the authors and the publisher.

declined during the forties, and then returned in popularity.[1,2] The departmentalized classroom organization provides a "teacher-specialist" for each of the subjects taught. In the self-contained classroom, one teacher instructs a class of children of a given grade in all the curricular areas. The advocates of departmentalization have emphasized the superiority in having a specialist teaching each subject, the implication being that greater learning would accrue.

A review of the available research on achievement under elementary classroom departmentalization yielded few carefully designed studies, with considerable inconsistency in findings. Hosley found significantly greater grade placement gains for the self-contained organizational pattern in most achievement areas.[3] Jackson found no differences in arithmetic achievement of sixth-graders under departmentalized and semi-departmentalized classroom organization.[4] Gibb and Matala found higher achievement for departmentalized science but not for arithmetic.[5] Gerberich and Prall reported significant differences in certain achievement areas, but with inconsistency in direction, favoring both patterns of classroom organization.[6] Other studies have yielded inconclusive results due in part to the absence of statistical treatment of their data.

It is apparent from the review of the literature on departmentalization that no general conclusion can be drawn regarding its relative instructional efficiency in arithmetic or in other curricular areas. The present investigation attempted to employ a more comprehensive statistical approach in analyzing elementary school achievement in arithmetic reasoning, arithmetic concepts, and arithmetic computation under departmentalized and self-contained classroom organization.

PROCEDURE

The investigation used two neighboring Los Angeles City elementary schools for the experimental and control samples. Both schools had three full

[1] R. C. Anderson, "The Case for Teacher Specialization in the Elementary Schools." *Elementary School Journal*, LXII (1962), 253–60.

[2] J. J. Goodlad, "Classroom Organization," in *Encyclopedia of Educational Research*, ed. C. W. Harris and Marie Liba (3rd ed.; New York: The Macmillan Co., 1960), pp. 221–26.

[3] C. T. Hosley, "Learning Outcomes of 6th Grade Pupils Under Alternate Grade Organization Patterns" (Unpublished Ed.D. thesis, Stanford University, 1954).

[4] J. Jackson, "The Effect of Classroom Organization and Guidance Practice upon the Personality Adjustment and Academic Growth of Students," *Journal of Genetic Psychology*, LXXXII (1953), 159–70.

[5] E. Glenadine Gibb and Dorothy C. Matala, "Study on the Use of Special Teachers of Science and Mathematics in Grades 5 and 6," *School Science and Mathematics*, LXII (1962), 565–85.

[6] J. R. Gerberich and C. E. Prall, "Department Organization Versus Traditional Organization in the Intermediate Grades," *Elementary School Journal*, XXXI (1931), 671–77.

classes of fifth-grade pupils, with an overflow into a fifth-sixth combination class. These pupils placed in the combination classes were eliminated from the study because of the contaminating effect of the additional variable of multigrade grouping and the inconsistency in selection criteria. The four departmentalized teaching assignments were social studies, reading, English and science, and arithmetic and art. Each teacher also taught physical education on a rotating schedule. Each school attempted to make teacher assignments on the basis of special competence and interests.

All subjects were administered the California Test of Mental Maturity (1957 S-Form) and the California Arithmetic Tests (Form W) in October 1963 as part of the regular testing program. In June 1964 the three SRA Arithmetic Tests (Form A) were given to all pupils in the experimental and control classes. Usable results on 173 subjects were obtained, 97 and 76 for experimental and control schools respectively. In addition to the test data, the participating teachers and administrators of the two schools were given questionnaires in order to elicit relevant nontest factors.

The statistical design utilized a $2 \times 2 \times 2$ (classroom organization, by level of intelligence, by sex) multiple analysis of covariance. Before testing for significance was done, this model statistically equated the groups on each of these variables: age, language IQ, nonlanguage IQ, total IQ, and the pretests (the CAT Arithmetic Reasoning Test and the CAT Arithmetic Fundamentals Test). The statistical equating was indispensable, since the control school had somewhat lower pretest performance. The comparative data for the experimental and control subjects on the SRA Arithmetic Reasoning, Concepts, and Computation Tests were analyzed using the BIMD 14 computer program, which allows inequality of cell frequencies. The IBM 7094 computer at the Western Data Processing Center performed the statistical analysis, for which gratitude is expressed.

RESULTS

The unadjusted means and standard deviations for the experimental and control group on the SRA Arithmetic Tests, California Arithmetic Tests, and the California Test of Mental Maturity (CTMM) are found in Table 1.

Since the groups differed significantly in IQ and pretest achievement, only *after* the groups were equated on critical variables such as IQ and pretest scores through the use of multiple analysis of covariance could a meaningful comparative evaluation be made. The requirements of parallel regression lines and homogeneous variances were tested and satisfied. The results from such analyses of covariance are given in Table 2.

Only one of the twenty-one comparisons reached the .05 level of significance; an interaction of minor consequence was observed between or-

TABLE 1

Unadjusted Raw Score Means and Standard Deviations of Dependent Variables and Covariants

	Control (N = 76)		Experimental (N = 97)	
	$\overline{X}$	s	$\overline{X}$	s
Dependent Variables *				
SRA Achievement Series				
Arithmetic reasoning	26.29	9.32	31.23	7.56
Arithmetic concepts	12.36	4.71	14.78	3.25
Arithmetic computation	22.78	8.84	26.49	5.94
Covariants †				
Age (in months)	123.76	4.06	123.00	4.39
California Test of Mental Maturity				
Language IQ	104.76	17.48	117.21	15.35
Nonlanguage IQ	103.07	21.47	116.51	18.22
Total IQ	104.04	17.69	117.03	14.39
California Achievement Tests				
Arithmetic reasoning	25.63	7.40	32.16	4.94
Arithmetic fundamentals	30.26	8.60	36.36	7.42

* Tests administered in June 1964.
† Tests administered in October 1963.

TABLE 2

F-Ratios from Covariance Analysis on the SRA Achievement Series *

Source of variation	SRA Achievement Series in Arithmetic			
	df	Reasoning	Concepts	Computation
Classroom organization (CO)	1	1.04	c	3.45
Intelligence†	1	c‡	2.16	c
Sex	1	c	c	c
CO × intelligence	1	c	10.45§	c
CO × sex	1	2.26	c	1.97
Intelligence × sex	1	c	c	c
CO × intelligence × sex	1	c	c	1.98
Error MS	159	31.42	7.37	26.73
	166			

* F-ratios, degrees of freedom, and error mean squares only are given; all other desired data can be reconstructed from these, since a fixed-effects analysis-of-covariance model was employed.
† Intelligence was used as a covariant, therefore no significant intelligence main effect would be expected; intelligence levels were above and below IQ 110.
‡ c = F < 1.0
§ P < .01

ganizational pattern and intelligence level on arithmetic concepts. This interaction resulted from relatively less achievement differential between high and low intelligence groups under departmentalization, although total group means did not differ.

A fifteen-item questionnaire was returned by five of the six personnel involved in each of the schools. The items pertained to teacher load, learning time, pupil interest, scholarship, teacher knowledge of pupils, classroom control, subject-matter emphasis, teacher responsibility, teaching specialization, supervision, and equipment use. Both groups tended to favor the purported "logical advantages" of departmentalized approach in relationship to each of the above factors. Differences between the two groups' responses were not statistically significant.

SUMMARY

The findings of this investigation indicated that departmentalization with its "teacher-specialists" was not associated with higher achievement in the three areas of arithmetic skills measured by the SRA Arithmetic Reasoning, Concepts, and Computation Tests, even though the teachers viewed it as being advantageous. A clear implication from the study is that classroom organization is no panacea and does not, per se, increase pupil achievement in arithmetic at the intermediate grades, at least during its initial year. Perhaps, with additional experience, the "logical advantages" of departmentalization can be tapped to allow superior arithmetic achievement.

It should be noted that the experimental school used the same curricular scope-and-sequence guides as the control school. A differing organizational pattern, such as departmentalization, may necessitate curricular revision to take full advantage of any unique feature it offers.

A Teaching Strategy for Culturally Deprived Pupils: Cognitive and Motivational Considerations

David P. Ausubel

The possibility of arresting and reversing the course of intellectual retardation in the culturally deprived pupil depends largely on providing him with an optimal learning environment as early as possible in the course of his educational career. If the limiting effects of prolonged cultural deprivation on the development of verbal intelligence and on the acquisition of verbal knowledge are to be at least partially overcome, better-than-average strategies of teaching are obviously necessary in terms of both general effectiveness and specific appropriateness for his particular learning situation. Yet precisely the opposite state of affairs typically prevails: the learning environment of the culturally deprived child is both generally inferior and specifically inappropriate. His cumulative intellectual deflcit, therefore, almost invariably reflects, in part, the cumulative impact of a continuing and consistently deficient learning environment, as well as his emotional and motivational reaction to this environment. Thus, much of the lower-class child's alienation from the school is not so much a reflection of discriminatory or rejecting attitudes on the part of teachers and other school personnel—although the importance of this factor should not be underestimated; it is in greater measure a reflection of the cumulative effects of a curriculum that is too demanding of him, and of the resulting load of frustration, confusion, demoralization, resentment, and impaired self-confidence that he must bear.

An effective and appropriate teaching strategy for the culturally deprived child must therefore emphasize these three considerations: (*a*) the selection of initial learning material geared to the learner's existing state of readiness; (*b*) mastery and consolidation of all on-going learning tasks before new tasks are introduced, so as to provide the necessary foundation for successful sequential learning and to prevent unreadiness for future learning tasks; and (*c*) the use of structured learning materials optimally organized to facilitate efficient sequential learning. Attention to these three factors can go a long way toward insuring effective learning for the first time, and toward restoring the child's educational morale and confidence in his ability to learn. Later possible consequences are partial restoration of both intrinsic and extrinsic motivation for academic achievement, diminution of anti-intellectualism, and decreased alienation from the school to the point where his studies make

Reprinted from "A Teaching Strategy for Culturally Deprived Pupils: Cognitive and Motivational Considerations," *The School Review* (Winter 1963), pp. 454–463, by David P. Ausubel, by permission of The University of Chicago Press.

sense and he sees some purpose in learning. In my opinion, of all the available teaching strategies, programmed instruction, minus the teaching-machine format, has the greatest potentialities for meeting the aforementioned three criteria of an effective and appropriate approach to the teaching of culturally deprived pupils.

Readiness.—A curriculum that takes the readiness of the culturally deprived child into account always takes as its starting point his existing knowledge and sophistication in the various subject-matter areas and intellectual skills, no matter how far down the scale this happens to be. This policy demands rigid elimination of all subject matter that he cannot economically assimilate on the basis of his current level of cognitive sophistication. It presupposes emphasis on his acquisition of the basic intellectual skills before any attempt is made to teach him algebra, geometry, literature, and foreign languages. However, in many urban high schools and junior high schools today, pupils who cannot read at a third-grade level and who cannot speak or write grammatically or perform simple arithmetical computations are subjected to irregular French verbs, Shakespearean drama, and geometrical theorems. Nothing more educationally futile or better calculated to destroy educational morale could be imagined!

In the terms of readiness for a given level of school work, a child is no less ready because of a history of cultural deprivation, chronic academic failure, and exposure to an unsuitable curriculum than because of deficient intellectual endowment. Hence, realistic recognition of this fact is not undemocratic, reactionary, or evidence of social class bias, of intellectual snobbery, of a "soft," patronizing approach, or a belief in the inherent uneducability of lower-class children. Neither is it indicative of a desire to surrender to the culturally deprived child's current intellectual level, to perpetuate the status quo, or to institute a double, class-oriented standard of education. It is merely a necessary first step in preparing him to cope with more advanced subject matter, and hence in eventually reducing existing social class differentials in academic achievement. To set the same *initial* standards and expectations for the academically retarded culturally deprived child as for the non-retarded middle- or lower-class child is automatically to insure the former's failure and to widen prevailing discrepancies between social class groups.

Consolidation.—By insisting on consolidation or mastery of on-going lessons before new material is introduced, we make sure of continued readiness and success in sequentially organized learning. Abundant experimental research has confirmed the proposition that prior learnings are not transferable to new learning tasks unless they are first overlearned.[1] Overlearning, in turn,

[1] See R. W. Bruce, "Conditions of Transfer of Training," *Journal of Experimental Psychology*, XVI (1933), 343–61; C. P. Duncan, "Transfer in Motor Learning as a Function of Degree of First-task Learning and Inter-task Similarity," *Journal of Experimental Psychology*, XLV (1953), 1–11, and his "Transfer after Training with Single versus Multiple

requires an adequate number of adequately spaced repetitions and reviews, sufficient intratask repetitiveness prior to intra- and intertask diversification,[2] and opportunity for differential practice of the more difficult components of a task. Frequent testing and provision of feedback, especially with test items demanding fine discrimination among alternatives varying in degrees of correctness, also enhance consolidation by confirming, clarifying, and correcting previous learnings. Lastly, in view of the fact that the culturally deprived child tends to learn more slowly than his non-deprived peers, self-pacing helps to facilitate consolidation.

Structured, sequential materials.—The principal advantage of programmed instruction, apart from the fact that it furthers consolidation, is its careful sequential arrangement and gradation of difficulty which insures that each attained increment in learning serves as an appropriate foundation and anchoring post for the learning and retention of subsequent items in the ordered sequence.[3] Adequate programming of materials also presupposes maximum attention to such matters as lucidity, organization, and the explanatory and integrative power of substantive content. It is helpful, for example, if sequential materials are so organized that they become progressively more differentiated in terms of generality and inclusiveness, and if similarities and differences between the current learning task and previous learnings are explicitly delineated.[4] Both of these aims can be accomplished by using an advance organizer or brief introductory passage before each new unit of material, which both makes available relevant explanatory principles at a high level of abstraction and increases discriminability. Programmed instruction can also be especially adapted to meet the greater needs of culturally deprived pupils for concrete-empirical props in learning relational propositions.

Although programmed instruction in general is particularly well suited to the needs of the culturally deprived child, I cannot recommend the small-frame format characteristic of teaching-machine programs and most programmed textbooks. In terms of both the logical requirements of meaningful

---

Tasks," *Journal of Experimental Psychology,* LV (1958), 63–72; L. Morrisett and C. I. Hovland, "A Comparison of Three Varieties of Training in Human Problem Solving," *Journal of Experimental Psychology,* LV (1958), 52–55; and J. M. Sassenrath, "Learning without Awareness and Transfer of Learning Sets," *Journal of Educational Psychology,* L (1959), 202–12.

[2] See Duncan, "Transfer after Training with Single versus Multiple Tasks," *op. cit.;* Morrisett and Hovland, *op. cit.;* and Sassenrath, *op. cit.*

[3] D. P. Ausubel and D. Fitzgerald, "Organizer, General Background, and Antecedent Learning Variables in Sequential Verbal Learning," *Journal of Educational Psychology,* LIII (1962), 243–49.

[4] D. P. Ausubel, "The Use of Advance Organizers in the Learning and Retention of Meaningful Verbal Learning," *Journal of Educational Psychology,* LI (1960), 267–72; D. P. Ausubel and D. Fitzgerald, "The Role of Discriminability in Meaningful Verbal Learning and Retention," *Journal of Educational Psychology,* LII (1961), 266–74, and their "Organizer, General Background, and Antecedent Learning Variables in Sequential Verbal Learning," *op. cit.*

learning and the actual size of the task that can be conveniently accommodated by the learner, the frame length typically used by teaching machines is artificially and unnecessarily abbreviated. It tends to fragment the ideas presented in the program so that their interrelationships are obscured and their logical structure is destroyed.[5] Hence it is relatively easy for less able students to master each granulated step of a given program without understanding the logical relationships and development of the concepts presented.[6] In my opinion, therefore, the traditional textbook format or oral didactic exposition that follows the programming principles outlined above, supplemented by frequent self-scoring and feedback-giving tests, is far superior to the teaching-machine approach for the actual presentation of subject-matter content.[7]

MOTIVATIONAL CONSIDERATIONS

Thus far I have considered various environmental factors that induce retardation in the culturally deprived child's intellectual growth, as well as different cognitive techniques of counteracting and reversing such retardation. These factors and techniques, however, do not operate in a motivational vacuum. Although it is possible separately to consider cognitive and motivational aspects of learning for purposes of theoretical analysis, they are nonetheless inseparably intertwined in any real-life learning situation. For example, school failure and loss of confidence resulting from an inappropriate curriculum further depress the culturally deprived pupil's motivation to learn and thereby increase his existing learning and intellectual deficit. Similarly, although a number of practice and task variables are potentially important for effective learning in a programmed instruction context, appropriate manipulation of these variables can, in the final analysis, only insure successful long-term learning of subject-matter provided that the individual is adequately motivated.

Doing without being interested in what one is doing results in relatively little permanent learning, since it is reasonable to suppose that only those materials can be meaningfully incorporated on a long-term basis into an individual's structure of knowledge that are relevant to areas of concern in his psychological field. Learners who have little need to know and understand quite naturally expend little learning effort; manifest an insufficiently meaningful learning set; fail to develop precise meanings, to reconcile new ideas with existing concepts, and to formulate new propositions in their own

[5] S. L. Pressey, "Basic Unresolved Teaching-Machine Problems," *Theory into Practice*, I (1962), 30–37.

[6] D. G. Beane, "A Comparison of Linear and Branching Techniques of Programed Instruction in Plane Geometry" ("Technical Report," No. 1 [Urbana: Training Research Laboratory, University of Illinois, July 1962]).

[7] Pressey, *op. cit.*

words; and do not devote enough time and energy to practice and review. Material is therefore never sufficiently consolidated to form an adequate foundation for sequential learning.

The problem of reversibility exists in regard to the motivational as well as in regard to the cognitive status of the culturally deprived pupil, inasmuch as his environment typically stunts not only his intellectual development, but also the development of appropriate motivations for academic achievement. Motivations for learning, like cognitive abilities, are only potential rather than inherent or endogenous capacities in human beings; their actual development is invariably dependent upon adequate environmental stimulation. Cognitive drive or intrinsic motivation to learn, for example, is probably derived in a very general sense from curiosity tendencies and from related predispositions to explore, manipulate, and cope with the environment; but these tendencies and predispositions are only actualized as a result of successful exercise and the anticipation of future satisfying consequences from further exercise and as a result of internalization of the values of those significant persons in the family and subcultural community with whom the child identifies.

Intrinsic motivation.—The development of cognitive drive or of intrinsic motivation for learning, that is, the acquisition of knowledge as an end in itself or for its own sake, is, in my opinion, the most promising motivational strategy which we can adopt in relation to the culturally deprived child. It is true, of course, in view of the anti-intellectualism and pragmatic attitude toward education that is characteristic of lower-class ideology,[8] that a superficially better case can be made for the alternative strategy of appealing to the incentives to job acquisition, retention, and advancement that now apply so saliently to continuing education because of the rapid rate of technological change. Actually, however, intrinsic motivation for learning is more potent, relevant, durable, and easier to arouse than its extrinsic counterpart. Meaningful school learning, in contrast to most kinds of laboratory learning, requires relatively little effort or extrinsic incentive, and, when successful, furnishes its own reward. In most instances of school learning, cognitive drive is also the only immediately relevant motivation, since the greater part of school learning cannot be rationalized as necessary for meeting the demands of daily living. Furthermore, it does not lose its relevance or potency in later adult life when utilitarian and career advancement considerations are no longer applicable. Lastly, as we know from the high dropout rate among culturally deprived high-school youth, appeals to extrinsic motivation are not very effective. Among other reasons, the latter situation reflects a limited time perspective focused primarily on the present; a character structure that is oriented more to immediate than delayed gratification of needs; the lack of strong internalized needs for and anxiety about high academic

[8] F. Riessman, *The Culturally Deprived Child* (New York: Harper & Bros., 1962).

and vocational achievement, as part of the prevailing family, peer group, and community ideology; [9] and the seeming unreality and impossibility of attaining the rewards of prolonged striving and self-denial in view of current living conditions and family circumstances, previous lack of school success, and the discriminatory attitudes of middle-class society.[10]

If we wish to develop the cognitive drive so that it remains viable during the school years and in adult life, it is necessary to move still further away from the educational doctrine of gearing the curriculum to the spontaneously expressed interests, current concerns, and life-adjustment problems of pupils. Although it is undoubtedly unrealistic and even undesirable in our culture to eschew entirely the utilitarian, ego-enhancement, and anxiety-reduction motivations for learning, we must place increasingly greater emphasis upon the value of knowing and understanding as goals in their own right, quite apart from any practical benefits they may confer. Instead of denigrating subject-matter knowledge, we must discover more efficient methods of fostering the long-term acquisition or meaningful and usable bodies of knowledge, and of developing appropriate intrinsic motivations for such learning.

It must be conceded at the outset that culturally deprived children typically manifest little intrinsic motivation to learn. They come from family and cultural environments in which the veneration of learning for its own sake is ont a conspicuous value, and in which there is little or no tradition of scholarship. Moreover, they have not been notably successful in their previous learning efforts in school. Nevertheless we need not necessarily despair of motivating them to learn for intrinsic reasons. Psychologists have been emphasizing the motivation-learning and the interest-activity sequences of cause and effect for so long that they tend to overlook their reciprocal aspects. Since motivation is not an indispensable condition for short-term and limited-quantity learning, it is not necessary to postpone learning activities until appropriate interests and motivations have been developed. Frequently the best way of motivating an unmotivated pupil is to ignore his motivational state for the time being and concenrate on teaching him as effectively as possible. Much to his surprise and to his teacher's, he will learn despite his lack of motivation; and from the satisfaction of learning he will characteristically develop the motivation to learn more.

Paradoxically, therefore, we may discover that the most effective method of developing intrinsic motivation to learn is to focus on the cognitive rather than on the motivational aspects of learning, and to rely on the motivation that is developed retroactively from successful educational achievement. This is particularly true when a teacher is able to generate contagious excitement and enthusiasm about the subject he teaches, and when he is the kind

[9] A. Davis, "Child Training and Social Class," *Child Behavior and Development*, ed. R. G. Barker, J. S. Kounin, and H. F. Wright (New York: McGraw-Hill Book Co., 1963), pp. 607–20.
[10] *Ibid.*

of person with whom culturally deprived children can identify. Recruiting more men teachers and dramatizing the lives and exploits of cultural, intellectual, and scientific heroes can also enhance the process of identification. At the same time, of course, we can attempt to combat the anti-intellectualism and lack of cultural tradition in the home through programs of adult education and cultural enrichment.

Extrinsic motivation.—The emphasis I have placed on intrinsic motivation for learning should not be interpreted to mean that I deny the importance of developing extrinsic motivations. The need for ego enhancement, status, and prestige through achievement, the internalization of long-term vocational aspirations, and the development of such implementing traits as responsibility, initiative, self-denial, frustration tolerance, impulse control, and the ability to postpone immediate hedonistic gratification are, after all, traditional hallmarks of personality maturation in our culture; and educational aspirations and achievement are both necessary prerequisites for, and way-station prototypes of, their vocational counterparts. Hence, in addition to encouraging intrinsic motivation for learning, it is also necessary to foster ego-enhancement and career-advancement motivations for academic achievement.

As previously pointed out, however, the current situation with respect to developing adequate motivations for higher academic and vocational achievement among culturally deprived children is not very encouraging. But just as in the case of cognitive drive, much extrinsic motivation for academic success can be generated retroactively from the experience of current success in schoolwork. Intensive counseling can also compensate greatly for the absence of appropriate home, community, and peer-group support and expectations for the development of long-term vocational ambitions. In a sense counselors must be prepared to act *in loco parentis* in this situation. By identifying with a mature, stable, striving, and successful male adult figure, culturally deprived boys can be encouraged to internalize long-term and realistic aspirations, as well as to develop the mature personality traits necessary for their implementation. Hence, as a result of achieving current ego enhancement in the school setting, obtaining positive encouragement and practical guidance in the counseling relationship, and experiencing less rejection and discrimination at the hands of school personnel, higher vocational aspirations appear to lie more realistically within their grasp. Further encouragement to strive for more ambitious academic and vocational goals can be provided by making available abundant scholarship aid to universities, to community colleges, and to technical institutes; by eliminating the color, ethnic, and class bar in housing, education, and employment; by acquainting culturally deprived youth with examples of successful professional persons originating from their own racial, ethnic, and class backgrounds; and by involving parents sympathetically in the newly fostered ambitions of their children. The success of the Higher Horizons project indicates that an energetic program organized along the lines outlined above can do much to reverse the effects of cultural deprivation on the development of extrinsic motivations for academic and vocational achievement.

Individual Projects in Creative Arithmetic

Claire Sprague

For two years I taught an experimental class of seventh-grade "gifted" and "very able" pupils at Daniel Webster School, in Stockton, California. These children were selected from their records on tests, such as California Mental Maturity and Iowa Skills Tests, and on teacher recommendations. They came to my class daily for one forty-five-minute period of enrichment. The rest of the day they spent in their regular classes. Our special period was a happy time and the boys and girls had experiences in science, math, music, debating, choral reading, and creative writing. We leaned heavily on the help of resource speakers and on the services of our audio-visual department and our librarian.

A number of our ideas could be used in a normal classroom that had only five or six gifted or very able children. Anyone with an IQ of 125 should have some enrichment experiences.

The gifted or very able child sometimes becomes a discipline problem because he works the assignment quickly and has time on his hands. "Read something if you are finished," sounds to him like a worn-out record. "Do ten more problems" isn't the answer either; he wants a different assignment, not more of the same. In our class we filled that need by doing creative arithmetic whenever other work was finished. The children's original problems were expressed in terms of current life situations.

We began with a problem in the area of recreation. I said, "We are going to the ball game and have two dollars to spend. How shall we spend it?" "If the sign says, 'Hamburgers 20 cents each, 6 for $1.00,' do we save any money buying six at once?" "Can you make a problem about milk shakes and hamburgers at a game?" The class usually thought up many other problems—on the price of tickets, uniforms, balls, cafeteria meals, and so on, as well as problems involving batting averages and scores.

This kind of lesson is fun because the child creates the type of problem he can handle; one child may think of decimals, another of fractions, another of per cent, while someone may be using base-two or binary numbers. Here

Reprinted from *The Instructor*, Vol. LXVIII No. 1 (September 1958), pp. 34, 95, by permission of F. A. Owen Publishing Company.

we are reaching the needs of all members of the class and stimulating the very able and gifted.

After this start, we put boxes in our room, labeling them: *Recreation, Transportation, Music, Health, Communication, Religion, Education, Government,* and *How Men Make a Living.* As a child thought of an original problem, he would write it out, put the answer on the back of his paper, and put it in the appropriate box. One day a week I read all the problems and initialed them, correcting if necessary.

When a problem had been accepted, it could be put on a 7″ x 11″ sheet of tagboard and illustrated. The children enjoyed working on the tagboard and it was sturdy enough to withtsand much handling. The problems created by their pals were more fun for the girls and boys than the ones in their textbooks.

Children who are gifted or very able are someimes interested in surveying. Constructing their own transit and measuring the heights of trees and telephone poles hold their interest. A working vocabulary should be on the board—*tripod, stadia rod, plumb, angles, signals,* and so on.

Holidays provide much material for creative math. If valentines cost 3 for 5¢, how much will the valentines for this class cost?

A capable group could make a study of comparing our number system with the metric system. An assignment to precede this would be to list words that contain the word *meter,* meaning measure.

Others may be interested in working with figures related to the stock market.

Children who like science can be challenged with such words as *fusion, fission,* and *temperature.* We turn to the dictionary first before attempting to create original problems.

Another group may be interested in statistics and can do some research on the number of people in their community who earn their living in specified areas. Here we have correlation between arithmetic, social studies, and language arts.

A discussion of Bizmac and other mechanical brains will provide a stepping stone to further reading on electronic computers and how they are used today on quiz programs. Figuring the take-home pay of TV winners always has a timely interest.

Another excellent activity for the gifted and very able students is the development of cross-math problems. A discussion of crossword puzzles should precede this lesson. The next step is to list on the board a variety of arithmetical terms to start the children thinking of arithmetic problems. Our list included: *sum, difference, bisect, area, perimeter, quotient, degree, average, decimal,* and so forth. A few reminders, such as: "Any number multiplied by one will give the same number in the answer" and "Any number multiplied by 0 will give 0 in the answer," are helpful. A box in the room is labeled *Cross-Math Problems.* When enough problems have been created so each child can have one, we have a lesson wherein each child works at least one problem.

Cross-Math problems can be devised on different ability levels so that every child in an average classroom will have success. Gifted children can edit the puzzles and assemble them in booklet form.

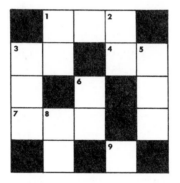

Horizontal

1. Find the average of 20, 30, 0, 230, 360, 4160, 100
3. How many beats are there in 14 measures of ⅝ time?
4. 7 degrees more than a right angle
7. $608 \times 0 + 607 + 7$
9. . . . . . . feet = 1 nautical fathom

Vertical

1. $0 \times 49 + 52 - 1 + 23$
2. ⅓ of .27
3. How many half pecks in 102 bushels?
5. $356 + 350 + 6$
6. 20% of 220
8. $40 \times 2 \div 5$

In a normal class, the gifted and very able children could assemble and illustrate an arithmetic book developed by the class. The gifted could serve as an editing committee and would be expected to create other problems to fill the gaps so all the problems would not be of the same type. Social studies areas—transportation, recreation, and so on—would make good chapter headings. Other headings might be: *Etymology, Entomology, Mechanical Brains, Foreign Languages, Hobbies, Metric System.*

BIBLIOGRAPHY

An upper-grade arithmetic book shelf.

Building Mathematical Concepts in Elementary School, by Spencer and Brydegaard (Henry Holt).

Developing Mathematical Understandings in the Upper Grades, by Breuckner and others (Winston).

Enrichment Program for Arithmetic, by H. D. Larsen (Row Peterson). There are packages of pamphlets for grades 3 through 6. The entire set has much value.

New Applied Mathematics—Third Edition, by Lasley and Mudd (Prentice-Hall).

Practical Classroom Procedures for Enriching Arithmetic, by Herbert F. Spitzer (Webster).

Refresher Arithmetic with Practical Application, by Edwin I. Stein (Allyn and Bacon).

Using Mathematics—Book 7, by Henderson and Pingry (McGraw-Hill).

Wonderful World of Mathematics, by L. T. Hogben (Garden City Books by Doubleday).

Magazines

The Arithmetic Teacher and *The Mathematics Teacher* are published six times yearly by the National Council of Teachers of Mathematics, 1201 16th St., N.W., Washington 6, D.C.

Developing Mathematical Concepts Through the Inductive Learning Process

Don Alkire

Certain mathematical concepts permeate the arithmetic curriculum from the grade school through the high school. One key concept: Finding the whole quantity when a part is known—is embodied in the following set of problems:

If $\frac{1}{2}$ of a pie costs 30 cents,
then $\frac{2}{2}$ of a pie costs 2×30 cents or 60 cents.
If $\frac{3}{5}$ of Joe's weight $= 45$ pounds,
then $\frac{1}{5}$ of Joe's weight $= \frac{1}{3}$ of 45 pounds or 15 pounds;
and $\frac{5}{5}$ of Joe's weight $= 5 \times 15$ pounds or 75 pounds.
If $\frac{3}{7}$ of Jane's marbles $= 42$ marbles,
then $\frac{1}{7}$ of Jane's marbles $= \frac{1}{3}$ of 42 marbles, or 14 marbles;
and $\frac{7}{7}$ of Jane's marbles $= 7 \times 14$ marbles or 98 marbles.

If $2\frac{3}{4}$ inches on a map represent 165 miles,
(i.e.) if $\frac{11}{4}''$ on a map represent 165 miles,
then $\frac{1}{4}''$ on a map $= \frac{1}{11}$ of 165 miles or 15 miles,
then $\frac{4}{4}''$ on a map $= 4 \times 15$ miles $= 60$ miles,
and $5''$ on a map $= 5 \times 60 = 300$ miles.
If 13% of the weight $= 1560$ pounds,
then 1% of the weight $= \frac{1}{13}$ of 1560 pounds or 120 pounds,
and 100% of the weight $= 100 \times 120$ pounds or 12000 pounds.

Reprinted from *California Journal of Elementary Education,* Vol. 30, No. 1 (August 1961), 43–49, by permission of the California State Department of Education.

If 37½% of the bill = \$48,
(i.e.) if ⅜ of the bill = \$48,
then ⅛ of the bill = ⅓ of \$48 or \$16,
and ⁸⁄₈ of the bill = 8 × \$16 or \$128.

If ⅔% of the weight = 1560 pounds,
then ⅓% of the weight = ½ of 1560 pounds or 780 pounds,
and ³⁄₃% of the weight = 3 × 780 pounds or 2340 pounds,
then 100% of the weight = 100 × 2340 pounds or 234,000 pounds.

What are the ideas that emerge from working such problems? I hope that children would acquire an awareness of the relationship of a part of a thing to the whole thing. Using the first problem as an example;

If ½ of a pie costs 30 cents,
then ²⁄₂ of a pie costs 2 × 30 cents or 60 cents.

The important ideas are that ½ is *half as much* as ²⁄₂, and ²⁄₂ is *twice as much* as ½. Also ²⁄₂ of a thing is all of a thing.

Another idea I hope children would acquire is illustrated in the second problem;

If ⅗ of Joe's weight = 45 pounds,
then ⅕ of Joe's weight = ⅓ of 45 pounds or 15 pounds;
and ⁵⁄₅ of Joe's weight = 5 × 15 pounds or 75 pounds.

An important idea is that ⁵⁄₅ of a thing is *all* of a thing.

(i.e.) If ⅗ of Joe's weight is part of Joe's weight,
then ⅕ of Joe's weight is part of Joe's weight–
and is ⅓ of ⅗ of Joe's weight
and ⁵⁄₅ of Joe's weight is all of Joe's weight.

An awareness of the relationship among parts of a whole thing is equally important. For example:

If ⅗ of Joe's weight = 45 pounds,
then ⅕ of Joe's weight = ⅓ of (⅗ of Joe's weight).
If ⅗ of Joe's weight is 45 pounds,
then ⅕ of Joe's weight is ⅓ of 45 pounds or 15 pounds.
If ⅕ of Joe's weight is 15 pounds,
then ⁵⁄₅ of Joe's weight is 5 times 15 pounds or 75 pounds.

Mathematics is more than doing such exercises as $3\overline{)79}$. Mathematics embodies logical argumentation. Get the if-then argumentation of mathematics under way. Consider the following problem:

If ⅔ of the class is 20 pupils, how many pupils are in the class?

Children might profit from discovering that they don't even need to know how many pupils comprise $\frac{2}{3}$ of the class in order to begin working on the problem. The phraseology plays an important part of the learning process.

> If $\frac{2}{3}$ of the class is 20 pupils,
> then $\frac{1}{3}$ of the class must be $\frac{1}{2}$ of 20 pupils, or 10 pupils;
> if $\frac{1}{3}$ of the class is 10 pupils,
> and $\frac{3}{3}$ of the class is all of the class,
> then $\frac{3}{3}$ of the class is 3 times 10 pupils, or 30 pupils.

The comparative factor is important in mathematics. Seek to compare like-named things. Learn to make comparisons; find the patterns; learn to make analogies; learn to make discriminations.

Mathematical principles are not acquired by working one problem. Finding the patterns may take many problems worked over a long time span.

The mathematical ideas noted in the previous discussions are applicable to similar mathematical problems used throughout the elementary school and junior high school. Such ideas are also appropriate to working problems involving proper fractions, mixed numbers, improper fractions, per cents, mixed per cents, and the like. Certain kinds of mathematical problems involving the concepts discussed may be identified in terms of difficulty and categorized by grade level as follows:

Finding the Whole Quantity When a Part Is Known

A. Lower grades
  1. If 2 pencils cost 10 cents,
     then 1 pencil costs ________.
  2. If $\frac{1}{2}$ of a pie cost 30 cents,
     then $\frac{2}{2}$ of a pie cost ________.

B. Middle grades
  1. If $\frac{2}{3}$ of the class is 20 pupils,
     then $\frac{1}{3}$ of the class is $\frac{1}{2}$ of 20 or 10 pupils,
     and $\frac{3}{3}$ of the class is 3×10 or 30 pupils.
  2. If $\frac{3}{5}$ of Joe's marbles is 15 marbles,
     then $\frac{1}{5}$ of Joe's marbles is $\frac{1}{3}$ of 15 or 5 marbles,
     and $\frac{5}{5}$ of Joe's marbles is 5×5 or 25 marbles.

C. Junior high
  1. If $2\frac{3}{4}$ inches on a map represents 165 miles,
     i.e.) if $\frac{11}{4}$ inches on a map represents 165 miles,
     then $\frac{1}{4}$ inch on a map represents $\frac{1}{11}$ of 165 or 15 miles,
     and $\frac{4}{4}$ inches on a map represents 4×15 or 60 miles.
  2. If 13% of the weight is 1040 pounds,
     then 1% of the weight is $\frac{1}{13}$ of 1040 or 80 pounds,
     and 100% of the weight is 100×80 or 8000 pounds.
  3. If $\frac{2}{3}$% of the county budget = \$12,500,
     then $\frac{1}{3}$% of the county budget = \$6250,
     and $\frac{3}{3}$% of the county budget = \$18,750,
     therefore 100% of the county budget = \$1,875,000.

4. If p pens cost q cents,
   1 pen cost 1/p of q or q/p cents,
   r pens cost r × q/p or rq/p cents.
   This type of problem is often asked in civil service examinations in various areas of work.
5. Problem: A merchant pays $120 for a coat. Find the selling price (S.P.) so as to allow 12½% for overhead and 25% for profit, each based on the selling price.

100% of the S.P.

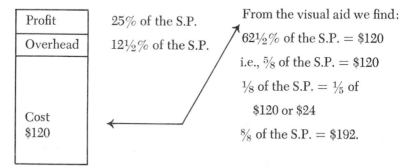

From the visual aid we find:

62½% of the S.P. = $120

i.e., ⅝ of the S.P. = $120

⅛ of the S.P. = ⅕ of

$120 or $24

⅛ of the S.P. = $192.

A generalization (or rule) of great importance in the arithmetic program pertains to operations with fractions. The rule may be inferred from consideration of the following questions:

$$\text{Does } \tfrac{1}{2} = \frac{1 \times 3}{2 \times 3} = \tfrac{3}{6}? \qquad \text{Does } \tfrac{2}{3} = \frac{2 \times 3}{3 \times 3} = \tfrac{6}{9}?$$

$$\text{Does } \tfrac{1}{2} = \frac{1 \times 2}{2 \times 2} = \tfrac{2}{4}? \qquad \text{Does } \tfrac{4}{6} = \frac{4 \times 2\tfrac{1}{2}}{6 \times 2\tfrac{1}{2}} = \tfrac{10}{15}?$$

$$\text{Does } \tfrac{2}{3} = \frac{2 \times 2}{3 \times 2} = \tfrac{4}{6}?$$

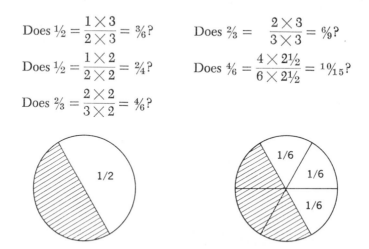

Partitioning circles in this manner may be helpful to certain children in arriving at an affrmative response to the first question. As a result of considering questions of this nature, children can infer the rule that you may multiply the numerator and denominator of a fraction by any number you choose (except zero) without changing the value of the fraction.

Another generalization (or rule) of great importance in the handling of fractions may be inferred from consideration of the following questions:

$$\text{Does } \tfrac{4}{8} = \frac{4 \div 2}{8 \div 2} = \tfrac{2}{4}? \qquad\qquad \text{Does } \tfrac{6}{9} = \frac{6 \div 3}{9 \div 3} = \tfrac{2}{3}?$$

$$\text{Does } \tfrac{4}{8} = \frac{4 \div 4}{8 \div 4} = \tfrac{1}{2}? \qquad\qquad \text{Does } \tfrac{10}{15} = \frac{10 \div 2\tfrac{1}{2}}{15 \div 2\tfrac{1}{2}} = \tfrac{4}{6}?$$

Again, using visual aids such as

1/8	1/8	1/8	1/8	1/8	1/8	1/8	1/8

1/4	1/4	1/4	1/4

certain children may be helped to perceive that an affirmative response is appropriate to the first question. As a result of considering questions of this type, children can, without prompting, infer the rule that the numerator and denominator of a fraction may be divided by any number you choose (except zero) without changing the value of the fraction.

The generalizations (or rules) mentioned above are the mathematical authority for performing certain techniques in arithmetic. We shall mention a few. Consider the following questions:

Why can a person annex zeros onto the end of decimals
Why can one write for .12 the quantity .120?

$$.12 = \frac{12}{100} = \frac{12 \times 10}{100 \times 10} = \frac{120}{1000} = .120\text{---which was to be shown.}$$

Why can one "move" decimal points in division, as:

$$.3\,\overline{)\,2.1\,6\,}$$

$$.3\,\overline{)\,2.16\,} = \frac{2.16}{.3} = \frac{2.16 \times 10}{.3 \times 10} = \frac{21.6}{3} = 3\,\overline{)\,21.6\,} \text{ --- which was to be shown.}$$

Why, in division of fractions, may one invert the second fraction and multiply?

$$\tfrac{2}{5} \div \tfrac{3}{7} = \frac{\tfrac{2}{5}}{\tfrac{3}{7}} = \frac{\tfrac{2}{5} \times \tfrac{7}{3}}{\tfrac{3}{7} \times \tfrac{7}{3}} = \frac{\tfrac{2}{5} \times \tfrac{7}{3}}{1} \text{ or } \tfrac{2}{5} \times \tfrac{7}{3} -$$

which was to be shown.

In each of the above types of mathematical problems, the rule which states that you may multiply the numerator and denominator of a fraction by any number you choose without changing the value of the fraction (except zero) was applied. It is the mathematical authority or support of many of the "rules of thumb" that have evolved in arithmetic.

Children also need to know the source for the shorthand rules for working mathematical problems. The reasons which premise the rules of thumb must be made clear to the child, however, if the child is to be knowledgeable and effective at the operational level with mathematics.

Curriculum leadership personnel has the responsibility for helping teachers identify the important mathematical concepts and carry the ideas across to children. Through providing situations from which children may have sufficient experiences over a long-enough time period to take note of recurring elements in problems, children can make the generalizations, infer the principles, and develop for themselves those rules of thumb which are helpful.

Some of you at this conference have asked me to comment on a problem that often arises in the arithmetic program. What might a teacher do to demonstrate that in $.12\frac{1}{2}$ the $\frac{1}{2}$ may apparently be changed to a 5, yielding $.125$.

On the chalkboard a teacher might write the following to summarize appropriate discussion:

Does $.12\frac{1}{2} = .12$?
No, $.12\frac{1}{2}$ is more than $.12$
　$.12\frac{1}{2}$ is $.12 +$ some more.

Again, after further relevant questioning which culminates in a commitment by his class:

Does $.12\frac{1}{2} = .13$?
No, $12\frac{1}{2}$ is less than $.13$.
Surely $.12\frac{1}{2}$ cannot equal $.14$ or $.62$
since it is not as large as is $.13$.

A teacher willing to encourage pupils to hypothesize must be prepared to entertain the following suggestion from a pupil:

$.12\frac{1}{2} = .12 + \frac{1}{2}$.

Although this suggestion is in error, a teacher should help a student test this suggestion. The test leads to:

$.12\frac{1}{2} = .12 + \frac{1}{2}$
$= .12 + .5$
$= .62$

Since the class has committed itself to the acceptance of the idea that .12½ is less than .13, surely it cannot possibly be as large as .62. Hence, a pupil making the hypothesis above has earned the right by way of the personal conviction route to abandon that hypothesis.

The teacher is now ready to develop relevant experiences designed to enable pupils to furnish the following demonstration:

$$.12\tfrac{1}{2} = .12 + \tfrac{1}{2} \text{ of } \tfrac{1}{100}$$
$$= .12 + \tfrac{1}{2} \text{ of } \tfrac{10}{1000} \quad \text{(featuring an important generalization regarding}$$
$$= .12 + \tfrac{5}{1000} \quad\quad \text{fractions)}$$
$$= .12 + .005$$
$$= .120 + .005 \quad \text{(annexing zero onto the end of a decimal)}$$
$$= .125$$

A pupil inquiring about "changing" the ½ to 5 on .12½ wishes some demonstration with that ½. He is more likely to be satisfied with the demonstration above than with the following one, which in itself is a model of deductive logic.

Since .12½ = ⅛
and .125 = ⅛
therefore .12½ = .125

This is a logical demonstration. Psychologically, for some students, it may be a little wanting.

I have not made reference to anything which might be labeled as "newer mathematics." I have emphasized the need for "better teaching." I have not addressed myself to content, rather have I emphasized inductive learning, the identification and comparison of recurring elements among similar kinds of problem situations, the discovery of principles, and the thinking process characteristic of logical argument. These aspects of the arithmetic program have been emphasized by various mathematics study groups.

Children need to be able to give mathematical support for mathematical operations performed. Let us consider whether it is advisable to state the generalizations and show the shorthand rules of mathematics to children at the beginning of a teaching-learning situation. Let us consider the possible values which might accrue from learning through discovery—from inductive learning. A pupil might gain arithmetic knowledge of a more permanent nature, and as a result become more functionally competent in the subject himself, if he were furnished a teaching-learning climate which would encourage and promote such procedures as advancement of hypotheses, testing hypotheses through relevant experiences, and arriving at the end of the teaching-learning process with a generalization formulated by him in a form which he sees to hold promise of being employed to advantage.

Science and the New Math

Paul C. Rosenbloom

Almost every elementary science project now under way is wrestling with the problem of providing the mathematics that is needed for the science that should be taught. Educators and scientists are at long last realizing that these disciplines are vitally related even at the elementary level, and that the natural or social sciences cannot adequately be presented without a satisfactory mathematics program. Relating the new mathematics to the child's science experiences is not for the purpose of helping him to see that learning pays off in practical applications, for much that the child learns cannot immediately be related to a specific learning problem. But the child can recognize that without mathematics there cannot be science and without science there cannot be social growth.

Mathematics is an inseparable part of most inquiries and disciplines. In particular, science and math share a compatible process of inquiry: (1) the analysis of a situation, (2) the mathematical description of it, (3) the analysis of the mathematical model, (4) the translation of mathematical results into conclusions, (5) the testing of inferences by comparison with observations, and then, if necessary, (6) a revision of the original analysis.

This type of literacy is a necessary skill we seek to develop at all levels, from kindergarten through graduate school, in jobs, and in daily life. Yet, in the elementary and secondary schools, there is insufficient application of mathematics to other areas, outside of common bookkeeping, shopping, and such. The integration of knowledge is not practiced as much as the separation of the isolated disciplines.

Present mathematics curricula, at all levels, concentrate almost exclusively on the third stage of inquiry—the analysis of the mathematical model. The "story problem" in math textbooks is mainly a linguistic problem; it teaches the student to translate from English into mathematical terms and back again, often with some confusion. In teaching mathematics, we rarely concern ourselves with where the problem comes from or what anyone would do with the answers. It is obvious, however, that children must gain some understanding of *where* mathematical ideas come from and *how* they help us understand the working of the universe. Such understanding is important as part of a general, liberal education, as well as essential for future users of mathematics.

Qualitative judgments are often substantiated by quantitive evidence. We usually test suppositions and hypotheses quantitatively. An early awareness of this makes a sound base for the elementary child who is pursuing scientific

Reprinted from *The Instructor* (October 1965), 25, 87, 125, by permission of F. A. Owen Publishing Company.

investigation. The boy who boasts that he can run twice as fast or throw the ball twice as far often is convinced that he can, when in reality he can run somewhat faster and throw somewhat farther. Enclosing a garden containing 20 square feet can require as little as 18 feet of fence, or as much as 42 feet, but this is not readily accepted unless the student recognizes the relation between the elements of a product.

We really cannot teach the application of mathematics properly unless pupils understand the science to which we are applying it. There is a parallelism between the two subjects; the development of science instruction serves the new math, and vice versa.

THE VITAL "SET" CONCEPT

A simple example of this parallelism can be seen in the concept of "sets," which has been considered a sort of hallmark for the "modern" mathematics curriculum.

For purely mathematical purposes at the elementary level, we need only the term "set," the idea of one-to-one correspondence, and the union of sets without common members in the teaching of addition of integers and in geometry. The notations or the techniques of the algebra of sets are not needed, for in solving simultaneous equations, the solutions are in the intersection of the graphs of the equations in the system. Any more extensive treatment of sets hangs in midair, since there is nothing for the students to do with this knowledge.

The first place in school mathematics where we can do something non-trivial with sets is in probability theory. (Except for a chapter in the SMSG eighth-grade text, and some enrichment material, such as that of Glenn and Johnson, little on probability has been written for school use below the twelfth-grade level.) As long as we stick to a pure mathematics curriculum, the critics who claim there is overemphasis on sets in school math are entirely justified.

But classification by sets is fundamental to the science curriculum. The whole system of Linnaeus for classifying plants and animals consists of constructing sets, genera, families, and species, which form a structure of sets and subjects.

Some persons would recommend throwing out the discussions of intersections of sets, but science uses this concept extensively. The classification of objects with respect to several properties relies upon the intersection-of-sets concept.

For another example, let us consider the process of abstraction. It is easy for a first-grade child to make a hardness scale. If he has four rocks, he can take two at a time and find out which rock scratches the other. How many pairs, i.e., sets of two elements, can be made from a set of four? We find six. If A scratches B, and B scratches C, can we predict the result of comparing A with C, without actually doing it? Do we need to make all six comparisons? What is the best strategy? The solution lies in simple application of set concepts.

In another experiment of ordering a set of four liquids with respect to viscosity, the child takes two at a time, and compares them by stirring, or by dropping a marble into each test tube and seeing which falls to the bottom first. How many comparisons of pairs can we make? Do we need to try all six pairs? Can we apply what we learned in the hardness experiment to design the best viscosity experiment?

We have here a concrete example of the concept of isomorphism and a *practical* use of the abstract concept of transitive relation.

SCIENCE HELPING MATHEMATICS

We might also look at two basic examples where we need science to help us teach mathematics. For one, we wish to teach multiplication graphically so children will be able to multiply any two real numbers.

After teaching coordinates early in third grade, we want the child to multiply by 3, by joining the origin (0,0) to the point (1,3). This gives the line for multiplying by 3. To multiply 4 by 3, for example, start at (4, 0), go up to the diagonal line, and then go to the left to the y-axis. Read off the answer ($y = 3 \cdot 4$) on the y-scale.

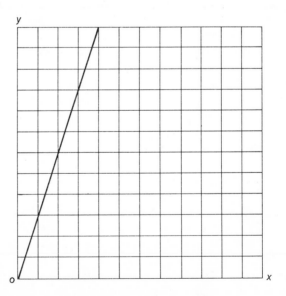

This is fine mathematically. Our problem is to give the child a reason for wanting to find the answer. When science and mathematics are coordinated, we *know* what experiments the child is doing and can gear mathematical studies to them.

Perhaps he will be measuring sticks and shadows. If a one-foot ruler casts a three-foot shadow, the child will find that he uses this line to predict the length of shadow cast by an x-foot ruler. He can then use the graph to find the height of a tree by measuring its shadow. This is a good application of the inverse operation of division.

We have taught in fourth grade the concept of *vector*, addition of vectors, and multiplication of a vector by a number. We can also give an economic interpretation in terms of the stocks of two commodities in a store. All this works.

But we do not really know how to teach the concept of the scalar product of two vectors. It is easy to give a well motivated economic interpretation. If we keep track of the stock of milk and cookies in the store, then $+ 3M - 2C$, the *change vector*, represents an increase of 3 quarts of milk and a decrease of 2 pounds of cookies. If the *price vector* is $21M + 15C$, i.e., milk costs 21 cents a quart and cookies are 15 cents a pound, then the *change in value* of the stock is $(3 \cdot 21) + (-2 \cdot 15)$ cents.

This leads easily to the expression of the scalar product in terms of co-ordinates. (But the price vector is really in a different space, the so-called dual space, from that of the change vector, and therefore the angle is, in the concrete interpretation, meaningless.)

We can give a natural, purely mathematical discussion of the scalar product *if* we can give a good reason for being interested in the square of the distance between two points. This is easy if we already know the Pythagorean theorem. If we don't know this theorem, would we ever dream of comparing areas of squares in order to investigate the lengths of the sides of a triangle?

But if science can teach the concept of *work* before fifth grade, then our mathematical problem is solved. We have a good reason to investigate just the quantity we wish to introduce. I am confident that we shall ultimately be able to teach scalar product this way, because the scientists must discuss conservation of energy, and they will need the concept of work to deal with potential energy.

From these few examples we see reasons why a good elementary mathematics program is impossible without a good elementary science curriculum. Neither mathematics nor science educators working in isolation can produce the kind of curriculum we need. But neither can they produce it working together unless there are materials, texts, and trained classroom personnel to activate these principles.

The connections that have already developed in primary-grade materials encourage us to expect that ultimately experiment and mathematical analysis of data will be closely coordinated.

At the elementary level, the self-contained classroom has a very great advantage. There is only one teacher to deal with both mathematics and science, and he can point out to his pupils which mathematics goes with which science. This of course means that teachers must be prepared well in two fields.

But at present, since the Minnemast science program is about two years behind our mathematics program, we often give upper-grade children mathematical descriptions of phenomena before they have had experiences in observing the phenomena. Our goal should lie in the area of emphasis on measurement and concrete interpretations of mathematical ideas which blend especially well in the coordination of mathematics with science.

Learning by Discovery: Instructional Strategies

Bert Y. Kersh

What characterizes the discovery approach? What difference does it make whether the learner "invents" a principle of mathematics or simply is told the principle? The expected answer would be that learning is more "effective," even though it may take the learner longer to learn by discovery. What advocates of discovery learning generally mean by by effective learning is not often spelled out in detail. However, many would agree that when the student learns by discovery he (1) understands what he learns, and so is better able to remember and to transfer it; (2) he learns something the psychologist calls a "learning set," or a strategy for discovering new principles, and (3) he develops an interest in what he learned.

It is becoming increasingly more evident that the somewhat inconsistent findings by researchers in recent years may actually reflect different learning outcomes, resulting from two or three quite different processes of learning by discovery. Moreover, if people in a group were each asked to give a concrete example of the discovery approach, I would expect a number of different responses. In the final analysis, it is highly probable that we do not all have precisely the same idea of the discovery approach after all.

Research has indicated that there are subtle, but highly important, differences in the way teachers guide the learning process when students are attempting to "discover" mathematical principles.

Let's start with an example of teaching a mathematical "principle" by the

Reprinted from *The Authentic Teacher,* Vol. 12, No. 6 (October 1965), 414–417, by permission of the author and publisher.

discovery approach. The principle may be stated as follows: The sum of the first n odd numbers is n^2. For example, the sum of the first four odd numbers (1, 3, 5, and 7) is 4^2 or 16. This particular principle has been used frequently in educational research because, like many mathematical principles, it can be learned in a variety of ways. For example, the rule may be taught as if it were an isolated fact, or it may be interrelated with other information which the learner already knows. For instance, a student may learn to explain the principle in terms of the symmetry of the series, or he may learn to explain the principle geometrically in terms of the area of a square, the side of which is n units in length.

Imagine a learner at his desk working an exercise consisting of ten addition problems. Each problem is a series of odd numbers beginning with one (for example, $1+3+5$; $1+3+5+7$; etc.). He has been instructed to find a shortcut for summing each series.

Now, ask yourself, "What are we trying to teach in this exercise?" As advocates of discovery learning, we should say we want to teach (1) the mathematical principle, (2) a procedure for identifying mathematical principles from examples, and (3) a desire to learn more about numbers in series. Why are we using the discovery method? Because we feel the learner will attain all three objectives through discovery.

Instead of saying that the mathematical principle is taught, a researcher might say "answer-giving" behavior is taught to the learner. Also, instead of saying that a procedure for identifying mathematical principles from examples is taught, he might say that we teach "answer-seeking" behavior. Answer-*giving* behavior characteristically involves information processing which produces a solution to the problem at hand, in this case, the shortcut n^2. When the learner performs arithmetical operations, replaces numerals, and factors, he is engaging in answer-giving behavior. The end result, or product, of his behavior is an answer, right or wrong. Answer-*seeking* behavior is different in that it deals exclusively with actions the learner takes in preparing for answer-giving. The result is a plan of action or a decision about what to do next. It involves separating out the various features of a mathematical expression and deciding which to "focus upon" in answer-seeking behavior; deciding what kind of information will be needed to accomplish the task at hand, and what to do with the information once it is obtained is answer-seeking behavior. In short, answer-seeking behavior is deciding what to do, and answer-giving behavior is actually doing whatever has been decided.

Let us return to our hypothetical student. You are sitting with the learner, watching him in his efforts to find the short-cut. He is having difficulty, but you are resisting the temptation to help him, because the discovery method dictates that you withhold instructions. However, does this mean that you must avoid interacting with the learner at all? Certainly not. A teacher's job is to facilitate learning.

A careful analysis of the learning task in this case would indicate that we can interact with the learner in at least two different ways. Each way is characterized by withholding instructions and, at the same time, assisting the learner in his efforts to achieve an instructional objective. This is possible because there is more than one instructional objective. Let us consider each of these two discovery methods separately.

PROVIDING "ANSWER-GIVING" INSTRUCTIONS AND WITHHOLDING "ANSWER-SEEKING" INSTRUCTIONS

One discovery approach results when the teacher guides the learner by revealing the mathematical principle through "hints" which are provided one at a time. Skillfully employed, the procedure effectively leads the learner into pathways of meaning and understanding where he otherwise might not venture or which he might simply overlook. The worst that can be said for it is that it is comparable to dangling a carrot before a donkey in an effort to make him move. At best, the learner will complete the task with a clear and meaningful knowledge of the principle involved. Unless he is skillfully taught, however, the learner may as well have been told the answer in the first place with little or no explanation of it.

For example, the learner might be told to look at the symmetry of the series and to notice that the numbers following the midpoint increase, just as those preceding the midpoint decrease in magnitude. If this does not prove successful, the instructor might suggest that the learner find the arithmetic mean of the series and compare it with the "middle numeral." The procedure almost guarantees that the learner will find the answer during the course of instruction. On the other hand, he may or may not improve his ability to seek answers. He may even learn undesirable approaches.

GIVING "ANSWER-SEEKING" INSTRUCTIONS AND WITHHOLDING "ANSWER-GIVING" INSTRUCTIONS

This procedure is the opposite of the first. Although the teacher may not give the learner any hints which reveal the answer to him, the teacher *is* permitted to suggest alternative plans of approach in problem-solving strategies. In other words, the teacher may facilitate the discovery or problem-solving process without revealing the principle itself. Mathematicians employ a variety of problem-solving strategies, some of which are quite formalized and others of which are best described as informal approaches. "Persistence" and "flexibility in thinking" are examples of the latter.

Imagine that our learner is a junior high school student who is just beginning algebra, and we are interested only in fostering the informal problem-solving techniques. The instructional strategy is to ask the learner to report what he is thinking in the process of working the problems. We ask him to "think out loud." Whenever we determine that the learner is being persistent and flexible, we will praise his efforts and offer encouragement. Whenever the learner appears to persevere in one problem-solving approach, we instruct him in how to proceed on a different tack, hopefully one which will lead more directly to the solution. Finally, if the learner shows signs of giving up, we will persuade him to continue in hopes that his efforts will soon be rewarded. All this help and encouragement is to be provided regardless of how successful the learner is in finding the shortcut.

A specific set of instructions designed to suggest a different strategy to the learner, without indicating the answer, might be, "Try comparing the problems on your answer sheet. See if you can benefit by what they have in common and what is different about each of them." This instruction tells the learner how to begin processing the information before him, and hopefully produces some observations about the number series which will suggest the shortcut. The approach is generally a good one. Your next instruction may be, "Decide what is the most important element that these problems have in common. Think about this one feature, and tell me how you think it might help you find the sum."

Instructions such as these do not reveal anything to the learner about the shortcut he is seeking. Rather, they channel his thinking in a way which will increase the probability of his finding the answer. There is no guarantee that he will, however. From what we know about human behavior under these circumstances, it is likely that the learner will *not* find the shortcut while working in your presence. Since we have told him essentially how to approach the problem and let him know when he has employed good answer-seeking behavior, it would seem more than likely that the learner will profit from this aspect of his experience. In other words, whereas the first instructional strategy almost inevitably will teach the mathematical principle involved, the second one almost certainly will teach a technique for identifying principles—one which applies to other problem-solving situations as well.

COMPARISON OF THE TWO APPROACHES

Each of the two approaches described are properly identified as discovery approaches, because the instructor withholds information and the learner must find it out for himself. These two approaches differ only in the type of information provided and withheld. Both approaches could teach the mathematical principle and the skill in identifying principles. However, each method emphasizes a different instructional objective, specifically that which relates to the information which the teacher provides the learner. We cannot be at all certain that the learner profits much from the "unguided" experience he has. We can conclude only that some learners profit from unguided experiences and others do not.

We have considered two instructional strategies and discussed them with reference to the first two of three objectives identified earlier. The objective which has not been discussed is that which pertains to developing interest in mathematics. Max Beberman defends the use of the discovery method in the UICSM curriculum on the grounds that ninth-graders are attracted to the "what-would-happen-if" question, regardless of its practicality from the adult point of view. The fact that the learner can discover for himself is all the learner needs to justify mathematics. Actually, there is very little evidence in the research literature that bears on this reaction to discovery learning. Researchers have attempted to measure the emotional reaction of the learners to discovery-type tasks in various ways. The results of some indicate heightened interest. Others did not indicate increased interest.

Personally, I believe that this phenomenon of interest which sometimes results from discovery learning is a cognitive motive which might be related to a drive for mastery or simply reflect our native curiosity. The drive to master a task sometimes is aroused when we are engaged in a task requiring the manipulation of objects or ideas. This drive is particularly evident in the behavior of young children who may persist at a manipulative task for long periods of time. Curiosity, on the other hand, may be aroused in situations which have elements of surprise, perplexity, or doubt. In our number series example, for instance, many learners appear to hit upon the solution unexpectedly. This surprise reaction may tend to pique their curiosity. Undoubtedly, many of you have used effectively the technique of "torpedoing" an hypothesis which your students offer as conclusive. Demonstrating the vulnerability for some mathematical principle produces doubt in the student's mind, which in turn results in some further exploration and study. Perplexity or "puzzlement" may be produced by reviewing the rich associative structure of an apparently simple principle. Each of these techniques is often involved in the discovery approach.

We may conclude that interest could be aroused by either of the strategies outlined previously. However, the extent to which interest is aroused may be a function of skillful questioning and ordering of experiences for the learner. It may also depend on whether or not the learner is successful in discovering the shortcut, as well as upon some rather complex characteristics of the learner about which we know very little. In any event there is certainly no guarantee that the discovery approach will result in increased interest in the task at hand.

CONCLUDING STATEMENT

Two instructional strategies, both of which involve discovery experiences, but which may be expected to produce different learning outcomes, have been outlined. One fosters answer-giving behavior, the other answer-seeking behavior.

What the student learns probably is related more to the instructions which the teacher provides than to those which he withholds. If instructions on how to seek alternative ways for producing answers are provided and instructions on how to carry out the plans are withheld, we may expect that the student will learn how to seek answers in general, but may not actually learn the answer he is seeking. An instructional strategy must produce the behavior which is to be learned; that is, the learner must do what you want him to learn as best he can so you can act upon the imperfect performance in an effort to help the learner perfect it. By selectively withholding instructions, the teacher may cause the learner to engage in the kind of behavior the teacher is interested in, but instruction may not be effective until the teacher provides instructions designed to guide behavior in the desired direction.

The two different instructional strategies described elicit different behaviors for the teacher to act upon. Consequently, the learning outcomes may be different. Perhaps it is time for us to analyze rigorously our instructional techniques to identify the particular behaviors each technique may be expected to elicit. In this way, we may be able to predict the learned outcomes of our instruction more accurately. Also, it may result in our becoming more critical of those who label instructional strategies "the discovery method" or "the lecture method" and who evaluate them as good or bad accordingly.

5

Problem-Solving

For many years, that complex mental process of problem-solving has been of concern to the teacher. The intent of this section is to explore problem-solving, to discover what certain aspects or factors will be revealed and, further, what this exploration will say about the nature and function of problem-solving in the entire process of mathematics thinking and development.

What are the major components of problem-solving? Is problem-solving related solely to the teaching of mathematics? When is a child engaged in problem-solving? What kinds of structuring of the environment is a teacher capable of establishing? What can the teacher do to assist the child to develop problem-solving ability? What useful procedures might a teacher suggest to her children? What considerations serve to increase the interest in problem-solving? Is there a difference between mathematical problem-solving and other forms of problem-solving? Are there some general principles to be emphasized in the development of problem-solving ability? Can problem-solving be taught?

Vitalizing Problem Solving

Margaret Godfrey

Motivating and interesting students in problem solving has always required the expenditures of great effort. The atomic age and the changing world we live in can influence and even alter the natural curiosity of children. An inquisitive child may find challenge and interest in movies, television, and print mediums. A quiet, retiring child, on the other hand, may become over-

Reprinted from *Education* (Indianapolis: The Bobbs-Merrill Company, March 1962), 416–418, by permission of the publisher.

254

whelmed by this barrage of information. A third child may find amusement and joy in the ready-made entertainment forms and become passive and indifferent in the classroom.

These children's reactions to the present-day world will not help the classroom teacher in motivating them to learn. Problem solving in arithmetic especially causes difficulty because the child can be easily discouraged in his efforts if he is left unguided. Lack of success will stifle further initiative and cause more disappointment in the progress of the arithmetic program because problem solving requires an active participation of the child's mind.

Starting a program to improve children's ability to solve problems would necessitate evaluating their present ability. Achievement scores are the first means of measurement available. Then the teacher can take small groups of children whose achievement scores in the problem solving are on the same grade level and make further evaluation by having the children solve orally arithmetic problems on their grade level. In this way the teacher can get a better idea of the children's grasp of problem solving.

The development of a systematic method for solving problems would advance the pupils' arithmetic powers. However, the curriculum of the elementary school is crowded with pressures to use group work in skill subjects, committee work, and special projects for special students. Therefore, I feel that this work in developing problem-solving skills would necessarily be a continuous process spread over the six elementary school years. Evaluation of present abilities would give each teacher a fresh look at the weaknesses and strengths in their previous training.

DEVELOPING A SYSTEMATIC METHOD

Problem solving requires "thinking." The teacher faces the task of building the framework of needed steps in this thinking process. Problem solving in any area of arithmetic must be undertaken only after concept development of that process in arithmetic is in the child's mind. In solving arithmetic problems, the child's mind must reverse these arithmetic concepts. That is, the child must fit the details of the problem into a framework of thought which will lead to the problem itself.

The excitement of discovery advocated in today's arithmetic texts can be used here in finding the concept involved.

Most texts emphasize using three steps to determine the answer: first, defining the facts; second, determining the question asked; and third, determining the processes required to find the answer. I added the concept of "more or less" to this list as an aid to the children's thinking. Determining if the answer would be more or less would first relate to any previous concept development and would, secondly, categorize the processes to be used in the solution.

Thus, in one-step problems, a conclusion reached by the child of "more" would mean to add or multiply, and "less" would relate to subtract or divide. In two-step problems this thinking of "more or less" will certainly allude to the direction of the answer and the processes which will be used as part of the solution. This type of thinking will also correlate with the process of estimating used in today's arithmetic development.

These questions emerge as a guide: (1) What does the problem tell? (2) What does the problem ask? (3) Will the answer be more or less? (4) What must I do to find the answer?

The teacher may start the lesson by reading a problem: "Suppose this class had a party and there were 216 cookies to share among 27 children. If the cookies were shared equally, how many would each child get?" The solution will be found by dividing 216 by 27. The answer of 8 cookies will be obtained. Do a few more problems orally.

Ask the children if they know the thoughts they went through automatically in solving the problem. Then ask the children to make a list of steps their minds went through in solving the problem. You will probably get some of the questions I have previously enumerated as a guide and may get others. Add any of the four guide questions that have been omitted by the class.

Continue the lesson by having the children analyze problems with these four questions in mind. For example, you might use the problem: "Suppose mother had just baked 30 cookies and you wanted to share them among five people. How much would each person get?"

The question "What does the problem tell?" will be answered by the first sentence of the problem. The second sentence will answer the second question, "What does the problem ask?" Then the idea of estimating will be incorporated into the third question, "Will the answer be more or less?" The reply should undoubtedly be "less." If you find your children do not know that the answer will be less, you will have uncovered a weakness in their ability to solve problems.

If enough time is spent analyzing problems continuously but not constantly through the elementary school years, the children, even the slower ones, will gain insights into problem solving and will gain in proficiency.

EVERYDAY LIFE SITUATIONS

The present-day aims of arithmetic emphasize it as a socially important subject. This emphasis can be exploited advantageously in teaching problem solving to elementary school pupils. Classroom needs to solve arithmetic problems will arise when the milk money needs to be counted, or the cost per person for a bus for a class trip, or the cost of a class party must be figured. Do not overlook these occasions.

The children can relate their own experiences with numbers in their daily lives: receiving change at the grocery store, making their allowance last for the week, or saving for something special. Economics will also be introduced as the children denote saving or spending money, scarcity of some goods or money.

Newspaper advertisements, financial reports, and other topics in our newspapers show figures in use in our world today. These can be collected and displayed on the bulletin board or used as the basis for original class problems. Commercial charts and pictures are also good to display.

CHILDREN'S CREATIVE ABILITY

The creative ability of the children can be used to spark up the arithmetic lessons in three ways: first, because the children love to challenge each other with their own problems; and second, because children may feel a more active role in problem solving and the arithmetic concepts involved in working out their own problems; and third, real life situations can be injected into this work.

Children's awareness of the fact that questions in problems denoting different processes, such as adding, subtracting, multiplying, and dividing, can be emphasized more easily when the children write or make their own problems.

I had a bright class of fifth-graders write their own problems. When they challenged the class orally with the problems, I enumerated the questions in the category of the solution needed. Thus I collected these questions:

Add
  How many did he have then?
  What was the total cost?
  How much would you have?
Subtract
  How much would you have left?
  How much more do I have to save?
Multiply
  How many pencils did she have?
  How many cookies do I need to get?
Divide
  How much will each child get?
  How many stamps does the boy get?

Slower classes and younger children are less apt at writing problems, but they will be able to think up problems and present them orally to the class. You could still derive a list of questions this way and put them on a chart for the class's use. This would show the children how different shades of meaning in a question contribute to the meanings of arithmetic conceptions and thus help the child in the solution.

ing to avoid here is to say that these questions always denote cer-
cesses, because there is really no guarantee they always will.

other important aspect of problem solving that must be stressed is
there are often several ways to reach a conclusion. Have different children illustrate their thinking processes in solving the problems to show the
varied methods of arriving at the answer.

As children delve to solve problems and inject real life into them, they
will begin to see the great need for arithmetic in their daily lives.

Teaching Problem-Solving

J. D. Williams

The problem-solving process has relevance to learning both as a means and
as an end: it is involved both in the acquisition of new responses and in
their application to new situations. Few educators would deny that this is
so, but the extent of this involvement might be made clearer by an examination of the nature of problem-solving, the acquisition of responses, and
their application in new situations.

A problem is normally said to arise when progress towards a goal by an
obvious route is not possible, and less obvious ways of reaching the goal
have to be sought. In this sort of situation, the problem-solving behavior that
results can take many different forms, but it always involves more than the
mere reproduction of a learnt response; the appropriate response may need
to be selected from several possible responses, or it may need to be formed
by the integration or modification of learnt responses. Say, for example, the
child wants the apple that is hanging high in the tree. The obvious means
of getting the apple—reaching for it—is out of the question, for the child is
not tall enough; a less obvious means must be sought. The child might think
of several ways of dealing with this sort of situation: "Stand on a chair, as I
do to get the jam from the shelf—not high enough; throw something at it,
as I do to get conkers—might hit the glasshouse; lassoo it, as they would in
a film—branches would get in the way; use the long handle of my fishing
net—ah yes!" Thus, from several likely responses, themselves chosen from a
wide range of possible responses, the child *selects* an appropriate one. In
this case, the child must do more than merely select—he must modify a
previously-learnt response, for, hitherto, the fishing net has been used only

Reprinted from *Educational Research* (November 1960), 12–36, by permission of the
National Foundation for Educational Research in England and Wales.

for reaching for fish, and now it must be used for knocking down apples. Suppose, now, the fishing net handle proved to be too short, after all. The child might think of using the net while standing on the chair. In this case, he would have *integrated* two responses in order to solve the problem.

Problem-solving behaviour of this sort occurs more generally in the learning situation than might be thought. Consider the acquisition of a new response. Sometimes, in this process, problem-solving is very evidently involved, as when the response in question is a problem-solving technique that is acquired by solving an actual problem. But sometimes the problem-solving is not so noticeable as this: even in what might appear to be rote learning a certain amount of problem-solving is likely to take place; the pupil will seek underlying unities and relationships in the material he is learning in much the same way as he would seek the solution to a problem.

Suppose that the pupil were learning his nine times table—an operation that might often be described as "memorizing." He might have trouble in learning nine times eight. This would constitute a problem for him. Quite commonly, this sort of problem is solved by an integration of other knowledge about the multiplication tables: "I know that ten eights are eighty, and that nine eights will be one eight less than this." In "memorizing" a great deal of search for similarities, differences and other relationships between the present situation and past ones, and between the different components of the present situation is likely to take place; essentially, this sort of search is problem-solving, these relationships the solutions. All the time during learning, categories and relationships are being selected, modified or created in order to give meaning to the learning situation. Unfortunately, the person who might well be least of all likely to notice the problematical nature of the learning situation, is the teacher himself. He, of all people, is likely to be familiar with the responses he is trying to get his pupils to acquire, and for him, the components of the learning situation will no longer need to be organised and interrelated. Even "problem mathematics" will tend to become a set of automatic exercises for him; it can only be hoped that he can remain, while teaching, fully conscious of the difference between the automatic way in which he can go through a series of well-practised operations, and the searching, re-organising and interrelating that his pupils will need to engage in before these operations will mean anything to them.

It is held by some that explicit problem-solving, of the sort that is employed in the teaching of mathematics and science, should be made to play an even greater part in learning. These recommend the "problem-solving approach" to the teaching of not only mathematics and science, but other subjects also. We shall examine evidence bearing on the effectiveness of this approach later on.

Consider now the *application* of learnt responses. The form in which a response is learnt is seldom the form in which it will subsequently be used. Even if the response *is* used in roughly the same form as that in which it is learnt, its relevance to a new situation will need to be seen, for no two situations are quite the same. Thus, selection and modification of responses is necessary not only in those activities that most conspicuously involve problem-solving, but in all sorts of applications of responses to new situations.

To illustrate this, we could take a fairly simple sort of response: a newly-learnt word. Perhaps it has been learnt merely in the sense that it has been equated with its definition, or perhaps some of its uses in various contexts have been seen. In the former case none, and in the latter, by no means *all* of its possible uses will have been specifically learnt; in both cases the pupil will be faced with the problems of adapting its meaning to new uses and selecting the word, when it is needed, from the total of his vocabulary. Where the situation in which the word is required is similar to that in which it has been learnt, there will not be much of a problem. Where the two situations differ appreciably, however, a certain amount of problem-solving will be necessary before the word can be applied. So thin, it seems, is the line between what is usually considered to be problem-solving, and other applications of learnt responses, that one might even go so far as to say that a problem has been solved every time a way has been found of applying a learnt response.

This way of looking at the application of learning has important implications for the teacher, for, as we shall see later, the sort of teaching that leads to the quickest acquisition of responses is not necessarily the same as that which will conduce to the problem-solving activities that are involved in applying these responses. In considering some of the factors that influence problem-solving we might well arrive at some indication of how, in teaching, to increase the likelihood that what is learnt can later be used.

But the relevance of problem-solving to teaching consists not *solely* in the fact that it enters into learning and its application. The ability to solve problems could be regarded as highly important in its own right. In fact, if one were asked to justify the teaching of mathematics and science to children who were never going to use them in later life, one might well point out that they provide practice in problem-solving. It would be difficult to question the usefulness in adult life of the ability to solve problems.

In this article an attempt will be made to acquaint teachers with research findings relevant to the teaching of problem-solving. Some of these findings derive from situations very close to those in which teaching is normally carried out, but this cannot be said of all of them. Many are derived from experiments upon adults instead of children, laboratory experiments, experiments using problems extremely unlike those to be found in the classroom; for example, in the usual experimental problem only relevant data are given, and there is only one correct solution, whereas in real-life problems it is usually necessary to discard much redundant data before the problem can even be formulated, and there is seldom a *single* correct solution. But by means of such "artificial" experiments it has often been possible to isolate and examine factors that would have been obscured in the classroom.

It is not expected that teachers will be able to see direct applications for all of these findings, but much that psychological research has to offer the teacher is not *directly* applicable to any of the many complex classroom situations that he has to face. Some of these findings can be said to constitute rules of action: they point directly to ways of improving teaching methods; others should be regarded as rules not of action but of interpretation: in the light of these the teacher should be able to follow the problem-solving activities of his pupils more insightfully and to work out for himself how to improve his teaching methods.

PLAN

Three determinants of success in solving problems will be considered:

1. Factors in the problem-solving situation.
2. Factors in the problem-solver's previous training.
3. Characteristics of the problem-solver.

Studies bearing on these will be examined, and an attempt will be made to indicate their relevance to teaching.

In addition to this, the advisability of "The Problem-Solving Approach" to teaching in general will be considered.

FACTORS IN THE PROBLEM-SOLVING SITUATION

With an understanding of the factors that facilitate problem-solving the teacher can make it much easier for the pupil to acquire problem-solving techniques. Further, by imparting this understanding to the pupil he can help the pupil to direct his own problem-solving activities in a more efficient manner. The factors examined below: concrete presentation, verbalisation, graphical representation, "brain-storming," group problem-solving and some motivational factors, are by no means the only determinants of ease in problem-solving, but have been selected because we know something about them and their implications for teaching are fairly clear.

CONCRETE PRESENTATION

It is often assumed that when presented "concretely," or in a "life-like" setting, a problem is easier to solve and its solution is higher in quality than when presented numerically or verbally.

Lorge and others tried to test this assumption. Using adults as subjects, they posed the problem of formulating a way of getting five men across a mined road. This problem was presented on four different levels of reality: (a) verbal description, (b) photographic representation, (c) as a miniature scale model allowing no manipulation of its parts, and (d) as a miniature scale model allowing manipulation of its parts. They found that the quality of the solutions was not affected by the level of reality at which the problem was presented.

In other experimental settings, concrete presentation has been shown to have considerable facilitative effect on problem solving. Gibb found that children were better able to solve three different types of subtraction problem when these were presented concretely, and Long and Welch found that six- to eight-year-olds were better able to generalize a reasoning principle when it was presented concretely.

Thus, seemingly, there is conflicting evidence on the usefulness of presenting problems concretely. However, in interpreting the results of these experiments the following points should be borne in mind:

1. Slight details of the experimental set-up can make all the difference. For example, one of the advantages of concrete or "real-life" presentations is that more information is available to the solver. In the experiment described above by Lorge and others, subjects working at all levels of reality were given any extra information they asked for, so that this particular advantage of real-life presentation was minimised.

2. It is perhaps significant that the experiments on children gave positive results. There is much evidence that children's thought is concrete in nature, so it is not surprising that their problem-solving should gain more from concrete presentation.

3. The advisability of concrete presentation will depend upon the criterion of performance to be used. Although, when the problem is presented concretely, superior solutions are not produced, there may be an advantage in speed. It might be solved more quickly because of the greater familiarity of the terms in which it is presented. Moreover, its solution might lead to greater transfer because of the meaningfulness of the problem-solving activity, or the pupil might find the problem more "interesting" and for *this* reason perform better.

In conclusion it can be said that there are some proven, and several conceivable advantages to presenting priblems to children in concrete terms. The usefulness to children of structural and life-like representations of problems might well be underestimated by the adult, who is much more capable of symbolic thinking.

Verbalisation

Although it is by no means *necessary* for the solution of problems, one is not surprised that in some cases verbalisation has been shown to help a great deal.

In an experiment in which subjects were required to discover the correct sequence in which to turn off a set of lights, Ray found that those subjects who were required to formulate their responses before making them solved the problem much sooner. Here, verbalisation helped the subjects to make their responses more explicit, so that they could more easily relate them to one another and to their hypotheses.

Again, Thompson showed that children allowed to verbalise steps in the solution of a mechanical puzzle, solved it in half the time taken by children prevented from verbalising. In this sort of problem it is necessary to make frequent reference to the sequence of the different steps; when they are labelled, their sequence can be reviewed more easily.

There are many different ways in which verbalisation can help in problem-solving. Kurtz and Hovland found that children recognised and recalled objects better after naming than after merely encircling them. Probably it is partly due to this particular advantage of verbalisation that in one experiment young children were found to be much better able to solve a simple multiple-choice problem when names were given to each of the choices. Words are our most effective tool for carrying out a host of operations that are involved in problem-solving. They help us to discriminate, designate, classify, and, by providing a bridge between present problem and past experience, they often enable us to see the relevance of previously-learnt materials and techniques. So that maximum use can be made of this tool pupils should be encouraged to discuss problems as much as possible and even to formulate on paper an analysis of the problem and their plan of attack. The more explicitly a technique of solution is formulated, the more probably will its relevance to a new problem be seen.

Despite the abundance of evidence in favour of verbalisation there are some experimental situations in which it has proved a handicap rather than a help, so it should not be prescribed indiscriminately. In some cases a clearer and less cumbersome idea of the problem can be framed in spatial terms. Again, some individuals find it easier to think without verbal formulation. In particular, it must be remembered, as was pointed out in the previous section, that children are much less capable of symbolic thought than adults, and they might well be able to engage in problem-solving processes on a concrete level without being able to translate these processes into an adequate verbal form.

GRAPHICAL REPRESENTATION

Verbalising is not the only way of making a problem more explicit or easier to grasp. Sometimes the problem lends itself to *graphical* depiction. Katona, in his "Organising and Memorising," suggests the use of diagrams to encourage relational thinking in mathematics. In an early study of the subject Clark and Vincent showed that graphical accompanied by verbal analysis of problems was a great help. Euler's diagrams too are a classical method for simplifying problems involving class-inclusion.

Interrelationships between key items can be depicted simply and helpfully by graphical means. The following problem provides an example:

"John gave Joe twice as much as Jim gave George. Joe gave George half of what he received. If Jim gave George 6d., how much did George receive altogether?" This becomes much easier to understand when the interrelationsips are presented graphically:

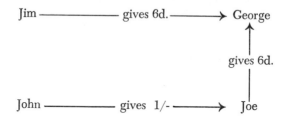

In the diagram it is quite evident that George receives 1/-.

As with verbalising, though, this device has its limitations, and there is experimental evidence that it is not helpful in *every* type of problem.

BRAINSTORMING

A. F. Osborn, in his book "Applied Imagination", suggests that creativity in problem-solving is increased by separating the process of *forming* hypotheses from that of *evaluating* them. In this way, one's habitual modes of thought are less likely to determine which hypotheses one produces and less likely to preclude the production of unusual ones.

Meadow and Parnes have put this suggestion to experimental test, and shown that more hypotheses of better quality are produced by:

a. subjects who have undergone a course of training based on this suggestion;
b. subjects told to produce hypotheses irrespective of their quality, as opposed to those who are told to produce only good hypotheses.

They also found that subjects who have had practice in brainstorming benefit more than others from instructions to produce hypotheses irrespective of quality.

These results indicate that the teacher can over-emphasize the importance of critical thinking. Naturally, it is important that pupils should learn to subject their ideas to critical examination, but they should be made aware that a critical frame of mind can very often inhibit the production of an idea at a point in its developmen at which it is impossible to assess its true value.

Children are given a great deal of training in critical thinking, but could do with much more encouragement to *produce* and *elaborate* ideas. Teachers in all subjects could well set aside time for 'brain-storming' sessions, in which they posed their children a problem and gave complete licence for the production of hypotheses no matter *how* impracticable or bizarre. The hypotheses could be recorded and sorted out later.

Fear of having silly ideas can sometimes cripple the problem-solver. Hypotheses that appear to have no support from his past experience should be welcomed, for problem-solving is to a large extent *un*learning.

Problem-solving in Groups

Often it is convenient and often it is desirable for children to work together in groups instead of individually. Various aspects of the efficiency of problem-solving by groups have been investigated.

Klugman found that children working in pairs solved more problems than did individuals, but took more time to do so. He attributed this result to the fact that more hypotheses were presented, discussed and rejected by the pairs.

Taylor and Faust found that groups of two and groups of four were superior to individuals in terms of the number of problems solved and the speed of solution, and that the number of failures decreased in proportion to the size of the group. However, the groups of two were by no means *twice* as efficient as individuals, and the groups of four by no means *twice* as efficient as the groups of two.

The group method of solving problems was shown by Lorge and others to have other advantages. The quality of group solutions was shown to be much higher than that of solutions by individuals, and this was attributed to the fact that groups asked more questions and gained more relevant information than did individuals. In another study by the same investigators, it was found that whereas individuals tended to overestimate the quality of their solutions, groups tended to *under*-estimate that of theirs.

The work of Shaw provides further evidence of the relatively higher standards of self-criticism obtaining in group problem-solving. She found that far more incorrect solutions were rejected by the group.

It has been suggested that group superiority is due merely to the fact that there is a greater chance of a group's *containing* a good problem-solver than of an *individual's being* one. In support of this view, Marquart repeated Shaw's experiment, but instead of comparing the results of a group of three with those of *one* individual, she compared them with those of *three* individuals. She found little difference between groups and individuals.

We can conclude from the above evidence that group problem-solving is at any rate in some ways more efficient than individual problem-solving, and produces solutions of higher quality. It is therefore desirable that pupils should be given the opportunity to develop the technique and habits of mind that are necessary for this sort of activity. This sort of development cannot take place without plenty of practice, of course, but with the complicated inter-actions that can take place between the members of a group, much can go wrong, unless its activity is guided by the teacher, who should make sure that each child willingly accepts his part in the group's activity, contributes to the discussion, keeps to the subject, permits others to voice their views, can bring himself to abide by majority decisions when there is little to be gained by questioning them but will not be afraid of trying to change the course of the group's activity when there is good reason for doing so. Groups should be carefully composed of members who are not too disparate in ability, fluency or dominance.

Working in groups can be recommended not only as an efficient way of getting problems solved, but also as a useful method of improving the problem-solving abilities of the individuals participating. Since their approaches to problems are bound to differ in many ways, individuals can be expected to learn a great deal from observing one another engaged in the various activities that are involved in solving problems.

SOME MOTIVATIONAL FACTORS

Three motivational variables known to enter into the problem-solving process are: anxiety, frustration and confidence.

In a later section, anxiety is shown to reduce the subject's ability to change his approach to a problem. Anxiety has been found to impair children's performance on complex tasks much more than on simple tasks so it is possible that teachers using anxiety-promoting approaches to the teaching of simple skills will find that these approaches produce good results and will incline to use them in teaching the more complex problem-solving techniques; here they will find less success. Problem-solving proceeds most efficiently under conditions of minimal anxiety.

In his book on frustration, Maier has shown how this condition can produce just the rigid, stereotyped, non-adaptive behaviour that is antithetical to successful problem-solving. It has been found that frustration reduces fluency in nine-year-olds, that it reduces the constructiveness of children's play, and that it can reduce one's ability to solve problems. It is important, therefore, that teaching should be such as to minimise the sorts of frustration that can so easily arise in the problem-solving situation as a consequence of over-difficult problems for example, or a premature introduction to abstract problems, meaninglessness of terms and lack of a procedure for dealing with an unstructured problem situation.

There is evidence that failure to solve a problem is often due to *fear* of failure. Lack of confidence probably inhibits the exploration of the problem, the production of hypotheses and the persistence of endeavour that are so necessary in the initial stages of problem-solving. On the other hand, it appears that one *can* be *over*-confident. It has been found that confidence correlates with the length of time wasted in unsuccessful attempts at solving problems. Thus, confidence should be accompanied by enough caution to permit a realistic evaluation of hypotheses.

One very effective way of reducing anxiety, precluding frustration and inspiring confidence, is to make sure that the child is capable of coping with the problems that he is posed. Updegraff and Keister have shown that when, in their training, children have begun on easy problems and progressed through graded stages of difficulty to harder ones, they approach new problems with greater persistence and confidence. The teacher should continually check that the pupil is faced with problems that do not take him far out of his depth.

It is claimed for structural methods of teaching arithmetic that, by presenting the pupil with problems in a way that enables him to cope with them, such methods avoid the development of attitudes and fears which may permanently hamper him in solving arithmetical problems.

Another means of ensuring that the pupil is not disheartened in his first attempts at developing a problem-solving technique is the use of 'crutches'—devices that ease his introduction to a new problem-type and can later be discarded. For instance, in learning to perform subtractions involving carrying, children at first can be encouraged to write down the number they have borrowed and the number remaining in the column from which they have borrowed it, as shown in the example.

$$
\begin{array}{r}
7\,{}^{3}\!\!\!\not{4}\,{}^{1}2 \\
-4\ 2\ 7 \\
\hline
3\ 1\ 5
\end{array}
$$

When they have mastered the technique sufficiently they can solve the problem without doing this. Brownell found that children encouraged to use such crutches understood the process better and computed more accurately. Often, the use of crutches is objected to on the grounds that it establishes habits that have to be unlearnt before the most efficient form of the technique can finally be acquired. In some cases this is a valid objection, but in many, the crutch is automatically short-circuited out of the technique when a sufficient degree of skill has been reached. Any disadvantages there may be attached to the use of crutches, are probably well out-weighed by the advantages of training the pupil upon problems presented in a manner that does not arouse anxiety, that precludes frustration and that establishes a confident approach.

FACTORS IN THE PROBLEM-SOLVER'S PREVIOUS TRAINING

Now we shall examine eight areas of research in which factors affecting the ease with which problem-solving techniques can be acquired and transferred to new situations have been investigated. These eight areas have dealt with: understanding of essential principles, the use of a variety of training problems, teacher guidance in learning, feedback to the pupil, timing, explicit training in problem-solving approaches, set, and training in creativity.

UNDERSTANDING ESSENTIAL PRINCIPLES

One would expect that mechanical memorisation of problem-solving techniques would be a far less efficient method of learning them than a method involving understanding of the principles behind them, and there is a vast amount of experimentation to support this expectation. Brownell reports an experiment in which children taught the principle of place value performed the operation of 'borrowing,' transferred their knowledge to new problems, and re-learnt it after a period of time, far better than others who had been taught to borrow mechanically.

Others, working with both children and adults have produced evidence that problem-solving techniques are better remembered and transferred when the principles underlying them are understood. In his *Organising and Memorising*, Katona, for example, describes how he taught college students card tricks in two different ways: one group memorised the tricks, while the other was shown the principle behind them. The *memorising* group did not retain the tricks or perform new tricks as well as the other (the *understanding*) group.

But there is evidence that there are conditions under which the 'understanding of principles' policy should be modified. Some investigators find little difference between understanding and memorising methods in their effect on recall or transfer to *simple* tasks, but that understanding is superior in facilitating transfer to *difficult* tasks. Hilgard and others, who were responsible for one of these investigations, point out that where reliance is placed upon understanding, limited understanding can be a source of error. Often, too, the relevance of the taught principles to new problems is less easily appreciated than in the case of the particular transfer situations used above; there is plenty of evidence from both the psychological laboratory and the classroom that an understanding of underlying principles does not *automatically* ensure the solution of a problem.

Corman, using one of the problems Katona had used in some of his experiments, found that information about *method* of solution produced more solutions and better transfer than did information about *underlying principles*.

He also found that abler subjects benefited from additional knowledge of principles more than did less able subjects.

It seems then, that there are limitations to the use of understanding methods. On the whole, understanding methods are to be recommended. They enable particular operations to be unified into general principles, which, because of their greater generality, are more likely to transfer to new problem situations. But:

a. in the case of simple problems, the application of a memorised technique might be easy enough without an understanding of the principles underlying it,

b. the relevance of some principles to new problems might be more difficult to see than that of the appropriate techniques, and

c. less able subjects might be less capable of utilising information about underlying principles.

TRAINING ON A VARIETY OF PROBLEMS

It is usually assumed by teachers that variety in training-problems facilitates the abstraction of essential principles of solution, thus making easier transfer to other problems. Harlow supports this view, maintaining that variety of training-problems *teaches* the solver how to *learn* to deal with the new problems. Experiments in the laboratory and in the classroom have shown that both adults and children transfer problem-solving techniques better after practising them on a variety of problems.

The principle of variety in training might seem so much in accordance with common sense, and so much supported by every-day teaching experience that it is superfluous to demonstrate and absurd to question it.

However, as in their work on understanding, psychologists have shown that this principle can do with some qualification. Adams found that adults trained on a single sort of problem transferred to a new problem *better* than those trained on a variety of problems. This apparent contradiction was explained by Morrisett and Hovland, who pointed out that increasing the variety of problems decreases the rate of learning to solve any one sort of problem, and that Adams' multiple-problem subjects transferred relatively poorly only because they had mastered their training problems less well.

These investigators showed:

a. that when only a little training was given, subjects transferred better after training on a single sort of problem;

b. that when a great deal of training was given, subjects transferred better after training on a variety of problems.

In situations where training to a high degree of proficiency is not possible (when the time is short, the problem-solving technique difficult, the pupil dull) it appears that more training on fewer types of problems is indicated.

Where training to a high degree of proficiency *is* possible, however, the greater the variety of problems, the better.

TEACHER GUIDANCE VERSUS DISCOVERY

There is plenty of experimental evidence that discovering for himself the solution to a problem increases the pupil's ability to transfer his technique of solution to other problems. In one study it was found that pupils who were merely told where they had gone wrong in solving problems learnt and transferred better than those who were told the solutions to the problems in advance. In another, it was found that students could transfer a principle in physics better if they had puzzled over a problem exemplifying it before learning the principle, than if they had learnt the principle before puzzling over the exemplification.

One could expect discovery to encourage transfer, for in seeking the solution to a problem the subject will

a. re-organise the information available in a way that is meaningful to him,
b. deal with the same (problem) situation as he will be faced with in the case of a new problem,
c. learn new ways of solving problems ("learn to learn" as Harlow says).

However, there is also a great deal of evidence that discovery by itself is inferior to teacher-directed ways of solving problems.

In training adults on verbal problems, Craig found that teacher-guidance in the form of directing the subject's attention to underlying principles led to avoidance of more errors while learning, and greater transfer to new problems.

Brownell found that children allowed to solve arithmetical problems without guidance may reach a certain level of proficiency by using an inefficient mode of attack but that they may need to be guided on to a more efficient mode, otherwise satisfaction with some measure of success may prevent the learner from making further progress.

An important variable in experiments on discovery versus guidance is intelligence. In an experimental study of the relationship between intelligence and social atmosphere in group problem-solving, it was found that a permissive, non-prescriptive atmosphere favoured intelligent students, while a traditional, prescriptive atmosphere favoured the less able. However, in another study it was shown that intelligent students were more able to utilise guidance than the less intelligent ones, so it seems that intelligent subjects benefit more under either of these conditions.

Since discovery of a problem-solving technique by the pupil is desirable, but can lead to a great deal of wasted effort and time, and might lead to the development of sub-maximally efficient techniques, a compromise is called for. Such a compromise is provided by what Frandsen describes as "teacher-guidance of pupils' self-discovery experiences." Instead of demonstrating, illustrating, explaining, etc., the teacher guides by questioning, dropping hints, and generally arranging the situation so that the pupil can discover without too much fruitless effort or error the right things for himself. Allowances can be made for the pupil's ability. Brighter pupils will need less guidance but will be able to make better use of the guidance they get.

One can imagine many ways in which the pupil's discoveries could be guided: the teacher could present him with a problem and correct his errors until the technique had been perfected; the technique could be introduced on problems analogous to those to which its application is eventually to be discovered; an analogous technique could first be taught and the pupil could be left to discover the appropriate form of it; hints could be dropped appropriate to the pupil's level of progress, to point the direction his next exploratory move should take; a sequence of prescriptive questions could be asked, the pupil's answers to which would lead him in the direction of the discovery.

A useful illustration of some of these methods has been reported by Thiele. In this case, the pupils needed to learn how to multiply whole numbers by mixed numbers. They already knew that the size of the product was directly related to that of the multiplier, and to bring this back to their notice they were asked to find the products in the examples shown below.

$$6 \times 8 = 48 \qquad 3 \times 8 = 24$$
$$5 \times 8 = 40 \qquad 2 \times 8 = 16$$
$$4 \times 8 = 32 \qquad 1 \times 8 = 8$$

Next, they were asked to look for significant relationships between the products. Eventually they formulated the fact that products diminished as multipliers diminished. After this, $\frac{1}{2} \times 8$ was written below 1×8, and extrapolating from their observations of the behaviour of whole number multiplications, pupils were able to infer that the product would be half of eight. Next, $\frac{1}{4} \times 8$ and $\frac{1}{8} \times 8$ were added on to the column, and pupils were able to work out the products of *these*. In this way they discovered how to find the products of fractions and whole numbers.

Luchins and Luchins provide a further example of this sort. They show how children can be led to discover a generalised procedure for finding the areas of various figures. Dienes has based a structural system of teaching mathematics on this principle and has worked out in detail many applications of it.

FEEDBACK TO THE PUPIL

When faced with a problem, the pupil produces several provisional hypotheses. Unless he can ascertain their appropriateness his progress in solving the problem will be impeded. Likewise, in learning a problem-solving technique, the pupil will need to be fed back some information concerning its effectiveness in the solving of problems on which it has been tried. This information the pupil receives concerning the effectiveness of his efforts can be described as "feedback."

There is much experimentation to show that feedback is necessary in the learning of simple skills, but less to show its value in the development of problem-solving techniques. All the same, there is *indirect* experimental evidence of its value. Brownell, in the study mentioned in the previous section, showed that children become habituated to inefficient modes of problem-solving unless continually fed back with information as to their progress. The efficiency of teacher-guided conditions of learning is largely attributable to the opportunities it provides for feedback. This same factor probably accounts for the high quality of the solutions produced by groups in the experiment we considered earlier by Lorge and others; within a group, individuals can check and criticise one another's hypotheses.

Without immediate and informative feedback, children are likely to waste more time pursuing erroneous hypotheses, develop and learn faulty techniques, and, in the case of the multi-stage problems, to make at an earlier stage, errors that invalidate perhaps correctly-performed operations at a later stage.

There are various ways of increasing the immediacy of feedback: early marking of books, self-marking by pupils, development of quick approximation techniques so that pupils can tell at least the *order* of the correct answer, development of self-checking techniques, such as solving the problem in more than one way. One of the advantages of structural methods of teaching arithmetic like those of Dienes and Stern, is that when the sum does not "add up" the children know at once, for the blocks do not fit.

Holland, in discussing ways of teaching long division, suggests a way of making feedback more informative: eight common types of error are listed, and code letters standing for the type of error made are written by the teacher at the side of the pupil's examples in marking.

THREE ASPECTS OF TIMING

a. Intervals Between Learning Periods. The question of the maximally efficient length of intervals between learning periods is a classical one in the psychology of learning and has been studied extensively in connection with the learning of simple tasks. In a review of several studies in this area, Underwood hypothesised that periods of work on a problem should be close together at the beginning to facilitate discovery, but further apart during the later stages to facilitate fixation. However, attempts to test this hypothesis have produced no clear-cut evidence in favour of it. Probably the length of the rest periods required at the different stages in training on a problem depends on the nature of the problem and the ability of the problem-solver. If problem and solver are such that the problem is solved and explored in the first work period, then subsequent work periods will all be "fixation" rather than "discovery" periods.

b. Pacing. If the pupil determines for himself when he will proceed from one problem, or stage in a problem, to the next, his learning is described as "self-paced." If the point at which he proceeds is not determined by himself, his learning is described as "paced."

Although there is some limited evidence that paced learning of a technique can be more efficient than self-paced learning, it is usually held that for the learning of complicated techniques, self-pacing is the more effective method. Pacing has the advantages of forcing the learner to aim for speed of execution and to schedule his operations more deliberately. However, as we shall see in a later section, hurry in the learning of a technique, tends to discourage flexibility in its application. Again, pacing can lead to over-practice of the initial stages of the technique, and under-practice of the later stages.

Despite this, it is difficult for the teacher to avoid pacing the pupils: only by pacing can they all be taught the same thing at the same time. This class-pacing introduces a further difficulty—it cannot accommodate the variations in speed of learning that exist among members of the class.

If self-paced learning could take place, the pupil's progress would still need to be controlled by the teacher to a great extent, for the pupil could not always be expected to know automatically when he had practised one technique, or stage in a technique, sufficiently to proceed to the next.

We can conclude then, that the teacher needs to pace the pupil's learning to a certain extent, but, in doing so, should as far as possible take into account each individual's readiness to proceed.

c. Steps in Problem-Solving. So that his teaching could be in phase with the pupil's progress in developing a problem-solving technique, the teacher should bear in mind that the pupil might require different treatment at different points in his progress. We have touched on this point in the section on brainstorming. In *The Art of Thought,* Wallas suggested that creative thinking proceeds by four steps: preparation (in which relevant facts are investigated), incubation (in which the thinker may allow the problem to rest), illumination (a sudden insight into the solution), and verification (an evaluation of the solution). Evidence has been produced that some types of creative thinking do follow this pattern.

More recently, Johnson has maintained that only three stages can be distinguished: orientation to the problem,· production of relevant material ("search" and "free play" of thought) and evaluation of the solution. Others have offered other analyses of the stages by which problem-solving proceeds.

In view of the great variety of approaches to problems found by investigators who have examined individual differences in problem-solving patterns, it woud be unwise to accept any of these schemes as universal, but they do serve the purpose of showing that different types of intellectual operation might be needed at different points in the solution of a problem. Preparation of the problem and evaluation of the solution need to be carried out in a careful, analytical, critical frame of mind, whereas production of hypotheses requires enthusiasm, fluency, and a certain amount of abandon.

As pointed out in the section on "brainstorming," account should be taken of the differences between approaches required at different stages in the solution of a problem.

EXPLICIT TRAINING IN PROBLEM-SOLVING APPROACHES

There have been many reports of improvement at problem-solving following training in ways of approaching problems.

In some cases there has been success after previous practice of what might be called *abilities*, rather than *approaches*. The solution of many problems, of widely different varieties, depends on the mastering of abstract verbal relationships, and it has been shown that the ability to solve such problems can be improved by training in interpretation and discussion of the printed word, and in logical analysis.

There is some evidence that improvement in problem-solving can result from training in *general approach*. Glaser, for instance, found that of all the aspects of thinking he tried to train, an attitude of *thoughtfulness* was the most susceptible to improvement.

Advice on solving problems has often proved useful. Bloom and Broder compared the problem-solving behaviour of successful and unsuccessful students and devised a checklist which provided an approach to solving problems; they found that training on this checklist improved performance on new problems.

In addition to training in the techniques necessary for solving problems, it is often found necessary to *make explicit* the fact that these techniques can be transferred to other problems. It has often been found that a *readiness* to transfer learnt techniques, produced by instructions during training, makes all the difference to whether or not transfer later occurs.

As an example of the sort of explicit general advice that can help children to tackle problems, here is a routine suggested by Frandsen in "How Children Learn." He suggests that children should proceed, in solving arithmetical problems, by the following eight steps:

1. Determine what is wanted.
2. Find which of the given facts are relevant.
3. State in a single sentence what is wanted as a function of the data given.
4. Restate this in arithmetical language.
5. Try to recognise this statement as one of the standard operations used in arithmetic, and plan the solution.
6. Estimate an answer.
7. Make necessary computations.

8. Check the solution. (*a*) Does the answer approximate to the estimated answer? (*b*) Perform any possible arithmetical check.

Explicit training in abilities, attitudes, techniques and procedures appears to be beneficial, and its benefit appears to increase when its relevance to future problems is made clear to the pupil. But in addition to this, the teacher could well help the pupil to understand some of the *processes* at work in problem-solving. Part of the improvement that results from practice in problem-solving is due to increased insight into how best to *manage* one's self in preparing for, and engaging in this activity. There is no reason why this sort of insight should not be taught more directly to older pupils by giving them some sort of an understanding—even if only a rudimentary one—of the psychological laws governing their thinking. Not only in problem-solving, but in many other areas it should be possible to improve the pupil's learning and performance by direct instruction in how to analyse and to some extent manipulate one's own thinking.

THE EFFECT OF SET

Failure to solve a problem cannot always be attributed to lack of intelligence, knowledge or motivation. Often, the problem-solver fails because he is "barking up the wrong tree," or, in other words, has an inappropriate "set" that he cannot change.

Sometimes this inappropriate set has actually been implanted by the training the problem-solver has received. Having learnt to solve certain problems using a particular technique, he tries to use this technique on other, similar problems to which it is inappropriate. Many of the studies of this "method-set" have involved training the subject on a series of problems requiring the use of a certain technique, then testing him either on problems that permit but do not necessitate the use of a different technique, or on problems that cannot be solved without changing to a different technique; his disinclination or inability to change from an established technique to a more appropriate one is taken as a measure of what can be called "problem-solving rigidity."

Many factors in the learning situation have been found to contribute to the development of problem-solving rigidity. Naturally, these will interest the teacher, whose objective will be to teach problem-solving techniques in such a way as to minimise the likelihood of their being applied rigidly. Here are some determinants of rigidity:

a. Amount of training. Generally, it has been found that the set to use a particular technique rigidly, and despite its inappropriateness, increases with the amount of training on it. This is what one might expect: there are many situations in everyday life in which one becomes habituated to a certain way of doing things and as a result becomes less attentive and tends "mechanically," "automatically," "without thinking" to carry on in this way even when circumstances have changed.

There is some evidence, though, that this mechanisation increases with practice only up to a point. One investigation indicates that beyond this point mechanisation might even be reduced. Perhaps when a technique has become very familiar the subject begins to try out alternative approaches—or perhaps he gains enough insight into the principles underlying it to see the limitations of its applicability.

Since the effect of practice is by no means *always* to increase rigidity, and since practice is desirable for various reasons, we shall consider removing not practice but certain rigidity-producing conditions under which it can take place.

b. Distribution of Training. It is found that rigidity in application of a problem-solving technique is reduced when training in it is interspersed with rest periods.

c. Speed. Rigidity is reduced by enforcing a pause between the presentation of training problems and their solution, and increased by instructing the subject to hurry through the training problems. In order to speed, the subject has to reduce his attentiveness to problem-requirements and mechanise the technique as much as possible.

Teachers often encourage speed when training their pupils—it is often used as a criterion of success. It certainly *does* indicate a *sort* of mastery of a problem-solving technique, but conduces to mechanisation and thus reduces the pupil's ability to modify the technique when faced with a somewhat different problem situation. A more leisurely learning of the technique allows the pupil to explore more aspects of it and encourages him to retain a greater attentiveness to features of the problem relevant to its applicability.

d. School Atmosphere. Luchins, who was to a large degree responsible for the interest that has been taken in this aspect of problem-solving, noticed that children from permissive and active schools were less handicapped by the development of a rigid method-set than were children from schools with a more authoritarian atmosphere. Whatever the merits of authoritarian teaching, it does not seem to be the best sort of preparation for problem-solving in a variety of situations.

e. Anxiety. Subjects scoring high on the Taylor Manifest Anxiety scale have been found to be more rigid than others, and less able to shift from a set technique in response to new problem-requirements. Likewise normal subjects become more rigid when made to feel anxious or too ego-involved in the problem-solving activity. Thus, there are some sorts of motivation that are likely to reduce the pupil's flexibility. The teacher can avoid these by encouraging interest in the problem-solving activity for its own sake instead of relying upon extrinsic motives such as fear of failure or the wish to impress.

f. Similarity of Training Problems. It was concluded in a previous section that training on a variety of problems usually leads to greater transfer of the technique. There is experimental evidence that it also results in a reduction in rigidity of the application of the technique. Perhaps this is because such varied training sustains attentiveness or perhaps it is because it encourages the development of a variety of alternative sets. Whatever the reason, it seems advisable in training to embody the technique in as many different types of example as possible (bearing in mind the reservations made previously, of course).

g. It has been shown that exposure to unsolvable problems during training increases rigidity. This underlines the necessity, pointed out previously, for care in aligning difficulty of training problems with the pupil's ability and skill.

The set to use a particular problem-solving technique is not the only sort of set that can hamper the problem-solver. He may interpret the problem-requirements in a misleading way and be unable to abandon this interpretation for another. Again, he may have to abandon a set idea of the function of certain materials or techniques before he can see their relevance to the problem.

The teacher can go a long way towards countering these interfering sets by training the pupil to keep an open mind when faced with a problem, to look at it from as many different angles as possible, to explore it freely and avoid repeating approaches that have failed. It should be clear that the sort of frame of mind established in "brainstorming" is likely to reduce interference due to set.

Training Creativity

A great deal of teaching is aimed at getting children to make responses that conform to adult standards. In problem-solving, however, responses of an original sort are often needed, and the child often has to break away from taught patterns of behaviour in order to make them. In fact, as shown in the section before this, established patterns of behaviour often impede the production of an original solution.

Recently the possibility of training subjects to produce original responses has been investigated by Maltzman and others. They have worked on the assumption that obvious, commonplace responses will be "high in the response hierarchy" (uppermost in the mind) and that original, unusual responses will be "low in the response hierarchy" (at the back of the mind). They found that they could get subjects into the habit of producing responses "low in the response hierarchy" by requiring them to give repeatedly different associations to certain words. After training of this sort, subjects produced significantly more original associations to other words, and performed better on a test of originality.

This is only a beginning in the exploration of this important field, but it does suggest that pupils would benefit by being more often encouraged to give unusual, "off-beat" responses rather than those that are most likely to be in line with accepted adult standards.

CHARACTERISTICS OF THE PROBLEM-SOLVER

Characteristics of the problem-solver are much less amenable to control than are variables in training and the problem situation. However, it is important that the teacher should be alert to them, so that he can make appropriate allowances in his handling of other factors in this situation.

In this section, individual differences in approach will first be considered, and then differences in performance due to age, sex, ability and personality.

INDIVIDUAL DIFFERENCES IN APPROACH TO PROBLEMS

Any attempt to understand and control the process of problem-solving must make allowance for the great differences that obtain between different individuals' behaviour in the problem situation. After observing over 500 subjects working on a variety of mathematical problems, Buswell concluded that individual differences in approach were so great that no precise recipe could be given for successful problem-solving.

Different investigators have classified differences in approach in different ways. Durkin found that three main types of attack were used: (i) trial and error, (ii) insight, and (iii) gradual analysis of the problem. She believed that these were not qualitatively different from one another or mutually exclusive. She observed that subjects often switch from one to another during the course of solving a problem.

Guest found that three different types of thinking were distinguishable: (i) superficial, illogical, (ii) concrete-specific, (iii) analytic-deductive.

Again, Chant distinguished between *these* different types of problem solving activity: (i) interpretative behaviour based upon the solver's established associations; (ii) analytical behaviour, emphasising comparisons of the stimulus materials.

It appears then, that an individual's approach to the problem situation can vary along many different dimensions. Taking with this the fact that problems themselves also vary widely, it is not surprising that great care has to be taken in advocating particular problem-solving procedures.

AGE

Although there are many obvious differences between the child and the adult in problem-solving, the experimental evidence supports Anderson's claims that "from early childhood to adult life, essentially the same mechanisms of problem-solving are found."

Heidbreider and Hazlitt both found what they called reasoning in children less than three years of age, but the reasoning was confined to concrete, personal and immediate situations. Hazlitt attributed Piaget's emphasis of the difference between adult and childish thinking to an over-valuation of verbal expression as a measure of thinking, and an exaggerated view of the logicality of adult thought.

Studies aimed at ascertaining whether pre-school children show insightful problem-solving indicate that a great deal of trial and error takes place before the solution is obtained. This does not mean to say that pre-school children are *incapable* of insightful solution of problems. On the contrary, there is a great deal of evidence of insight at this age. When the problem is such that the child has in his repertoire ways of interpreting and attacking it, he is much less likely to resort to trial and error; even adults will proceed by trial and error when there are no leads as to how else to proceed. So, if one hopes for insightful problem-solving from young children, one must take care to present them with problems that are intelligible to them.

In an earlier section some of the advantages of concrete presentation were indicated. Whereas adults often find concrete presentation of a problem helpful, to children it is usually very *necessary*. Children have much less capacity for ideation and symbolic thought than adults, but can cope with quite difficult problems if these are embodied in concrete form and can be solved by manipulating not symbols, but objects.

Thus, although children undoubtedly have less problem-solving ability than adults, it is easy to over-estimate differences in other respects. Children do not *inevitably* tackle problems by trial and error, but, because they are unable to interpret a problem, because they have not been shown how to deal with certain sorts of problems, or because the process of systematically solving the problem requires powers of symbolic thought that they do not possess, they are often forced to resort to this strategy. By presenting them with problems in concrete form, and in such a way that the solutions can be reached by the manipulation of objects, teachers can encourage even the youngest of their pupils to engage in the goal-directed, insightful activity that leads to a much greater understanding and will provide a foundation for the sort of problem-solving they will need to do in later life.

SEX

Many sex differences have been reported in the area of problem-solving, but often the differences have been discovered in experiments that have been mainly concerned with some other aspect of this activity; consequently we have only a fragmentary account of how the sexes compare. In general, though, it can be said that males have been found to be superior to females.

In some studies a comparison between the two academic activities of acquiring information and solving problems has been made. Bedell, for instance, found little difference between boys' ability and girls' ability to acquire science information by reading a passage, but found that boys were significantly superior in solving a problem that required them to draw information from the passage. Likewise, Billings found that the sexes were equally able to acquire information in eight different academic fields but that men were significantly better at solving problems in these fields. These findings are very much in accordance with the sort of distribution of abilities that one expects to find in the classroom. Girls are usually expected to be bad at maths—a subject in which much problem-solving is required—and, if they are good at some branch of science it is expected that this branch will be botany or zoology, which involve less problem-solving than other branches. On the other hand, in subjects like geography, history, etc., that involve less problem-solving and more acquisition of information, one expects to find less difference between the sexes.

But not *all* investigations have demonstrated sex differences in problem-solving ability, and one study suggests such differences as have been demonstrated might well be attributed to differences in sex-role identification. It would be interesting to find out which ingredients of the problem-solving process are tied to which aspects of the sex-roles. Perhaps women could be brought up to be better problem-solvers without losing the more indispensable features of their femininity.

ABILITY

There is evidence that ability to solve problems of one sort accompanies ability to solve problems of other sorts. To account for this, a general reasoning ability has been postulated.

However, considering the complexity of the thought processes that can take place in problem-solving and the variety of possible problem-situations, it is not surprising that problem-solving ability has been found to be analysable into many different components.

Considerable progress has been made in the analysis of problem-solving ability by Guilford and his associates at the University of Southern California. They find that intellectual ability can be divided into memory factors and thinking factors. Thinking factors—which are those that are more involved in problem-solving—consist of three sorts:

a. Cognition factors. These have to do with becoming aware of things—seeing relations, classifying, etc. These are what are involved in *understanding* the problem.

b. Production factors. After the problem has been understood, something has to be done about it. Analogies have to be sought, hypotheses produced. At this stage such abilities as fluency and flexibility come into play.

c. Evaluation factors. The final stage in problem-solving is that in which judgement of the quality or suitability of the solution takes place. Such factors as the ability to make perceptual judgements and to see logical inconsistencies operate at this stage.

Each of these classes of factors can be divided into sub-classes according to the content of the thought process (whether symbolic or behavioural, for example) and its end product (whether in terms of relations or classes, for example).

Dozens of these factors have been identified, and we can assume that many different sorts of abilities operate in problem-solving.

This sort of analysis of ability could have an important relevance to education, for:

a. with a knowledge of the abilities involved the teacher could assess far more accurately his pupil's strong and weak points in problem-solving;

b. this done, the pupil could be given selective training to make good his deficiencies.

Oriented in this way to the essential abilities underlying problem-solving, teaching could be much more economically carried out.

PERSONALITY

Like most other kinds of endeavour, problem-solving style and ability are affected by the personality of the individual engaging in it, and some useful leads on how best to deal with a pupil's learning in this area are sometimes suggested by certain personality characteristics. Thus, an impulsive, active, heedless sort of pupil could be expected to do well at the productive stage in problem-solving but less well at the evaluative stage. The persistent could be expected to cope with more difficult problems, the self-confident should be able to tolerate more failures. Rigidity has been much studied as a personality trait, and one can conclude from these studies that the pupil who is respectful and amenable to discipline, and so in some ways ideal, might well be incapable of the flexibility of approach that is necessary in problem-solving. Again, the anxious pupil will probably strive hard and achieve some success in subjects in which acquisition of knowledge is of prior importance, but where originality of response is required, as in problem-solving, the inflexibility of his thought, or his inability to suspend judgement might well prove to be a severe handicap. Another trait that is likely to have an effect on problem-solving ability is individualism.

The individualist will often be much less handicapped by conventional preconceptions than will others, and is more likely to produce unusual hypotheses and to persist in their elaboration. Although not invariably, he will sometimes be a potentially valuable originator. Unfortunately he might be unable or disinclined to make the conforming-responses that are so often interpreted by the teacher as indications of ability.

"THE PROBLEM-SOLVING APPROACH"

The main part of this article has been concerned with ways of teaching problem-solving techniques. In this section we shall consider the possibilities of using problem-solving as a tool in teaching.

The use of "problems" in the teaching of mathematics and science is, of course, standard practice—although even in these subjects the sort of "problem-solving" that goes on in many classes is a degenerate form, involving the mechanical insightless manipulation of well-worn rules and facts. In other subjects, though, there is less often even a pretence at using the problem-solving approach. There have been several attempts to show that the teaching of many subjects can benefit from this approach.

Cook and Koeninger, for example, found that students using the problem-solving approach in college sociology courses gained as much factual knowledge as other students, and improved much more than others in "attitudinal tendencies" and critical thinking.

Not all researches have favoured this approach so decisively. Quillen and Hanna tried to compare the effectiveness of the chronological, the topical and the problems methods of teaching social studies to high school children. They found only small differences between the three methods. Although pupils using the problems method improved more than others in certain skills and attitudes, the chronological method resulted in the greatest gains in information, and, surprisingly, the greatest improvement in research techniques. The topical approach, incidentally, fared by far the worst.

In a carefully-planned study Kight and Mickelson compared the effect of problem- and subject-centred types of presentation upon learning on the one hand factual information, and on the other, rules of action. They experimented on the teaching of English, science and social studies. In English and science, pupils gained more factual information from problem-centred teaching, but not in social studies. In all subjects pupils learnt more rules of action from a problem-centred presentation. Kight and Mickelson make the following recommendations for users of the problem-solving approach:

(i) The problem should be clearly stated and analysed into its sub-problems.
(ii) As far as possible pupils should be made to see that the problems are their own personal problems.
(iii) *Doing* rather than *knowing* should be emphasised.
(iv) Rules of action necessary for the solution of the problem should be taught clearly and specifically.
(v) A rationale should be given for the rules of action taught.

To these recommendations could be aded several that could be drawn from the researches described earlier in this article.

In attempting to assess the value of this approach, one must take into account the fact that it involves many new skills of teaching and learning. It has been observed that gains in its use grow considerably after the teacher has had some years' experience with it, and probably the pupil takes some time to learn how to learn by it. Even so, much of the research on the problem-solving approach indicates that it is superior to traditional approaches in most ways. There is some doubt that it is the most efficient means of inculcating factual information, but merely to do this is less often the teacher's aim, nowadays.

SOME FINAL POINTS

ACHIEVEMENT AND PROCESS ORIENTATIONS

In the introduction to this article it was pointed out that the results of many of the studies examined would not be *directly* applicable to teaching. One reason for this has already been indicated: there are so many different kinds of problem, so many different kinds of problem-solver and so many different kinds of activity involved in solving problems that there are bound to be difficulties in generalising findings from one sort of problem-situation to another. There is another reason though: that the psychologist approaches problem-solving from a different point of view from the teacher. The psychologist is interested in the processes underlying problem-solving and selects for study those aspects of the activity that will enable him to understand it. The teacher, on the other hand, is primarily interested in getting his pupil to attain certain academic ends, and needs information on the best procedures for bringing about this attainment. Since the psychologist is thus *process*-oriented and the teacher *achievement*-oriented, it is not surprising that a certain amount of alignment is needed before the findings of one will be of use to the other.

An alignment from *one* direction has been attempted in this article: an attempt has been made to select findings on problem-solving that are relevant to teaching and to present them in categories that emphasise their implications for teaching procedure. But an alignment from the other direction could be made: teachers could acquaint themselves with the processes underlying problem-solving and become more *process*-oriented in their teaching. Two benefits might accrue from this:

a. With an understanding of the psychological processes involved the teacher would have some means other than that of trial and error by which he could select appropriate teaching procedures, and would be better able to diagnose and remedy faults in these procedures.

b. It can be held that the attainment of particular academic ends is only incidentally important to the development of fundamental abilities and skills that have a much more general usefulness; e.g., in the case of problem-solving, the ability to think logically, to criticise, to produce hypotheses, to abstract the essential features of a situation. If the teacher analysed the teaching situation in terms of these he could encourage their development with much more economy.

ACQUISITION AND APPLICATION ORIENTATIONS

The simplest way of ascertaining whether or not a pupil has learnt to make a response is to get him to try to reproduce it. Where this sort of testing is used, no great allowance needs to be made for differences between the form in which the response is learnt and that in which it is applied. However, where the test involves solving problems—and, as pointed out in the intro-duction, most tests *do* involve solving problems—the subject has, almost by definition, to do more than simply *reproduce* a learnt response: he might have to modify it, or re-interpret it so that its relevance to the problem be-comes clear, or completely re-organise his learnt responses to reproduce a new response. Thus, where learning takes place with a view to solving prob-lems, allowance must be made for the likelihood that the form in which the response will be applied will be different from that in which it is acquired. This sort of learning could be called *application*-oriented, to distinguish it from learning merely to reproduce—which could be described as *acquisition*-oriented. Most of the suggestions contained in this article have been on how to orientate the learning of problem-solving techniques to their eventual application.

IMPARTING SELF-GUIDING SKILLS TO THE PUPIL

The distinction between acquisition and application orientations is rele-vant to a point made earlier.

In the case of acquisition-oriented learning, the teacher is present to guide the pupil at the stage that is of most importance in this sort of learning: that at which the responses are acquired. But in the case of application-oriented learning there is an important stage in the process at which the pupil's activities are no longer guided by the teacher: that at which responses are *applied*. Thus, in the case of application-oriented learning, the pupil will have to learn how to guide his own activities. This is why, in this sort of learning, it is particularly important that the pupil should be equipped with some sort of understanding of the psychological laws that operate in the application situation. Given advice based on such factors as are dealt with in the third part of this article, the pupil will be placed in a much better posi-tion to apply his training in the solving of problems.

But we should not stop here. Not *all* of the value of teaching is that the pupil learns to make responses and in some cases learns how to apply them in new ways; part of its value is, to use Harlow's phrase, that the pupil "learns to learn." In the course of learning he picks up techniques of learn-ing that help him to learn in other situations. This very important part of the learning process could be supplemented by imparting to the pupil some sort of sophistication about the learning process. Thus, advice to the pupil him-self could also be derived from the fourth section in this article.

BIBLIOGRAPHY

ANDERSON, J. A., *Psychology of Development and Personal Adjustment*. New York: Holt, 1949.

BAYLES, E. E., "Experiments with Reflective Teaching." *Kansas Studies in Educa-tion*, Lawrence Univ. of Kansas, Vol. VI, No. 3, 1956.

BEDELL, R. C., "The Relationship between the Ability to Recall and the Ability to Infer in Specific Learning Situations." *Kirksville Mo. Bull. of the Northeast Missouri State Teachers College*, Vol. XXXIV, No. 9, 1934.

BROWNELL, W. A., "A Study of Learning in One Phase of Arithmetic." *J. Gen. Psych.*, Vol. XXIV.

————, "When is Arithemetic Meaningful?" *J. Educ. Res.*, Vol. XXXVIII, 1945.

BLOOM, B. S., & BRODER, L. J., *Problem Solving Processes of College Students.* Univ. Chicago Press, 1950.

BUSWELL, G. T., *Patterns of Thinking in Solving Problems.* Univ. Calif. Publ. Ed., No. 12, 1956.

COOK, L. A., and COOK, E., *A Sociological Approach to Education.* New York: McGraw-Hill, 1950.

CRAIG, R. C., "Directed Versus Independent Discovery of Established Relations." *J. of Ed. Psych.*, Vol. XLVII, No. 4, 1956.

DIENES, Z. P., "The Growth of Mathematical Concepts in Children Through Experience." *Ed. Res.*, Vol. II, No. 1, 1959.

DURKIN, H. E., "Trial and Error, Gradual Analyses, and Sudden Re-organisation: An Experimental Study of Problem Solving." *Arch. Psych.*, N.Y., Vol. XXX, No. 210, 1937.

FRANDSEN, A. N., *How Children Learn.* New York: McGraw-Hill, 1957.

GIBB, E. G., "Children's Thinking in the Process of Subtraction." *J. Exp. Education.* Vol. XXV, 1956.

GLASER, E. M., *An Experiment in the Development of Critical Thinking.* Teachers' College Contributions to Educ. No. 843, N.Y., Columbia Univ., 1941.

GROSS, R. E., and McDONALD, F. J., "The Problem Solving Approach." *Phi Delta Kappan*, Vol. XXXIX, No. 6, 1958.

GUEST, M. F., *Process and Product in Generalising.* Doctoral Thesis, Univ. California, 1953.

GUILFORD, J. P., "The Structure of the Intellect." *Psych. Bull.*, Vol. LIII, 1956.

HARLOW, H. F., "The Formation of Learning Sets." *Psych. Rev.*, Vol. LVI, 1949.

HAZLITT, V., "Children's Thinking." *Brit. J. Psych.*, Vol. XX, 1930.

HEIDBREIDER, E., "Problem Solving in Children and Adults." *J. Genet. Psych.*, Vol. XXV, 1938.

HILGARD, E. R., EDGREN, R. D., and IRVINE, R. P., "Errors in Transfer Following Learning with Understanding: Further Studies with Katona's Card-Trick Experiments." *J. Exp. Psych.*, Vol. XLVII, 1954.

KATONA, G., *Organising and Memorising.* New York: Col. Univ. Press, 1940.

KIGHT, S. S., and MICKELSON, J. M., "Problem v. Subject." *The Clearing House,* 1949.

KURTZ, K. H., and HOVLAND, C. I., "The Effect of Verbalisation During Observation of Stimulus Object upon Accuracy of Recognition and Recall." *J. Exp. Psych.*, Vol. XLV, 1953.

LONG, L., and WELCH, L., "Influences of Levels of Abstractness on Reasoning Ability." *J. Psych.*, Vol. XIII, 1942.

LORGE, I., TUCKMAN, J., AIKMAN, L., SPIEGEL, J., and MOSS, G., "Solutions by Teams and by Individuals to a Field Problem at Different Levels of Reality." *J. Ed. Psych.*, Vol. XLVI, 1955.

LUCHINS, A. S., "Mechanisation in Problem Solving." *Psych. Monogr.*, Vol. LIV, No. 6, 1942.

————, and LUCHINS, E. H., "A Structural Approach to the Teaching of the Concept of Area in Intuitive Geometry." *J. Educ. Res.*, Vol. LX, 1947.

MEADOW, A., and PARNES, S. J., "Evaluation of Training in Creative Problem Solving." *J. App. Psych.*, Vol. XLIII, No. 3, 1959.

MALTZMAN, I., "On the Training of Originality." *Psych. Rev.*, Vol. LXVII, 1960.

MAIER, N. R. F., *Frustration: the Study of Behaviour Without a Goal.* New York: McGraw-Hill, 1949.

MARQUART, D. I., "Group Problem Solving." *J. Soc. Psych.*, Vol. XLI, 1955.

MORRISETT, L., and HOVLAND, C. I., "A Comparison of the Three Varieties of Training in Human Problem Solving." *J. Exp. Psych.*, Vol. LVIII, No. 1, 1959.

MUMFORD, S. C., *Factors Involved in Problem Solving with Special Reference to the Problem of Insight.* Unpub. Doctoral Thesis, Univ. Lond., 1937.

OSBORN, A. F., *Applied Imagination.* New York: Scribner's, 1947.

QUILLEN, I. J., and HANNA, L., *Education for Social Competence.* Chicago: Scott Foresman, 1948.

SHAW, M. E., "A Comparison of Individuals and Small Groups in the Rational Solution of Complex Problems." *J. Exp. Psych.*, Vol. XLIV, 1932.

SWENSON, E., ANDERSON, G. L., and STACEY, C. L., *Learning Theory in School Situations.* Minneapolis: University of Minnesota Press, 1949.

THIELE, C. L., "Fostering Discovery with Children." *Arith. Teacher*, No. 1, 1954.

TAYLOR, D. W., and FAUST, W. L., "Twenty Questions: Efficiency in Problem Solving as a Function of Size of Group." *J. Exp. Psych.*, Vol. XLIV, 1952.

UPDEGRAFF, R., and KEISTER, M. E., *A Study of Children's Reactions to Failure and an Experimental Attempt to Modify Them.* Iowa Univ. Studies in Child Welfare, Iowa City, 13, No. 4, 1937.

VAN DE GEER, J. P., *A Psychological Study of Problem Solving.* Haarlem: Uitgeverij De Toorts, 1957.

WALLAS, G., *The Art of Thought.* New York: Harcourt, 1926.

6

Textbooks and Other Instructional Materials

In a day and country where all forms of materials are found in abundance, it is somewhat difficult to accept the notion that much of the curriculum in today's schools is to be found in the textbooks. The elementary-school mathematics textbook is probably the major, and only, source for developing mathematics instruction. It governs what is taught and how it shall be taught. It is understood that the only place a school's mathematics program can be found is in the textbooks adopted by that school. Essentially the schools' programs are controlled by the textbooks.

It is agreed that the textbooks perform a unique function, offering both possibilities and limitations. When the textbook is the only source, certain limitations seem to be in evidence. It cannot be assumed that textbooks do, indeed, provide logical and psychological *insights* at appropriate times. When a textbook is not capable of conveying certain ideas or attitudes, how are they to be included in the curriculum? For example, in a study of geometry, would it not be to the benefit of a group of children to develop a unit on logic? Can we agree that the programs of the schools are controlled by the textbooks in use? Do the books presume to be all-inclusive? What happens when a book has not been written for a particular group of children?

On the other hand, what are its possibilities? Is it possible for a teacher to extend and use the textbook as a center of course work? Can we utilize the logical developmental sequence to good advantage? Does the programed nature of the materials offer advantages to the children? The sequential nature of the content offers the teacher a program which she cannot have if she is not articulate with mathematics. Does the mathematics textbook serve as evidence of the developmental nature for children?

We speak frequently of enrichment. How can the textbook serve as enrichment material? What are the possibilities of supporting materials? What kinds of supporting materials might be used to enhance, extend, and enrich the mathematics program?

Selection and Evaluation of Learning Materials

Mildred A. Carlson and Rodney Tillman

Jon's head was bent low over a maze of crisscrossed strings out of which identifiable geometric shapes were emerging. In his engrossment he seemed unaware of the children at near-by tables equally interested in shapes developing from their efforts. Nor did he seem disturbed by the small group of children in the alcove who were discussing which shapes they had observed in their environment since yesterday and selecting corresponding shapes from a box of models. Four children near an improvised screen were viewing a filmstrip and listening to an accompanying tape, but this did not distract him. Nor was he aware of the children with the teacher who were folding and matching felt rectangular pieces; one child was recording their observations about parallel sides, diagonals and angles.

Jon's attentiveness to his activity was not by chance. When various learning resources are available to assist with development of ideas or concepts, to fit the styles of learning of individual children, and to involve the child dynamically in the process of learning, many experiences can be in motion in the classroom. They can be so personal that each child is totally involved.

Learning resources can provide experiences that range along a continuum from the most concrete and personal to substitutes for the real. One's total environment provides resources for *direct experiencing*. Direct but *structured experiencing*—handling and observing realia, manipulating concrete materials, experimenting with things or processes—plays a vital role in a dynamic learning situation.

Vicarious experiencing may stem from a variety of sensory stimuli. Learning opportunities are extended through audio materials—radio, recordings,

"Selection and Evaluation of Learning Materials," by Mildred A. Carlson and Rodney Tillman, *Childhood Education,* January 1967, pp. 267–270. Reprinted by permission of Mildred A. Carlson and Rodney Tillman and the Association for Childhood Education International, 3615 Wisconsin Avenue, N.W., Washington, D.C. Copyright © 1967 by the Association.

listening posts—and through visual aids—flat pictures, overhead projectuals, slides, filmstrips, films, television. Other visual aids, some of them three dimensional, make particular contributions to learning—charts, tables, diagrams, maps, globes and models. Printed materials are among the most common visual resources—textbooks, workbooks, trade books, reference materials, newspapers, magazines. Programed materials with their carefully sequenced learning increments, whether machine or textbook style, are a verbal variation.

Tools for *interpretive experiencing* are still another kind of resource—props for creative dramatics, tonal or rhythmic instruments, art media of many kinds. Ingenious teachers add numerous materials to their learning environment as they collect colorful remnants of wrappings, unusual shapes in boxes, materials of varied texture and composition. Items bound for wastebaskets challenge the creative teacher, becoming treasures rather than trash.

SCHOOL SYSTEM SELECTS

Because of this myriad of possibilities, a school system needs selective processes to make available to teachers an adequate and qualitative variety of learning materials. Opportunities for teachers to get acquainted with new or changing materials grow out of many professional experiences, such as seeing displays of educational materials, attending staff-development meetings and trying sample materials. Both exploratory use and participation in research projects provide teachers with data and opinions about materials. The most appropriate and effective ones are identified and publicized in basic approved lists (textbooks, library books, supplies, equipment).

In recent years free and inexpensive materials have improved in quality and become increasingly available. Most school systems have established policies and/or procedures for selecting such materials.

Specific criteria developed by professional organizations assist school systems with the selection process; for example, ACEI's tested and approved list of recommended materials for nursery, kindergarten and elementary school.* Specialists in different content fields frequently suggest learning materials to implement the programs they describe and list criteria for their selection. Several such sources of criteria aided one school system in the development of its own criteria to guide in the selection of mathematics textbooks:

Philosophy:
Is consistent with curriculum guidelines.
Encourages use of a guided discovery approach.

* *Equipment and Supplies* (Washington, D.C. 20016: Association for Childhood Education International, 1964).

Encourages development of understanding by moving from concrete experiences to abstractions.

Content:

Contains the suggested concepts.
Presents accurate mathematics.
Encourages understanding of the structure of mathematics.
Is consistent and accurate in use of appropriate vocabulary.
Makes provisions for individual differences; e.g., reteaching, reinforcement, review, enrichment.
Can be used flexibly with total class, sub-groups, individuals.

Physical Format:

Has functional illustrations.
Is attractive and appealing to children.
Has a usable index, glossary, table of contents.
Is a convenient size and has a durable construction.

Teacher Aids:

Provides background information for the teacher.
Suggests additional references as resources to teachers.
Provides specific helps for diagnosis and evaluation.
Suggests supplementary experiences.
Gives suggestions for constructing concrete teaching aids.

Supplemental:

Has workbooks to meet special needs of individual children.

TEACHER SELECTS

Each teacher has autonomy in selecting from lists of available materials those particular materials which are to be a part of his classroom environment. His selection has the potential to create a drab or exciting environment, to restrict or extend the learning opportunities provided for children.

The teacher has a continuing role in selecting instructional materials. His beliefs about children and how they learn are primary determinants of the materials he selects. His values regarding active involvement in learning, inquiry and discovery, critical and creative thinking influence his choices among available materials. Curriculum guidelines provide guidance for his initial selection of materials. Additional selections are refined as his sensitivity to strengths and needs of the class, subgroups and individuals increases. His knowledge of children's interests, achievement status and thought processes influences the types and levels of difficulty represented in the chosen materials.

Teachers' choices of learning materials should make it possible for children to

Learn through one or several senses, depending upon the individual's style of learning. Materials should provide visual, auditory and/or tactile stimuli.

Proceed at different rates of learning: be challenged yet find that success is possible. Materials should vary as to type, difficulty and comprehensiveness. Children should not have to conform to the rates of their peers.

Select either the best or several contributing sources of data, depending upon the purpose of the experience. Many materials varying as to type and difficulty should be available. Materials should extend and enrich prior experiences.

Respond in one's own unique way, whenever this is appropriate. Materials should allow for differing responses, for open rather than closed experiences. They should encourage personal interpretations or creations.

Demonstrate initiative and develop self-reliance. Materials should trigger new ideas; they should help children "learn how to learn."

CHILD SELECTS

A child expresses his personal commitment to learning as he selects from experiences arranged for him in his school environment. His learnings could be positive or negative; they could be in depth or just shallow "covering" of content. Easy access to and purposeful use of many kinds of learning materials should contribute to development of positive and valued learnings.

While the child's criteria are less clearly defined, his selections tend to be influenced by such factors as

1. Personal interests and purposes.
2. Available materials.
3. Feelings of comfortableness as materials are used.
4. Available time.
5. Perceptions of teacher's expectations.
6. Lead-on possibilities for personal future application.

CHALLENGE IN CHOICES

In recent years instructional materials have increased in quantity and variety, much of this stemming from the availability of federal funds. With the increase in variety has come additional teacher responsibility in the making of choices. The teacher is challenged constantly to choose materials that will

1. Provide open rather than closed experiences.
2. Encourage rather than stifle creativity.
3. Stimulate original rather than uniform responses.
4. Provide variety and balance rather than excessive use of a single material.
5. Establish personal rather than impersonal relationships.

Concern for progressive acquisition of skills and understandings has led to preparation of many materials with projected logical sequences of learning. Sometimes this logic happens to match the developmental pattern of a child; sometimes the next unit or lesson or page fits like a well-fitting shoe. But it is also possible that the preplanned sequences may be too brief for understanding in depth or too detailed and lengthy to maintain interest; they may be too verbally oriented for some children. Since learning continuity occurs within rather than outside of each child, the sensitive teacher arranges for experiences and materials appropriate for individual children in the development of particular skills or ideas. The sensitive teacher chooses an array of materials of many kinds and levels to avoid overdependence upon work sheets, workbooks and other programed materials.

Learning opportunities in every classroom are largely determined by the ways in which the teacher arranges time, space and materials. Dynamic teaching has as its goal those arrangements which promote positive interactions among people and things. Materials are significant in this setting.

The Role of the Textbook

Donovan A. Johnson and Gerald R. Rising

The mathematics textbook is a major factor in determining what mathematics topics are taught and how they are taught. A textbook has often dictated the scope, the sequence, and even the pace of the mathematics program. Thus, the textbook is a powerful means of determining whether the new mathematics is brought into the schools or whether the old is maintained. This is all in addition to its basic function as a learning tool in the classroom. Its importance increases when instruction is inadequate. However, the mathematics curriculum should not be determined by the text; rather, the text should be selected on the basis of prior curriculum decisions.

Since the mathematics textbook is such a powerful influence in the mathematics classroom, it may be an invaluable servant or an intolerable master—depending upon the intelligence with which it is handled. Too often, it is overused. The greater variety of new textbooks available and the continuing development of new school mathematics curricula means an increasingly frequent change of textbooks.

From *Guidelines for Teaching Mathematics* by Donovan A. Johnson and Gerald R. Rising. © 1967 by Wadsworth Publishing Company, Inc., Belmont, California. Reprinted by permission of the publisher.

The mathematics textbook has a unique role in the classroom. The reasons are:

1. Direct experience, visual aids and classroom instruction cannot provide all the instruction necessary. Some of this instruction must be covered by reference to a textbook.

2. Teachers have too many pupils, preparations, and extracurricular assignments to make it possible for them to plan and write complete units and daily lessons without the aid of a text.

3. Mathematics requires a sequential study treatment, and the textbook provides a useful aid to this approach.

4. For mathematics teachers with an inadequate background in mathematics and in the methods of teaching mathematics, the textbook is a substitute (*albeit a poor one*) for this inadequacy.

5. Many schools are limited in resources such as library books, concrete and visual learning aids, community resources, duplicating equipment; and so the text provides the basic and sometimes the only resource.

6. Learning mathematics depends on the mastery of concepts and skills. Students may gain this mastery by performing the exercises of the text.

7. Mathematics requires a storehouse of facts, theorems, formulas, and definitions to which reference can be frequently made. In this way, the mathematics text is as necessary as a dictionary or encyclopedia in English or social studies.

THE CONTRIBUTION OF A GOOD TEXTBOOK

The superior mathematics textbook offers the following aids to teaching and learning:

1. It provides most of the content for a course. As such, it should contain appropriate, mathematically correct topics presented in a readable and orderly fashion.

2. It presents topics in a manner that builds understanding of concepts, structure, problem solving, and computations. In other words, it is a tool to be used in attaining the objectives of the course.

3. It provides the exercises, the experiences, the directions for attaining mastery through practice, review, application, and thought-provoking questions.

4. It provides a means for independent study and, hence, is useful for assignments, make-up work, remedial instruction, and independent study.

5. It provides a means of making provision for individual differences. By giving assignments tailored to different ability, by providing suggested enrichment materials, by permitting independent acceleration, the textbook can be a source of satisfying, challenging experiences.

6. It provides a compact reference book which is useful in building the structure of mathematics. Tables, definitions, formulas, graphs, sample problems, theorems, and proofs are available to make problem solving efficient.

7. It provides a basis for achievement testing. Chapter tests, review tests, practice tests, and accompanying semester tests provide ready-made devices for evaluation of content mastery.

8. It brings directly to the student the exposition of the writer or writers, often major figures in mathematics and mathematics education or master teachers.

9. It forms the basis for classroom instruction, which may and should often fol-

low a different but essentially parallel development. In this way the student is offered various approaches to a single topic.

THE PROPER USE OF MATHEMATICS TEXTBOOKS

Too often the text is misused, overused, or, at the other extreme, ignored. In this latter connection, many school administrators sometimes believe that they are introducing a new program by adopting a new textbook—when actually the teaching remains unchanged and the text is misused or ignored.

The following suggestions are given for the proper use of a textbook for the typical mathematics class:

1. A selection of topics to be taught should be made from the text. Only in rare circumstances should the entire content of a text be presented in a single course. Textbook authors purposely include more content than necessary so as to give a teacher the possibility of selection.

2. A decision should be made as to what topics which are not in the text should be included in the course. Every textbook needs to be supplemented by up-to-date material from sources such as library books, pamphlets, and other texts.

3. The text should be used as a resource and reference book. Rather than repeating the examples of the text or reading the text to the class, the competent teacher uses different examples and different explanations.

4. The text is used by students as well as teachers as a source for questions, exercises, reading material, and reference material. Students are expected to read the text, to answer the questions thoughtfully, to work the exercises, and to find information. At the same time the text should suggest problems, topics, or exercises related to independent study and suggest further study in other source books.

5. The students should be given instruction in how to use the textbook—for example, where to find material, how to read the narrative, how to use chapter summaries and tests, how to review, and how to solve problems.

6. The narrative or exercises of the text should be assigned with the students' differing abilities and needs in mind. The low-ability student works a greater proportion of easy problems and reviews frequently. The high-ability student works fewer and more difficult exercises. The suggested enrichment material, outside reading, references, or projects are used according to the interests of the students.

7. The assignment of textbook exercises is done carefully. The purpose of each assignment should be to improve the understanding, accuracy, efficiency, and retention of the students. These purposes must be made clear to the student who should never think of homework as mere drudgery.

8. Answers to at least some exercises should be provided to students working exercises so that they can know what success they are having. Correct answers then reinforce correct methods while errors suggest further study of concepts and rechecking computation.

9. The textbook exposition is supplemented by instruction that provides discovery exercises, audio-visual illustrations, references, and local applications.

10. The textbook exercises also are supplemented with learning activities, reports, projects, games, and surveys.

11. The textbook tests are supplemented with other tests such as unit tests, reading tests, diagnostic tests, essay tests, performance tests, and open-book tests.

12. The resources of the text are used to enhance instruction. The projects, references, historical sidelights, and enrichment topics should be recognized to be of as great a significance as the explanations and exercises.

13. The references support teacher-requests for school purchases of additional library books and other supportive material. Additional textbooks provide the teacher with a valuable resource library to help him with planning and executing his program. They are a source of different strategies, discovery exercises, enrichment, and test items. Often texts are supplied by textbook companies as a service and in hopes of adoption. However, it is not ethical for the teacher to request "free" books purely for supplementary material. Whatever supplementary materials are needed should be purchased by the school.

WORKBOOKS AND LABORATORY MANUALS

Workbooks were very popular a generation ago. They provided the teacher with many drill exercises and saved him time in preparing material. They also saved the student time by eliminating the need to copy exercises. However, the workbooks' emphasis on rote manipulation at the expense of understanding caused them to be discarded.

Workbooks do, however, have many possible uses if they are of good quality and are used properly. Workbooks can contribute to instruction in the following ways:

1. Workbooks of different levels in a single class provide one way of meeting the problem of individual differences.

2. They permit individual work at varying rates.

3. Workbooks provide a varied testing program with progress ratings and keyed remedial exercises.

4. They supplement the textbook in building meaning as well as skills.

5. Workbooks often provide discovery activities for each student to complete. He can write his responses in specially provided places.

6. Workbooks have the advantage of being the student's own property. The student's own work is organized for him, providing him with a valuable tool for review.

7. Workbooks provide for independent work and orderliness in the overcrowded classroom.

8. They provide the teacher with duplicated material written by experts.

In the future workbook-type activities may be printed by computers. The computer would be programmed so that exercises could be tailored to previous student achievement.

Another type of workbook will probably be developed in the future. This is the laboratory manual. These manuals would provide discovery activities of the kind discussed in Chapter 22. For example, it would seem appropriate to approach the topic of probability by a series of experiments. These experiments would provide the intuitive, empirical experiences to which formulas, definitions, and abstractions would later make reference.

PROGRAMMED TEXTS

At the present time an entirely new type of textbook is provided by the programmed text. A programmed textbook is a book designed in such a way that it guides the student by a series of short steps to understand the material being presented. These short steps are in the form of brief expository statements and questions, to which the reader responds by writing the answers in spaces provided. The reader checks his answers against those supplied by the book (often hidden by a slide or presented on the following page). The questions provide the learner with immediate knowledge of his progress. In some programs, called branching programs, incorrect answers may direct the learner to remedial work, but the most important function of the question-and-answer process is the deeper involvement of the reader in the learning activity. He is virtually forced by the questions to share responsibility for learning.

These texts are being advocated because they require each student to react to each question. In this way he is "led" to discover a generalization. In addition, answers are given to each question or problem so that correct answers are reinforced and errors are corrected.

Programmed texts also are advocated because they permit independent study at whatever rate the individual wishes to establish. This seems an ideal way of providing for individual differences. The slow learner progresses at a rate appropriate to him, and the talented can be accelerated. Also, the text might be used by a student to make up work missed during an absence or for remedial instruction by the student having difficulty.

High hopes were held for these programmed texts when they were first developed. However, research on their effectiveness has shown that these texts have some negative effects. It is much too monotonous for students, especially slow learners, to work independently day after day writing answers to questions. To the superior student, the questions seem trivial and time consuming. To the slow learner, the reading is difficult and his motivation wanes. In addition, the mathematics of the early programmed texts was out of date.

This unsatisfactory experience with programmed texts does not mean that they are not useful. Rather, it means that new ways of using these texts must be devised. The texts themselves need improvement in content and format. Attempts are being made to correct these faults. Classroom discussion, experimentation, and group activities need to be combined with programmed texts. Perhaps their major role is to supplement instruction by presenting remedial work or enrichment topics. Another possible use is as a text for correspondence lessons or television courses.

As is true for all instructional aids, programmed texts do not replace the teacher. Instead they supply a new teaching tool to be used to improve instruction.

THE DANGERS OF "TEXTBOOK TEACHING"

Many teachers are strictly textbook teachers, more concerned to "cover" the text than to "uncover" ideas. Their focus is on the text rather than on the learner. Some of the following results have been noted:

1. The mathematics textbook becomes the mathematics curriculum. To bring the curriculum up to date merely means the adoption of a text with a recent copyright date.

2. The content of the text becomes the total content of the course, with rate and sequence rigidly prescribed. Some teachers even divide the number of pages of their text by the number of school days in the year to get the daily average rate. Confining the class content to that indicated by the text gives students a limited experience and increases the danger of poor attitudes and little appreciation of the elegance of mathematics.

3. The tendency of textbooks to emphasize given rules and procedures defeats the possibilities for discovery, independent thought, and intellectual curiosity. Even where discovery questions are included, the answers usually appear on the next page and students find it easier to look ahead than to discover the concept.

4. Student memorization of the language of the text and stated definitions and rules does not nourish skill in communication or the development of understanding. Students need experiences in stating generalizations in their own words even though these may lack precision.

5. The constant use of the textbook kills interest by its monotonous, formal treatment. Learning needs a variety of meaningful, interesting experiences.

6. The blind regimentation of textbook teaching loses the slow learner and bores the rapid learner. It is a discouraging experience to see teachers using the same text examples and exercises for all students in a given class.

7. The narrow emphasis on the text ignores the importance of objectives such as attitudes, problem solving, creativity, appreciations, or values. These are the objectives which seem of greatest importance today. They are seldom attained and rarely tested by the textbook teacher.

From this discussion, it is apparent that "textbook teaching" is highly unsatisfactory. Dependence on the text and only the text is one mark of an unsuccessful teacher.

THE QUALITIES OF A GOOD MATHEMATICS TEXTBOOK

If a mathematics textbook is to serve its proper function, it must be a good text. It needs qualities such as the following:

1. *Topics:*

   a. The topics are those that will attain the objectives of the course.

   b. The topics allow selection to fit the sequence: building on the previous course and foreshadowing the course to follow.

   c. The topics are appropriate in terms of interest, difficulty, and usefulness to the students electing the course.

   d. The topics are in harmony with current curriculum emphasis.

2. *Mathematics:*

   a. The mathematics is correct.

   b. The structure of each topic is clear and concise.

   c. The level of the rigor and precision is appropriate for the course.

   d. The use of symbols is correct but reasonable, accurate, and not overly cumbersome.

3. *Language:*

   a. The narrative is readable and comprehensible.

   b. The abstractions and symbols are made meaningful.

   c. The language is interesting and thought-provoking.

   d. The definitions and explanations use only those terms which the student can be expected to understand.

4. *Pedagogy:*

   a. Material is included to create interest and motivate learning.

   b. Terminology and content is justified in terms the students understand so that they can see how it relates to them.

   c. Material is included to make it possible to meet the needs of different levels of ability.

   d. The strategies used are based on sound learning principles.

   e. Concepts are introduced by providing opportunity for the student to discover ideas through reflective thinking, problem solving, experimentation, analysis, and generalization.

   f. Tests for the evaluation of achievement by student and teacher are included.

5. *Mastery:*

   a. Exercises emphasize reflective thinking and problem solving rather than manipulation.

   b. Adequate exercises of different difficulty levels are included.

   c. Review and remedial materials are included.

   d. Some exercises require the student to generalize, others to consolidate concepts, and still others to improve skills or to apply what is learned to new situations.

6. *Enrichment:*

   a. Enrichment topics are included in the text.

   b. Suggestions are given for independent study.

   c. Research topics, projects, and independent experiments are suggested.

   d. References for enrichment reading are included.

7. *Aids to Learning:*

   a. A teacher's manual with suggestions for teaching.

   b. An answer key with worked solutions.

   c. Achievement tests.

   d. Overhead projectuals.

   e. Accompanying workbook, laboratory manual, or programmed text.

8. *Physical Characteristics:*
    a. The format of the pages is attractive and inviting.
    b. The arrangement, headings, and type make the location of material convenient.
    c. The use of color and illustrations is functional in terms of text content.
    d. The size of the book is convenient.

The qualities listed above may be made into a checklist format and form the basis for the selection of a text. If each item is rated on a scale such as "inadequate," "satisfactory," or "excellent," information will be provided for the comparison of different texts. Each item should not be counted as equal in importance, and it is the responsibility of the teacher making the selection to determine the value of each attribute.

SELECTION OF A MATHEMATICS TEXTBOOK

Selection is not easy and should be done, ideally, by a group rather than an individual. The selection of a text should be only a part of an over-all curriculum study. Such a study should involve activities such as these:

1. The group which is to select a text should consist of teachers who are to use the text, teachers of a previous grade, teachers of a following course, a mathematician, and a curriculum coordinator.
2. The group should first decide what the contribution of mathematics is to their total educational program; that is, the text will be selected on the basis of the goals of the specific mathematics course involved.
3. They must be informed of the current trends in mathematics education. Only when the group understands the changes in school mathematics can they make an appropriate choice.
4. The text selected must be suited to the abilities and backgrounds of the students in the course. For a given grade, several texts should be selected according to the ability groupings for that grade.
5. The text selected must also be suited to the competencies of the teachers who will use the text. Often the text itself needs to be used for inservice training before it is used with students.
6. The committee members must be informed about all available texts. Then the criteria listed above should be applied to these texts.
7. The selection of a text for a specific course must be made with the program for the preceding course and the course to follow in mind. Criteria for the selection of a text series for several grades or courses are the same as for the selection of a single text.
8. If at all possible, several texts should be used on a trial basis. Only after a text is used can its strengths and weaknesses be accurately identified.

In making a textbook analysis, one will need to sample parts of the text for intensive study. Preferably, one should compare on the basis of the treatment of the same topics in each text. A checklist should be devised so that the different qualities of the texts may be compared. A value judgment will be the basis of the final choice.

Although a committee has been selected and has made its recommendations, the final decision and responsibility for a selection should probably be that of an administrator, preferably the mathematics supervisor or department head.

LEARNING EXERCISES

1. Compare a modern textbook with one of a generation ago. How do they differ?

2. Make a critical evaluation of a modern textbook in terms of the qualities listed in this chapter.

3. Observe a master teacher teach a lesson. What is the role of the textbook in his class?

4. Review a research study of the use of a programmed text.

5. Find a programmed text on a topic that is new to you. Use this text to study this topic. What are the strengths and weaknesses of this text?

6. Select a short topic. Write this topic in programmed format for independent study. Have a class learn this topic by the independent study of your program.

7. Why isn't a textbook the basis for a mathematics curriculum? What aspects of a curriculum are provided by a textbook? What aspects are not provided?

8. What material do you need for the mathematics course you are currently teaching that is not in your text? Where can you obtain this material?

9. Make a collection of definitions from different texts to illustrate differing levels of mathematical sophistication.

10. Suppose that you were to write a textbook for the mathematics course you are now teaching or studying, how would it be different from the text you are now using?

11. Select a textbook and determine a readability score for it.

12. Make an analysis of the enrichment material of a given text. How should this material be used? For what level of ability is it most appropriate? Why?

13. Compare a modern text and an old text in terms of the percent of space devoted to exercises, explanatory material, enrichment, reviews, and tests.

Mathematics in a Living Laboratory

Richard Mariani

When you were a youngster in school would you have given up a play period for a chance to stay indoors and do mathematics? The chances are you would not—unless you were extra fond of addition and subtraction.

Reprinted from *Grade Teacher* (May 1959), 94–95, by permission of the author.

Mathematics is not a subject which our youngsters choose in preference to baseball and other athletic activities, yet in our Elmwood Park schools the seventh and eighth-graders *Do Just That.* The reason?

It is because our classroom is a learning laboratory. In this laboratory the children engage in a wide variety of concrete, meaningful experiences in which numbers pay an essential role such as solving problems, carrying on discussions of uses in measuring things, constructing models, grouping and manipulating objects and discovering the meaning of numbers and of all the number operations.

The children work with manipulative materials and visual aids that will make number operations meaningful to them. These activities are conducted in such a way that the children will discover the answers for themselves. In this laboratory I direct the activities, ask the questions and lead the discussion, but the pupils discover facts, generalizations and relationships. Pupils are never called upon to memorize facts or practice operations that they do not understand. Undoubtedly the most valuable form of practice is the application of a principle or process in a variety of social situations such as a learning laboratory can provide.

Our boys and girls are doing such things as measuring exact-scale model cars and airplanes to determine the size of the real thing; measuring the thickness of an aluminum sheet with a micrometer; weighing water; using the pound, ounce and gram scales; measuring the height of the school's flagpole with a transit; using a map and the mapmeter to find distances of various places in the United States and to determine speed and cost of air travel; or determining the number of people that can be seated in our auditorium.

They look things over, experiment with them, and when they have examined them to their satisfaction, they say, "I see." They mean, of course, "I understand."

If, in the mathematics classroom, we ask boys and girls to absorb highly abstract information with few, if any, opportunities for observing or handling or constructing, they will lose interest in finding out about new things. And they will begin to have trouble learning facts. Adolescent boys and girls need rich, concrete experiences in order to understand and master such concepts as percentage, signed numbers, formulas or practical science problems in our world of today.

Following are some of the things that are done to objectify the topics taught in our up-to-date general mathematics course so that all will have a chance to like it and "get it."

Percentages. Use newspaper and magazine clippings that show the uses of percentage for a class project. Each student is to look for such materials as household budgets, allocations of funds by governmental departments, population distributions, tables and graphs showing dollar allocations for various purposes, changes in cost of living and wages, major or minor league baseball standings. Exploratory questions about these clippings will reveal how much the class already knows or does not know about percentages.

Employ actual objects showing percentages. Have students bring in such items as test papers with percentage scores, bills with percentage discounts, bankbooks, or lists of bank rules for payment of interest.

Cup, pint, quart, gallon and peck measures are used to help clarify the abstractions of percentage. Pour out a cup of water from a full quart jar. Ask the students why they know this cupful is 25% of the quart. (4 cups make a quart.) Ask, when they make this comparison, whether they are comparing two different things or comparing part of something with all of it. Point out that the water left in the quart jar is 3 times or 300% of the water in the cup. In this case they are not comparing all of something with part of it; they are comparing two things. Other questions might include, "Explain how you know that a pint of water is 50% of a quart of water." "How do you know that a quart is 200% of a pint?"

Formulas. Assign the finding of newspaper and magazine clippings for a bulletin board display of formulas as a class project at the opening of the unit. Such clippings will serve to show the function of formulas in today's world and might include such examples as the formula for splitting the atom and other scientific formulas. List formulas used in other school subjects such as science or shop, and in everyday uses, for instance, simple engineering formulas such as speed of light, train travel and jets.

Circular objects can be measured to determine the value of pi. Have the students measure the circumference and diameter of several circular objects such as a clockface, jar and plate bottoms, and then divide to find an approximate value of pi.

Drawings of one-inch squares can be cut up and rearranged into other designs to bring meaning to area. This activity helps boys and girls understand that the area of a plane figure is independent of its shape, and that square units can measure the area of any figure. We use many wooden figures of different shapes and thicknesses to find the volume and areas in square and cubic centimeters, inches, feet and yards. Our students make models showing various formulas at work such as the distances apart, altitude and speed of ships and aircraft.

Signed numbers and general mathematics. A bulletin board display may be made of pictures and news stories showing occupations and activities where a knowledge of mathematics is essential. Examples might include the work of astronomers, physicists, mathematicians, ballistics experts and engineers.

Graphs, tables and charts show the use of signed numbers and their meanings. Examples include heights and depths, weight changes, temperature changes and profits and losses. We display these to show that the plus and minus signs, when used in this way, show direction from a starting point.

Direct measurement. We have the most common measuring instruments in our mathematics laboratory such as scales, clinical thermometers, stopwatch, sewing tape measures, steel tape measures used by surveyors, calipers, vernier caliper, r.p.m. meter, mapmeter, thousandths gauge.

We use the ruler with inches and centimeters marked on it. We have the students measure as many things as possible in our classroom, using both kinds of measurement.

Metric measurements. We use the meter stick and other instruments showing liter measure and kilogram weight, to give our students experience in using these measurements so that they can become familiar with the common English-metric equivalents through actual practice. (They use our ounce, gram and pound scales.)

Vocational measurements. Our students find and bring in examples of measures such as the board foot, the fluid ounce, a liquid quart and a dry quart. Discussion brings out the important part measures play in our everyday vocation.

Angle measurements. With the compass, protractor and transit our students measure the height of buildings, flagpole and trees with the clinometer and transit. They work out problems such as the area of the schoolgrounds, walls, window area and others. We use mapmeters and roadmaps. Our students pick out a certain town or state and follow the route with the mapmeter as it records the distance. The students then multiply the scale of the map by the reading on it and this gives the distance traveled.

Indirect measurement. Pictures, tables and charts that illuustrate heights, depths and distances that cannot be measured by ordinary direct means are used to show the need for knowing how to make indirect measurements. We make a list of things in the immediate vicinity which the class can measure by indirect methods and then give students the opportunity to get outdoors and try out the shadow and sighting methods.

Congruent and similar figures. We display to the class examples of congruent things such as shop parts, screws, wheels and many other parts used in our machine age. We also use dishes, forks, glasses, buttons. We suggest that they watch displays in store windows for other examples to share with the class.

Class observation of surveying. We let the students discover uses of the tangent ratio in any surveying project that may be carried on nearby.

Mathematics in the business world. We study rates of railroads, air express and parcel post. (If the tables in our textbook are out of date because of recent changes, I appoint a committee to get information on the latest rates from transportation officers and report to the class.) Then we let the class make up problems involving local rates to nearby localities. We also appoint a committee to find out about rates for other transportation methods such as air parcel post, which may not be covered by our text or another text.

Wholesale and retail prices. A committee is appointed to find out wholesale prices of various commodities. Then the class attempts to determine reasonable retail prices. They must remember that overhead and other things are to be taken into consideration before they can quote a reasonable sales price.

Insurance policies. Students examine various types of policies such as automobile theft, fire and life. In the case of fire insurance, we have a committee find out the rates for the local community and how they vary from other nearby communities.

Mathematics of finance—banking. Students study actual passbooks, deposit slips, banknotes, statements and checks. We have them make out blank checks. We have them examine all types of bank papers and contracts and we discuss the rules that are involved in banking and savings.

When mathematics is taught in a laboratory and closely related to life, there is no reason why every student cannot make a good start in understanding this science, liking it and applying it in his own living.

Cuisenaire Materials in Elementary Math

William M. Alexander and Nicholas J. Vigilante

The Cuisenaire-Gattegno materials, more commonly recognized as the Cuisenaire rods, are a vivid example of materials capable of generating interest, knowledge and dialogue in mathematics—teaching materials in keeping with the modern mathematics curriculum. The Cuisenaire Company of America, Inc., 235 East 50th Street, New York City, produces the rods along with booklets for teachers, materials for children, a newsletter and films.

The Cuisenaire-Gattegno materials consist of a set of 291 wooden rods varying in color and length, used to demonstrate number relationships. The colored rods are one centimeter square in cross section and vary in length from one to ten centimeters. The rods consist of five color families. The red family represents the quantities in terms of unity 2, 4, 8, the blue-green family (3, 6, 9), the yellow family (5, 10), the black rod (7), and the white cube (1).

Since the rods are not affixed with numerals, children who have not yet developed an adequate number background use the materials to explore logic as well as relationships between quantities. For example, which is longer? Yellow and white, or purple and red? Or in comparing the white cube with the red rod, the child notices that two white cubes are as long as one red or three white cubes are as long as one green.

Reprinted from *Education News* (January 8, 1968), 17, by permission of the publisher.

Children possessing basic number awareness work with the rods in terms of principles identified with particular number operations. For example, what are the facts of six (one dark green rod)? Six white cubes (1) equal one dark green (6, 1); three red (2) equal a dark green (3, 2); two light green (3) equal a dark green (2, 3).

The four booklets that accompany the set of rods treat such topics as cardinality, ordinality, factors, equivalence, permutations, transformations, complements, various forms of measurement, inequalities, proportions, basic whole numbers and rational number operations, number properties, and so forth. While the booklets are concerned with various aspects of basic mathematics, they can, by no means, be considered as a complete program.

The program develops a strong understanding of the number system but lacks in social application. It therefore is desirable for teachers to continue to emphasize social applications when working with the Cuisenaire-Gattegno materials. More than the accompanying booklets are necessary if teachers are to use the rods effectively. Again, merely having the new materials available does not ensure success. In the hands of a teacher not familiar with the Cuisenaire-Gattegno philosophy, their use would, no doubt, be another one of the pedantic exercises we see too frequently in classrooms.

The Cuisenaire-Gattegno materials have been used with children possessing a varied range of abilities: deaf, mentally retarded, emotionally disturbed and gifted. One teacher adapted the rods for use with blind children marking the rods in Braille. Because of their simplicity and universal character, the rods are utilized in many countries around the world.

Researchers report obvious gains in knowledge and speed with the rods. However, the research, thus far, is not conclusive. It appears that wherever the rods were considered successful, there was a direct relationship to the fervor of the teacher who had been exposed to a training period. The Madison Project includes the Cuisenaire rods among their materials primarily because of the potential for discovery and their application as laboratory materials.

The Cuisenaire materials are compatible with the spirit of the modern mathematics movement, which allows a learner the freedom to choose a process of abstraction, one he can devise and which develops confidence through discovery. It appears that experience with the rods does provide the tactile and visual manipulations necessary to reinforce number awareness among children who cannot deal with abstract work.

One aspect of the Cuisenaire rods which garners little attention is their extremely important use as model builders. The effective teacher utilizes models to help her students think and recognize relationships. Much can be made for the case that strengthens the link between the thought processes of children and the reality of nature. The rods facilitate communication: verbal and nonverbal. As a child manipulates the rods, what cognitive factors are called into play?

The student paper-and-pencil materials that accompany the rods require the child to record certain number operations. One might ask if transfer really takes place? Might children have the facility to manipulate and not record? Are we to assume that when he physically manipulates the rods, he also possesses the necessary verbal and symbolic instruments?

On the other hand, how adequate are our present evaluative instruments for assessing cognitive development that results uniquely from use of the Cuisenaire rods? As the Peanuts Cartoon reads, "How can I do modern mathematics with an old math mind?"

The brightly colored rods seem to be easily lost by the children. Too frequently learning situations are stifled by a teacher concerned with "keeping track" of rods.

Used judiciously along with other models and approaches now available and carefully associated with a comprehensive mathematics program, the Cuisenaire-Gattegno materials do have a place in the modern mathematics curriculum as supplemental materials.

The necessary components for good teaching continue to be: a knowledge of the over-all content of mathematics in the elementary school; discriminate use of teaching materials; insight into how children learn; and a deep desire for teaching.

7

Research in Elementary School Mathematics

The aims of the researcher in mathematics education are quite clear. The researcher is seeking to isolate those forces which are acting on all of the considerations discussed in Section 2. He is isolating the forces which are shaping the changes related to content, how children learn, and affective teaching-learning strategies. In an era of rapid change, the researcher, and in some ways the theorist, seems to be emerging as the most influential force. He is reflecting the latest values and attitudes related to mathematics education and professional direction, alerting us to the wide spectrum of alternatives which we are to consider not only with respect to what is taught but also how it shall be taught and the organizational form it shall take.

What research has been done in mathematics education? What kinds of direction can we get from the study of mathematics education? What areas of research do you feel profitable to follow during the next few years? What are the voids? How can we draw on and make use of that body of research that has already been accumulated? What aspects do you consider viable areas for research in elementary school mathematics: the teacher, the content, the learner, instruction, instructional materials, the environment, or school organization?

Research in the years to come will undoubtedly increase in scope and improve in quality. This more sophisticated research will better assist in providing some of the more basic understandings on the structure of the discipline, children, teaching, materials, and other important considerations related to teaching and learning mathematics in the elementary school. What wise choices will be made?

Mathematics Curriculum: Needed Research

Thomas A. Romberg and M. Vere DeVault

The purpose of this paper is to identify needed research in mathematics curriculum. To achieve this purpose, the task is undertaken in two parts. The first is to identify the components which influence mathematics curriculum and to present a model showing how these components are related. The second is to organize a discussion of needed research in terms of the model. Any effort to discuss needed research in mathematics curriculum must begin with a clarification of the meaning of the term curriculum. A variety of definitions have been useful to curiculum specialists (Goodlad, 1960). Generally, these may be classified as 1) those which focus essentially on the content to be taught, and 2) those which consider the major interacting forces which influence classroom learning.

Three points of view are commonly found in the first group of definitions, all of which deal somewhat statically with the concerns of content. The simplest definition holds that curriculum is defined entirely by its scope. A good example is a description of a course in a college catalogue. Another popular definition of curriculum specifies, in addition to the scope, the sequence or order in which the content is to be taught. Textbooks and the usual school curriculum guides are examples of the use of the term in this manner. Finally, the most inclusive definition of this type requires a statement of behavioral objectives to be given in conjunction with scope and sequence. In this view, curriculum is a carefully detailed set of behavioral objectives which orders the content to be covered in a hierarchical network. Noticeably absent from these content-centered definitions are the components of the classroom social setting: the tactics of instruction, the role of the teacher, and the nature of the learner.

The second category of definitions places emphasis not only on the content to be taught but also is concerned with the context of learning in the classroom. The term curriculum is used in this sense to mean "the organization and sequence of a subject matter in which statements about that subject, methods of teaching, and the activities of the learners are carefully interrelated to form a single entity." (Shulman and Keislar, 1966) This is usually called a systems approach to curriculum in which the planning for both what is to be done and how it is to be done are specified. The key to this conceptualization of curriculum is that the components which interact in the classroom with content and objects are included. In this interacting sense, curriculum may be considered either to be the plans for the interaction or the actual experiences of learners in the process of interacting.

Reprinted from *Journal of Research and Development in Education,* Vol. 1, No. 1 (Fall 1967), 95–112, by permission of the College of Education, University of Georgia.

Of the two sets of definitions, those which focus on content, and those which focus on the interaction of content with other components in the classroom, it is the latter which gives direction to the development of the model presented in this paper. Research which effectively investigates the nature of learners' mathematics experiences must give appropriate consideration to a variety of aspects within each of four elements: 1) mathematics, 2) learners, 3) teachers, and 4) instruction.

Mathematical Curriculum Research Model

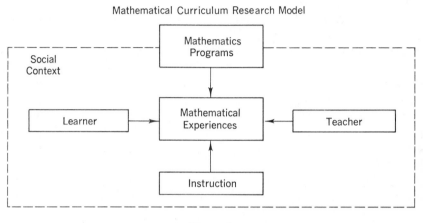

Figure 1

MATHEMATICS CURRICULUM: A RESEARCH MODEL

Ralph Tyler, who has been long interested in curriculum theory, defines theories in the behavioral sciences as conceptualizations revealing relationships, structures and processes which characterize complex situations. (Tyler, 1960) In this spirit, we now turn to the development of a model which organizes the components identified above into a unified structure which can serve as a guide to examine processes. Figure 1 graphically portrays such a model.

MATHEMATICS PROGRAMS

Certainly one of the components which must be considered in any conceptualization of mathematics curriculum is the mathematics program. The program is detailed in terms of goals, content and behavioral objectives. Goals are the statements of intent which give direction and meaning to both choice of content and statements of behavioral objectives. They may include utilitarian goals, stated in terms of the importance of mathematics to the learner; or cultural goals, stated in terms of the importance of understanding the spirit of mathematics. Broudy (1967) has characterized utilitarian goals as vocational, citizenship and self-development. That is, mathematics is important to the learner because it is vocationally useful, it increases his ability to be a good citizen, and it aids in the development of his individuality. Buck (1965) listed six cultural goals for mathematics instruction. It is clear that he intends that the role and character of mathematics in our culture should be understood by the learner.

Content, of course, includes more than just a set of facts to be learned. Included are facts (assumptions, definitions, symbols, etc.), principles (associations between facts), conceptual schemata or structure (the organization of a set of facts and principles), skills (replicative performance with respect to a few selected principles, usually called algorithms), and methods (the ways in which mathematicians use facts, principles, conceptual schemata, and skills).

For behavioral objects, as Walbesser (1964) points out, the key requirement is that the objectives be denoted in terms of observable activities (action verbs). This implies that the general non-observable verbs used in stating goals (to know, to understand, to appreciate, etc.) must be translated into performance variables. From a research point of view, this translation of content into behavioral objectives is important since statements of observable performances give direction to the development of measuring instruments needed to evaluate learning.

A very large number of studies, both basic and applied, have resulted in products, guidelines, or hypotheses concerning the mathematics component of the model. Three representative examples are presented here as illustrations. The first is the task analysis procedure typified by the work of Gagné. This procedure provides evidence relative to the hierarchical sequencing of materials and thus provides a guide to the selection of variables and the creation of hypotheses concerning the system's content component. Examples of task analysis may be found in a number of studies done by Gagné and his associates (e.g. 1962, 1963, and Gagné and Paradise, 1961). While the construction of content hierarchies has been useful, further work needs to be undertaken to remove the important limitations which characterize the set of experiments reported to date. The value of attempting to build hierarchies is uncertain since the work reported so far deals only with rudimentary notions. To be sure, Gagné et al. are primarily interested in the psychology of learning and for such work this restriction may be only a tolerable technical consideration. The implication for mathematics curriculum research is much stronger, however. The classroom necessarily deals with complex concepts and it is the analysis and ordering of these which sets the challenge to curriculum researchers.

The Cambridge Conference Report (ESI, 1963) content outline is an example of another kind of effort which attempts to give direction to the development of the content component of the research model. The significant questions this report raises, from the standpoint of curriculum research, relate to the other components of the model as well as content. The conference participants have themselves recognized some of the questions and, indeed, have set in motion a number of activities seeking answers to them. Chiefly, the means of embodying advanced concepts in simple forms and the techniques of implementing such forms in successful instructional sequences remain to be found. The Cambridge Conference has gone on record in favor of a spiral curriculum sequence, which is the focus of the third illustration of activity in the content component of the systems model.

The spiral organization of content, ably characterized by Bruner (1963), has been proposed by many curriculum experts. However, the research literature concerning spiral organization of content is meager. Thus consistent evidence concerning the effectiveness of this kind of content sequencing is in short supply. The experience of the 1890's (Wilson, 1952), during which the spiral curriculum was very popular, led to a general abandonment of the practice in the early 1900's mainly on the grounds of its inefficiency. Certainly this suggests a source of research questions. A more recent example of a deliberate attempt to organize a spirally organized textbook is the calculus text of Moise (1966). It is to be hoped that other talented authors will contribute their efforts to exploring the potential of the spiral approach. However, the efficacy of the spiral organization is a fundamental question which should be explored by mathematics curriculum researchers.

LEARNER

The second system component, the learner variable, has been extensively researched and a vast fund of information, some of it useful to mathematics curriculum research, has been developed. The emerging picture of the learner gained from this work can be briefly summarized. The nature and quality of the mathematical experiences of learners in the classroom are influenced by both cognitive and affective behaviors. The cognitive behaviors of the learner are dependent upon his developmental level, his intellectual power, his learning style, and his past mathematical experience and learning. Affective behaviors are dependent upon personality, perceptions of self, and motivation. Any given mathematical experience is influenced by these cognitive and affective behaviors and learning which results from such experience is determined to a large extent by these behaviors.

Again, three examples have been selected for discussion which illustrate the usefulness of information about the learner to mathematics curriculum researchers. The studies by Suppes and his associates illustrate the attempt to dig deeper into the development of an adequate psychological theory of mathematics learning. (Suppes, 1967) For example, the Suppes and Groen (1967) study on counting models for performances on addition facts at first grade contributes to our knowledge of time requirements in mathematical learning and thus provides an example of specific hypotheses relative to that variable.

A second illustration from the studies of the psychology of motivation is typified by the work of Kagan. (1966) He has described the goals that motivate the child's learning in three broad classes. The first class is characterized by "a desire for nurturance, praise and recognition of significant others." The second is "the child's desire to increase his perceived similarity to a model who is (1) seen as commanding desirable resources (such as power, competence, affective) and (2) in possession of some attributes that are also shared by the child." And, "the third class of intrinsic motives involves the desire for competence and self-worth."

Learning styles have been the subject of considerable research pertinent to the learner element in the research model. The third illustration of significant research is chosen from this area. French (1963) found two distinct problem-solving styles for the solving of the same set of problems. One he characterized as spatial and the other as analytic. Dienes (1967) has also discovered distinct styles with respect to learning of operation.

Each of these illustrations not only represents standards of excellence in past research but suggests new directions for further work. Extending the point of application of Suppes' work will undoubtedly need to be done. The evidence uncovered by French, Dienes, and others on learning styles touches only the surface of this important large domain.

TEACHER

The third component in the model which influences the nature and quality of the curriculum is the teacher. The research literature reveals the teacher, too, is a complex set of cognitive and affective behaviors. In addition to his role in the selection and organization of instructional tasks, the teacher is a person having unique qualities which influence the characteristics of the mathematical experience of learners in the classroom. Thus, curriculum research related to the teacher component of the system looks appropriately at not only what the teacher does but also what the teacher is. The determination of what the teacher is requires, in turn, that research look at a teacher's professional background, his self-perceived role in the classroom, and his perception of the learner and learner's needs.

The teacher variable as it relates to mathematics has been the subject of less research than the other components of the research design. Nonetheless, the work of Ryans (1960) on the characteristics of teachers, of Dutton (1951) on teacher attitudes, and of Grossnickle (1951) and Orleans et al. (1952, 1954) which investigate the mathematics understanding of elementary teachers provide a source of information useful in the development of variables to consider in the teacher component of the design. A few are cited here.

Ryans' study, *Characteristics of Teachers*, dealt with teacher behavior patterns observed in the classroom, teacher characteristics, background and environmental variables, and observed pupil behaviors. The findings of this study and the methods used to characterize teachers illustrate concerns important to curriculum researchers. The three major patterns of teacher classroom behavior found in the study were:

Pattern X—warm, understanding, friendly versus aloof, egocentric, restricted teacher classroom behavior.
Pattern Y—responsible, businesslike, systematic versus evading, unplanned, slipshod teacher classroom behavior.
Pattern Z—stimulating, imaginative versus dull, routine teacher classroom behavior.

This suggests that studies might well be done matching teacher patterns with varying learner characteristics.

Dutton studied the attitudes toward arithmetic of 211 students in his undergraduate course for elementary school teachers. The study was designed "to guide students to define their attitudes toward arithmetic and to isolate, if possible, some of the factors causing them." The students were asked to identify their most important favorable attitudes and their most important unfavorable attitudes toward arithmetic. Seventy-four percent of all responses were unfavorable. Responses were carefully analyzed and tabulated. Sixty-five percent of the unfavorable responses were identified with seven statements: "Lack of understanding, teaching disassociated from life, pages of word problems, boring drill, peer teaching, lack of interest and peer motivation, and fear of making mistakes . . ." The investigator felt that the responses showed ". . . deep-seated highly emotionalized attitudes that have persisted from childhood and are prominent in the thinking of prospective teachers . . ." Among the favorable statements, 67 percent were accounted for in the four most frequently made responses: "Enjoyment of arithmetic because of proficiency in it, good teachers who explained the work and made it meaningful, appreciation of arithmetic as a vital subject in the curriculum, and enjoyment of advanced mathematics." It is evident that further curriculum research on the nature of causes of both favorable and unfavorable attitudes would be valuable.

INSTRUCTION

The fourth system component is instruction. Three aspects of instruction have received wide attention in the literature: instructional tasks, instructional materials, and the organizational context of instruction.

Instructional tasks are those things a teacher does to facilitate learning. These tasks include planning, teaching, assigning, diagnosing, and prescribing. Planning is that part of decision making concerned with content, sequence, and the selection of activities that is left to the teacher prior to and during the act of teaching. Teaching is the face-to-face confrontation of teachers and pupils, and is held to be the most important of the instructional tasks. Selection of assignments is an important part of planning, for here the teacher assists the learner in the next cycle of his mathematics inquiry. Diagnosing and remedial action are the ways in which teachers guide the learning process, reduce the risk of failure, and correspondingly increase the chance of success.

In addition to instructional tasks, the types of materials and the organizational context have been researched since they also influence the experiences of learners. Instructional materials may include textbooks, programmed texts, computer assisted instruction, multisensory media devices, etc. Organizational context is the setting in which the mathematical experiences are to take place, i.e., large class, small class, laboratory, study carrel, team teaching, flexible scheduling, and type of grouping.

Instructional variables have been under investigation by a wide variety of researchers in and out of the mathematics education community. One popular teaching strategy, called discovery teaching, is central in such programs as the University of Illinois Committee on School Mathematics (Beberman, 1964), and the Madison Project (Davis, 1964). The research on this topic and the implications have been recently discussed at a conference reported in *Learning by Discovery* (Shulman & Keislar, 1966). The importance of the concept of discovery to curriculum is widely recognized. Research relative to the concept, however, has not been very helpful because of lack of clarity in defining the units of behavior in the teaching act. Because the concept of discovery has been so important in mathematics education, further critical analyses of the process are valid sources of mathematics curriculum research.

In presenting new topics to learners, Ausubel and Fitzgerald's work (1962) suggests the effectiveness of using advanced organizers in instruction. This study has raised some interesting questions relative to the organization of learning experiences. They report that the learning of unfamiliar material is enhanced by using an antecedent organizer. The organizer in their study was a 550-word introductory passage which provided ideational anchorage. They conclude that when a new topic is first introduced, care should be taken to fit the new topic into a larger scheme, drawing on the learners' past knowledge and giving direction to future learning. Substantial problems remain to be investigated with regard to a theory to guide the building and to explain the function of organizers.

Programmed instruction has been the topic of countless studies in the past decade. The recent NEA *Teaching Machines and Programmed Learning, II: Data and Questions* (Glaser, 1965) lists over 1200 references on the topic. In many cases this research has direct relevance to experimental methodology for curricular research. In fact, Galanter (1959) has stated that programmed learning is "a theory of teaching." The dissection of the teaching act accomplished by introducing concepts like pacing, promoting, confirming, and reinforcing, is theory building and thus had direct implications to instructional strategies other than programming.

MULTI-ELEMENT CURRICULUM RESEARCH

System components which influence the kinds of experiences a learner has with mathematics have been presented as content, learner, teacher, and instruction. Research designed to investigate the effectiveness of mathematical experiences in the production of desired learning must consider the four components of the model in the selection of variables and experimental or statistical controls. If, for instance, some aspect of the mathematics program is to be an independent treatment variable, the characteristics of learners, the teacher and the instructional elements also need to be considered in the experimental design. Mathematics curriculum research most likely to produce useful results with relatively direct application to school situations is that which utilizes all four elements as independent or control variables (De Vault, 1966).

It is only recently that the efforts of researchers working within each of the elements have produced results which now make the interaction among elements worthy topics of detailed investigation. During the past decade we have witnessed a great outpouring of creative effort in the development of new mathematics content and ideas for our schools. Significant contributions concerning the nature of children's learning and of instructional strategies designed for the improvement of learning in the schools have been made by mathematicians, psychologists, and educators. Missing has been a comparable thrust in the area of mathematics curriculum research. The emphasis on mathematics curriculum research is coming after the new efforts in related areas, for it must be recognized that the successful use of the research model presented in this paper is dependent upon the quality of the ideas which make up the input for each of the components. Drawing upon the results of the creative developmental activity underway throughout the mathematics education community, however, we find ourselves currently in a fortuitous position for the identification of significant input for various kinds of curriculum research appropriate to the research model.

SOCIAL CONTEXT

In the mathematics curriculum research model, the social context within which schools function in the total community has been illustrated (Fig. 1) by the dashed boundary to indicate this set of uncontrollable variables which influence mathematical experience. In any curricular research, these variables act in a variety of ways to constrain classroom interaction and are not under control (Biddle, 1964). However, inasmuch as needed mathematics curriculum research must be undertaken in actual classrooms the influence of these variables must be acknowledged.

THE FUTURE ROLE OF MATHEMATICS CURRICULUM RESEARCH

There are at least three kinds of research which aptly illustrate the manner in which the model may be used. The first is evaluative research. Those who advocate new content, newly designed instructional materials, or particular instructional strategies need evidence of the effectiveness of their recommendations. Likewise, those responsible for the adoption and adaptation of these recommendations need evidence concerning the success in achieving expected outcomes as they might be observed and measured in schools. Useful evaluations can be made only when they are based on results dependent upon the context of the total learning environment. Only when evaluation takes place in such a context can those responsible for learning in our schools make judgments upon which they may have reasonable confidence. Cronbach (1964) and Scriven (1965) have made a useful distinction between formative and summative evaluations. Cronbach has pointed out the importance of making continuous evaluations throughout the development of any innovation which implies an ultimate direct application in the schools. The purpose of a formative evaluation procedure is to identify those aspects of a course where revision is necessary. This implies that every performance objective associated with the innovation is evaluated. It also implies that this evaluation is based on criterion behavior—"the determination of the characteristics of present performance or output in terms of specified standards." (Glaser & Klaus, 1961) Formative evaluation, done in the context of the model presented in this paper, makes it possible to observe and measure the effectiveness of aspects of the innovation as they are being developed. The measures can then be used in the alterations and adaptations which are usually made throughout the process of adopting a new program within a school system.

Summative evaluations, on the other hand, were suggested once alternative innovations have been completely developed and are ready for widespread use in the schools. Choice among alternative sets of material should not be left to preferences of those who would be swayed by the propaganda of the moment. Informed choices can be made only with the help of trustworthy evidence as to what each of the competing programs can accomplish in similar situations. Summative evaluations must include as criteria all the objectives of the competing materials, both common and unique. The outcome of such evaluation will be a set of comparisons between competing programs.

In spite of all the innovations in the development of new mathematics content for the schools, exemplary formative research efforts in mathematics are difficult to find at this time. Probably the best available example of formative research is associated with the AAAS Elementary Science: A Process Approach (Walbesser, 1964). As they have developed various units of study, efforts have been made to gather information about their effectiveness in the context of the school settings in which they are ultimately to be used. In addition to content variables, attention has been given the effectiveness of the materials with the variety of learner types, under the instruction of teachers with known science and mathematics understandings, using specified instructional methods.

A second kind of mathematics curriculum research is designed to investigate the relationship of various system components of the curriculum as they exist in practice. None of the variables manipulated as experimental treatments and data are usually gathered on a large number of variables in a large population. Two recent examples of this type of research are the SMSG National Longitudinal Study of Mathematical Abilities (Cahen, 1963) and the International Study of Achievement in Mathematics (Husen, 1967). Other standard examples include status studies, factor analytic studies, and survey investigations. The purpose of these studies is to provide information and insight into the nature of specific relationships between curriculum variables, thus making it possible to build tentative hypotheses which may be tested in more rigorously designed experiments. Unfortunately, these are too often undertaken hurriedly, with inadequate resources, with inadequate samples, and poorly designed data gathering instruments. The result has been a general degradation of research of this nature. Nonetheless, it must be recognized that much value can be derived from such studies when they are designed with care and with the expectation of providing information useful in the development of theories out of which hypotheses may be established.

The National Longitudinal Study of Mathematical Abilities exemplifies correlation techniques in mathematics curriculum research. Students have learned mathematics from a variety of textbooks including recently published modern texts and traditional texts published in the early fifties. Extensive data were collected about the other three elements of the mathematics curriculum research model. Regarding learner characteristics, information was obtained relative to mental abilities, attitudes, personality constructs, and mathematical experience. Teacher information included attitudes toward mathematics, education in general, and orientation toward scientific methods. The weakest link of this study, in terms of the research model, is the instructional variable. Although no information was gathered concerning the instructional methods used by the teachers, information relative to school organization and instruction and instructional materials used in instruction was obtained.

A third major purpose of mathematics curriculum research is to identify generalizations about the influence of the four system components on the mathematical experiences of learners. If evaluative studies can properly be called product-oriented, then research which attempts to identify generalizations about the learning of mathematics may be called theory-oriented.

MacDonald and Raths (1963) review the literature on curriculum research and indicate the need for theory-type research studies in mathematics curriculum which are "guided by the use of models, theories, and paradigms if hypotheses that can be related meaningfully to a body of knowledge are to be generated." Such research draws upon and utilizes the small amount of theory which already exists for the formation of researchable problems. In turn, such research should result in a fund of information which increasingly serves a wide variety of situations and becomes useful in the further development of mathematics curriculum theory.

Product-oriented, relational, and theory-oriented studies are essential mathematics curriculum enterprises. Implications drawn from any of these studies, unless they are well designed and carefully implemented, are difficult to support; and, indeed, add little to the expert opinions of teachers, supervisors, and curriculum directors.

Effective mathematics curriculum research which meets the requirements of the model increasingly is being discussed, designed and implemented. There are those who say that it cannot be done. They bemoan the lack of cooperation from supervisors, principals, and teachers in the schools. Some reject the idea of such extended research involvement on the part of schools because of parental objection. But there is also a real commitment developing among school personnel and patrons of the schools to the idea that research can assist in the clarification of the problems they face. Needed are improved approaches to research, approaches which make it possible for schools to depend upon the results of research as valid and reliable. Unfortunately, the typical study in which schools are asked to cooperate is irrelevant to their problems, inadequately designed, inappropriately implemented, and without any follow-up attempt designed to assist the schools in the utilization of the results of the study in the improvement of their own curriculum. Mathematics curriculum research should be designed to include a wide range of efforts extending from those which distil appropriate generalizations from a variety of research efforts to the dissemination of their findings in useful ways for schools. Few investigators have effectively selected generalizations and hypotheses from the wealth of research information which has been steadily accumulating within each of these components. There are notable exceptions.

A few studies within the last thirty years have been harbingers of mathematics curriculum research. Two of these studies were undertaken by Brownell and Moser (1949) and by Swenson (1949).

The Brownell-Moser study fits the Mathematics Curriculum Research Model as an experimental study using each of the four components either as treatment or control variables. The content of the program was varied as two different procedures for substraction were taught. These procedures were identified as the decomposition and the equal additions methods. Two instructional methods were employed; namely, the meaningful and the mechanical. The learner variable included measures on intelligence, mental age, and chronological age. The teacher variable (perhaps the least treated of the four components) included volunteers who taught the treatment of their preference. The dependent variable included measures of computational rate and accuracy.

The investigators at this early date observe that "The present investigation has shown the . . . necessity of taking into account many factors which condition the advantages of the two procedures. Among these factors are: age of pupils (or, better, amount and kinds of arithmetical backgrounds), methods of teaching and procedures, outcomes set in teaching the skill of borrowing. Hence the decision to teach D (decomposition) or EA (equal additions) must be relative, and must be made with due consideration for these factors." (Brownell & Moser, 1949)

The Swenson study is another example of a mathematics curriculum research study completed twenty years ago which represents the research model presented in this paper. Content of the program study in that study was limited to the 100 addition facts. The manner in which other aspects of the mathematics program were to be treated during the duration of the study was carefully delineated. The major experimental variable was instruction and included: 1) a generalization method in which children were encouraged to build up inter-relationships among addition facts; 2) a drill method in which children were told the facts presented via some authoritative source. Learners in the final analysis included 332 second graders whose fourteen (originally fifteen) classes were randomly assigned to treatments from stratified groups according to mean MA scores; sex and mental age were both taken into consideration in the data analysis. Teachers were assigned to specific methods with their classes and were given detailed assistance in the way of training for the experimental teaching. Dependent variables included measures of learning during the period of instruction, measures for transfer of training, and measures of retroactive inhibition. Analysis of covariance was used as the major statistical tool in 24 separate analyses (at a time several years prior to the development of computers).

NEEDED RESEARCH

The context in which research is to be accomplished determines to a large extent the quality of that research. Any discussion of needed research should consider the nature of general problems which confront those who would improve the quality of mathematics curriculum research. For example, the improvement of attitudes throughout the research community, the selection of relevant problems for research, and the need for theory out of which to build testable hypotheses are but a few of the general areas which must be considered if mathematics curriculum research is to make significant contributions.

RESEARCH ATTITUDE

If the research which is required is to be accomplished, positive attitudes among the education community need to be developed and encouraged. The relevance of research is not understood and appreciated by those responsible for the direction and improvement of school programs, or by teachers whose work should be based on research results and on whose cooperation many significant research studies depend. Among those who conduct research, there needs to be an improvement in attitude in the direction of fostering greater openness to alternative hypotheses. Only as these attitudes are improved concurrent with the improvement of mathematics curriculum research design efforts, can one expect an improvement in the expectations of teachers and curriculum directors whose responsibilities are directly related to the improvement of mathematics education in the schools.

PROCESS DESCRIPTION

Education is a process; to be useful, the components of curriculum need to be described in terms of behavioral processes. For example, research done on problem solving, or discovery teaching will result in more useful implications if problem solving and discovery teaching are described behaviorally. The analysis and translation of gross and often-times inadequately defined concepts into behavioral descriptions is essential in order to conduct effective mathematics curriculum research.

THEORY BUILDING

Perhaps the time has come when a series of major efforts in building mathematics curriculum theory could prove feasible. Theories relative to the sub-systems of the model as well as theories which relate aspects of these sub-systems or elements should prove to be rewarding enterprises. For instance, theories are needed which attempt to clarify the relationship between learning theory and the kind of specific goals or objectives to be achieved. Clarification is also needed concerning the relationship of the personality structure of learners and the kind of organizational setting in which instruction takes place. Theories in mathematics curriculum research cannot at this time be expected to be rigorous in the sense that the mathematician is accustomed to thinking of theory or even as psychologists theorize, but it does seem appropriate and essential that beginnings in such theorizing be undertaken.

Mathematical learning theory of the nature that Suppes (1967) and Scandura (1967) are currently proposing is needed. Certainly, theories regarding motivation are needed and although these theories have been developed in the psychological literature, they have not been translated into theories in mathematical curriculum contexts nor have they been utilized in mathematics curriculum research. Several people currently propose instructional theories (Davis, 1964; Bruner, 1966) but these need to be tested through the building of hypotheses for research in the mathematics curriculum context.

RESEARCH TEAMS

If mathematics curriculum research does, indeed, need to draw upon the four components of the research model described herein, it follows that much of the effective research in the area will need to be either team research or research which draws heavily on consultants, appropriately representing the four components of the design. Those interdisciplinary teams which include psychologists, mathematicians, mathematics educators, measurement and research specialists, and classroom teachers, as well as curriculum theorists may be expected to make the most significant contributions through well conceived theoretical positions and well designed and implemented research studies.

LONGITUDINAL STUDIES

Longitudinal and long-term studies in mathematics curriculum research are very much needed. Six weeks is seldom long enough to evaluate the effects of a mathematics curriculum research study. Needed are those studies which include instruction over a period of several months or over a period of several years. It seems unreasonable to expect that many studies of the type currently reported in the literature could have been extended both in terms of the experimental treatment and in terms of the measurement of the independent variables over a period of time without undue increase in efforts and funds. Such extension of time allows the investigation of questions concerning both the retention of learned behavior or the transfer of this behavior to later learning experiences.

RELEVANCE

Perhaps one of the major needs in mathematics curriculum research is improvement in the relevance of research hypotheses to current problems facing those responsible for building curricula for the schools. Many expressions have been made concerning the need to develop, to research, and to disseminate. Many of these expressions have alluded to dissemination as the weakest element of the research link. If this is the weakest link, it is likely due to the fact that the information ready for dissemination as a result of research is not directly related to the real concerns and problems as perceived by teachers and curriculum directors. Both the perceptions of those who work directly with children in school and the process of problem selection by researchers may be faulted on this point but if mathematics curriculum research is to contribute significantly to the improvement of learning in the schools, there must be an improvement in the congruence between the problems perceived by curriculum specialists and those perceived and selected for study by mathematics curriculum researchers.

ILLUSTRATIVE MATHEMATICS CURRICULUM RESEARCH

The problem of presenting examples of needed research confronts one with the choice of treating a number of plausible topics very briefly or giving more detailed attention to one or two illustrative examples. The latter alternative was chosen and two examples of mathematics curriculum research are presented. One is an evaluative study and the other an experimental proposal.

An Evaluative Proposal

In its broadest context, the problem under investigation in this first illustrative proposal is: How does one teach any content? With all the new content innovations during the past decade, very little research has been conducted which properly defines the role of instructional procedures relative to content. To be sure, the prophets have extolled the virtues of using computers, discovery teaching, programmed instruction, multi-media aids, individualized programs, flexible groupings, etc.; but rather than subscribe to any one tactic or set of materials, it seems most plausible that a proper educational design calls upon a tactic at a certain point in the sequence, for a certain period of time, following and preceding certain other tactics; and, no conclusion can be drawn about the tactic considered by itself (Cronbach, 1965).

For the illustrative project discussed here, the content to be worked with is the real numbers as taught in the primary grades. It is appropriate content for this study, in part, because there are a variety of types and a wide range of levels within the content to be taught; and, in part, because young children will react differentially to the various materials and tactics. Choosing appropriate materials and tactics to be used in any instructional unit is a difficult task. Gagné (1965) suggests that the type of learning implied by the content should influence the tactics of instruction. A procedure of trying to connect content with fundamental psychological learning elements will be followed in this study.

This project is presented in terms of the mathematics curriculum research model (Fig. 1). For purposes of this proposal (at least at the early stages of development) both the learner and the teacher are conceived as fixed. The mathematics goals are also considered as fixed, but the choice of content used to achieve these goals can vary. Primarily, materials and tactics or methods will be studied in this project.

The purpose of this project is to investigate systematically the instructional variables related to the teaching of mathematics content. To accomplish this objective, four sequential phases are envisoned: analysis, pilot examination, validation and development. How these are related is illustrated in Figure 2.

Steps in Developing an Instructional System

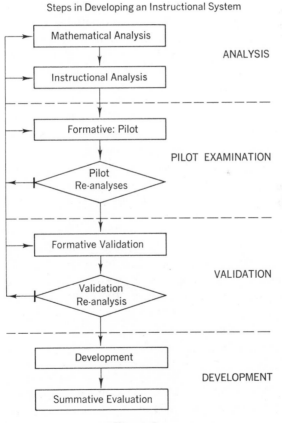

Figure 2

The first phase, analysis, begins with the mathematics program element of the research model. This implies that goals, content and behavioral objectives are chosen and detailed. In addition, the behavioral objectives are rewritten in terms of their more fundamental psychological learning elements (i.e., concept attainment, and rule learning).

This is followed by instructional analysis. It is here that attempts are made to conceptualize how best to teach each learning element. Variables from the other aspects of the research model are also considered: learner variables (age, sex, developmental level, mathematics history, etc.); teacher variables: stimulus variables (stimuli which maximize sensory and motor experiences, etc.); reinforcement variables, etc. From these considerations, materials and procedures will be chosen or created and put together into planned instructional units for each learning element.

The pilot examination phase follows the analysis phase and consists primarily of exploratory pilot research. It should be apparent that a number of planned units will probably not work as expected. Each procedure needs to be tried out with a few students in a normal classroom with their regular teacher. Formative evaluation procedures will be followed to assess the effectiveness of each procedure in accomplishing that which was intended.

The pilot re-analysis step is the decision point relative to the pilot research. If results are favorable, then one goes ahead; if unfavorable, then one recycles and starts over. Conceptually, this could be a never ending loop. It should be recognized that too often the demand for the production of a product forces premature release from the recycling process.

Assuming that a procedure has proven to be feasible in its pilot-tryout, the next phase is validation. The materials and methods need to be tried out in a variety of regular classrooms with other kinds of learners, other kinds of teachers and in different social contexts. Formative evaluation procedures will be used again to make decisions about the effectiveness of each procedure (validation re-analysis).

The development phase is the last phase. If training on fundamental psychological learning elements proves to be valid, then and only then will an instructional system be designed utilizing the materials and methods found to facilitate the learning of mathematics. Once a system has been developed it may then be compared with other systems via summative evaluation procedures.

An Experimental Proposal

Our second illustrative proposal is an experimental rather than an evaluative design. The well-entrenched concept of the elementary school teacher as a generalist has been challenged by recommendations and by some efforts to develop teachers with special competences for elementary schools. One problem immediately confronted by those who propose such specialization is the lack of patterns of school organization which optimally utilize such specialists. One of the most promising organizational proposals which has been rather widely adopted is team teaching. Unique competences of teachers are supposedly advantageously employed in team teaching through the appropriate use of grouping which employs the use of small group, class-size group, and large group instruction. It has frequently been said that the use of mathematics specialists in the context of team teaching could be particularly useful.

The major questions of such a study are centered in the interactions among the four components of the research design. The purpose of the study is to determine what kind of content is most effectively taught within what size group unit, by specialist or nonspecialist mathematics teachers, to what kinds of learners. Any question which is directed to a single element alone is likely to produce results in which the significant differences are covered up by the interaction with components of other elements. The unitary question, "What size group is most effective?" would likely end with results which say either, "The smaller the better," or "It makes no difference." Neither is a useful answer and it may be that neither answer tells the whole truth.

The content of mathematics program element in such a study might be divided into three major sets of objectives: those dealing with concept development (facts, principles, and structures), with skills, and with applications. Instruction directed toward each of the three sets of objectives would be among the three types of grouping within each of the instructional populations. It might be expected that the number of pupils in the small group would affect the outcome; and thus in each of the experimental schools, the size of the small groups would vary to include the following: 6, 9, 12, and 15; whereas the class-size group would contain 25–30 pupils; and the large group from 75–90.

The mathematics specialist and the regular elementary classroom teacher represent the two levels included in the teacher element. One might suggest that the teacher with the least mathematics understanding (assuming that the quality of teaching remains constant) would be most effective with the large group in contrast to his effectiveness with other groups. This suggestion is made on the assumption that careful planning for a large group presentation in which there are few questions to be answered spontaneously can protect the teacher from pupil questions which put him in areas in which his understanding is weak. The best use of the teacher with the best mathematics understanding might be in the small group, or in the class-size group instructional setting in which interaction with individual learners is more likely to occur.

Turning to learner characteristics, many variables seem worthy of research concern, but two should be specifically considered. First, is mathematics understanding. It might be hypothesized that the small seminar groups are of particular value for the learners at the extremes of the mathematics understanding continuum on the assumption that teaching to class-size groups and to large groups is usually directed to the middle of the achievement range. Personality characteristics might also be related to the effectiveness of group size and should be studied with correlation techniques.

Finally, the dependent variables need to be carefully identified. Certainly, achievement tests which measure concepts, skills and applications would be essential. Attitudes toward mathematics and independent approaches to the study of mathematics are among the variables which should be given consideration.

CONCLUSION

In summary, the position taken in this paper is that mathematics curriculum deals with the interaction process between the learner and mathematics; and that research revelant to this interaction must first take into account the forces which influence the interaction, and second, be conducted in realistic educational settings.

What we have attempted to do is to identiify major classes of variables which must be considered in terms of a model of mathematics curriculum research, to state some general needs if research is to be productive, and to illustrate the kind of studies which need to be done.

In conclusion, it must be noted that to conduct mathematics curriculum research as viewed here is no easy task. Subtle questions need to be posed and examined through elaborate and intricate research designs with patience and ingenuity. Rather than decry the difficulty of doing such research, the problems encountered should be a challenge to creative scholars. Mathematics curriculum research fills a particular need which must be met if we are to improve educational practice.

REFERENCES

AUSUBEL, DAVID P. and FITZGERALD, DONALD. Organizer, General Background, and Antecedent Learning Variables in Sequential Verbal Learning. *Journal of Educational Psychology*, XXXIII, 1962, p. 243–249.

BEBERMAN, MAX. An Emerging Program of Secondary School Mathematics. In R. W. Heath (Ed.), *New Curricula*, New York: Harper and Row, 1964, p. 9–32.

BIDDLE, BRUCE J. The Integration of Teacher Effectiveness Research. In B. J. Biddle and W. J. Ellena, (Eds.) *Contemporary Research on Teacher Effectiveness*. New York: Holt, Rinehart and Winston, Inc., 1964, p. 1–40.

BROUDY, HARRY S. *Education for 1985*. A position paper prepared for the Research and Development Center for Cognitive Learning at the University of Wisconsin, 1967. To be published as an occasional paper.

BROWNELL, WILLIAM A. and MOSER, HAROLD E. *Meaningful vs. Mechanical Learnings: A Study in Grade III Subtraction*. Duke University, Research Studies in Education, Number 8, Durham: Duke University Press, 1949.

BRUNNER, JEROME S. *The Process of Education*. New York: Vintage Books, 1963.

————. *Toward A Theory of Instruction*. Cambridge: Harvard University Press, 1966.

BUCK, R. CREIGTON. Goals for Mathematics Instruction. *The American Mathematical Monthly*, LXXII, 1965, p. 949–956.

CAHEN, LEONARD S. An Interim Report on the National Longitudinal Study of Mathematics Abilities. *The Mathematics Teacher*, LVIII, 1965, p. 522–526.

CRONBACH, LEE J. Evaluation for Course Improvement. In R. W. Heath, (Ed.), *New Curricula*, New York: Harper & Row, 1964, p. 231–248.

————. The Logic of Experiments on Discovery. In L. S. Shulman and E. R. Keislar, (Eds.), *Learning By Discovery*, Chicago: Rand McNally & Company, 1966, p. 76–92.

DAVIS, ROBERT B. The Madison Project's Approach to a Theory of Instruction. *Journal of Research in Science Teaching*, II, 1964, p. 146–162.

DEVAULT, M. VERE. What is Mathematics Curriculum Research? *The Arithmetic Teacher*, XIII, 1966, p. 636–639.

DIENES, ZELTAN P. Some Basic Processes Involved in Mathematics Learning. In J. M. Scandura (Ed.), *Research in Mathematics Education*. NCTM, 1967, p. 31.

DUTTON, WILLIAM H. Attitudes of Prospective Teachers Toward Arithmetic. *Elementary School Journal*, LII, 1951, p. 84–90.

EDUCATIONAL SERVICES, INCORPORATED. *Goals for School Mathematics*, Boston: Houghton Mifflin, 1963.

FRENCH, JOHN W. The Relationship of Problem-solving Styles to the Factor Composition of Tests. *Educational and Psychological Measurement*, XXV, 1965, p. 9–28.

GAGNÉ, ROBERT M. Learning and Proficiency in Mathematics. *The Mathematics Teacher*, LVI, 1963, p. 620–626.

————. The Acquisition of Knowledge. *Psychological Review*, LIX, 1962, p. 355–365.

————. *The Conditions of Learning*. New York: Holt, Rinehart and Winston, Inc., 1965.

———— and PARADISE, NOEL E. Abilities and Learning Sets in Knowledge Acquisition. *Psychological Monographs*. No. 518, 1961.

GALANTER, EUGENE. The Ideal Teacher. In E. Galanter, (Ed.), *Automatic Teaching: The State of the Art*, New York: John Wiley & Sons, Inc., 1969, p. 1–37.

GLASER, ROBERT, (Ed.) *Teaching Machines and Programmed Learning II*. Washington, D. C.: National Education Association, 1965.

GLASER, ROBERT and KLAUS, DAVID J. Proficiency Measurement: Assessing Human Performance. In R. M. Gagné, *Psychological Principles in System Development*. New York: Holt, Rinehart, and Winston, Inc., 1962, p. 419–474.

GOODLAD, JOHN I. The State of the Field. *Review of Educational Research*, 30: p. 185–198; June, 1960.

GROSSNICKLE, FOSTER E. The Training of Teachers in Arithmetic. In *The Teaching of Arithmetic*, 50th Yearbook, Part II, National Society for the Study of Education. University of Chicago, 1951, p. 203–231.

HUSEN, TORSTEN (Ed.) *International Study of Achievement in Mathematics; A Comparison of Twelve Countries*, (2 Vols.), New York: John Wiley and Sons, 1967.

KAGAN, JEROME. Motivational and Attitudinal Factors in Receptivity to Learning. In S. Bruner (Ed.), *Learning About Learning*, Cooperative Research Monograph, No. 15, 1966, p. 34–39.

KEISLAR, EVAN R., and SHULMAN, LEE S. The Problem of Discovery: Conference in Retrospect. In L. S. Shulman and E. R. Keislar, (Eds.), *Learning by Discovery*, Chicago: Rand McNally & Co., 1966, p. 181–199.

McDONALD, JAMES B., and RATHS, JAMES D. Curriculum Research: Problems, Techniques, and Prospects. *Review of Educational Research*. XXXIII, 1963, p. 322–329.

MOISE, EDWIN E. *Calculus*. Palo Alto, California: Addison-Wesley Publishing Company, Inc., 1966.

ORLEANS, JACOB S. *The Understanding of Arithmetic Processes and Concepts Possessed by Teachers of Arithmetic*, CCNY, 1952.

——— and JULIA L. SPERLING. Arithmetic Knowledge of Graduate Students. *Journal of Educational Research*, 48: p. 177–186; 1954.

RYANS, DAVID G. *Characteristics of Teachers*, Washington, D.C.: American Council on Education, 1960.

SCANDURA, JOSEPH M. Research in Mathematics Education—An Overview and Perspective. In J. M. Scandura (Ed.), *Research in Mathematics Education*, NCTM, 1967, p. 115–125.

SCRIVEN, MICHAEL. The Methodology of Evaluation. Mimeographed Report of the Social Science Education Consortium, February, 1965.

SHULMAN, LEE S. and KEISLAR, EVAN R., (Eds.). *Learning By Discovery*, Chicago: Rand McNally & Company, 1966.

SUPPES, PATRICK. The Case for Information-Oriented (Basic) Research in Mathematics Education. In J. M. Scandura (Ed.), *Research in Mathematics Education*, NCTM, 1967, p. 1–5.

——— and GROEN, GUY. Some Counting Models for First-Grade Performance Data on Simple Addition Facts. In J. M. Scandura (Ed.), *Research in Mathematics Education*, NCTM, 1967; p. 35–43.

SWENSON, ESTHER J. Organization and Generalization as Factors in Learning Transfer and Retroactive Inhibition. *Learning Theory in School Situations*. University of Minnesota Studies in Education, Minneapolis: University of Minnesota Press, 1949.

TYLER, RALPH W. The Contribution of the Behavioral Sciences to Educational Research. In F. W. Banghart (Ed.), *First Annual Symposium on Educational Research*, Bloomington, Indiana: Phi Delta Kappa, 1960, Chapter 4, p. 55–70.

WALBESSER, HENRY. An Evaluation Model and Its Application. AAAS Commission on Science Education. *Science—A Process Approach*, Document #65–9, 1964.

WILSON, GUY M. Arithmetic. In *Encyclopedia of Educational Research*, Revised Edition. New York: The Macmillan Co., p. 45, 1952.

Some Implications from Research in Arithmetic

Lorraine Sherer

We have no long-term studies in arithmetic research on the development of quantitative abilities of the same children, comparable to studies of other aspects of growth and development. Research in arithmetic consists mainly of brief, cross-sectional investigations, inventories, short experimental studies, and test samplings of children's concepts, interests, uses, and abilities. We need to assess what they mean viewed together.

In this article, an attempt is made to view arithmetical research in broad perspective and to single out some of the most important highlights. Implications have been drawn from four types of research: the development of concepts (2, 11, 19, 20, 21, 26, 31, 35); children's interests in arithmetic in their out-of-school activities (8, 25, 30, 32); children's uses of arithmetic in their school activities (9, 14, 29, 32, 36, 39); and children's quantitative abilities (1, 2, 3, 4, 5, 6, 7, 12, 13, 21, 22, 23, 26, 27, 28, 31, 33, 34, 42, 43).

Two groups of closely related studies are analyzed; one on children's interests in arithmetic in their out-of-school activities, the other on their voluntary uses of arithmetic in school activities. Children's interests in and voluntary uses of information and skills are indices of maturity and readiness to learn, and as such are criteria for the timeliness of instruction. The meanings of these studies, whose schemes of organization differ, are not clear unless the data are studied under the categories of number, size (measurement), form, and position. The two groups show substantially the same broad over-all picture when the data in both sets are analyzed under the same categories, and when all measurement is considered under one category.

All investigators use *grade*, not *age*, in inventorying interests in and uses of arithmetic. The studies as a group cover kindergarten through sixth grade.

WHAT CHILDREN'S INTERESTS SHOW

One fact that stands out clearly from the studies is that children's interests in arithmetic are primarily functional and children use arithmetic functionally in two ways: (1) in thinking and communicating facts and ideas about number, size, form, and position, and (2) in solving their own particular problems, which may or may not require computation.

Communication is a dominant interest in all grades; in the lower grades it is a predominant interest. Children ask questions: how many, what order, which one, and how much. They talk about the shapes of things. They use a great variety of expressions for position and positional relationships. They compare and estimate. In short, children use arithmetic functionally, as do adults, in thinking and communicating quantitative facts and ideas. The difference is degree of maturity.

Problem-solving is used in a wide variety of situations, accompanied by much talk, especially among younger children. Interest in computation increases with age. The activities determine the types of arithmetic which children use and how they use it. Another fact, equally clear, is that children use a breadth of arithmetic, or "mathematics"—number, measurement, form, and position—in their activities.

Both outside of school and in school, children use *number* in all kinds of ways, in its cardinal, ordinal, and denominate senses. Kindergartners and first graders do a great deal of rote and rational counting, just for fun. They count by ones, twos, fives, and tens. In situations calling for computation, children of all ages use integers and the processes of counting, adding, subtracting, multiplying, and dividing. Their proportional use of these fundamental processes is not clearly established. They use a few fractions, and simple decimals when dealing with money and speed. How well they use number is not known.

Children are interested in *measurement*, "how much" of almost everything—money, time, speed, distance, weight, liquids; how big, how high, how far, how fast, how heavy, how long, what time, ad infinitum. They use denominate number in exchanging ideas, and in connection with activities which require actual measurement. They compare, estimate, and use instruments of measure. Among children of first and second grades, interest in and uses of measurement and of number are about equal. Among third and fourth graders, measurement exceeds all other interests and uses. Fifth and sixth graders show sustained interest in measurement; they use denominate numbers in simple computation.

Only two studies included form and position, but these show that children are much interested in both the shapes and the positions of things.

The studies give a rough picture of children's interests in and voluntary uses of arithmetic in their in- and out-of-school activities. Trends are detectable, and clues suggested. We know too little about the children or the circumstances to make many implications. Teachers can, however, find out about the quantitative interests and quantitative behavior of the children in their own classrooms by setting up studies of their own.

IMPLICATIONS FROM RESEARCH

Taking what we do know of children's interests as a basis for further study, there are implications of ways in which school people could use children's interests to generate interests in learning arithmetic:

1. Recognize that children, from early years on, are becoming aware of the quantitative characteristics of their experiences—number, size, form, position; that they are endeavoring to understand these quantitative aspects; that they are learning the words and symbols which express these facts and ideas.

2. Provide all possible assistance to children in their efforts to think quantitatively and to communicate these facts and ideas.

3. Supply breadth of mathematical experiences in all grades, emphasize measurement in the grades where it is an all-out interest, and give attention to the development of understanding all along the line.

4. Take into account that children's needs for computation and their abilities to reason increase as they grow older, and match expectancies to the tempo of expansion of these needs and abilities.

5. Recognize that number, to be serviceable to children in thinking, communicating, and computing, must be sufficiently meaningful to them that they use it volitionally in their own real situations.

Arithmetic has been regarded as a skill subject, with high priority on computation. If it is conceded to be a system of thinking, of which computational skills are but one important part, the same procedures will apply to it as to development of meanings and of reasoning along other lines.

The processes which children use in developing quantitative concepts and skills are not clearly defined in arithmetical research, but clues support the suggestions just made. Research in child development suggests that the development of quantitative competence is interwoven with other aspects of development. To date, on the basis of research, we know very little about this.

The most significant implication from studies of children's interests in and uses of arithmetic is the importance of quantitative thinking and communication throughout childhood. Emphasis on concept development and quantitative communication might capitalize on children's interests, help children in school subjects in which quantitative thinking and communication are foundational, and assist them in other aspects of arithmetic. It would help children in learning to deal with abstractions in the three R's.

Arithmetic is not a separate language, but the quantitative aspect of language plus symbols for quantitative facts and operations. Understanding quantitative words precedes the understanding of their abstract arithmetic counterparts.

Among young children, quantitative expression develops as a normal part of language development. As they become familiar with the meanings of things, they gradually become aware of quantitative characteristics, as number, spatial relations, and size. At all ages, some children are more aware of quantitative characteristics than other children are, and deal with them more maturely. Research shows this (2, 7, 11, 21, 24, 26, 31). Observe children's quantitative behavior, listen to children, and you can prove it yourself.

The first years in school children are often expected to deal with abstractions in reading and writing and sometimes in arithmetic. This is too heavy a load for many of them. They need many concrete experiences, and much help from the teacher in discerning quantitative characteristics in these experiences. They need help with quantitative words and ideas, and ample opportunities to use these words and ideas in play activities, spontaneous talk, and interesting discussions.

Such experiences as trips to markets, airports, and post offices, the reproduction of such places in authentic playworthy constructions, and the interpretation of the activities of the people through dramatic play, supply vivid quantitative perceptions and stimulate quantitative thinking (32).

First-grade teachers know that children are helped if their concrete quantitative experiences are related, recorded, and then read. They make experience charts every day. Children see in writing what they know and have tested in experience, and they recognize the written symbols for what they know aurally and orally. Later, they learn to write their own quantitative ideas. Notation is only one part of the writing.

Quantitative thinking and communication include more than listening-speaking, reading-writing. They include the use of such mathematical forms of communication as tabular forms, maps, graphs, and equations.

Concepts of form, position, and measurement are basic to thinking intelligently about spatial relations, speed, and other magnitudes; basic, also, to using globes, maps, and other means of communication. Do we supply enough concrete experiences as children progress through school and the load of abstractions gets heavier? Are we giving children adequate help in measurement? Should third- and fourth-grade programs in arithmetic be examined to be sure we are not bearing down heavily on abstract number combinations during a period when children are most receptive to assistance in measurement and denominate number? What does the paucity of data on form and position mean?

Children in the lower grades use such tabular forms as calendars, tables of contents, schedules of daily programs, lists of "things we need," simple inventories, and tables in connection with their experiences. They are making maps with concrete objects when they lay out segments of small communities which they have constructed. These concrete maps are forerunners of pictorial maps, which are in turn forerunners of symbolic maps. Equations and formulae—mathematical sentences—should give little trouble if concrete experiences are translated into symbols often enough.

As children grow older, more and more tabular forms, maps, and graphs appear in the books which they are required to use. These books are also heavy with quantitative facts and ideas which require, in order to be comprehended, an ample background of concrete experiences and a meaningful quantitative vocabulary. Concept development and accurate terminology are lifelong tasks, but children need all the help they can use at their ages.

Research shows that children can understand arithmetic (1, 2, 3, 4, 22, 27, 33, 34). But—research stresses a longer period of concrete number experiences, and a more gradual transition into abstract number. It emphasizes that *the processes children use on the concrete and semiconcrete levels should be the processes which they will use when dealing with abstract number* (2).

Measurement is open territory in research. However, since measurement is not a system as is the number system, but several systems, each with its own units and instruments of measure, this aspect can be handled in connection with children's activities.

Several attempts have been made to find ways of relating *number* to children's activities (14, 15, 16, 18, 32, 40, 41). Numerous researches have been made to find effective methods of teaching number (1, 3, 4, 5, 6, 22, 33, 34). Most of these have been made on the basis of existing grade placements and subject matter. No one has found satisfactory answers.

The underlying problem of helping children with arithmetic is not simply supplying interesting activities for children, but rather of using interesting experiences as a solid foundation for the development of understanding. We may find better going *if* communication and quantitative thinking are admitted into the curriculum as a legitimate function of arithmetic, *if* number ideas and skills are allowed to mature gradually, and *if* size, form, and position are admitted as partners of number.

The whole area of the development of quantitative abilities should be studied carefully, and on a long-term basis. Professional literature supplies promising hypotheses, which could and should be tested. Arithmetical research supplies many clues, but insufficient scientific evidence to settle such questions as how children learn arithmetic successfully, what to expect at different ages, or how success or failure in developing quantitative competence affects children's success or failure in other aspects of development. We need a teamup in research—between teachers who understand children and experts who understand arithmetic—to explore this aspect of child development.

BIBLIOGRAPHY OF RESEARCH IN ARITHMETIC

1. ANDERSON, G. LESTER. "Quantitative Thinking as Developed under Connectionist and Field Theories of Learning," *Learning Theory in School Situations.* Minneapolis: The University of Minnesota Press, 1949. Pp. 40–73.

2. BROWNELL, WILLIAM A. *The Development of Children's Number Ideas in the Primary Grades.* Supplementary Educational Monograph, No. 35. Chicago: The University of Chicago Press, 1928. Pp. 241.

3. BROWNELL, WILLIAM A. and CARPER, DORIS V. *Learning the Multiplication Combinations.* Durham, N.C.: Duke University Press, 1943.

4. BROWNELL, WILLIAM A. and Others. *Arithmetic in Grades I and II.* Research Studies in Education, No. 6. Durham, N.C.: Duke University, 1941. P. 175.

5. BROWNELL, WILLIAM A. and Others. *Learning as Reorganization.* Research Studies in Education, No. 3. Durham, N.C.: Duke University, 1939. P. 87.

6. BUCKINGHAM, B. R. and MacLATCHY, JOSEPHINE. "The Number Abilities of Children When They Enter Grade One," *Report of the Society's Committee on Arithmetic,* Part II, Twenty-ninth Yearbook of the National Society for the Study of Education. Bloomington, Ill.: Public School Publishing Company, 1930. Pp. 473–524.

7. COWARD, E. "The Development of Number Concepts in the Pre-school Child." Unpublished Master's thesis, University of Minnesota, 1940.

8. CULVER, MARY MARJORIE. "A Study of Children's Interests in Arithmetic as Indicated by Their Spontaneous Quantitative Expressions in Life Situations." Unpublished doctoral dissertation, Stanford University, 1941. P. 166.

9. ELLSWORTH, ELMER E. "Number Experiences of 390 Children from Grades 3–6 in an Urban Area," *Education* (April 1941), 61:485–87.

10. FRIEDMAN, KAPPLE C. "Time Concepts of Elementary School Children," *Elementary School Journal* (Feb. 1944), 44:337–42.

11. GRAHAM, V., JACKSON, T. A., LONG, L., and WELCH, L. "Generalization of the Concept of Middleness," *Journal of Genetic Psychology,* 1944, 65:227–237.

12. GRANT, ALBERT. "Analysis of the Number Knowledge of First Grade Pupils According to Levels of Intelligence," *Journal of Experimental Education* (Sept. 1938), 7:63–66.

13. GUNDERSON, AGNES G. "Number Concepts Held by Seven Year Olds," *Mathematics Teacher* (Jan. 1940), 33:18–24.

14. HANNA, PAUL R. (Chairman). "Opportunities for the Use of Arithmetic in an Activity Program," *The Teaching of Arithmetic,* Tenth Yearbook of the National Council of Teachers of Mathematics. New York: Teachers College, Columbia University, 1935. Pp. 85–120.

15. HARAP, HENRY and BARRETT, URSULA. "Experimenting with Real Situations in Third Grade Arithmetic," *Educational Methods* (Jan. 1937), 16:188–92.

16. HARAP, HENRY and MAPES, CHARLOTTE E. "The Learning of Fundamentals in an Arithmetic Activity Program," *Elementary School Journal* (March 1934), 34:515–525.

17. HELBING, MARY E. "Evaluation of the Procedures of a Modern Elementary School in Terms of the Subsequent Adjustment of Its Pupils," *California Journal of Elementary Education* (Feb. 1940), 8:137–146.

18. HIZER, IRENE S. and HARAP, HENRY. "The Learning of Fundamentals in an Arithmetic Activity Course," *Educational Method* (June 1932), 11:536–39.

19. LONG, LOUIS. "Conceptual Relationships in Children: The Concept of Roundness," *Journal of Genetic Psychology* (1940), 57:289–315.

20. LONG, LOUIS and WELCH, LIVINGSTON. "The Development of the Ability to Discriminate and Match Numbers," *Journal of Genetic Psychology* (Dec. 1941), 59:377–387.

21. MARTIN, WILLIAM F. "Quantitative Expression in Young Children," *Genetic Psychology Monograph* (Nov. 1951), 44:147–219.

22. MCCONNELL, T. R. *Discovery vs. Authoritative Identification in the Learning of Children.* University of Iowa Studies in Education, Vol. IX, No. 5, Sept. 15, 1934.

23. MCLAUGHLIN, KATHERINE. "Number Ability of Pre-school Children," *Childhood Education* (May 1935), 11:348–53.

24. MEYER, EDITH. "Comprehension of Spatial Relations in Pre-school Children," *Journal of Genetic Psychology* (1940), 57:119–151.

25. MORTON, JOHN AUSTIN. "A Study of Children's Mathematical Interest Questions as a Clue to Grade Placement of Arithmetic Topics." Unpublished doctoral dissertation, Stanford University, 1945. Pp. 215.

26. MOTT, SINA M. "Number Concepts of Small Children," *Mathematics Teacher* (November 1945), 38:291–301.

27. OVERMAN, JAMES R. *An Experimental Study of Certain Factors Affecting Transfer of Training in Arithmetic.* Baltimore: Warwick and York, Inc., 1931. Pp. 235.

28. POLKINGHORNE, ADA R. "Young Children and Fractions," *Childhood Education* (May 1935), 11:354–58.

29. REID, FLORENCE E. "Incidental Number Situations in First Grade," *Journal of Educational Research* (September 1936), 30:36–43.

30. ROBINSON, CLARK N. "Elementary School Children's Arithmetic Needs Arising in the Home Environment." Unpublished Master's thesis, Stanford University, 1938. Pp. 90.

31. RUSSELL, NED M. "Arithmetical Concepts of Children," *Journal of Educational Research* (May 1936), 29:647–63.

32. SHERER, LORRAINE, "How to Improve a Curriculum—Mathematics, for Example." Unpublished doctoral dissertation, Stanford University, 1946. Pp. 544.

33. SWENSON, ESTHER J. "Organization and Generalization as Factors in Learning, Transfer, and Retroactive Inhibition," *Learning Theory in School Situations.* Minneapolis: The University of Minnesota Press, 1949. Pp. 9–39.

34. THEILE, C. L. *The Contribution of Generalization to the Learning of the Addition Facts.* New York: Bureau of Publications, Teachers College, Columbia University, 1938. Pp. 84.

35. THRUM, M. E. "The Development of Concepts of Magnitude," *Child Development* (1935), 6:120–140.

36. TOMKINS, JEAN B. and STOKES, CLAUDE N. "Eight-Year-Olds Use Arithmetic," *Childhood Education* (March 1940), 16:319–21.

37. WAHLSTROM, E. L. "Computational Arithmetic of Social Experiences of Third Grade Children," *Journal of Educational Research* (Oct. 1936), 30:124–29.

38. WHITE, HELEN M. "Does Experience in the Situation Involved Affect the Solving of a Problem," *Education* (April 1934), 54:451–55.

39. WILEY, ROY DE VERL. "A Study of Uses of Arithmetic by Pupils of Selected Elementary Schools in Santa Clara County, California." Unpublished doctoral dissertation, Stanford University, 1940. Pp. 212.

40. WILLIAMS, CATHERINE M. "Arithmetic Learning in an Experience Curriculum," *Educational Research Bulletin* (Sept. 14, 1949), 28:154–168.

41. WILSON, GUY M. "New Standards in Arithmetic: A Controlled Experiment in Supervision," *Journal of Educational Research* (Dec. 1930), 22:251–60.

42. WOODY, CLIFFORD. "Arithmetical Backgrounds of Young Children," *Journal of Educational Research* (Oct. 1931), 24:188–201.

43. WOODY, CLIFFORD. "Knowledge of Arithmetic Possessed by Young Children," *Bulletin of the School of Education* (Indiana University) (July 1930), 60:50–85.

Arithmetic Research That Has Made a Difference

Paul C. Burns

This articles describes twenty-four examples of arithmetic research. These twenty-four examples were selected, not because they are the most valuable in all situations, but because they hold an answer to the question, "When did research ever influence the teaching of arithmetic?"

Research should influence teaching, we are told, but we are not always aware of the studies that have influenced arithmetic instruction over the years. Because most of the research discussed here is well known, the methods and results will be described only briefly. Certain other aspects of the studies will be discussed at greater length to see why they have had such a powerful influence on the arithmetic curriculum and related areas.

A BALANCED PROGRAM

The first of the classic studies is the Wilson study made shortly after the turn of the twentieth century (1). Wilson sought answer to the questions: What social situations require arithmetic? What aspects of arithmetic are useful in these situations? Wilson held that arithmetic content should have a clear relationship to the life needs of adults as determined by the arithmetic used in their vocational and non-vocational activities.

After Wilson reported his findings, other investigators promptly set out to base arithmetic on the theory of social utility. The social utility movement reduced the content of the arithmetic curriculum and established beyond any doubt the fact that arithmetic has a social aim. Because of the contribution

Reprinted from "Arithmetic Research That Has Made a Difference," *The Elementary School Journal,* Vol. 65, No. 7 (April 1964); pp. 386–392, by Paul C. Burns, by permission of The University of Chicago Press.

that arithmetic could make to effective, intelligent daily life, this subject was assured a place in the elementary-school program.

Still later, in the twenties, interest developed in the mathematics of arithmetic. This interest led to attempts to organize arithmetic programs on the basis of "unit skills" used in the fundamental operations. The works of Knight and Brueckner illustrate this approach (2, 3), the effects of which are still evident in arithmetic materials. The influence is apparent, for example, in materials that use denominators as the basis for organizing the teaching of the addition of proper fractions. These materials take into account fractions that have like denominators, as $\frac{1}{3} + \frac{1}{3}$; fractions that have unlike but related denominators, as $\frac{1}{2} + \frac{3}{8}$; and fractions that have unlike and unrelated denominators, as $\frac{1}{3} + \frac{3}{4}$.

A still different approach that led to many disagreements during this period investigated the mental maturity needed for various arithmetic operations. The standards that were established provided a limited basis for discovering when children can best be taught various arithmetical operations, but many textbooks and teachers were influenced by the findings and immediate effects were noted on the arithmetic curriculum. The chief effect of this approach was that the study of many arithmetic topics was deferred until later years (4).

In the thirties, an effort was made to emphasize the learning of arithmetic through an activity program. The Harap and Mapes study illustrates research based on this approach (5).

As one looks back over the research on arithmetic, one can discern a striving to create a balanced program—a program that took into account the needs of society, the needs of the subject matter, and the needs of the child. The striving for a balanced arithmetic program continues to the present.

BEGINNING ARITHMETIC INSTRUCTION

Brownell's *Arithmetic in Grades 1 and 2* is a memorable study for all who are interested in arithmetic in the primary grades (6). The study deals with pupils' readiness to begin systematic instruction in arithmetic in the primary grades. Before Brownell's study, arithmetic was not universally taught systematically in Grades 1 and 2. Rather, an incidental approach was commonly used.

Brownell posed an important question: Is the primary-grade pupil intellectually capable of benefiting from systematic instruction in arithmetic? In answer to the question, Brownell showed that children knew a great deal about arithmetic before school instruction and that there were many social needs for arithmetic.

Earlier, Buckingham and MacLatchy had presented the idea that most third-grade arithmetic textbooks began at an immature level and ignored the arithmetic that children learned before formal schooling and during early formal instruction (7). Such ideas helped to place arithmetic in the primary grades on a more solid footing by supplying evidence that readiness is determined, not by age or grade alone, but also by the kind of arithmetic experiences pupils have had.

TEACHING METHODS

More than three decades ago, in 1928, McConnell presented evidence on the value of meaningful teaching and learning of arithmetic (8). In his study he reported the transfer values of teaching arithmetic so that the children understood the processes.

Concurrently, Olander and Overman did considerable work on transfer in arithmetic (9, 10). Their studies found a high degree of transfer of learning from taught to untaught situations in addition and subtraction under appropriate teaching. Students of arithmetic will admire the thoroughness of these studies even though they may not agree with the authors' definitions of *transfer*. These studies were followed by Thiele's study, which attempted to measure pupils' ability to use newly acquired learnings in novel situations and to generalize (11).

One outcome of the research on transfer and generalization has been the rather wide acceptance of the objective of teaching arithmetic for meaning rather than for computational efficiency only. Brownell and Moser provided further evidence on transfer value when the skill of borrowing in subtraction is taught meaningfully: "When subtraction examples were understood and rationalized by pupils, there was greater transfer to untaught examples than when initial instruction had been mechanically associative" (12).

These were important early studies of the values of drill as opposed to understanding. There may still be some confusion as to just what is meant by "meaningful arithmetic," but the emphasis of drill has been markedly reduced.

Such telling research on drill culminated in the "meaning theory" of arithmetic. This approach is the popular one today. Advocates stress understanding. Arithmetic is viewed as a system of understandable ideas, principles, and processes. Drill, which was important in the traditional program, still has a place; but drill is offered only after the children understand a new step.

TEACHER EDUCATION

In 1948 Glennon did a frontier type of research study to test meanings in arithmetic (13). He noted the paucity of research studies in the area of testing for meaning and concluded that this was one of the most neglected educational problems of the day. His findings suggested that many teachers were still not making meaningful teaching one of their primary objectives in elementary arithmetic.

A considerable number of studies followed this work, which attempted to sample pupils' understanding as well as their ability to work arithmetic exercises. The checking of pupils' understanding of arithmetic has been followed by studies evaluating teachers' understanding of arithmetic. These studies, in turn, have led to intensified research on teacher preparation in arithmetic. Perhaps the most extensive recent study on teacher preparation was reported by Grossnickle in 1951 (14).

DIAGNOSIS AND REMEDIATION

Research on diagnosis and on the remedial teaching of arithmetic has not advanced to the point where many questions on the relative merits of specific procedures can be answered with assurance. Buswell and John made one of the first major investigations of research on diagnostic and remedial activities with the four fundamental operations (15). They attempted to catalog pupils' operational habits in each of the four operations. Teachers promptly showed more concern about corrective arithmetic.

After the Buswell and John investigations, other significant studies of a related nature were carried out by Brueckner and other authorities on arithmetic (16). The findings of such studies were incorporated in Brueckner's *Diagnostic and Remedial Teaching of Arithmetic*, a book that has strongly influenced instructional practice and the construction of diagnostic tests (17). Such earlier studies have encouraged further research on types of errors in fundamental operations, difficulties pupils encounter in certain aspects of arithmetic, and general factors that affect success and failure in learning arithmetic.

OTHER FACTORS

Yeldham's *Teaching Arithmetic through Four Hundred Years*, an example of the historical method of research, describes the long and gradual development of methods and practices (18). This historical survey has proved useful. It gives teachers considerable confidence in what they advocate in the teaching of arithmetic; it provides a background against which current teaching can be measured; and it establishes a basis for continued research on methods and materials. The study provides evidence that instruction is not based on the personal whim of individual authors or teachers but is the result of generations of trials in the classroom. Other examples of scholarly historical research include *History of Mathematics* by Smith; *The Writing of Arabic Numerals* by Wright; and *One Hundred Years of Arithmetic Textbooks* by Smith (19, 20, 21).

Other studies are worthy of mention. Several leave unanswered questions and suggest that more comprehensive studies need to be carried out. A list of studies that have influenced teaching practice would certainly include some that treat specific aspects of the fundamental operations, such as estimating the quotient in long division. It should be noted that studies of tests and measurements of arithmetic learnings have had a marked influence on research in arithmetic. Still, procedures and technique for evaluating the outcome of arithmetic learnings have not had an appropriate influence on instructional procedures. Certainly, research in problem-solving has not yet answered many of the questions in this important area of instruction.

More recently, some studies have compared arithmetic teaching, programs, textbooks, and performance in the United States and in other countries (22, 23). Ideas of genuine merit that are being used in the schools of some foreign countries may well be incorporated into our teaching procedures. Various groups have tried out so-called modern content. Their experiments have obviously resulted in some changes in instructional arithmetic materials for elementary-school children (24). Such recent influences are difficult to assess from a historical point of view.

CHARACTERISTICS OF STUDIES

Five generalizations stand out in this survey of studies that have strongly influenced instruction in arithmetic.

First, each study was influenced by other research in related areas. In the field of child or educational psychology, the debate over learning with understanding as opposed to isolated drill had an effect. Statements of educational objectives by authorities and national organizations such as the National Council of Teachers of Mathematics also had an effect. Studies on children's thinking—Piaget's work, for example—have also been influential. And, more recently, the need for many highly trained persons has influenced research in arithmetic. Each of the studies cited here pointed ways to important future studies. At times the research supported new goals, and at other times it led to new goals.

Second, the studies vary in research design. Some are general surveys (Glennon, Grossnickle, Wilson); some are laboratory studies (Brueckner, Buckingham and MacLatchy, Knight); some are teaching investigations (Brownell, Brownell and Moser, Buckingham, Harap and Mapes, McConnell, Olander, Overman, Thiele); some are diagnostic studies (Brueckner, Buswell and John); some are historical surveys (D. Smith, H. Smith, Wright, Yeldham). Each design fits the explicit purpose of the investigation.

These differences imply that the continued attack on problems of instruction in teaching arithmetic can be varied.

Third, each study was closely connected to the problems of its day. The Wilson study coincided with some phases of the social utility movement. The studies by McConnell, Olander, Overman, and Thiele gave basic data about the meaning process in the days when psychology was beginning as a science. The Brownell studies are closely associated with the development of theories of transfer. The study by Glennon was an adjunct to the idea of "meaningful" arithmetic. Interest in arithmetic in foreign schools and "modern" content was given impetus by the launching of the first artificial satellite in 1957. Each study had impact because it was closely related to the context in which it was made. As we look to the future, we must continue to ask, "What is relevant and pressing?"

A fourth mark of these studies is the simplicity of their design and statistical analysis. Good planning at the beginning can eliminate the necessity for intricate statistical analysis. One of the finest features of the older studies is their careful planning. These features are worth emulating. Today's researcher may not be acquainted with many of the new technical developments, and so the team approach, especially at the planning and analysis stages of the study, would seem to be desirable. While today some of the finest research is done by individuals, individual researchers in arithmetic will be wise to consult other experts.

A fifth characteristic of the studies is that they were concerned with a variety of problems. They represent the tremendous scope in arithmetic and suggest even greater possibilities for the future in arithmetic. This scope involves teaching methods, arithmetic vocabulary, children's motivations, emotional and personality concomitants of arithmetic instruction, and the general problems of arithmetic all around the world.

Much more still needs to be done. We hear much about providing for gifted pupils and low achievers. We read of differences among individuals, but what can be done about the neglected area of intra-individual differences? The whole area of arithmetic has hundreds of possibilities to be tried and tested. We do not do enough research, or use enough of it, but the record shows that arithmetic research has influenced and will continue to influence practice. Research *can* make a difference.

NOTES

1. GUY M. WILSON. *Survey of the Social and Business Usages of Arithmetic.* Contribution to Education No. 100. New York: Bureau of Publications, Teachers College, Columbia University, 1919.

2. F. B. KNIGHT, E. M. LUSE, and G. M. RUCH. *Problems in the Teaching of Arithmetic.* Iowa City, Iowa: Iowa Supply Company, 1924.

3. LEO J. BRUECKNER and FRED KELLEY. "A Critical Evaluation of Methods of Analyzing Practice in Fractions," *Research in Arithmetic,* Twenty-ninth Year-

book of the National Society for the Study of Education, Part II, pp. 524–34. Bloomington: Public School Publishing Company, 1930.

4. C. W. WASHBURNE. "Mental Age and the Arithmetic Curriculum—Summary of the Committee of Seven," *Journal of Educational Research*, XXIII (March, 1931), 210–31.

5. HENRY HARAP and CHARLOTTE MAPES. "The Learning of Fundamentals in an Arithmetic Activity Program," *Elementary School Journal*, XXXIV (March, 1934), 515–25.

6. WILLIAM C. BROWNELL. *Arithmetic in Grades 1 and 2*. Durham, North Carolina: Duke University Press, 1941.

7. B. R. BUCKINGHAM and JOSEPHINE MACLATCHY. "The Number Abilities of Children When They Enter Grade One," *Research in Arithmetic*, Twenty-ninth Yearbook of the National Society for the Study of Education, Part II, pp. 473–524. Bloomington: Public School Publishing Company, 1930.

8. T. R. McCONNELL. *Discovery vs. Authoritative Identification in the Learning of Children*, pp. 11–62. Iowa City, Iowa: University of Iowa Studies in Education, Volume 9, 1934.

9. H. T. OLANDER. *An Experimental Determination of the Degree of Transfer between Taught and Untaught Combinations in Simple Addition and Subtraction*. Unpublished doctoral dissertation. Pittsburgh, Pennsylvania: University of Pittsburgh, 1930.

10. J. R. OVERMAN. "An Experimental Study of Certain Factors Affecting Transfer of Training in Arithmetic," *Educational Psychological Monographs*, No. 29. Baltimore: Warwick and York, 1931.

11. C. LOUIS THIELE. *Contributions to Generalizations to the Learning of Addition Facts*. Contributions to Education, No. 673. New York: Bureau of Publications, Teachers College, Columbia University, 1938.

12. WILLIAM A. BROWNELL and ARNOLD E. MOSER. *Meaningful vs. Mechanical Learning—a Study in Grade 3 Subtraction*. Research Monograph No. 8. Durham, North Carolina: Duke University Press, 1949.

13. VINCENT J. GLENNON. *A Study of the Growth and Mastery of Certain Basic Mathematical Understandings on Several Educational Levels*. Unpublished doctoral dissertation. Cambridge, Massachusetts: Graduate School of Education, Harvard University, 1948.

14. FOSTER E. GROSSNICKLE. "The Training of Teachers in Arithmetic," *The Teaching of Arithmetic*, Fiftieth Yearbook of the National Society for the Study of Education, Part II, pp. 203–31. Chicago: University of Chicago, 1951.

15. G. T. BUSWELL and LENORE JOHN. *Diagnostic Studies in Arithmetic*. Supplementary Educational Monograph No. 30. Chicago: University of Chicago, 1926.

16. LEO J. BRUECKNER. "Analysis of Errors in Fractions," *Elementary School Journal*, XXVIII (June, 1928), 760–70; and "Analysis of Difficulties in Decimals," *Elementary School Journal*, XXIX (September, 1928), 32–41.

17. LEO J. BRUECKNER. *Diagnostic and Remedial Teaching of Arithmetic*. Philadelphia: John C. Winston, 1930.

18. Florence Yeldham. *Teaching Arithmetic through Four Hundred Years*. London: Harrap and Company, 1936.

19. DAVID EUGENE SMITH. *History of Mathematics.* New York: Ginn and Company, 1958.
20. G. G. NEIL WRIGHT. *The Writing of Arabic Numerals.* London: University of London, 1952.
21. HENRY L. SMITH. *One Hundred Years of Arithmetic Textbooks.* Bloomington: Indiana University, 1954.
22. GUY T. BUSWELL. "A Comparison of Achievement in Arithmetic in England and Central California," *Arithmetic Teacher,* V (February, 1958), 1–9.
23. KLASS KRAMER. "Arithmetic Achievement in Iowa and The Netherlands," *Elementary School Journal,* LIX (February, 1959), 258–63.
24. Projects known as School Mathematics Study Groups: University of Illinois Mathematics Project; Greater Cleveland Mathematics Program; Madison Project; and others.

8

Evaluation in Elementary
School Mathematics

The evaluation of a child's progress in elementary school mathematics is no simple task. Did the evaluation consider what the child knew or what he did not have the opportunity to reveal? Did the evaluation measure the child's understanding of an important concept or his ability to analyze a problem? Did the evaluation consider divergent thinking patterns? In our concerns for the improvement of mathematics skills, and where standardized tests are used, can we justify devoting a block of time specifically to skill development? Do we use tests and teach to the tests? Are the evaluation instruments and guidelines properly balanced, and do they take into consideration all aspects of a well-balanced program of mathematics for elementary school children? If we are too preoccupied by how children do on tests, does this concern misdirect what a good mathematics program could and should do? What should we evaluate? How he feels or what he knows? What are the objectives of the program? Are we teaching what we say we are teaching? Are our objectives consistent with the testing instrument or plan?

Recently, mathematics education programs have been redesigned. Have we redesigned our evaluation instruments and procedures too? We continue to organize new programs, devise new materials, and seek to build new inservice programs, but we lack instruments to measure this newness. Do we revert to the use of established standardized tests that do not measure this new emphasis? Is this why some programs are inferior? How can we justify the use of an antiquated concept of evaluation to evaluate new programs? Remember the Peanuts cartoon, "How can I do the new math with an old math mind"? What does the diagnosis-prescription cycle have to offer to the child? What kinds of abilities, skills, and insights must the teacher possess? What do teachers, mathematicians, and mathematics educators need to know about research in the area of mathematics education?

Testing, Diagnosis, and Follow-up in Arithmetic

Leo J. Brueckner

Testing in arithmetic, broadly considered, involves the use of analytical procedures, both standardized and unstandardized, that enable the teacher to evaluate the achievement and performance of the learner.

The chief contributions of testing and evaluation to arithmetic instruction are:

1. The selection and clarification of objectives which serve as guides for testing and instruction
2. The determination of the rate of growth and the progress made by each learner in achieving accepted objectives
3. Provision of a basis on which teachers can set up educational experiences adapted to the needs, interests, and ability of the learners
4. Motivation and guidance of learning, especially by helping children to evaluate their own responses and behavior
5. The location, diagnosis, and treatment of learning difficulties
6. The basis for coordinating improvement programs in related fields such as arithmetic, reading, science, and social studies.

The primary functions of the arithmetic program are: first, development of ability to perform the various number operations intelligently and skillfully; second, provision of a wide variety of learning experiences that will ensure the ability to apply arithmetic skills and quantitative procedures and thinking effectively in social situations—both in and out of school.

The most effective way to evaluate the arithmetic program of an elementary school is to determine by tests and other suitable procedures the growth that the children make as they progress through the school.

Reprinted from *The National Elementary Principal,* Vol. 39, No. 2 (October 1959), 33–36, by permission of the publisher. Copyright 1959, Department of Elementary School Principals, National Education Association. All rights reserved.

MAKING ARITHMETIC MEANINGFUL

In recent years, forward-looking schools have placed emphasis on making arithmetic meaningful to children. It is generally agreed that children must understand the structure of the number system. They must also understand how the number system operates in the performance of number operations —for instance, the transferal that must be made in carrying in addition or in regrouping in subtraction. When the learner also understands the meaning of the various number operations, it is likely that he will be able to apply them in solving arithmetic problems.

To make number operations meaningful to children the teacher must provide experiences in which they make number discoveries involving the use of exploratory manipulative materials, visual aids, and the study of abstract presentations and explanations found in textbooks.

STRESSING EFFICIENCY OF WORK

Knowing the meaning of a number of operations does not ensure efficiency in its manipulation. When meanings are stressed, the emphasis is often placed on resourcefulness in arriving at solutions of examples and problems. The result is that children sometimes invent procedures that are meaningful to them but actually are roundabout and not very efficient. Children should learn to perform the various number operations intelligently and skillfully and gradually learn efficient thought processes.

When children work numerous types of examples which they do not understand, they usually make many errors. When they persist in the use of incorrect and roundabout procedures, these procedures are likely to become learned responses which may become set patterns. Once an incorrect response pattern is established, it is difficult to correct the thought processes involved. Good teaching seeks to guide the learning activity in such a way that efficient meaningful thought patterns are established.

Drill to establish any particular step or skill should never be assigned until the teacher is certain that the child understands the procedure to be used in the solution and has in mind the sequence of steps in an efficient algorism: that is, a meaningful way of thinking through and writing out the solution. The slogan should be: meaning first, then practice to develop skill.

STEPS IN EVALUATION

There are five basic steps in testing and evaluating outcomes: 1) formulating general and specific objectives; 2) defining the objectives in terms of pupil behavior; 3) designing or selecting suitable means of appraisal; 4) securing a record of behavior or performance; 5) interpreting and evaluating the information secured.

Teachers at various grade levels should define the objectives in terms of the behavior to be expected at different levels of development and progress. For example, a basic objective of arithmetic in the middle grades is the development of skill in the four fundamental operations with whole numbers and the ability to apply them effectively in social situations. This general objective may be more specifically defined in terms of pupil behavior as: control of knowledge of the basic number facts involved; an understanding of the meanings of the four operations and their interrelationships; skill in performing the operations involved; and the ability to apply them in solving real and vicarious problems. The use of suitable means of testing enables the teacher to evaluate the responses of the learner related to each aspect.

THE MEANS OF EVALUATION

The means of appraisal that are available or which teachers can devise as needed include:

1. Standardized tests for measuring achievement.
2. Informal paper and pencil procedures and objective type tests that should be used as an integral element of the on-going instructional program.
3. Free and uncontrolled observation of pupil behavior and responses in daily work, in dealing with problematic situations, during drill and study periods, in free periods, etc.
4. The evaluation of some product, for example, a graph, a report, or a construction.

Less formal records of behavior not readily tested by paper and pencil procedures can be secured by using anecdotal records, interest inventories, photographs, motion pictures, tape recordings, questionnaires, interviews, and similar methods. The procedures used will depend on the type of behavior to be evaluated.

The teacher must make value judgments as to the merit of the pupil responses. For standard tests, norms of achievement based on the performance of large numbers of children at the various grade levels assist in evaluating the performances of individual children. The teacher must also use the results of tests found in textbooks and tests that are teacher prepared and administered frequently during the year to make a continuing study of the pupil's growth.

The teacher must also consider the results of the less formal appraisal procedures listed above. Interests cannot be measured directly, but the teacher can estimate their value as observed in the pupil responses in the course of daily work. Similarly, the ability of the pupil to utilize quantitative thinking and quantitative procedures in social situations cannot be measured directly, but it can be estimated.

The important point to bear in mind in interpreting test scores is that standards of achievement should not be the same for all children in a particular grade group because of differences in their capacity to learn, the rates at which they learn, their experiential background, their social, emotional, and physical maturity, and their basic interests and purposes. Individual progress goals meaningful to the learner should be set up for each pupil, especially if the individual has serious learning difficulties, and growth should be measured by progress in achieving these goals.

Standard tests usually reveal a wide range of ability in arithmetic in practically all classes. In appraising the performance of any particular child on a standard test, the teacher should give consideration to his mental level, health and physical limitations, social and emotional adjustment, and home background. The teacher should also bear in mind that a typical standard test will show the level of his achievement, but it does not give a dependable indication as to how well he understands the steps tested or of the efficiency of his work methods or thought processes. These factors must be evaluated by more penetrating diagnostic test procedures.

TYPES OF CASES

Four kinds of cases emerge when the results of survey and diagnostic tests are analyzed.

Type 1: Cases whose performance is at or above the level that can ordinarily be expected of children of their ability and grade level.

Type 2: Cases of simple retardation whose performance is somewhat below the normal level but for whom the regular program is probably adequate. The deficiency usually responds readily to carefully directed instruction.

Type 3: Specific disability cases, such as a child who for some reason has a marked weakness in subtraction or a reading disability which interferes with reading and solving word problems usually included in tests and textbook exercises. There is something fundamentally wrong with the pupil's performance that should be studied carefully by the teacher. There always is some interfering habit or an ineffective approach in this type of disability and a remedial program based on a systematic diagnosis of the difficulty is necessary.

Type 4: Complex disability cases include the more complicated, subtle kinds of weaknesses. Such children are often normal in intelligence. Even though they may be severely retarded in arithmetic, they may be capable in other areas such as reading. These children have developed blockings, tensions, and faulty attitudes that make them ineffective learners of arithmetic.

With the passing of time, these tensions become more severe and the children demonstrate fear and worry and often a lack of desire to learn. This group should be given careful individual attention under the guidance of clinical specialists, if available.

These four categories should be regarded as descriptive designations. There actually is no clear line of demarcation between them. It should also be pointed out that all elements of the total learning situation have a bearing on the success the pupil has in learning arithmetic, including the curriculum, methods of instruction, the adequacy of learning materials, environmental conditions, and the social interrelationships of the members of the class group.

DIAGNOSING LEARNING DIFFICULTIES

Standard and survey tests give the teacher a general indication of the pupil's level of achievement. They indicate the broad areas of strength and weakness so that the teacher can plan the instructional program intelligently.

There also are available analytical diagnostic tests that enable the teacher to locate specific weak spots in some major skill.

For instance, an analytical diagnostic test of division by two-place numbers consists of separate tests of each major skill involved in this process. An analysis of the division example . . . shows that the underlying basic skills are:

$$
\begin{array}{r}
2 \\
27\overline{)80} \\
54 \\
\hline
26
\end{array}
$$

1. Ability to divide to estimate the quotient figure. In this case, the estimated quotient, 4, $(2\overline{)\ 8\ })$, is too large and must be corrected, a difficult step.
2. Placing the quotient correctly
3. Multiplying the divisor by the quotient
4. Addition as needed in carrying in multiplication
5. Subtracting to find the remainder.

A well-constructed analytical diagnostic test will test each of these basic skills. The results enable the teacher to identify deficiencies in specific areas which may be the root of an apparent disability in division. Research has shown that, in some cases, a single deficiency, for example in subtraction, is the basic cause of incorrect work in division; in other cases, weaknesses in several of the component skills require attention. It is necessary to examine the results for each pupil to discover the factors that may be at the root of his trouble.

Analytical diagnostic tests should be used systematically in the regular instructional program so that weak spots can be promptly diagnosed and corrected. For example, a series of such tests in the addition of common fractions in grades five and six should include tests for these units.

1. Addition of like fractions—no carrying involved—as in ¼ + ¼, or 3¼ + 2¼
2. Addition of like fractions involving carrying, as in ¾ + ¾, or 2½ + 4½
3. Addition of related fractions, as in ½ + ¼, or 3⅓ + 4⅚
4. Addition of unrelated fractions, such as ⅓ + ¼, or ¾ + ⅚.

Analytical diagnostic tests are provided in a number of arithmetic textbooks. When they are not available, the teacher can quite easily prepare them according to directions given in the reference below.[1]

Analytical diagnostic tests *locate* specific areas of weakness. However, they do not in themselves reveal the nature of the underlying difficulty, how well the child understands the steps in the solution, the effectiveness of his thought processes and his methods of work, or the kinds of computational errors as such that cause incorrect work.

These are the diagnostic procedures that have been found helpful in studying the work of individual pupils having difficulties in learning arithmetic:

1. Analysis of the pupil's written work to discover faulty procedures, misunderstood steps in solutions, and purely computational errors, such as lack of knowledge of basic number facts or incorrect operations
2. Having the pupil give orally the steps he uses in working an example to discover faulty procedures, roundabout methods of thinking, etc.
3. Questioning the pupil to see how well he understands the steps involved, his thought processes, attitude toward arithmetic, study habits, experimental background, and so on
4. Observation of the pupil's behavior to discover evidence of faulty methods of work, counting, poor work habits, emotional maladjustment, lack of interest, extent of effort made to learn
5. Securing from school records pertinent information that may be of value in making a diagnosis.

Similar procedures of diagnosis may be used to determine reasons for poor work in problem-solving, in the use of instruments of measurement, and in ability to apply arithmetic in other subject matter areas.

PRINCIPLES OF FOLLOW-UP

When the instructional program in arithmetic is adjusted to the needs and abilities of the pupils, the number who do not make reasonably good prog-

---

[1] Brueckner, Leo J., and Bond, Guy L., *The Diagnosis and Treatment of Learning Difficulties*. New York: Appleton-Century-Crofts. 1955. Chapters 8 and 9.

ress is reduced to a minimum. Minor difficulties usually respond quickly to corrective treatment. However, under existing conditions, it is almost inevitable that in almost every class there will be pupils who encounter unusual difficulties. Teachers must learn to use diagnostic procedures such as those described above to determine the underlying nature of the problem. The teacher has the responsibility of planning the corrective work that will most likely lead to improvement in the learner.

The following principles may be regarded as basic in the management of an improvement program for pupils having serious difficulty in arithmetic:

1. Base treatment on a diagnosis and make it individualized.
2. Secure the interested cooperation of the learner so he will be likely to attack his problem aggressively and willingly.
3. Attack specific difficulties directly. Begin reteaching at the point where there is likely to be success in the corrective work from the start, so that the learner will take satisfaction in the progress he makes.
4. Take steps to correct any physical, emotional, and environmental factors that are likely to niterfere with progress in mastering the difficulty.
5. Proceed on a tentative basis in the correction of weaknesses. Do not hesitate to modify the steps being taken when progress is slow and uncertain.
6. Select instructional procedures and materials that are of demonstrated value in making operations meaningful to the learner.
7. Integrate the corrective and developmental program so that the individual will not feel isolated and will feel that he still is a member of the group.
8. Take steps to assure the growth of all aspects of the learner's personality. Do not focus on the correction of deficiencies to the extent that such positive values as interests, attitudes, and appreciations are neglected.

The Ability of Elementary-School Children to Learn the New Mathematics

Patrick Suppes

Since 1956 I have been involved with the introduction of various nontraditional mathematical concepts to elementary-school children. These concepts are "nontraditional" in terms of the curriculum ordinarily offered to elementary-school children; they are not necessarily new from a mathematical standpoint. For example, in 1958 and for several years thereafter, Newton

Reprinted from *Theory into Practice* (April 1964), 57–61, by permission of the publisher.

Hawley and I experimented extensively on the introduction of geometrical constructions to primary-grade children.[1]

Beginning in 1959 I turned my attention to the basic arithmetic curriculum, and since that time have been developing the *Sets and Numbers* series as a new basic, but very much enriched, curriculum in elementary-school mathematics.[2] Work on the Sets and Numbers project is continuing, and by this time next year we hope to have completed the preliminary editions for grades 4, 5, and 6.[3] In the present article, however, I shall stress certain special aspects of research with which we have been concerned for the past several years. I have divided this paper into three sections. The first section discusses the work in mathematical logic that we have conducted with gifted fifth and sixth graders since 1960. The second section deals with our current project of vertically accelerating in mathematics a group of 40 gifted first graders for the entire period of their elementary-school education. Finally, the third section describes some of the psychological experiments on mathematical concept formation, which we have been conducting in conjunction with the pedagogical program.

MATHEMATICAL LOGIC IN THE ELEMENTARY SCHOOL

In modern times, logic has gained depth and breadth as a subject for study. Only in recent years have the systematic relations between logic and mathematics been established and a completely explicit theory of inference formulated which is adequate to deal with all the standard examples of deductive reasoning in mathematics and the empirical sciences.

The concept of axioms and deduction of theorems from axioms is at the heart of all modern mathematics. The purpose of this project has been to introduce the academically gifted elementary-school child to modern mathematics and mathematical methods at a level that is rigorous but simple enough in presentation and context to permit fairly easy comprehension.

A pilot study in the teaching of mathematical logic to a group of selected fifth-grade students was begun at Clifford Elementary School in Redwood

[1] For an evaluation by persons outside the project, *see* Thomas Denmark and Robert Kalin, "Suitability of Teaching Geometric Construction in Upper Elementary Grades—A Pilot Study," *The Arithmetic Teacher*, February, 1964, *11*, 73–80.

[2] The initial year of the Sets and Numbers project has been described in Patrick Suppes and Blair A. McKnight, "Sets and Numbers in Grade One, 1959–60," *The Arithmetic Teacher*, October, 1961, *8*, 287–90. The work of subsequent years has been described in Patrick Suppes and Shirley A. Hill, "The Concept of Set," *Grade Teacher*, April, 1962, *79*, 51, 86–90; and Patrick Suppes and Shirley A. Hill, "Set Theory in the Primary Grades," *New York State Mathematics Teacher's Journal*, April, 1963, *13*, 46–53. Volumes for the series from grades K to 3 are now available from L. W. Singer Company, Syracuse, New York.

[3] Some of the test data on the project appear in Suppes and Hill, "Set Theory in the Primary Grades," *op. cit.*

City, California, in the autumn of 1960. The class consisted of 25 students selected from the several fifth-grade classes in the school on the basis of their arithmetic achievement scores. The children had been given the arithmetic test during the seventh month of their fourth-grade year; only students who had scored at the sixth-grade level or above at that time were selected for the logic program. The class was taught in 1960–61 and in 1961–62 by members of the project staff.

Eleven classes with a total of 260 fifth-grade students began the study of logic in the fall of 1961; they were taught by their classroom teachers. During the preceding summer, an intensive four-week course was given to ten teachers and three of the school principals. These same teachers were offered a second course in the fall of 1962 for the continuation of their classes during the academic year 1962–63. Eleven classes of sixth graders consisting of 215 students took part in the second year of study.

During this two-year course, the classes met, on the average, three times a week for about 30 minutes. The chapters of the experimental text had the following titles: Chapter 1. "Symbolizing Sentences in Sentential Logic"; Chapter 2. "Logical Inference: Deriving Conclusions from Given Premises Using Standard Rules of Sentential Inference"; Chapter 3. "Truth and Validity: Diagrams of Truth Value, Conditional Proofs, Indirect Proofs, Invalidity, Consistency"; Chapter 4. "Truth Values and Tautologies"; Chapter 5. "Symbolizing Sentences in Predicate Logic: Terms, Predicates, Universal Quantifiers"; Chapter 6. "Universal Specification and Law of Identity"; Chapter 7. "A Simple Mathematical System: Axioms for the Theory of Addition"; Chapter 8. "Universal Generalization, General Theorems."

Two Stanford University logic classes were used as control groups. These classes consisted of students taking elementary mathematical logic at the customary age and educational level. These two university classes met in the autumn quarters of 1961 and 1962.

Two tests were given to the college group of 186 students in the fall of 1961. The first of these tests was also given to all eleven fifth-grade classes (260 students). This test was on the recognition of the logical structure of sentences and beginning work in formal proofs. For the college group, the mean was 91, the median 97. For the fifth-grade group, the mean was 76, the median 83. Seven fifth-grade classes (164 students) took the second test, which dealt primarily with the symbolic manipulations involved in formal proofs within the framework of sentential logic. The two groups had highly comparable scores on this test. For the college group, the mean was 70, the median 72; for the fifth-grade group, the mean was 67, the median 77.

It should be emphasized that the two control groups of Stanford students were themselves a highly select body of undergraduate college students, with an ability range very comparable to that of the selected fifth graders. As the test scores I have cited indicate, the performance of the fifth graders was comparable to that of the college students. More detailed analysis supports this conclusion. From our work on this project, two conclusions of some significance emerge:

1. The upper quartile of elementary-school students can achieve a significant conceptual and technical mastery of elementary mathematical logic. The level of mastery is 85 to 90 per cent of that achieved by comparable university students.
2. The more dedicated and able elementary-school teachers can be given sufficient training in five or six semester hours of instruction to teach classes in elementary mathematical logic. It is important that a teacher-training program of no more than six semester hours be very closely geared to the actual program of instruction that the teacher will follow in his own classroom.

Finally, in the summer of 1963 we selected the ablest students from the initial group of 260 and gave them an additional intensive course for four weeks. In the last part of this program, the students were given Boolean algebra in axiomatic form and elementary topology. With their prior training in formal logic, they found it extremely easy to master the technique of thinking intuitively about these new mathematical systems and writing down appropriate proofs of elementary theorems. Our work during this summer suggests that any able group of students who received a broad mathematical training in the last years of elementary school is prepared for an intensive and rich mathematical curriculum during the six years of secondary school.[4]

VERTICAL ACCELERATION OF GIFTED FIRST GRADERS

Beginning with the current academic year, we have undertaken an intensive accelerated program of mathematics for a group of gifted first graders selected from four elementary schools in the Palo Alto Unified School District. As the first step in selection, the New York Test of Arithmetical Meaning was given to all entering first-grade students in the four schools. Students ranking above the 70th percentile on this test of first-grade achievement were then tested more intensively; most of them were given individual Stanford-Binet's. This procedure resulted in the selection of 40 children having IQ's ranging from 122 to 166 with a mean of 137. At the present time, these children are being taught mathematics in the four schools in small groups of 9 to 12 pupils. The classes meet four days a week with each session lasting not more than 35 minutes.

For each of the 40 students, we are collecting data on the number of problems worked and the errors made each day. During the first seven weeks, a typical child in the *bottom* quartile of the group worked approxi-

---

[4] Further details on this mathematical-logic project are contained in the final report, "Experimental Teaching of Mathematical Logic in the Elementary School," written by the author and Frederick Binford, on deposit with the Cooperative Research Program, U.S. Office of Education.

mately 2,500 problems. In terms of the *Sets and Numbers* mathematics series, the topics covered in working these problems are: sets; notation for sets; identity of sets; union of sets; number of things in a set; addition of numbers; place-value system of notation for numbers; difference of sets; subtraction of numbers; applications: telling time, linear and liquid measures, changing money; recognition of triangles, quadrilaterals, pentagons, and circles; inside and outside of a simple closed figure; figures of the same shape and size; figures of the same shape but of different sizes; equilateral triangles; perimeter of simple polygons. During the same period, the children in the top quartile of the group also covered the introduction of the numbers 11 to 19, with considerable practice on their properties, the place-value notation to hundreds, the concept of *subset*, and the corresponding numerical concept of *less than*—a total of more than 500 additional problems.

At the present rate of progress, most of the students in the selected group will complete our already enriched second-grade curriculum by the end of the first grade. At the same time, they will also have worked through Book 1 of *Geometry for Primary Grades* as supplementary material. Children in the top quartile will have covered up to half of the third-grade curriculum in the Sets and Numbers program. We are, of course, impressed with the rapid progress that these children are making. The students in the top quartile have been working at an enormous rate; during the second week, for example, they averaged more than 150 problems a day, and during the first seven weeks they did not fall below the rate of 50 problems a day during any single week. Naturally, we expect this rate to slow down as they advance in the curriculum and come to more difficult material. It is, however, indicative of the speed with which brighter children can cover modern mathematical topics designed for a standard curriculum and absorption by all children.

Figure 1 shows the rate of progress during the first seven weeks of the top four students in the group of 40. The decline in rate from the second week to the fifth week is a result of the increasing difficulty of the material in *Sets and Numbers,* Book 1B. The increase in rate from the fifth to the seventh week is due to the fact that at this point the children had begun *Sets and Numbers,* Book 2A, which is the first half of the second-grade course; the early part of this book spends a good deal of time reviewing the concepts introduced in the first grade. The error rate for the four students represented in Figure 1 averaged less than 3 per cent for the seven weeks.

Before completing this part of the discussion, I want to make the point that the ability to learn the new mathematics concepts is not restricted to gifted children. I have attempted to show how rapidly gifted children advance through the new concepts organized in terms of the standard curriculum aimed at the average child. We also have in our project files data on achievement records with a class of mentally retarded students ranging in age from eight to fourteen years who worked with the first-grade books.

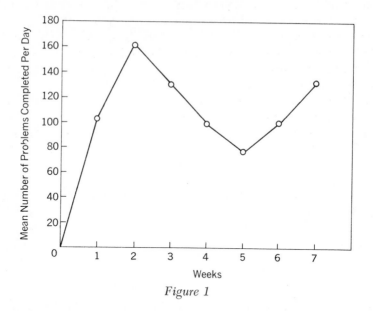

Figure 1

Their achievement scores indicated that they were mastering the basic concepts and were showing an ability to move ahead, though at a slow pace. It is perhaps already obvious that with proper pacing and presentation all students are able to learn the concepts of modern mathematics. Probably the more important point to be drawn from our own research is that the brighter children—those, let us say, in the upper quartile—are able to cover a great many more mathematical concepts and to learn a good deal more mathematics during their elementary-school years than we have been willing to admit in the recent past.

RESEARCH ON MATHEMATICAL CONCEPT FORMATION

Since 1959 we have also been conducting in our laboratories at Stanford an extensive program of psychological research on mathematical concept formation in children. The evidence of these experiments, which I shall not attempt to report in detail here, clearly indicates that many of the concepts of mathematics not traditionally taught in the elementary school are easily within the range of the average child. A few examples will illustrate this point.

In an experiment conducted by Erline Stoll, one group of kindergarten children was taught to recognize triangles, quadrilaterals, and pentagons; and another group was taught to discriminate between acute, right, and obtuse angles. Most of the subjects were able to satisfy the rather strong criterion of nine successive correct responses, even though only minimal instructional aids were provided by the experimenter.[5]

In another experiment, five- and six-year-old subjects were taught to recognize the notational pattern of the numbers 4 and 5 in the binary number system. Most of the children were able to master this relatively simple concept in one experimental session.[6]

We have also experimented extensively with the learning of the concept of identity of sets and equivalence of sets. First-grade children who had had no systematic instructions in set concepts made very good progress in a tightly controlled and tightly structured experimental setup in which only minimal instructions were given by the experimenter.[7]

Shirley Hill made an extensive empirical study of the logical abilities of children. She gave a test instrument consisting of 100 items to 270 children ranging in age from six to eight years (first, second, and third grades). Each of the 100 items, presented orally, consisted of two or three verbal premises plus a conclusion formulated as a question. The subject was asked to affirm or deny the conclusion as presented. The 100 items were divided equally between positive and negative answers. The first part of the test consisted of 60 items drawn from sentential logic. Each conclusion or its negation followed from the given premises by the sentential theory of inference. The second part consisted of 40 items drawn from predicate logic, including 13 classical syllogisms. The predicate-logic items also included inferences using two-place predicates together with existential quantifiers.

Every attempt was made to construct the items in such a way that the omission of one premise would make it impossible to draw the correct conclusion. To provide a behavioral check on this aspect of the items, a baseline group of 50 subjects was given the test with the first premise of each item omitted. This group got an average of 52.02 per cent of the items correct, which does not significantly differ from chance.

The major results of the complete test follow. The first graders got 71.18 per cent of the items correct; the second graders got 79.54 per cent of the items correct; and the third graders got 85.58 per cent correct. This study provides substantial evidence that even six-year-old children are able to deal very effectively with verbal premises that call for hypothetical reasoning and are by no means limited to "concrete" operations.[8]

[5] See Erline A. Stoll, "Geometrical Concept Formation in Kindergarten Children." Doctoral dissertation, Stanford University, 1962.

[6] See Patrick Suppes and Rose Ginsberg, "Application of a Stimulus Sampling Model to Children's Concept Formation with and without Overt Correction Responses," *Journal of Experimental Psychology*, April, 1962, 63, 330–36.

[7] See Patrick Suppes and Rose Ginsberg, "A Fundamental Property of All-or-None Models, Binomial Distribution of Responses Prior to Conditioning, with Application to Concept Formation in Children," *Psychological Review*, March, 1963, 70, 139–61.

[8] See Shirley A. Hill, "A Study of the Logical Abilities of Children." Doctoral dissertation, Stanford University, 1961.

The program of psychological experimentation as an extension and adjunct to our pedagogical program is continuing. It is fair to say that we do
not yet have a clear idea of the full potentialities of below-average, average,
and bright children for learning the concepts of mathematics. The problem is
a complex one. I am sure that we shall not be able to solve it definitely in the
next few years. We do hope, however, to continue to make contributions to
its solution.

Learning Mathematics: A Survey of 12 Countries

Alexander W. Astin

These two volumes report on a comparative study of the mathematics
achievement of school children in Australia, Belgium, England, Finland,
France, Israel, Japan, the Netherlands, Scotland, Sweden, the United States,
and West Germany. The data were collected in the early part of 1964 by
means of a series of standardized multiple-choice tests especially devised
for international use. These were administered in each country to samples
of 13-year-olds and of pupils finishing secondary school. Although "the tests
were not devised primarliy in order to make total score comparisons between
countries possible and certainly not as yard sticks for an "international contest" (vol. 2, p. 26), such comparisons seem to have been encouraged by
the publisher's press release, which declared, among other things, that
"some nations do a far better job than others in teaching mathematics . . .
the best overall job of mathematics instruction in public schools appears to
be done in Japan. The United States is among the least effective." Thus, in
a subsequent article entitled "Why Johnny Can't Add," *Newsweek* (13
March 1967) reported that "Japanese schools do the best overall job of math
instruction and U.S. schools do just about the worst."

The principal scientific goal of the project was to use these comparative
international data in order to identify social and educational practices that
influence the student's achievement in mathematics. Presumably such information would be of great value in many aspects of educational planning,

particularly in curriculum development. Since the comparability of data from the respective countries was thus vital to the success of the project, a great deal of care was devoted to the sampling procedures. The basic plan was first to sample schools within each country and then to sample pupils within schools. The adequate sampling of schools was considered important because of the possibility that there would be substantial differences among the schools of any one country. Except for two or possibly three of the countries, the stratified sampling of schools within countries appears to have been well carried out. It is much less clear, however, how representative the within-school sampling was; the authors give only sketchy information on this point: "some countries attached importance to testing whole classes while others did not" and "the subsampling process . . . appears to have given difficulty in some cases" (vol. 1, pp. 161–62). Since the local school officials were usually given the responsibility for selecting the pupils who were to take the tests at each school, it is unfortunate that no independent checks on the representativeness of these subsamples were made. Ideally, each participating pupil should have been asked to report data (for example, marks in recent courses) which could have been checked against comparable statistics based on all pupils in the school. The pupils tested did give their parents' occupations and educational levels; these data, which are summarized by country in the report, could have been checked against comparable data from national censuses as a rough measure of representativeness. In the absence of such independent checks, the representativeness of the samples of pupils tested, and hence the validity of the international comparisons, are open to question.

Most of the second volume is devoted to formulating and testing hypotheses about how differences in the organization of schools, in curricula, in instructional methods, and in social factors affect mathematics achievement. Unfortunately, the results of most of these analyses are ambiguous, because of the cross-sectional design that was used. For example, while it was frequently found that the average achievement in one type of school differed from the average achievement in another type, the data offer no way of determining whether these differences are due to the schools' different effects on achievement or to one school's being more attractive to able students than the other. A longitudinal study, in which relative changes over time in the achievement of pupils in different schools were compared, would have helped greatly to resolve many such ambiguities.

Although the authors recognize that "the design of this study does not allow for the confirmation of imputed causal relationships" (vol. 1, p. 31), the discussion and conclusions frequently betray an uncritical acceptance of certain causal interpretations even when equally plausible alternative explanations suggest themselves. For example, positive associations between the child's mathematics achievement and his parents' educational level, which were found for 13-year-olds in nearly every country, are consistently interpreted as attributable to environmental influences in the home: "It appears that parents with high socio-economic characteristics do a better job of preparing their children for school" (vol. 2, p. 254). The possibility that these relationships may be mediated, even in part, by genetic factors is given virtually no consideration. A similar attitude is revealed in the authors' recurrent use of the term "social bias" in reference to the marked tendency, in every country, for those students who finish secondary school to come from better-educated families than those who do not finish.

Potential consumers of the findings based on between-country correlations should be cautioned that some of these correlations may be seriously in error because of mistakes in the calculations for one country, Finland —mistakes that the editor discovered when the volumes were in galley form. While some approximations to the correct data for Finland are provided in an appendix to the second volume, the possible effects of the miscalculations are not discussed. A comparison between these last-minute approximations and the data used for Finland in the text, however, shows a startling shift in that country's relative ranking on mean total scores. In one of the populations of 13-year-olds (there were two samples of this age group in each country), Finland drops from third place to last place among the 12 countries in total mathematics achievement; in the other 13-year-old population, the drop is from fourth to 11th place. Apparently, the entire text was written without knowledge of this error.

That these errors in Finland's data have markedly distorted many of the between-country correlations can be seen if one recomputes some of the coefficients, using the data in Table 2.2 and the corrected achievement mean for Finland. For example, in calculating by hand just a few trial coefficients, I found striking changes in magnitude and even reversals in sign. The Spearman rank-difference correlation between total mathematics achievement and "number of subjects taken in grade 12" changed from +.32 to −.10. Conversely, the correlation between total mathematics achievement and "student opportunity to learn all items" jumped from a modest .62 to a highly suggestive .95. As another consequence of the change in Finland's relative position, the tentative conclusion (vol. 2, p. 68) that late entry into school (age 7) may have a detrimental effect on mathematics achievement at age 13 is greatly strengthened. The 13-year-olds of the only two countries uniformly employing this later age of school entry (Finland and Sweden) show the lowest mean mathematics achievement.

In the interests of correcting any false impressions that might be created by the discussions based on these erroneous between-country correlations, the authors might want to consider recomputing the coefficients and distributing a revised presentation and interpretation of these findings.

The magnitude of the observed differences in performance between students in different countries is not trivial: for instance, the average 13-year-old student in Japan answered correctly nearly twice as many items (about 31) in the 70-item test as did the average 13-year-old in either the United States or Sweden (about 16 items each). If one assumes that the within-school sampling was random in each country and that these mean scores are therefore truly representative of national achievement levels in mathematics, what evidence does the study provide concerning the possible reasons for these differences? The simplest and perhaps most plausible explanation would seem to be that the countries varied considerably in the extent to which their curricula provided opportunities to learn the types of material covered in the test. We have already noted that the students' opportunity to learn the test material (as judged by their teachers) correlated very highly (.95) with between-country differences in mean achievement. The *within*-country correlations between these variables were consistently positive (median $r = .19$), although the range among countries was from nonsignificance to more than .50. It seems likely that the nonsignificant correlations in certain countries can be explained by the relative homogeneity of the mathematics curriculum within these countries. If the causal relations implied here can be accepted, an important task for curriculum experts in this and other low-scoring countries is to determine whether this apparent lack of fit between the test questions and the student's opportunity to learn this type of material is a fault of the curriculum or of the test. If the test questions can be accepted as an appropriate and reasonably representative sample of tasks in modern mathematics, then this may be one situation where "teaching for the test" makes good sense.

Considering that more than 130,000 students, 13,000 teachers, and 5000 schools from the 12 countries participated, this project stands as a major technical and, perhaps, diplomatic achievement. The educational and scientific value of the findings is much less clear, however, because the method used was not entirely adequate to the job. It can only be hoped that the planners of the next large-scale international study, which is scheduled to begin in 1968, will most seriously consider the advantages of using a longitudinal design.

Evaluation and Creative Mathematics

Alvin M. Westcott and James A. Smith

> . . . *If a man does not keep pace with his companions,*
> *perhaps it is because he hears a different drummer. Let*
> *him step to the music which he hears, however measured*
> *or far away.*
>
> HENRY DAVID THOREAU, *Walden*

HOW CAN WE EVALUATE?

Creative teaching of mathematics is the result of teacher planning. It is deliberate, not accidental. It is the result of planning in terms of clearly defined objectives, selecting methods to meet the objectives, and identifying evaluation techniques to appraise pupil progress and help plan future objectives. The most reliable and defensible evaluation of a mathematics lesson is in relation to the objectives prescribed in advance. This is the frame of reference against which the occurrences within the lesson *can* be evaluated.

TOWARD A MORE CLINICAL ANALYSIS OF CREATIVE TEACHING

To attempt to analyze creative teaching in a clinical manner is in many respects analogous to attempting to hold a moonbeam in your hand. Creative teaching, by many experts' definitions, is so varied, individualized, and inconsistent that it would seem to defy any kind of objective analysis. Yet what is highly creative teaching but a modification and/or variation of the teaching act? If we can determine the behavioristic norms of the teaching act as such, why can we not also determine those behaviors that are inherent in highly creative teaching?

In observing some teachers of mathematics, one might detect a great many behaviors that are apart from the behavioristic norms of the teaching act, others would give evidence of fewer variations. For this reason, creative teaching is a relative commodity. It is inaccurate to conceptualize two distinct classifications of teachers—creative and noncreative. There are some creative aspects to *every* teacher's classroom performance. But supervisors and administrators in our public schools generally agree that there are teachers who are immensely different from their colleagues in terms of their ability to develop new ideas, construct original teaching aids, and see unusual relationships among subject-matter areas. It is this group of teachers, whom their peers and supervisors quickly identify as "creative," that the profession needs to examine more clinically.

We have in the past been satisfied with tossing around very loosely the phrase "creative teacher." It would be extremely helpful in terms of promoting excellence in teaching to analyze those aspects of the highly creative teacher's performance which will lend themselves to objective observation and measurement. If this can be accomplished, the outcome might be used to help other teachers. Do highly creative teachers perform their teaching act intuitively, or can they explain their thought processes? Do highly creative teachers of mathematics differ in any significant ways from highly creative teachers in general? These and many other important questions relative to the highly creative teacher remain unanswered by research.

IDENTIFICATION AND EVALUATION OF CREATIVE TEACHING NEED NOT BE CRUDE

Clinical analysis of creative teaching is in its infancy. There are, however, two accepted bases from which evaluation can emanate.

1. *Highly creative teaching is performed by creative personalities.* There has been a great deal of research on the nature of the highly creative personality. The Thematic Apperception Test, Rorschach Test, and Minnesota Multiphasic Personality Inventory have assisted greatly in identifying the characteristics that differentiate highly creative persons from less creative ones. The work of Hargreaves (1927), Guilford and associates (1957), MacKinnon (1960), and Torrance (1959) (see Chapter 2 of this book), to name only a few, has given us a firm basis from which to draw evaluative criteria. To summarize: researchers have provided us with a great deal of information relative to the nature and behavior of the highly creative personality.

2. *No matter what definition of the teaching act one may choose to employ,* all *teachers engage in three common behaviors.* Regardless of their abilities and professional training, all teachers:

    a. Establish objectives for their teaching (either consciously or unconsciously).
    b. Plan activities, materials, and experiences to meet the objectives.
    c. Devise techniques and instruments to measure, evaluate and report students' progress in terms of the objectives.

The manner in which a teacher engages in the three basic behaviors inherent in the teaching act can be observed, measured, and evaluated on a relative scale. Conventional and unconventional methods can be objectively identified. Therefore, creative approaches to at least these three aspects of the teaching act can be identified on a relative scale of frequency.

THE HIGHLY CREATIVE TEACHER APPROACHES THE TEACHING ACT UNIQUELY

The highly creative teacher of mathematics undertakes the task of determining objectives for teaching in the following ways:

1. The objectives may be expressed in some type of unique written form.
2. The objectives may encompass a wider range of interrelationships between mathematics and other areas.

Remember that the highly creative individual frequently perceives relationships where average individuals do not. This was demonstrated recently while the authors were observing a student teacher present a mathematics lesson. The lesson was aimed at demonstrating the mathematical relationships that exist among intersections of sets, prime numbers, and least common denominators. The relationships the student teacher demonstrated were new not only to the students she was teaching but to most of the adults observing her lesson. This student teacher had determined the mathematical relationships while thinking through a method for teaching the determination of least common denominator (addition of fractions). Creative thinking was the means by which she had evolved the novel mathematical relationships.

A teacher at the intermediate level of the elementary school uses set concepts in discussing the relative position of his community in the world. For example, the United States is a member of the set of nations of the world. Then there is the set of the fifty states of the United States, of which the northeastern states constitute a subset. And the states contain a set of counties, which in turn contain subsets of townships and cities. The application of the set concept to political divisions is an unusual but useful one for a teacher to make.

The highly creative teacher of mathematics also introduces variations commensurate with the objectives for the lesson in the selection, construction, and implementation of classroom activities and teaching aids. In like manner, the highly creative teacher makes innovations in the task of testing and evaluating student achievement in mathematics.

Two Human Elements in Evaluating the Teaching-Learning Process

There are two human elements that must be accounted for in evaluating the teaching-learning process: the behavior of the teacher(s) and the students (considered individually and as a group). As stated previously, a teacher may manifest much creative behavior in his teaching act, yet there is no guarantee that this will precipitate creative behavior in his students. Conversely, students sometimes engage in overt creative behavior while the classroom teacher gives much evidence of being a rigid, tightly structured personality.

A more ideal teaching-learning situation exists when the teacher and his students serve to stimulate creative thinking and overt creative behavior in each other. But we must be aware that creative teaching behaviors do not always beget creative responses from students.

The Two-Headed Evaluation Task

In order to evaluate a mathematics lesson, one must have data pertaining to the manner in which the teacher behaved during the mathematics lesson as well as performance data relative to the students who experienced the mathematics lesson. Therefore, evaluation of creative behavior in mathematics involves testing, measuring, and evaluating the behavior of both the students and the teacher. This is a monumental task, to say the least. The greatest obstacle at present is the fact that there is no clear-cut description of what constitutes highly creative teaching behavior in mathematics or, for that matter, of what constitutes highly creative student behavior in mathematics. Even with the Torrance list of characteristics, it is possible to produce deductively a list of only very general behaviors that constitute highly creative behavior in mathematics.

All behavior can be plotted on a relative scale. At present, the single most reliable criterion for plotting creative behavior seems to be the *uncommonness* of the behavior, which, unfortunately, disregards whether or not the behavior is of a constructive or destructive nature.

A response may be uncommon coming from one individual yet common in terms of the individual's peer group. Uncommon student performance in mathematics is best judged by a teacher who is familiar enough with the individual to recognize the uncommonness as such.

What Does a Creative Response Look Like?

In order to measure or assess a creative response, the teacher needs to have a mental picture of what a creative solution or response looks like (see Figure 1).

The circled P in the diagram composing Figure 1 represents a mathematical word problem to which a group of thirty children have been exposed. Each child is asked to make a list of as many solutions as he can think of, and he is encouraged to construct as many answers as possible.

Assuming that all the children in the class have at least a general conception of what the problem asks for, their solutions can be compared and charted. We have not charted the *methods* the children used, but rather the *solutions* each child offered independently. The small circles containing the letter S represent the galaxy of solutions the class offered. Note that there is also a number included with each S; this represents the number of students in the class of thirty children who suggested this particular solution.

The thirty students suggested a total of forty-nine solutions in all. Of these only seven were different; the rest were repeats of the same solutions. There were three solutions that were offered only once, by one student. These three represent the most *uncommon* suggested by that particular class—not neces-

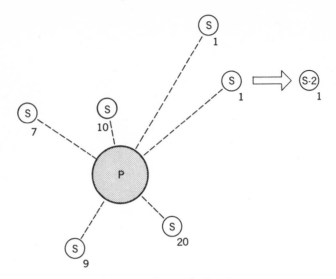

Figure 1. A diagram of responses

sarily the most practical, but the most unique in terms of the group and therefore the *most creative*.

The solution labeled S-2 in Figure 1 is an example of "hitchhiking" a solution, meaning that the child evolved a solution as a result of being mentally triggered by another solution.

If, as a teacher, you work several years with the same *basic* mathematical material, you come to know what constitutes a typical response to mathematical word problems and which responses are very different—atypical.

The number of solutions that each child has on his list is a rough estimate of his *fluency* with ideas—in this case, ideas as applied to the given problem. This fluency factor is particularly significant, since we do know that creative people tend to consider *more* solutions, as well as a wider range of solutions, to a problem.

One more thing: Each child's list of answers must be viewed by the teacher in the context of the child's personality. The aim is to help the child become more creative. Consequently, the teacher must ask himself whether the child's responses represent creative growth for this particular child.

The mathematics teacher who desires to evaluate children's creative thinking abilities must construct test situations such as the above, in which children are asked to provide as many different methods of solving a problem as they can and/or as many different solutions to a problem as they can. From this type of test, the teacher of mathematics can determine the quantity and uniqueness of ideas that each child can provide within a specified time element. This type of mathematical testing is noticeably absent in some modern mathematics programs.

OBJECTIVES FOR TEACHING AND EVALUATION OF STUDENTS' LEARNING

One basic function of the teaching act is to establish teaching objectives that serve as pivotal points from which all of the other teaching functions take on meaning. These objectives, however, become more meaningful for evaluation purposes when they are expressed in *behavioristic terms*.

All teachers engage in the identification and implementation of teaching objectives. This process may be conscious or unconscious, deliberate or unintentional. To evaluate teaching effectiveness with a reasonable degree of objectivity and accuracy, the evaluator can only concern himself with children's behaviors that develop intentionally as a result of a planned teaching act. During any mathematics lesson (as with lessons in other subject-matter areas), incidental, unintentional, peripheral objectives may be accomplished; but highly creative mathematics teaching cannot depend upon random and/or unintentional accomplishment of objectives. The quality of a mathematics lesson must be evaluated in terms of the predetermined objectives for the lesson. If the objectives have been poorly conceived, the lesson is seriously handicapped.

Ease of testing and evaluation are directly related to the specificity of objectives. The reader will discover that the more specifically objectives for a lesson are written, the easier it becomes to devise tests and evaluation procedures for those objectives.

TESTING CHILDREN'S ACHIEVEMENT IN THE DISCOVERY METHOD OF TEACHING MATHEMATICS

In order to plan future learning for students in an intelligent fashion, we, as mathematics teachers, need to test and measure student achievements. The conventional conception of testing in mathematics applies largely to testing the end product (the answer). Of course there will always be a need to do just that; it would be foolhardy not to be concerned with the accuracy of a solution to a mathematical problem. But standardized tests and the teacher-made variety tend not to test divergent thinking. In testing students' achievement in the discovery method of teaching, such tests are relevant only to step four. If we strive to promote a galaxy of answers or solutions from children, tests which look for a single "right" answer are often inappropriate.

Teacher-made and standardized tests that permit a wide range of "right answers" are needed for the teacher who desires to test the range of flexible creative thinking in children. At the present time, such tests are relatively scarce. Therein lies a challenge for the classroom teacher to develop tests to ascertain how many variations a child can make in an answer and still keep the answer within the realm of possibility.

The discovery process contains at least four steps. Thus far the galaxy of final solutions has applied only to step four. Tests that reflect children's behavior at steps one and three can yield revealing information as to children's creative thinking abilities.

It is in a student's sensitivity to and perception of the problem (step one) as well as in his experimental behavior (step three) that he reveals his openness to and facility with the creative process. The teacher who wants to assess the nature and scope of a child's creative thinking in the discovery *method* needs to collect evidence about the child's behavior relative to steps one and three of the discovery *process*.

Creativity involves a process and a product; so does the discovery method of teaching. This is one reason why this method is such a fine teaching vehicle for promoting creativity. As a teacher of mathematics, you need to be as concerned about the process a child uses to find an answer as about the answer itself. The end product is much easier to test and evaluate than the process. But a description of the child's thinking processes within the discovery method (steps one and three) can reveal the quantity of solutions the child considered before settling on an answer.

Teacher observation of student behavior in step one of the discovery method is one technique of collecting evidence (anecdotal in character). The verbal responses students give (number of and type) during the discussion of a mathematical problem constitute important data, and the technique of soliciting responses from children constitutes a type of informal testing.

It is possible to construct paper and pencil tests that will test a student's understanding of a mathematical problem. The test questions need to be phrased in such a way that the student is encouraged to individually brainstorm all of the ramifications of the problem that he can think of. After reading a mathematical word problem on the test, the students are *not* requested to compute an answer to the problem. (Now, this is a switch, isn't it?) Instead, there are some printed test questions about the mathematical problem itself. The test is not designed to see if the student can figure out a correct answer to the mathematical problem; its purpose is to ascertain how sensitively and flexibly the student perceives the mathematical problem. In other words, this test is aimed at obtaining some test data relative to step one of the discovery method. The test might consist of one mathematical word problem. The student is asked to answer questions about the word problem, such as:

1. Is there any information that is not given in the word problem that could affect the answer to it?

2. How many *different* algorisms can you construct which would depict the word problem?

3. Do you see any problems "within the problem" which should be considered?

4. If you could change the wording of the problem in any way you wanted, what changes would you make and why?

It is just as difficult to appraise students' achievement in step three of the discovery process as in step one. Step three involves ideation, flashes of insight, hunches, etc. Until we understand more fully the inner working of the mind, step three will remain somewhat of a mystery to the teacher and the student. If some type of elaborate machine that could trace the thought processes of a human being was available, we could gather some electronic data as to the complexities and subtleties of creative thinking. At present we will have to test step three through teacher observations of students and students' verbal descriptions of the mental processes they employ in solving mathematical problems. Trial and error certainly is employed by some students in step three, but it is the least sophisticated method of attacking a problem.

And so step three of the discovery method—the essence of creative thinking—eludes and, at times, seems to defy analysis. An effective teacher can only set conditions for it to occur and attempt to observe and describe its nature.

TESTING AND EVALUATING MATHEMATICAL SKILLS AND KNOWLEDGES CREATIVELY

Creativity can be used in determining the *manner* in which teachers test, measure, and evaluate the mathematics progress of their students. The job of the mathematics teacher is two-fold. Mathematics as a discipline contains a body of ideas and skills, many of which society expects children to master. Therefore, in addition to appraising the students' creative behavior in mathematics, the mathematics teacher needs to identify, test, measure and evaluate students' progress toward the acquisition of the knowledges and skills prescribed by the curriculum. Unfortunately, this job is the only one to which many mathematics teachers address themselves. They avoid the sticky task of attempting to appraise the quantity and quality of students' creative behavior in mathematics. Both tasks are important.

How Can a Teacher Be Creative in Testing, Measuring, and Evaluating Children's Progress in Mathematics?

It is impossible to tell someone "how to be creative." An act is classified as creative because of its relationship to the particular setting in which it occurs.

Rather than attempt the impossible, the authors elect to describe some variations and modifications of conventional testing, measuring, and evaluating procedures and devices. This may give the reader a general understanding of creative variations from conventional practice. The authors suggest that the reader engage in reference reading relative to the many varieties of tests, such as readiness tests, achievement tests, diagnostic tests, nonverbal tests, performance tests, etc. Likewise the reader will need to study the mechanics of test item construction; true-false, multiple-choice, completion, matching questions, etc.

Evaluation involves interpreting the measurement data so that the teacher and others concerned with the learner can form an accurate picture of the learner's performance in relation to his past performance, the performance of his peers, and national norms if they are available.

EXAMPLES OF CREATIVE TESTING

The conventional method of attacking the testing task is to have children take a paper and pencil test of representative algorisms. Pencil and paper mathematics tests serve valuable purposes at times, but what other exciting materials and techniques might the teacher use to test his students? The following are some unusual techniques and devices that teachers have employed to test children relative to some aspect of mathematics:

Teacher A dictates a mathematics test on a tape recorder. Individually or in groups, children can listen to the test and work out the answers at their own speed.

Teacher B, a primary-level teacher, acts as store clerk for the play store set up in her classroom. One by one she asks the children to come to the store and shop for three items. She tells each child the cost of each item. The child, using paper and pencil, is requested to figure out how much he owes the store clerk. The papers upon which the children figure their bill serve as test papers.

Teacher C passes rhythm band instruments to each member of his class. He reads aloud a mathematical problem, allowing the class some time to think about the problem. The students are instructed to make a noise with their rhythm band instrument whenever they hear a correct answer to the problem. Then Teacher C reads aloud a list of possible answers. He makes mental notes of which children consistently make an incorrect response.

Teacher D acts as moderator for a mock television quiz game dealing with mathematical problems. The responses of individual children are recorded on a tape recorder throughout the game. Replaying the tape later enables Teacher D to determine which children seemed to be having difficulty with specific types of mathematical problems.

Teacher E uses a modification of the NUMBO game described in Chapter 2 as an informal test device.

Teacher F, using the opaque projector and some simple sketches, projects various groupings of objects on a screen. The children record on their papers number sentences that represent the groupings of objects projected on the screen.

Teacher G uses a puppet to administer a mathematics test. The puppet, dressed in a space pilot's suit, whispers in the teacher's ear each question for the test. Acting as central mission controller, the teacher repeats the puppet's directions to the students. The students compute on their papers various aspects of the "flight" as it is given to them by central control.

The number of methods of testing children in mathematics is limited only by the imagination of each teacher.

Evaluating a School Mathematics Curriculum

Donovan A. Johnson

In view of the current ferment in mathematics education we are all interested in ways to improve our judgment as we make decisions regarding new programs. How are we going to decide what mathematics to teach? How can we determine the best way to attain a given objective? How can we decide when a given concept should be taught?

It is going to be extremely difficult to make valid judgments of the relative effectiveness of different curricula. Many of our decisions will be based on subjective value judgments. Many decisions will have to wait until long-range effects are determined. Other decisions will need the cooperative judgment of specialists in several fields.

In discussing mathematics programs, I am confining myself to the specific curriculum proposals now being made by various groups and individuals. The evaluation of the mathematics program of a specific school often includes many factors beyond the curriculum. For example, the Evaluative Criteria used by secondary school administrators take into account the school's facilities, staff, registrations in given courses, and length of period, as well as courses and course content.

Evaluation is more than measurement, although it is usually based on measurement. Evaluation involves the use of judgment. In evaluation, we usually decide whether certain measurements, actions, or materials are good, bad, or indifferent. In evaluation we compare and then render judgment regarding the order relation of the items involved.

If we are to render value judgments regarding curricula proposals, we need certain criteria as guide lines. What should these criteria be? For our

Reprinted from *Leadership Role of State Supervisor of Mathematics,* Bulletin 1962, No. 1, 46–53, U.S. Department of Health, Education, and Welfare.

discussion today, I would like to suggest criteria of the following four types: mathematical, psychological, pedagogical, and philosophical.

MATHEMATICAL CRITERIA

There are several aspects of the mathematical content of a given curriculum to consider. The first of these is that the mathematical content of an acceptable curriculum must be *good mathematics*. By this, I do not necessarily mean modern mathematics or classical mathematics. Good mathematics is mathematics that is correct, precise, and elegant. Good mathematics uses the terminology, the processes, the sequence, and the symbolism that are as correct, clear, and complete as possible at the level for which the mathematics is prepared. To attain the proper degree of rigor for a given level is one of our most difficult problems.

Evaluating the mathematical content of a given program requires mathematical sophistication beyond that of many elementary or secondary teachers. In the current national experimental programs, however, attaining the proper degree of rigor for a given level is not much of a problem since the materials usually have been produced by groups composed of competent mathematicians.

However, the mathematical content must not only be good mathematics. It must also be appropriate mathematics. To be appropriate mathematics, it needs to be adapted to the students involved. It should meet the needs of the students, currently and in the future. In view of the uncertainty of what mathematics our students will need in the future, this choice is difficult. Thus, it would seem that the mathematics should emphasize flexibility, procedures, and broad principles rather than specific facts. It should provide experiences in applying concepts and skills as well as present the esthetic aspects of mathematics. It should provide experiences that develop good learning habits as well as a desire to learn.

The National Council of Teachers of Mathematics has appointed a committee on the Analysis of Experimental Programs, with Philip Peak of Indiana University as chairman. This committee will visit experimental projects and collect information relative to nine questions.

1. *Placement.* Various topics are being introduced at a number of different grade levels. The question is: *At a particular grade level, what topics can be developed most effectively?*

2. *New Topics.* Many topics hitherto not commonly included in mathematics programs are now being taught. The question is: *Which of these topics should become an integral part of the school mathematics program and at what level?*

3. *Structure.* There has been much discussion recently on the need for studying mathematical structures. The question is: *What emphasis should be*

placed on the study of mathematical structures to result in a better understanding and use of mathematics?

4. *Social Applications.* Social applications of mathematics are being discussed by those concerned with better mathematics instruction. The question is: *How much emphasis should be placed on the social applications of mathematics and what should be the purpose and nature of these applications?*

5. *Vocabulary.* An individual's language develops as he develops his ideas and has relevant experiences. The person developing a language of mathematics proceeds in this same way. The question is: *How rapidly can an individual be led from the use of a general unsophisticated mathematical language to the use of a very precise, sophisticated mathematical language?*

6. *Concepts Versus Skills.* Mathematics has value as a tool to be used by other disciplines, but it also involves abstract ideas or concepts. The question is: *What relationship shall exist in the mathematics programs between the function of developing concepts and that of developing the manipulation of symbols?*

7. *Proof.* There are many possible grade levels and degrees of rigor at which proof might be introduced into the mathematics program. The question is: *At what grade level should proof be introduced, and with what degree of rigor; and how rapidly should the learner be led to the position where he recognizes and appreciates rigorous proof?*

8. *Organization.* Topics and areas of study may be organized in a number of ways. The question is: *Is there a principle of organization that supersedes other principles by providing a better learning pattern, more retention, or more efficiency?*

9. *Correctness of the Mathematics.* There is no question as to whether or not one should use correct mathematics, but the question here is: *What constitutes correct mathematics as determined by either logic or acceptable authority, and why is the particular authority the acceptable one?*

PSYCHOLOGICAL CRITERIA

Since our real concern is learning the mathematics we have selected, we must next consider criteria based on principles of learning. Can the selected mathematical concepts, skills, habits, and attitudes be learned?

Let us remind ourselves that we can't force a student to learn mathematics. If he is to learn, the student must be ready, willing, and able to learn the ideas we propose to teach. Furthermore, he will learn only if he reacts, responds, or participates.

Our first psychological criterion should be this matter of readiness. When should a concept be taught? From experiences with mathematical concepts such as those of Professor Suppes (Stanford University) in teaching geometry in first grade and those of Professor Davis (Syracuse University) in teaching quadratic equations in fifth grade, it appears that young children learn anything more readily than adults do. Thus, the conclusions reached nearly half a century ago by the Committee of Seven concerning a fixed time schedule for presenting topics in arithmetic now seem to have been in error. It appears that at this time we cannot render judgment, *on the basis of level of difficulty,* what is the proper time to present a given arithmetical topic.

A second requirement for learning is that the learner be motivated so that he is willing to learn. This seems to be a major strength of new proposals. Here is what Ferguson reported at the regional conferences sponsored by the National Council of Teachers of Mathematics last fall.

Some of us who have taught the old traditional mathematics feel it is a miracle that some of our students became mathematicians considering the way we taught them. The evidence we have to date is simply this: teachers are much more enthusiastic about the new mathematics programs and the new techniques of teaching them. The students show more interest and enthusiasm for mathematics than ever before. Almost all (if not all) teachers who have tried teaching the new programs (the University of Illinois Committee on School Mathematics—UICSM—the School Mathematics Study Group—SMSG—and the University of Maryland Mathematics Program—UMMaP, etc.) do not want to return to teaching the old traditional texts.

The mathematics in the new programs is not easier; it is not watered down, but it is more interesting and challenging to students and teachers alike. On traditional tests students taking the new programs have performed, so far as we can judge, about as well as the students taking the traditional program. If this is the case, the students taking the new programs have the same mathematical knowledge as the students taught in the traditional manner, plus many new ideas and topics. On power tests, such as the Advanced Mathematics Examination of the College Entrance Examination Board and the Contest Examination of the Mathematical Association of America, it is a different story. In schools that have used the UICSM Program for three or more years, the students in the UICSM Program have done significantly better than students of comparable ability who have had only the traditional courses.

However, in evaluating these enthusiastic results we must keep several factors in mind:

1. The courses are new and different.
2. The teachers and students are participating in an experiment.
3. The teachers are spending much time in preparation of lessons.

Much in this revolution is to be welcomed, and undoubtedly the mathematics teaching will be greatly modified and improved during the next decade. Many advantages will be gained thereby. But certain dangers need to be borne in mind. Perhaps the greatest is the danger that the revolution may go too far and confront students with courses so abstract that they exceed the youngsters' mathematical maturity, and thus result in bewilderment and revulsion against mathematics rather than increased knowledge. The community may expect that the skillful mathematicians pushing this revolution will bear such dangers in mind and make haste slowly in carrying out the generally useful changes they plan.

A requirement for learning concepts is that the student be *able* to learn the ideas being taught. Observe this editorial from the New York *Times* of November 28, 1960:

> To add meaning to what is taught requires intuition, participation, illustration, application, and proper language. Many of the new programs place emphasis on this aspect by having students discover the principle or idea involved. This is certainly an effective method of instruction, at least for reasonable size classes. On the other hand, some programs seem to lose interest in concrete representations, visualizations, or applications. It is unfortunate that very few scientists, economists, statisticians, or computer programmers have been involved in writing the new courses. Likewise, few experts in materials of instruction or psychologists have been consulted during the writing of experimental programs.

PEDAGOGICAL CRITERIA

Concerning methods of teaching the new mathematics programs, we should consider the following questions:

1. Do the teachers have the necessary background for the program? If not, can they be given it through inservice education?
2. Is sufficient time available for adequate presentation of the topics outlined? If too much is outlined can these topics be postponed or some eliminated? Can additional time be made available?
3. Does the curriculum have adequate materials, such as texts, units, and teacher guides?
4. Does the school have the resources to provide the teachers and the students with the necessary text material or facilities? (A given course is usually not teachable if text material is not available.)
5. Has the material been tried out experimentally? (This is one of the strengths of most current proposals, even some commercial programs. In evaluating the experiments, however, we must be realistic.) What kind of teachers were involved? How reliable are the teacher reports? What was the nature of the schools or students who participated?

Following is a preview of a typical SMSG experiment:

Twenty elementary teachers in the Twin Cities area will be selected to participate in this experiment. Ten of these will have taught the SMSG 4th-grade course in the academic year 1960–61. These teachers will teach the SMSG 4th-grade course to their pupils. The other 10 teachers will be selected to match the first 10 as closely as possible in regard to teaching experience and qualifications, but will have had no experience with SMSG materials. They will teach a conventional mathematics course.

The Sequential Tests of Educational Progress level-4 achievement test will be administered to both the experimental and control pupils at the beginning and at the end of the school year. In addition, an achievement test prepared by SMSG will be administered to all classes at the end of the school year. Also, achievement tests prepared by SMSG will be administered to the experimental classes at approximately 2-month intervals.

Another pedagogical question concerns the selection of a program that will provide the best possible mathematics education for all levels of ability. Thus we must ask the question: "For what level of ability is this curriculum the most suitable?"

PHILOSOPHICAL CRITERIA

We now come to the crucial basis for evaluation. What is the purpose of mathematics instruction? Where are we going? What are we striving to attain? It is not sufficient to know that we can teach a given concept at the fifth-grade level. We must decide whether we ought to teach it, whether it is more important than other ideas which we could teach.

To determine what we ought to teach we need to spell out our objectives. Although these goals may include general objectives such as responsible citizenship, or ethical character, I will assume that these have equal likelihood of being attained by traditional or new curricula. When you ask teachers to state the specific results they expect of mathematics instruction they usually come up with a list such as the following:

1. The student has a knowledge and understanding of mathematical processes, facts and concepts.

2. The student has skill in computing with understanding, accuracy, and efficiency.

3. The student has the ability to use a general problem-solving technique.

4. The student understands the logical structure of mathematics and the nature of proof.

5. The student associates mathematical understandings and processes with everyday situations.

6. The student recognizes and appreciates the role of mathematics in society.

7. The student develops study habits essential for independent progress in mathematics.

8. The student develops reading skill and a vocabulary essential for progress in mathematics.

9. The student is stimulated to participate in mental activities such as creativeness, imagination, curiosity, and visualization.

10. The student develops attitudes leading to appreciation, confidence, respect, initiative, and independence.

Now the problem arises as to what specific facts, processes, or skills you wish to teach. Here you must choose. Those appropriate for a given ability level or for given vocations will certainly vary. Not all mathematicians agree as to which are most suitable for college or for science. Most agree with Mr. Adler that classical as well as modern topics should be included. Most agree that basic computational skills are still needed. One of the things which the various curriculum groups should do is to spell out the specific competencies needed for success in business, government, and citizen activities, as well as in science and mathematics. Then we will have a basis for rendering judgment relative to the competence attained by a given program. Traditional tests are not satisfactory for this purpose.

Here are some specific recommendations of the Joint Commission on the Education of Teachers of Science and Mathematics:

1. SMSG might profit from a careful comparison between the present curricular projects and earlier ones. Such a study may reveal the factors which contribute significantly to a successful program. The following elements may be relevant: adequate support, development of text materials, experimental teaching, a favorable climate for getting relevant information to teachers and supervisors and for getting cooperation between school teachers and mathematicians.

2. In addition to defining the general objectives of curriculum projects, considerable effort must still be made in defining operationally the criteria which reflect the objectives (other than mathematical knowledge and skills) of the mathematics programs. Teachers, pupils, and parents react strongly to evaluative instruments (e.g., college board examinations); hence, SMSG should support efforts to construct tests reflecting all the many objectives of the programs.

3. Long-range follow-up studies, particularly of students who go on to college, should be made to find out whether the training provided by the new programs meets the demands made upon it and whether it produces the hoped-for results concerning attitudes towards mathematics.

4. SMSG should encourage joint research between mathematicians and behavioral scientists concerning the learning process and the formation of attitudes towards mathematics.

MEASUREMENT

If we accept these goals we then have a basis for measuring the achievement of our students. Can we do this so that we can render judgment as to the relative effectiveness of a given curriculum? In many ways this will be impossible. For example, in terms of facts and skills, only those common to both can be tested. This is likely to be an inadequate sample of the learning from either curriculum. New tests must be devised, not only on the common topics but on the common goals, such as problem solving, communication skill in reading, writing, and presenting mathematical ideas; attitudes, application, discovery, and creativeness.

Besides these we need long-range evaluations in terms of continued study of mathematics (what happens to registrations?), continued success in mathematics, success in related fields such as science, success in selected vocations, and success in citizenship.

SUMMARY

Finally, then, the evaluation of a school mathematics curriculum is not a single process. It will need the judgment of many specialists: the mathematician, the psychologist, the educator, the scientist, the research worker, and the teacher. It will need a comprehensive testing program which includes tests not as yet devised. It will need research in the form of comparison studies and follow-up studies that will require several years for completion. In the meantime, we must make our choices based on value judgments. In making our choices, however, we do have mathematical, psychological, pedagogical and philosophical criteria.

9

Preservice and In-service
Mathematics Education

The past decade has witnessed extensive inquiries into the education
of teachers, particularly of those who are teaching mathematics to
children in the elementary schools. We have noticed a gradual, yet
needed, increase in the number of mathematics courses required of the
undergraduate. These changes continue to influence undergraduate as
well as graduate programs. There are several reasons why this up-
grading has taken place and that explain the impetus for a re-evalua-
tion. The knowledge explosion, demographic conditions, diversified
school programs, studies in teacher education, the National Science
Foundation, federally supported programs, state department certifica-
tion standards, research efforts, and, most certainly, the "modern
mathematics" movement have all contributed to the refurbished image
of the elementary school teacher.

As we capture a glimpse of the changing view of mathematics education programs, questions continue to be raised. What is it that we
can do best during the preservice program? What can best be done
during the in-service program? Are certain aspects of mathematics education more desirable during the preservice or during the in-service
period? The education of teachers of elementary school mathematics
is a continuous process. How can we develop a developmental program?

How to develop and improve preservice and in-service articulation
remains as one of the major areas for exploration. Do preservice programs include a well-articulated sequence? Are mathematics education programs built around a continuous sequence? What should the
preservice elementary teacher experience during the first four years in
mathematics education? How do we go about offering an in-service program that has been undergirded by a strong preservice program and
that has provided for continuous contact? In this era, it is imperative

379

that the classroom teacher have continued contact with various aspects of mathematics. This offers the potential for elementary classroom teachers to become more complete teachers. What are the alternatives?

Modern Methods and Current Criticisms of Mathematical Education

Maurice L. Hartung

We are teachers. Probably we are all aware that some highly critical statements are being made about teachers these days. Educationists—a special variety of teachers that I happen to represent—are accused of undermining the educational system by promoting the use of modern methods in the schools. Critics say we aren't teaching the right things. Critics say pupils aren't learning as much as they should learn. Critics say the conduct of pupils has greatly deteriorated. Some of us teachers are among the critics, and we may say these same things ourselves—but usually only within our own groups, and not publicly. We may also note that the three complaints I have just mentioned are general criticisms. They are not directed specifically at mathematical education.

Some critics, when they say we aren't teaching the right things, assert that "intellectual" subjects like foreign languages and mathematics are being neglected. They point to the great variety of subjects now found in the lists of courses available in larger schools. The list may include Art, Home Mechanics, Driver Education, Foods, Stagecraft, and many others. It is true that some of these courses, as they are usually taught, are less demanding of intellectual abilities than, for example, science and mathematics. We should, however, be fair enough to admit that sometimes mathematics also is taught at a very low intellectual level. Moreover, a good teacher with bright pupils might choose to teach a so-called "non-intellectual subject" at a relatively high intellectual level.

Whether a school subject is more or less intellectual depends upon what happens in the minds of the pupils. This, in turn clearly depends upon their abilities and interests. It also depends upon the objectives deemed important by the teacher, and the teacher's skill in selecting and organizing learning experiences. It is therefore not very fruitful to try to prove in general that one subject field is better than another. The fact that we who are gathered

Reprinted from *School Science and Mathematics*, Vol. 55, No. 481 (February 1955), 85–90, by permission of the publisher.

here today happen to like science and mathematics may be evidence that studying these subjects has been good for us, but it does not follow from this alone that it is wise to require everyone to study them beyond the elementary school.

It certainly seems that some knowledge of these fields is useful to all citizens. It seems to me that we have too often tried to insure this by trying to establish "requirements" and by jockeying among the other subjects for time in the schedule. We act as though we are afraid no one will take our subjects unless we force them to do so. We are acutely aware of statistical data like those showing that in the year 1900 fifty-six per cent of the students in high school were studying algebra, but in 1949 only 27% were enrolled in algebra. The change for physics was from 19 per cent in 1900 to 5.4% in 1949. These data seem to alarm us, especially when we compare them with the tremendous growth of enrolment in subjects new to the curriculum in modern times. In short, fear that our favorite subjects are "losing out" in a competitive struggle for pupils seems to be exciting some of us.

I believe this fear is largely unjustified at the present time. Moreover, if some concern is justified, we are not in a position to blame the so-called modern methods. On the contrary, we should seriously examine the hypothesis that we are at fault because of unwillingness to modernize the curriculum and to introduce modern methods at a sufficiently rapid pace. If our product is not "selling" fast enough, perhaps it is because we have been too slow in modernizing it.

Befoer turning to a more detailed discussion of this hypothesis, we should consider a few more facts about the enrolment situation. As teachers of mathematics we are aware that in the calculation of rates in percentage, the base is of some importance. In the relative enrolment figures usually used, the base is the total number of pupils in the last four years of public secondary day schools. It is interesting to study the situation by using as a base the total population ranging from fourteen to seventeen years in age. The resulting per cents give an indication of the extent to which the public schools have made the study of certain subjects available to the *total youth population of appropriate age.* In 1900, only 4.7% of that population were enrolled in algebra. In 1949, the figure had increased to 17%. In 1900, 1.6% of the country's youth were taking physics. In 1949, the figure was 3.4%. Chemistry changed from less than 1% to 4.8% during the same period.

These and similar data make clear in quantitative terms what we already know but too often forget. Today we are trying to teach these subjects to a much larger fraction of the total population than was formerly true. Many of these pupils have little ability and no appetite for intellectual pursuits. The question remains as to whether what we are doing with them is the best we can do. We have, however, become very much more conscious of the wide range in individual differences among pupils at every grade level. The practice of promotion on the basis of age rather than achievement has wid-

382 MATHEMATICS IN ELEMENTARY EDUCATION

ened these differences and multiplied our instructional problems. Methods that once worked well now often seem to fail us. Successful teaching is much more difficult today than it used to be, and the use of modern methods is more important than ever before. Let us, therefore, briefly review some general features of these methods.

In the first place, modern teachers put much stress on meaningful learning. These teachers try to make sure that pupils see sense in what they are doing and really understand it. Teachers use a variety of ways of doing this. One popular way is to relate mathematics to situations in which it may be applied —in short, to stress the applications. This works in two directions. On the one hand, we can begin with problem situations familiar to the pupils and help them see the mathematics in them—to develop the new concepts by generalization and abstraction from familiar concrete situations. On the other hand, we can show the pupils situations—practical or even not very practical—new to them but in which familiar mathematical concepts can be applied. In either case, we hope that this process of relating mathematics to real and practical situations will make the concepts more meaningful.

If we examine the trends in the development of materials for children during the half-century just past, we can find clear and convincing evidence of progress toward this kind of meaningfulness. Arithmetic, of course, has always had a strong practical flavor. What we observe is that modern materials rely heavily upon problem situations chosen on the basis of the interests of children rather than those of adults. It is believed that these child-experience situations contribute more to the development of meaning with children than the more adult type of situation once prevalent. At the high school level the trend toward the use of more meaningful experiences is also evident. At this level, however, attention to more adult types of applications of mathematics is common and defensible.

There are, I believe, very few critics who will argue that this aspect of modern methods—that is, concern with the meaningfulness of experience—is not good. If there are some who do argue this way, their views run directly counter to the results of much substantial research by psychologists and others who have studied human learning. It is possible, however, to overdo this attention to the uses of mathematics, or the so-called "social meanings." This is particularly true when social or practical situations are used to introduce new concepts. We must be sure the mathematical aspects are brought clearly into focus and become objects of study. Sometimes this is not done, and although the children may arrive at a solution of a particular problem, they learn so little mathematics from it that they are unable to deal successfully with similar new situations.

A second popular way of helping pupils toward meaningful learning is to use visual or, more broadly, multi-sensory learning aids. The reasons for using these aids are well known to modern teachers, and we do not need to consider them here. The number and variety of such aids now described in the literature has increased much faster than the tendency to be critical about them. It is probably possible to devise a helpful model or aid of some kind to teach any topic you care to mention. Thus, we have aids available for teaching content that is of little or no value. When we examine an ingenious aid, we should ask: Why is it important for the pupil to learn what this aid is designed to teach? We sometimes waste time by skillfully teaching unimportant things.

Although the increased use of visual and mechanical aids is one of the characteristics of modern teaching, in most classrooms this kind of activity accounts for a relatively small part of the instructional time. It is difficult to see how this aspect of modern methodology can be blamed for the alleged deterioration of the schools.

A third and very modern way of helping pupils toward meaningful learning is to encourage them to participate in *planning* the learning experiences. This practice is, of course, in sharp contrast to the usual one in which "the assignment" is made by the teacher. Teacher-pupil planning and similar methods of encouraging interaction among members of the class are still seldom used in mathematics classes. Hence the alleged great deterioration in achievement can hardly be attributed to this as a cause. Similarly, the integration of mathematics with other subjects in a core curriculum is very infrequent. The core curriculum is a focus for attack by some vigorous critics of modern education, but teachers of mathematics are outside this line of fire.

This brief survey of some of the prominent features of modern methodology would be incomplete without some mention of "drill." It is certainly true that modern methods do not rely on "drill" as much as the older methods did. When learning is meaningful less drill is needed, but plenty of "practice," involving varied work with the same concepts rather than mere repetition, is invariably provided. Sometimes we discover pupils who have not learned what they are supposed to learn. I am sure that this is rarely the result of failure by their teachers to provide practice. Much more often it is the result of failure by the pupil to do the suggested practice because he does not understand the work and is poorly motivated.

In similar fashion and in greater detail we could analyse other aspects of modern methods and the extent to which they are actually used in schools. We would find that the foundation for these methods is well laid in learning theories and research. We would find that these methods are being used more and more by teachers, but that, in mathematics at least, instructional methodology today is nearly everywhere still much the same as it used to be years ago. Critics who assert that the educational process is being ruined by modern methods have greater faith in these methods than most of the teachers do. If the teachers were as "sold" on the modern methods as the critics seem to believe, it would be possible to see much more "modern" teaching in the schools.

Let us now return to one of the criticisms stated earlier. Are we teaching the right things? To this the answer should be "No, not entirely." Most schools are still a very long way from providing adequately for individual differences. For example, they are still trying to teach concepts from algebra and geometry to many pupils who are unequipped motivationally and intellectually to deal with these concepts in satisfying ways. As a consequence, these pupils do not learn very much and understand little of what they do learn. Sometimes they cause disturbances and get into trouble in other ways. You are all well aware of this, but I recall it here because it is another illustration of the fact that our difficulties are more a result of slowness in adjusting to modern conditions than of following the dicta of educational theorists.

Turning to the other and brighter end of the distribution of ability and interest, again we are slow in modernizing the curriculum. Criticisms of the traditional undergraduate curriculum in the colleges have become increasingly common in recent years. These criticisms come not from persons outside the field of mathematics but from those within it. The critics are highly respected mathematicians. They say that the traditional curriculum is barren of the content and point of view of modern mathematics. They say it is high time that courses be brought up to date. Materials for these new courses have been appearing with increasing frequency. To teachers who are wedded to traditional algebra, trigonometry, and analytic geometry these modernized courses are somewhat of a shock. For many experienced teachers these modern materials require considerable study before it is safe to appear before a class using them.

This same movement is beginning to be felt in the secondary schools. There is growing recognition that a semester of solid geometry as ordinarily taught may not be the best expenditure of time for college-bound students. Similarly, the essentials of trigonometry can be taught in less than a semester. Respectable groups are openly publishing statements that even plane geometry would profit from a somewhat drastic reorganization. In short, there is today more vigorous criticism of the mathematics curriculum than there has been for a long time, and most of it is coming from the mathematicians themselves.

I wonder what Moore, Klein, Hedrick, and other leaders of a generation or more ago would say if they were here today. In their day they were the lonely reformers. They would be fully justified in saying: Why didn't you make many of these changes years ago, before these modern critics came on the scene? In brief, if we choose our leaders carefully and if we avoid obvious opportunities to go to extremes, there is little danger that we will change things at too fast a rate. Valid criticisms will be found to be closely related to slowness in adopting modern content and modern methods. Criticisms that plead for a return to content and method of the past are for the most part invalid. They spring from lack of understanding of modern schools and modern methods and often from emotional rather than rational thinking.

We must recognize that progress can only be made by moving forward. We must maintain and renew our faith in the educational process. Mathematical education today is better than it ever was before, but we must keep on improving it.

In-service Education in Arithmetic: Three Approaches

Arden K. Ruddell and Gerald W. Brown

This article describes the co-operative efforts of a consultant and the administrative leaders of a comparatively large school district to bring about maximum involvement of the elementary-school teachers in an in-service program.

The school district, which is in southern California, is a growing, unified system that has thirty-seven elementary schools. The basic purpose of the program was to improve mathematics instruction in the first six grades.

Unfortunately there is very little empirical evidence to guide consultants and program-planners in organizing an in-service program which, by necessity, must be built around the busy schedule of the teaching staffs in the district. Many possibilities are available to planning groups, but because of the dearth of evidence final decisions are usually based on what seems to be most feasible and most expedient.

Most requests for consultant service fall in the "one-shot" category. Under this type of program, teachers are given a "one-shot inoculation" to cure their educational ills. The most appropriate time of the year for this inoculation seems to be early or late fall. Since there is usually neither time nor opportunity to examine and diagnose the "patient," the consultant must guess whether he should administer a corrective or a preventative antidote.

A series of small "doses" administered over an extended period of time is usually the alternative to the "one-shot" dosage. But when a series of doses is prescribed, the consultant competes with the many other demands, personal and professional, on the teacher's time. As a result, the meetings can rarely have the continuity necessary if the teacher is to benefit from them. In addition, it is much easier to bring great numbers of teachers together once on a day set aside for the purpose than to bring them together many

Reprinted from "In-service Education in Arithmetic: Three Approaches," *The Elementary School Journal*, Vol. 64, No. 7 (April 1964), pp. 377–382, by Arden K. Ruddell and Gerald W. Brown, by permission of The University of Chicago Press.

times during the school year. In spite of these drawbacks, many schoolmen consider long-range involvement in an in-service program superior to a single exposure.

The purpose of our investigation was to study the effect that three different programs of in-service leadership had on teachers and pupils. We did not propose to identify the one "best" program—the one that should be adopted by all schools. Rather, we proposed to describe the professional growth that teachers showed under each program and the effect on the pupils.

One group of teachers met with the consultant for six hours one day during orientation week early in September before school started. The teachers in this group, which we called Group A, did not meet with the consultant again at any time during the school year. The principals of the schools in which they taught, however, were permitted to attend regularly scheduled meetings conducted by the consultant for all elementary-school administrators and general supervisors in the district. Three teachers from the group registered at a nearby university for a two-unit course on modern mathematics for elementary-school teachers.

The other two programs were adaptations of a long-range program to meet the needs of great numbers of teachers. The first of these programs was for Group B, which is best described as a "partial attendance" group. Ten meetings were scheduled at evenly spaced intervals throughout the school year. Each meeting lasted for most of a school morning. At 7:45 A.M. there was a one-hour general session that all teachers in this group were permitted to attend. The general session was followed by a demonstration lesson at 9:15 A.M. at the primary-grade level and a demonstration lesson at 10:30 A.M. at the intermediate-grade level. The demonstration lessons were taught by the consultant and were attended by the primary- and the intermediate-grade teachers, respectively, at the appropriate time. To provide adequately for the children at each school, only half the teachers from each school at each grade level stayed for the demonstration lesson. The teachers alternated in attending the demonstrations, so that it was possible for each teacher to attend at least half of them. Principals of the teachers in Group B were permitted to attend the 7:45 A.M. sessions with the consultant, and four teachers in this group registered in the two-unit course on modern mathematics.

Like the partial-attendance teachers, the teachers in the third group, or Group C, participated in a series of ten meetings conducted as the meetings for Group B were. Unlike the teachers in Group B, who participated directly, the teachers in Group C were served by an intermediary. One intermediary at the primary level and one at the intermediate level from each school attended the general sessions and the appropriate demonstration lessons. The intermediaries for this group were selected by the local staff or by the principal of the school. No criteria were established for selecting intermediaries. They were not necessarily specially prepared in mathematics. It was their responsibility to report back to the teachers whom they were representing at the meetings. The hypothesis explored in this organizational pattern stems from the question: "How effectively can great numbers of teachers be served by a consultant through intermediaries?" Principals of the schools in Group C were permitted to attend the 7:45 A.M. meetings with the consultant, and two teachers registered for a course in modern mathematics.

Naturally, one would not expect any two intermediaries to feed back to their respective faculties in exactly the same way. On the whole, the intermediaries were very conscientious. They took copious notes at the general sessions and the demonstrations. Some prepared three- to six-page bulletins for distribution to their colleagues to serve as a basis for discussion. Others gave short reports on an individual as well as a small group basis. Still others prepared excellent demonstration lessons for the teachers whom they represented. Each intermediary used one or more of these techniques.

Thirty-seven elementary schools were classified by the general supervisory staff of the district according to the socioeconomic area they served (high, middle, or low). A stratified random sample for each of Groups A, B, and C was obtained by selecting at random one school from each of the socioeconomic groups and assigning it to an experimental group. Consequently, each group in the experimental program may be considered as fairly representative of the entire community in terms of socioeconomic levels. The number of children and teachers who completed all aspects of the program is shown in Table 1.

TABLE 1

Size of Sample of Experimental Groups A, B, and C by
Grade Level

Number of:	Group A	Group B	Group C
Teachers	68	42	45
Children			
Grade 1	254	198	194
Grade 2	282	155	183
Grade 3	290	156	170
Grade 4	197	161	183
Grade 5	245	179	165
Grade 6	246	195	193
Total	1,514	1,044	1,088

Pre- and post-tests of arithmetic achievement were administered to the children at each grade level. Each test, composed of eighty items, was specially prepared for this study to reflect the ideas, suggestions, and content presented in the in-service meetings. Glennon's Test of Basic Mathematical Understanding, Short Form, an unpublished test prepared by V. J. Glennon in 1948, was administered to all teachers in the three experimental groups during the first week in September. An alternate form of the same test was given to the same teachers after the in-service meetings were completed in May.

Only the tests of the children and the teachers who participated in the program from beginning to end were considered in tabulating and analyzing results. The t test was used to test differences between group means. The .01 level was established for determining significance.

Mean scores on the pre-test were obtained for each grade level in each of the experimental groups. In two instances there was a significant difference in mean scores: at the second- and the third-grade levels, children in Group B scored significantly lower than children in Groups A and C. These differences can be seen in Table 2.

TABLE 2

Mean Pre-test Scores and Mean Gains of Pupils, by Group and by Grade Level

	Group A		Group B		Group C	
Grade	Mean Pre-test Score	Mean Gain	Mean Pre-test Score	Mean Gain	Mean Pre-test Score	Mean Gain
1	22.98	26.72	21.94	26.35	23.23	26.75
2	41.75	19.53	38.16	17.92	41.28	18.68
3	44.46	17.32	40.95	21.13	45.26	18.94
4	33.91	19.71	33.59	21.63	33.80	16.27
5	18.89	13.22	18.66	18.99	20.12	10.01
6	31.92	10.70	31.11	16.22	30.99	12.37

The difference between the pre-test score and the post-test score was determined for each child. The mean gain was calculated for each experimental group by grade level. The results are shown in Table 2. At the first-grade level the differences between mean gains are nil. Not even a trend can be interpreted from these results.

Group A showed the greatest gain at Grade 2. Both Group A and Group C gained more than Group B, but no differences between mean gains were significant at the .01 level.

In Grades 3, 4, 5, and 6, significant differences between mean gains were found at every level. In each instance the gain is in favor of Group B. Children in Group B made greater gains than children in both of the other groups. At Grade 3 the difference in mean gain between Group B and Group C is not significant, and at Grade 4 the difference between Group B and Group A is not significant. All other differences are statistically significant.

The mean pre-test scores and the mean gains made by teachers on Glennon's Test of Basic Mathematical Understanding, Short Form, for teachers are recorded in Table 3.

TABLE 3

*Mean Pre-test Scores and Mean Gains
of Teachers, by Group*

Group	Number of Teachers	Mean Pre-test Score	Mean Gain
A	54	14.04	4.83
B	37	12.71	3.81
C	35	14.27	1.26

The form of the Glennon test used in this study had thirty items. Though Group B scored lower on the average than Groups A and C, the differences between mean pre-test scores were not significant. None of the groups made impressive gains on the test. Groups A and B made significantly greater gains than Group C, but there was no significant difference between the gains of Group A and Group B. The gain made by Group C may be attributed to chance alone.

The study included a careful evaluation of the job of the intermediary who served the third group. The results indicated that the teachers in this group showed the smallest mean gain in arithmetic understanding and that in general the pupils taught by these teachers showed the smallest mean gain in achievement. Thus one would conclude that the intermediary approach has little to recommend it as an in-service training plan and that the effectiveness of the intermediary might be considered irrelevant. The evaluation of the intermediary's role generally supports this conclusion. However, several interesting facets of the procedure were revealed by the data.

As described earlier, it was the responsibility of the intermediary to attend the general sessions and the teaching demonstrations and, through any procedure he chose, to report back to his local staff what he had perceived that would help his constituents in arithmetic instruction. The organization of the reporting sessions was left to the intermediaries. They were, however, encouraged to use their initiative and to avoid, if possible, a uniform approach.

In response to a questionnaire submitted to the teachers served by the intermediary, all reported that they knew who their intermediary was and that they had attended most of the reporting sessions. Eighty-four per cent of the teachers attended all the sessions held. However, 27 per cent reported that their intermediary did not report after each general session, and 77 per cent stated that the report was primarily a verbal one. However, 25 per cent stated that at one time or other their intermediary used children to show what went on at the demonstration lessons.

In remarking on the nature of the reporting sessions, only 6 per cent said the reports were enthusiastically received, and only 13 per cent said that they received "a great many helpful ideas." Sixty-seven per cent reported that they received a "few" helpful ideas and about the same proportion (66 per cent) said that the reports were well received and many questions were asked. The question was asked, "Did you use ideas you received from the reporting sessions in the classroom?" Only six teachers responded "a great deal," while seventy teachers gave the noncomittal response "some." Thirty of those responding did not answer this question. As a final attempt to obtain evidence as to whether the reports of the intermediary filtered down to the classroom, the question was asked: "Do you believe the teaching of arithmetic was genuinely affected by the information you gained from the reporting sessions?" Eighteen per cent of the responses were yes; 37 per cent, no; and 45 per cent, perhaps.

Thus one consistently receives the impression that those involved with the intermediary group were lukewarm about the effectiveness of the approach. Thirty-seven per cent stated flatly that arithmetic teaching was unaffected by the entire operation.

The intermediaries themselves were queried about their perception of the operation. Here again we see only a mild feeling that the approach was effective. The intermediaries were asked, "Do you feel the reporting sessions were of value to those who attended?" Only twelve of the sixteen answered yes. That is, 25 per cent of the intermediaries felt that their reporting sessions were of no value. The intermediaries were asked, "Do you feel that the teaching of arithmetic was genuinely affected as a result of the sessions you held reporting on the demonstration lesson?" The response of 37.5 per cent was no. Of the ten intermediaries (62.5 per cent) who answered yes to this last question, several qualified the answer in some way.

On the positive side, there is a thread of enthusiasm running through the entire evaluation of the intermediary that must be related to one or two intermediaries who carried off their responsibility with great effectiveness.

Under the most ideal conditions it is very difficult to exercise control over all variables that affect change in the school curriculum. In this investigation a school district used a consultant in three different ways in an effort to improve instruction in elementary-school mathematics. Each of three randomly selected sample groups was treated independently, and testing programs were administered to the teachers and the children.

Pupil gain in arithmetic achievement was used as an index of change in teaching effectiveness resulting from the in-service program. The authors have long contended that a consultant's efforts should ultimately be reflected in the child's work. It is their belief that this study has demonstrated (not conclusively, perhaps) that such an expectation is not unrealistic.

Interpretation of the test results leads to the following conclusions:

Some type of direct contact between the consultant and the teacher is necessary to bring about change in the teacher's mathematical knowledge and understanding.

The teacher's mathematical knowledge and understanding can be changed just as much from an intense "one-shot" program as from a slowly paced, long-range program. But this change is not reflected in the children's achievement.

Greater change in day-by-day classroom practices as reflected in pupil-achievement gain occurs on the part of teachers in Grades 3, 4, 5, and 6 who participate directly in a series of in-service meetings conducted over the entire school year. It should be noted that in this experiment the series of in-service meetings included teaching demonstrations.

The use of an intermediary in an in-service arithmetic program proved to be only mildly effective. The program should probably not be recommended in the light of the complexity of administering it. There is some indication that the effectiveness of the intermediary program depends on the intermediary selected. A hard-working, enthusiastic person, willing and able to organize an effective report can elicit favorable responses. Thus, if the procedure were to be used again, great consideration should be given to the choice of intermediaries.

As a group, the intermediaries assumed responsibilities far beyond those of teachers in any of the other groups. A great deal of ingenuity and effort was given to preparing materials, presentations, and demonstration lessons for the teachers in their own buildings. These people could very well form the nucleus of a group of potential leaders in the district for a program of self-examination and self-improvement in the area of elementary mathematics.

A Portable Mathematics Laboratory for In-service Teacher Education

Catherine M. Williams

Teachers of Grades I through VIII are providing instruction in arithmetic to one out of every six members of the nation's population. Even though so many children are involved, the quality of what generally takes place during the daily arithmetic period is disappointing. Arithmetic is the subject in which most elementary-school pupils do their poorest work. Unfortunately, too, most pupils are markedly less proficient in problem-solving—that important aspect which calls for intelligent application of processes and prin-

Reprinted from *Educational Research Bulletin* (April 13, 1960), 85–103, by permission of College of Education, Ohio State University.

ciples—than in computation skills. When children reach junior and senior high school, few elect mathematics; the majority take only the mathematics courses that are specifically required. By so doing, students close the door to opportunities both for learning how challenging the subject can be and for entering those occupations for which mathematical proficiency is a basic requirement.

We have reason to be deeply concerned about the quality of arithmetic instruction throughout the elementary grades.[1] Research reveals that an appalling number of elementary-school teachers are ill-prepared for the important task of teaching arithmetic; many of them are the victims of unfavorable mind-set. Several studies have brought to light the fact that the majority of elementary-school teachers of arithmetic admittedly fear and dislike the subject.[2] Such mind-set stems from the fact that the teachers are the products of a mathematical education which placed a premium on *knowing about* rather than on *knowing;* on memorizing book definitions and following prescribed rules of operation rather than on thinking and analyzing—the sort of learning which is characterized by experimenting to find solutions, generalizing from one's own experimental evidence, and testing to see whether the generalizations arrived at are valid. In view of the narrowly prescribed mathematical background of many elementary-school teachers, it is not difficult to understand their lack of security in situations which call for building a real understanding of and love for the subject.

Unfavorable mind-set is but one evidence of teacher insecurity concerning arithmetic. The teacher's edition of practically every leading arithmetic textbook contains all sorts of patterned how-to-do-it introductions to topics, step-by-step explanations, and step-by-step solutions to problems. Thereby problems become mere exercises. Publishers report that according to their polls teachers actually *want* such recipes for teaching. The widespread use of workbooks to supplement textbook exercises is yet another evidence that many teachers are reluctant to use a more creative approach. Use of the workbook routinizes classroom procedures and stereotypes arithmetic activities; it makes only a minimal demand on either the teacher's knowledge of the subject or his skill in teaching, since every exercise has a ready-made pattern and the answers are supplied. The cookbook type of teaching which frequently results from use of these materials in no way meets individual

---

[1] The author conceived this plan for a portable mathematics laboratory three years ago [1957]. At no time since that date have there been funds available for putting the plan into operation. It is set forth here with the hope that others may find ways of adapting it to their needs.

[2] Dutton, Wilbur H. "Measuring Attitudes Toward Arithmetic," *Elementary School Journal,* LV (September, 1954), pp. 24–31; Rappaport, David. "Preparation of Teachers of Arithmetic," *School Science and Mathematics,* LVIII (November, 1958), pp. 636–43; Weaver, J. Fred. "Crucial Problem in the Preparation of Elementary-School Teachers," *Elementary School Journal,* LVI (February, 1956), pp. 255–61.

needs. Moreover, it stifles individual initiative and imaginative approach on the part of either the teacher or the student.

There is also a very large group of elementary-school teachers who know the subject well but are unable to communicate to most of their pupils the *meaning* of arithmetical processes and principles. Hence, few of the pupils enrolled in their classes develop either proficiency or an abiding interest in arithmetic. Although many new instructional materials have been developed for the teaching of arithmetic, these teachers are unaware of them. Given proper guidance in the use of such tools, teachers could rapidly upgrade their programs so that their pupils could learn arithmetic and like it.

Some arithmetic teachers are, of course, doing a fine creative job of teaching the subject. In their classrooms pupils are learning to *know* arithmetic rather than just to *know about* it; they are enjoying the challenge of solving problems, of experimentally finding out for themselves the why's and how's of the processes. The pupils are all progressing—each at his own pace. This is good, but it is not good enough, because only a small number of the pupils enrolled in elementary schools are being so skillfully taught. The sort of teaching which will provide all children in elementary schools with full learning experience is needed.

A promising aspect of the present situation is the fact that a large number of the insecure teachers are aware of their insecurities and are sincerely anxious to overcome them. This points to a very real need for developing an in-service education program in the teaching of arithmetic on a scale not yet attempted.

In order to upgrade the teaching of arithmetic in an entire school program, it is necessary to reach all the teachers in the system, preferably while they are on the job. Thus, while they are being confronted with the actual problems of teaching, they will have opportunities for trying new approaches and materials. They will also have strong motivation for sharing and discussing among themselves discoveries, evaluations, ideas, and problems.

Most important, elementary-school teachers must become confident and practiced in new ways of teaching arithmetic. This must be done not only to improve the mathematical performance of the pupil at the time, but also to generate a favorable mind-set toward quantitative thinking and advanced work in mathematics in later years. Precisely such a program, planned three years ago, is presented here. It is not likely that anyone will want to adopt it in its entirety, but it is necessary to see the whole plan in order to determine ways in which parts of it might be adapted by readers to meet their local needs.

The project, as originally planned, was to involve supervisory personnel in the development, experimental use, and evaluation of a portable mathematics laboratory for the purpose of improving attitudes, instruction, and achievement in arithmetic in the elementary curriculum. Thus, persons both on the campus and in the field would collaborate in the venture, and the laboratory would provide school organizations with the basic resources to raise the level of arithmetical instruction and achievement throughout the state. The spirit of creativeness and experimentation would be a major element in carrying out the project.

Supervisory personnel are those most responsible for providing in-service help for elementary-school teachers. However, in their efforts to give their teachers the help needed in the area of arithmetic, most supervisors are blocked by their own mind-set, by lack of time set aside from other duties to permit them to organize good in-service education programs, and by lack of instructional materials of the right sort to help teachers learn new ways of teaching in their normal situations. The problem, therefore, is to help supervisors overcome these blocks so that they may in turn help their teachers approach arithmetic teaching creatively—with enthusiasm and skill.

The project proposed to help supervisors by means of a program which would evolve through five stages: participating in a summer workshop to develop the portable mathematics laboratory, conducting in-service workshops for teachers and preparing for evaluation after a year's use of the laboratory, participating in another summer workshop for the purpose of evaluation and improvement, during this same summer involving a new group of supervisors in the project, and carrying the program to a new set of teachers for use in the next academic year.

First, sixteen selected elementary-school supervisors, representing a variety of teaching situations in the surrounding territory, would come to a campus workshop for a four-week period during which they would cooperate in creating and equipping a portable mathematics laboratory. Through this endeavor the supervisors would not only become thoroughly familiar with the new materials for arithmetic instruction but would also have a strong motive for evaluating them. Constant analyses of their own workshop experiences would provide bases for critical judgments as they laid tentative plans for conducting workshops for their teachers.

The portable laboratory as conceived by the writer was intended to bring to the attention of participating teachers the various types of instructional materials and their proper use. These materials would include both commercially available resources and everyday items that could be made useful by applying imagination and skill. The following are potentially useful materials that might be incorporated in the laboratory:

1. Commercially prepared non-book materials such as an abacounter
2. Construction materials for devices to be prepared by the teacher or the teacher and the pupil
3. Projection equipment
4. Films (for example, *Understanding Numbers*) and filmstrips (for example, *The History of Measurement*)
5. Measuring devices, such as thermometers and liquid measures

6. Tape recorder and recordings (for example, Laura Zirbes' "Recordings for Teaching and Learning")

7. Wall charts (for example, "World Time Zones")

8. Manipulative materials, such as the abacus and inch cubes

9. Children's books (for example, *How Much and How Many*, by Jeanne Bendick)

10. Teachers' books on teaching arithmetic (for example, *Arithmetic: Children Use It*, by Edwina Dean)

There are several ways of making the mathematics laboratory portable. If funds are available, a small delivery truck of the Volkswagen type furnishes an efficient means of transportation. Specially designed carrying cases will be both space savers and time savers in packing and unpacking. However, a less expensive method is to use carrying cases designed to be transported in school buses at hours when they are not carrying children. If neither of these methods can be worked out, it is possible to fashion carrying cases from strong packing cartons and transport them in a privately owned station wagon. The writer suggests that two portable laboratories be assembled so that each could be available to the teachers for longer periods of time.

Second, the supervisors, individually, would have and use the portable laboratory for a three-week period during the academic year to conduct in-service workshops in their own local situations. It was intended that campus personnel would act in an advisory capacity during this year, maintain open lines of communication among the several supervisors, and involve all concerned in the record keeping necessary to make evaluation an integral part of the program.

In evaluating the program, varied kinds of information would be used. The supervisors would record their observations concerning the practices of individual teachers in teaching arithmetic prior to the workshop and at periodic intervals thereafter. Members of the project staff would conduct recorded interviews with the teachers to discover their psychological outlook before and after the workshop, and with school administrators and others in influential positions who control development of arithmetic teaching. Other evaluative materials include statements written before and after the workshops by the participants indicating what they feel they need in order to improve their arithmetic instruction; an inventory of aids available to the teachers and their degree of use before the workshop and at periodic intervals afterwards; a critique of book-type materials and methods of using them; "diaries" kept by teachers to report and analyze their experiences in teaching arithmetic; collections of examples of good and poor teaching of arithmetic and of common difficulties and their solutions; tests of arithmetical competence given to the pupils; and records of formal and informal research undertaken by field participants as a result of involvement in the project. It is most important that regular contact be maintained between the campus staff and the supervisors, particularly during the in-service workshop sessions and in the pre- and post-data gathering periods.

Third, at the end of the first year, the supervisors would return to the campus for a summer workshop to evaluate their experiences with their in-service workshops, to re-evaluate the portable mathematics laboratory, and to work out further additions and improvements. At this stage planning for development of distinctive materials was anticipated by the writer. These included a *filmstrip* to show the contents of the portable mathematics laboratory and the techniques for labeling, packing, transporting, and exhibiting these materials; and a *handbook* which would contain the following: (1) a report of those experiences and procedures that had been found worth while; (2) annotated listings of all of the books and other materials which were used, whether or not they were a part of the mobile laboratory; (3) the findings resulting from the evaluations; (4) other values, activities, and problems which grew out of the workshop experiences; and (5) an accounting of those changes which took place in both teaching and learning as a result of the in-service education program. At this time the contents of two additional portable units would likely be needed for use in the expanded program during the coming academic year.

Fourth, during the same summer, the original group of supervisors working in teams of two would conduct eight district workshops for still other supervisors. In each workshop there should be approximately twenty-four participants.

Fifth, these workshops would prepare the new persons to make use of the portable mathematics laboratories for their own in-service workshops during the next academic year. During these latter two stages of the program, the campus personnel would continue to assist in carrying forward a cooperatively designed evaluation of both the teaching procedures and the pupils' achievement. This evaluation would be included in the handbook, to be completed as soon as possible after this stage of the project was finished. The filmstrip would also be prepared at this time. If the experimentation up to this point proved successful, the idea of the portable mathematics laboratory could be "packaged" in a form useful to state departments of education, teacher-education institutions, and local school districts.

Ways of adapting this over-all plan to less comprehensive programs of in-service education may now be explored. A single city might well engage its elementary-school supervisory staff in creating and equipping a portable mathematics laboratory which could be moved from building to building for an agreed-upon period—three weeks seems to be a desirable length of time. During this period the teachers would be engaged in intensive study of the materials by actually trying them out in their classrooms and then sharing experiences, ideas, and evaluations in group meetings. If the school system were located in a city having a teacher-education institution, arrangements might be made whereby advanced education students could take over the teachers' duties during a part of each day of the workshop in order to free the teachers for sessions. If no institution of this type were available, similar arrangements might be worked out with qualified members of the school's Parent-Teacher Association. A county school system of two or more adjoining counties might co-operatively carry forward an in-service program of teacher education in much the same fashion. A research specialist either from the local school system or from the outside could give valuable aid in developing evaluation techniques and procedures.

The laboratory idea might be used on a more limited scale also. When it is not possible to involve an entire school system, an interested group of supervising principals or teachers or both might secure sufficient funds to develop a portable laboratory for use among themselves.

Through creative thinking and co-operative utilization of resources such as has been indicated by plans for the shared use of a portable mathematics laboratory, it is feasible to develop a challenging in-service education program on a large scale. Until some large-scale program for deepening the insights and raising the aspirations of elementary-school teachers of arithmetic is inaugurated, many elementary-school children will continue to be deprived of a rich and rewarding learning experience in arithmetic.

Great Challenges of Mathematics Education

Herman Rosenberg

A historian of mathematics has described mathematics as a ". . . constantly growing human thing . . . advancing in spite of its errors and partly because of them." [1] Allied with the tremendously rapid growth of mathematics has been the growth of its young "companion," mathematics education. Prior to the present decade, mathematics education, too, had a liberal share of unsolved problems. However, the present decade seems destined to surpass preceding decades for both the quantity and the quality of challenges to mathematics education.

The purpose of this article is to identify briefly some of the major challenges that may inspire or "haunt" mathematics educators during the early years of the present decade. To facilitate analysis, such challenges are presented below in three groups:

Reprinted from *The Mathematics Teacher* (May, 1962), 360–368, by permission of the author.

1. Challenges of content.
2. Challenges of method.
3. Other challenges in mathematics education.

CHALLENGES OF CONTENT

A central challenge to mathematics educators is the basic challenge to develop the best possible body of mathematical content suitable for presentation at each educational level from the elementary school through the graduate level of the university. In recent years, at least six related sub-challenges have been emerging:

Moderns Versus Traditionalists. There exists today a "modern" school of thought which recommends that the content of school mathematics should include a maximum amount of the newer mathematics uncovered in recent centuries. This recommendation is partially based on the hope of thereby providing for students mathematical material that may be less obsolete and more illuminating and interesting.

It has been said that there are two sides to every story. Thus, another school of thought—the "traditional" school—has recommended that the content of school mathematics should preserve the maximum amount of the fundamental mathematics uncovered in the earlier history of mathematics. This recommendation is partially based on the hope of thereby providing for students mathematical material that may be less abstract and more fundamental and useful. "Traditionalists" sometimes remind us that historians currently find considerable insight from the study of ancient and medieval history (e.g., ancient Athenian democracy as a source of study in the analysis of the "strategy" of modern democracy) and that the study of modern history does not necessarily displace the study of ancient and medieval history.[2]

However, as may be evident throughout this article, it is more proper to say that there may be more than one side to a story. For, among the rank and file of mathematics teachers may be found many who prefer varying amounts of "traditionalism" and "modernism." Some, for example, although inclined toward "tradition," favor the modern concept of sets as an excellent possibility for unifying and illuminating much of the basic traditional mathematics. Others, although favoring certain modern concepts, such as nondecimal numerals and/or vector concepts, oppose the set concept. Such opposition may be based on the conviction that, in the hands of untrained and unmotivated teachers and immature students, the entry of set concepts into traditional mathematics may be of little value or may even cause a loss of clarity and illumination. Mathematics teachers have varied degrees of reaction to the claim of the "moderns" that students may *easily* learn certain elementary concepts of modern mathematics. They vary also in their reaction to the countercharge of the "traditionalists" that children may easily learn concepts of even the most *useless* types of material and that the basic challenge is to select the most useful mathematics that may be taught in a very limited period of education. Thus, the challenge to mathematics educators is to determine—with the aid of careful research—the necessary and sufficient amounts of content of "modern" and "traditional" mathematics suitable for students of current school mathematics.

Mathematics Versus General Culture. Partly as a result of tensions created by the current "cold war" between the United States and Russia, the importance of mathematics in school curricula has been increasingly realized. On the one hand, some have asserted that, to meet the Russian challenge, the total school curriculum should be revised to include more mathematics for all students. On the other hand, others have asserted that our times demand a more vigorous total education which would properly treat other enlightening subjects in our general culture (subjects, such as the humanities, without which human lives may have limited meaning). The challenge, then, is to place mathematical and nonmathematical subjects in the proper perspective, and, thus, to determine the extent to which such subjects may even enhance each other on every level of the educational ladder.[3]

Pure Mathematics Versus Applied Mathematics. As current efforts are made to increase the content of "pure" school mathematics within allotted time limits, it becomes apparent that some aspect of school mathematics must "give." There are those who believe that concepts of applied mathematics should be among the first "victims" on the "sacrifice" list. The conviction here is that applications of mathematics may be learned "automatically" or easily in later years. There are also those who believe that concepts of applied mathematics should be relinquished only with the greatest of care. The conviction here is that such applications may not be learned automatically and may be vital and convenient vehicles not only for motivating instruction but also for providing mathematical insight and knowledge of our general culture.[4] The challenge here is this: What shall be the place for both pure mathematics and applied mathematics in the total evolving program of school mathematics?

Integration Versus Segregation. Several schools of thought are concerned with the proper type of organization of the content of school mathematics. Members of the "integration" school recommended that the content of school mathematics should be organized in a manner as integrated as possible. They feel, for example, that when several branches of mathematics are merged in one mathematics course, there may be significant gains for students in mathematical power, illumination, and appreciation. "Integrationists" point out that, because of isomorphisms (same abstract structure) of certain branches of mathematics (such as algebra and geometry), a student temporarily blocked in finding a solution via geometry may find the solution via algebra (or vice versa).[5] They argue that the trend in the development of modern mathematics is toward integrated mathematics and that school mathematics should reflect this trend.

Members of what may be called the "segregation" school of thought recommend that the content of school mathematics should be organized in a manner as "segregated" as possible; i.e., they prefer for teaching purposes "compartmentalization" of the branches of mathematics. They feel that an understanding of the structure of each branch of mathematics is best obtained by studying that branch in orderly "isolation" from other branches. They have the impression that integrated school mathematics is likely to be a bewildering "hodgepodge" for students, furnishing an effect similar to that of a meal in which all courses—including pickles and ice cream—are placed in one "mess kit."

Again, intermediate positions may be occupied between the "integration" and "segregation" schools of thought. Some mathematics teachers feel that, even when the teacher of "segregated" or "pure" algebra confronts a student with the elementary problem of adding $3x$ and $5x$, the necessity for student use of at least the skills of arithmetic may be a "natural" triumph for integration. Some point out that, in at least one sense, all effective learning may be "integrated" learning as a new concept is effectively "added" to previously learned concepts. Others insist that the fundamental concern is not the integration of one concept with a large set of concepts but rather the integration of two large sets of concepts (e.g., two branches of mathematics). And they emphasize the belief that learning may be facilitated if the purposeful integration of such sets of concepts takes place *after* each set has been learned separately. Thus, the challenge to mathematics educators is to determine the desirable amount of (and the strategic timing for) both the "segregation" and "integration" of concepts of school mathematics.

Revolutionaries Versus Conservatives. The wisdom of Felix Klein's remark that ". . . in mathematics, as everywhere else, men are inclined to form parties"[6] is further reflected in the current existence of variation of viewpoints on the proper rate of changing the content of school mathematics. Some educators have proposed what have been described as "sweeping" or "revolutionary" reforms in the content of school mathematics. The justification given for the rapidity of such revisions has often been the need for meeting the dangers involved in the rapid expansion of various foreign powers. Other educators have contemplated in "horror" the possibility of hasty crash programs that may destroy sound aspects of school mathematics that currently need conserving. They cite, for example, the extreme communication problem that might develop if every word in the English language were replaced overnight.

Between the extreme poles of "dynamic revolution" and "static conservatism" lies a group of educators who favor change of a gradual nature, i.e., "evolution rather than revolution." [7] Some feel that rapid, revolutionary changes in school mathematics programs may bewilder, confuse, and discourage unprepared teachers "ordered" to conform rapidly and that evolutionary change may permit for teachers a gradual, pleasant, stimulating growth. I. L. Kandel, noted for decades of research on problems of comparative (international) education, recently warned that a basic deterrent to young people from entering or remaining in the teaching profession may be what he called "frequent changes of pedagogical fashions." [8] Advocates of more rapid change argue that in dangerous times, such as the present, we may no longer afford the luxury of leisurely change in school mathematics. Thus, the challenge to mathematics educators is to determine the "correct" speed for reforming the content of school mathematics and the appropriate methodology for ascertaining this speed.

Diversity Versus Unity. On the one hand, members of a "diversity" school of thought prefer a maximum amount of experimentation with varied programs of content for school mathematics. This preference for variation is essentially based on two considerations:

1. The feeling that diversity in content is necessary for differing students, teachers, schools, etc., and is desirable for those who seek mathematical insight via alternative structures of the same content.
2. The hope that experimentation (such as that of the University of Illinois, University of Maryland, School Mathematics Study Group, etc.) may lead ultimately to the most desirable possibilities for selecting and organizing school mathematics.

On the other hand, members of a "unity" school of thought prefer a maximum amount of agreement on the nature of the content of school mathematics. This preference arises from consideration of questions, such as these:

1. Is it efficient in mathematical instruction to create many different symbols or terms for the same concept? For example, was there value in creating the two symbols arc sin x and $\sin^{-1} x$ for the same inverse sine concept? [9] May not the study of an excessive number of symbols for the same concept consume a disproportionate share of the time allotted for the study of school mathematics?
2. Assuming the ultimate "triumph" of the "diversity" school, may not an instructor of freshman college mathematics experience considerable difficulty if each of his students has been trained previously in radically different systems of mathematical language (terminology and notation)? May not such an instructor experience a "nightmare" in articulation (between college mathematics and high-school mathematics) if there is an acute problem of "shortages" and "excesses" in former learning among his varied students? [10]

Here, again, intermediate positions exist between the two schools of thought. Some prefer "unity" philosophy. However, they may justify the existence of "diverse" mathematical symbols in terms of the existence of many different national languages (including possible insight from such study in the general study of language) and in terms of further clarification of such mathematical concepts as the representation of a given number by many possible numerals.

Some prefer "diversity" philosophy and yet may justify the existence of "unified" content at such times as national emergencies. Using political analogies, some "unity" folk may point to the unfavorable military lessons of "disunity" among the medieval Italian city-state governments and to the "efficiency" of certain modern autocratic governments. "Diversity" folk may counter with references to the great flowering of Renaissance culture in disunited Italy and to the terrible sacrifice of freedom in "efficient" and "united" autocracies. Thus, the challenge to mathematics educators is to develop a program of school mathematics content that adequately reflects the efficiency advantages of unity within the beneficial experimental framework of diversity.

CHALLENGES OF METHOD

In addition to these challenges of content, many other challenges await mathematics educators. A basic challenge is the challenge to develop the best possible methodology for teaching mathematics at each educational level from the elementary school through the university. In recent years, at least five related subchallenges of this general methodology challenge have been emerging:

Logical Versus Psychological. At the present time, many mathematics educators have been very much concerned with a lack of rigor in much of school mathematics. Some, for example, may be well aware of the many logical holes discovered in secondary-school geometry,[11] and they may wonder about the possibility of using in secondary schools the more rigorous Hilbert approach to Euclidean geometry. Such views are frequently based on the feeling that mathematics must be presented logically if teachers are to achieve with their students all the potential disciplinary thinking values of mathematics.

However, such reasoning of the "logistic" school of thought may run counter to the reasoning of the "psychological" school, where the fear is that excessive amounts of formalism, abstractness, rigor, etc., may repel the mathematics student whose interest in the subject may be vitally needed.[12] Members of the "psychological" school favor liberal doses of concrete, intuitive school mathematics (identified as such to students) to prepare the way for subsequent careful presentations. Using analogies and comments, such as these, they may attempt to justify such "illogical" presentations:

1. In American films with locales in countries essentially non-English speaking, all foreign characters may speak English in spite of the "illogical" aspect of such speech. A breach in "logic" may be imperative here if the American audience is to attain understanding.

2. Honest identification of the "intuitive" nature of a mathematical presentation may be somewhat similar to the current emphasis on frank identification of a television program as being taped (and not "live") as a sequel to the exposure of former scandalous quiz programs whose preplanning was not so identified.

3. Initially, there may be "intuitive" levels of approach prior to more "rigorous" approaches in the sex education of young children and in the stages leading to more meaningful appreciation of the Bible, Shakespeare's works, and other classics.

4. At an early age, children are confronted with dictionaries, where definitions are not planned for mathematical purposes. One may hardly discuss with very young children in the elementary school definitions and theorems which are completely acceptable to mature mathematicians. As an example, the number concept is developed with increasing maturity as students move from the early stages of elementary-school instruction toward the college level.[13] In an evolving subject, such as mathematics, may even the mathematician ever achieve perfection in rigor?

In general, mathematics teachers realize that, as mathematicians, they wish the mathematics they teach to be as logical as possible. And, as teachers, they wish to teach that mathematics in accordance with the soundest findings of educational psychology. The challenge for mathematics educators, then, is to provide curricular experiences in mathematics that are soundly based on the best traditions of both logic and psychology.

Needs Theory Versus Subject Matter Theory. There are varying emphases given to the relative importance of the mathematics taught to students and the needs of such students. These needs, for example, may include adequate amounts of challenge and fun furnished by superior teachers and materials of instruction.[14] A basic challenge here is to develop methodology for improving the sensitivity of teachers and administrators to the importance of both mathematics and the mathematically oriented needs of their "charges."

Differentiated versus nondifferentiated. Recent decades have witnessed changing viewpoints with respect to the desirability of differentiating instruction to provide for tremendous individual differences in ability and interests among mathematics students.[15] Under the impact of the Sputnik race, respect for "homogeneous" grouping of mathematics students—a device formerly attacked with great frequency as "undemocratic"—has been increasing. Nevertheless, even among mathematics educators strongly convinced of the desirability of homogeneous grouping, there exists some division on questions, such as these:

1. At a given educational level, should groups of slow and rapid learners be taught the same basic mathematics content, or should differentiation be provided in content as well as in teaching-method?

2. Should groups of rapid learners experience acceleration in learning-time or enrichment of mathematical content?

3. Should different grading systems be used to distinguish between mathematical achievement in slow and rapid classes? (Growing public interest in such questions led playwright Gore Vidal recently to endorse a suggestion for adoption of nationwide minimum academic standards and rating systems.)

4. What is the optimum size for differentiated mathematics classes?

In general, the challenge to mathematics educators is to determine and increase the effectiveness of mathematics classes in which there has been differentiation with respect to mathematical content and/or teaching-methods.

Field Theory Versus Association Theory. Different psychologies of learning affect the choice of teaching-methods. Some educators favor the "association" theory (stimulus-response bond psychology), and, thus, they emphasize the importance of student learning of specific items of content with proper amounts of drill and programming. Others favor the "field" theory (Gestalt psychology), and, thus, they emphasize the importance of meaningful student insight into the whole structure of mathematics or mathematical systems. The challenge here is to develop a workable theory of maximum learning of mathematics, utilizing the best aspects of such theories as the "association" theory for learning the "small parts" of mathematics and the "field" theory for learning the "large wholes" of mathematics.[16]

Inductive Method Versus Deductive Method. Some mathematics educators have long employed in their textbooks and classrooms a "deductive" approach to the teaching of mathematics. Here, a mathematical generalization is presented first and is then followed by applications to specific situations. Others have advocated the use of an "inductive" approach, where specific situations are presented first and are then followed by student discovery of a mathematical generalization. The challenge here is to determine the conditions under which maximum learning is possible via both "deductive" and "inductive" approaches to the teaching of mathematics.[17]

OTHER CHALLENGES IN MATHEMATICS EDUCATION

In addition to the above challenges in mathematics education, other challenges arise from the relationship of mathematical content to teaching-method. Three final challenges are deemed by the writer as fundamental in mathematics education.

Teacher Education: General Practitioners Versus Specialists. Varied suggestions are available when one seeks a desirable program for the education of mathematics teachers. In the area of the preservice training of teachers of secondary-school mathematics, there exist differences in viewpoint on the proper relative amounts of specialization (college mathematics courses) and general education (nonmathematical courses). Here, too, there are different views with respect to the desirable distribution of specialization courses (and general-education courses) and the relative importance of content courses and courses in teaching-methodology.[18]

In the area of the preservice training of elementary-school teachers, a major difference in viewpoint exists with respect to the wisdom of having such training provide sufficient specialization to produce "expert" teachers of arithmetic. The New York University "Dual Progress Plan" (with the assistance of the Ford Foundation) is an example of an experimental program concerned with such questions. The problem arises, on the one hand, from the hope of securing well-prepared, highly motivated teachers of arithmetic in the elementary school, and, on the other hand, from the fear that the early education of the "whole child" may be disrupted by "departmentalized" teaching.[19]

Such problems of teacher-training have a possible far-flung significance in mathematics education. Consider, for example, the problem of the recruitment and retention of the most able mathematics teachers and the "controversial" suggestions which have been made of improving the situation via teacher rewards for the quality (as well as the quantity) of teacher-training and experience.[20] The challenge, then, is to evolve the best types of both general and specialized education of mathematics teachers—an education characterized by balance in both depth and breadth and in content and methodology.

Evaluation of Mathematics Instruction: Skills Versus Meanings. While the importance of evaluating instruction in mathematics has been generally recognized, there have been different identifications of the specific aspects of instruction needing evaluation. Some have insisted that the basic task in mathematics education is the development of student skills in mathematics and that, consequently, the basic job of mathematics evaluation is the testing of such skills. Others have maintained that the truly important task in the teaching of mathematics is the development for mathematics students of the meanings of mathematical concepts and that, consequently, the basic job of mathematics evaluation is the testing of such understandings.[21]

Thus, the determination of what should be evaluated depends upon the choice of the goals and potential values of mathematics teaching.[22] When seen broadly, the fundamental challenge to mathematics educators is the challenge to determine precisely those objectives of mathematics education that may assist in securing for students and society-at-large the "good" life and then to prepare a total program of evaluation of all aspects (meanings, skills, appreciations, etc.) of the program of mathematics education designed for those objectives.[23]

Leadership: School Versus Community. There have been pronounced differences in viewpoints with respect to the leadership role to be played by society, on the one hand, and school personnel, on the other hand. Some have advocated that the schools should not only utilize the local community for resources (or aids) in the teaching of mathematics but also encourage members of the community to assume a leading role in matters of school reforms (such as improvement of inadequate salary structures for mathematics teachers and removal of barriers tending to reduce time available to mathematics teachers for professional growth).

Some have successfully sought positive, dynamic leadership from school administrators. Others, however, have found here not leadership and inspiration, but rather dashes of desperation and despotism. There are those, like Myron Lieberman, who are critical of the current power structure in education and of "futile" appeals to the public-at-large and who forsee a new, forward-looking era emerging in educational leadership when teacher groups assert their great potential leadership.[24] The challenge, then, is to determine and to secure the finest types of educational leadership affecting mathematics education and to utilize the most able personnel from both the school and society.

NOTES

1. ERIC TEMPLE BELL, *The Development of Mathematics* (New York: McGraw-Hill Book Co., 1945), p. 12.
2. For further insight into the philosophies of the "traditional" and "modern" schools of thought, see Morris Kline, "The Ancients versus the Moderns, a New Battle of the Books," THE MATHEMATICS TEACHER, LI (October, 1958), 418–27; and Albert E. Meder, Jr., "The Ancients versus the Moderns—a Reply," THE MATHEMATICS TEACHER, LI (October, 1958), 428–33.
3. For further exploration of the background of this challenge, see Herman Rosenberg, "The Real Menace of the Sputniks to Mathematics Education," *School Science and Mathematics,* LIX (December, 1959), 723–30.
4. For illustrations of applications of mathematics which may have such values, see Herman Rosenberg, "Modern Applications of Exponential and Logarithmic Functions," *School Science and Mathematics,* LX (February, 1960), 131–38.
5. The publication in recent years of a large number of textbooks merging calculus with analytic geometry is a reflection of the "integration" point of view. For an analysis of the role of trigonometry as an integrating agent in school mathematics, see Herman Rosenberg, "The Changing Concept of Trigonometry as a School Subject," THE MATHEMATICS TEACHER, LI (April, 1958), 246–52.
6. FELIX KLEIN, *Elementary Mathematics from an Advanced Standpoint* (New York: Macmillan Co., 1939), II, 55.
7. For a recent textbook reflecting such "evolutionary" philosophy, see Francis J. Mueller, *Intermediate Algebra* (Englewood Cliffs, N.Y.: Prentice-Hall, Inc., 1960), p. v.
8. I. L. KANDEL, "Revival of American Education," *The Educational Forum,* XXIV (March, 1960), 272.

9. It is interesting to note the recommendation in Great Britain by Nunn that British mathematics teachers ". . . employ the continental notation arc sin x, arc tan x, in preference to our insular $\sin^{-1} x$, $\tan^{-1} x$, etc." See T. Percy Nunn, *The Teaching of Algebra (Including Trigonometry)* (London: Longmans, Green & Co., 1923), p. 514.

"Unity" people point also to the marring of the reputation of mathematics as a universal language of communication by the lack of international agreement on basic symbols for multiplication and division. (Consider, for example, the contrasts between the English and American placement of a dot to indicate multiplication and the use of what Americans would call a division sign as a sign of subtraction in Continental Europe.) For further background material, see *Fifteenth Yearbook: The Place of Mathematics in Secondary Education* (Washington, D.C.: The National Council of Teachers of Mathematics, 1940).

10. For further consideration of problems in articulation of college and high-school mathematics, see J. H. Neeley, "What To Do About a New Kind of Freshman," *American Mathematical Monthly* (August–September, 1959), 584–86.

11. See, for example, Commission on Mathematics of the College Entrance Examination Board, *Appendices* (Princeton: Educational Testing Service, 1959), 1909–11.

12. For a recent expression of such fear, see Rev. D. B. Smith, "Some Observations on Mathematics Curriculum Trends," THE MATHEMATICS TEACHER, LIII (February, 1960), 85–89.

13. See, for example, *Twenty-Fourth Yearbook: The Growth of Mathematical Ideas* (Washington, D.C.: The National Council of Teachers of Mathematics, 1959).

14. For a further discussion of such needs, see Herman Rosenberg, "The Real Menace of the Sputniks to Mathematics Education," *School Science and Mathematics*, LIX (December, 1959), 723–30.

15. See *Twenty-Second Yearbook: Emerging Practices in Mathematics Education* (Washington, D.C.: The National Council of Teachers of Mathematics, 1954).

16. For further material on philosophies of mathematical learning, see *Twenty-First Yearbook: The Learning of Mathematics* (Washington, D.C.: The National Council of Teachers of Mathematics, 1953). See also Henry S. Dyer and others, *Problems in Mathematical Education* (Princeton: Educational Testing Service, 1956).

17. For an illustration of research on this problem, see Max A. Sobel, "A Comparison of Two Methods of Teaching Certain Topics in Ninth Grade Algebra," *The New Jersey Mathematics Teacher*, XI (October, 1954), 15–16.

18. See for example, John J. Kinsella, "Preparation in Mathematics of Mathematics Teachers," *The Mathematics Teacher*, LIII (January, 1960), 27–32. See also Albert E. Meder, Jr., and others, "The Education of Mathematics Teachers," *American Mathematical Monthly* (November, 1959), 805–09.

Some educators, of course, have realized that teacher competence requires mastery of both subject matter and teaching techniques. Kandel, for example, has insisted that these two aspects of the same activity—professional competence—have been separated much too long. See I. L. Kandel, "Revival of American Education," *The Educational Forum*, XXIV (March, 1960), 278.

19. For a discussion of the problem of motivating teachers of arithmetic, see Herman Rosenberg, "The Role of Elementary Mathematics in General College Mathematics," THE MATHEMATICS TEACHER, LII (April, 1959), 260–64.

20. For a further discussion of teacher "rewards," see Howard F. Fehr, "How Much Mathematics Should Teachers Know?" THE MATHEMATICS TEACHER, LII (April, 1959), 299–300.

21. For an interesting article on the relation of mathematical skills to mathematical meanings, see George H. Meen, "Interaction of 'How' and 'Why' in Arithmetic," *The New Jersey Mathematics Teacher*, XIII (February, 1957), 3–6.

22. For a recent statement of the potential values of mathematics, see Herman Rosenberg, "Values of Mathematics for the Modern World," THE MATHEMATICS TEACHER, LIII (May, 1960), 353–58.

23. Considerable insight into the entire evaluation challenge may be found in the *Twenty-Sixth Yearbook: The Evaluation of Achievement in Mathematics* (Washington, D.C.: The National Council of Teachers of Mathematics, 1961).

24. Myron Lieberman, *The Future of Public Education* (Chicago: The University of Chicago Press, 1960).

Planning for the Improvement of Mathematics Experiences in the Elementary School

Wallace T. Stoebe

Title III of the National Defense Education Act of 1958 which provides federal funds for a period of four years has encouraged California school districts to enrich their programs in science, mathematics, and modern foreign languages. This opportunity has caused many school districts maintaining elementary schools to take inventory of their present programs, to plan for more enriched instruction, and to submit projects to achieve these goals.

The applications received by the Bureau of National Defense Education Act Administration of the California State Department of Education for the 1958–59 school year were for a total of 404 projects to be developed by the elementary schools or by elementary and secondary schools together. Of this number, only 77 were in the field of mathematics. In the applications for the 1959–60 school year there were 408 projects submitted which included 60 in mathematics. The number submitted for mathematics projects in comparison to the number submitted for science and foreign language projects would seem to indicate that (1) district personnel is satisfied with present programs of mathematics; (2) school districts are unaware of the possibilities for enriching their mathematics programs afforded by the pro-

Reprinted from *California Journal of Elementary Education*, Vol. 28, No. 10 (May 1960), 234–243, by permission of the California State Department of Education.

visions of the National Defense Education Act; (3) school districts lack trained personnel to work on the formulation of plans for the enrichment of the mathematics program; or (4) evaluation of present programs has not yet been undertaken.

Because of the growing importance of mathematics in our world today and because of demand by the general public for an improved program in mathematics instruction, it seems advisable to encourage school districts to take advantage of Public Law 864 in order to enrich their mathematics program. The following information should help school districts to develop carefully planned and well-organized projects which show promise of improving instruction in mathematics.

PLANNING FOR MATHEMATICS PROJECTS

Plans for the improvement of programs in mathematics should include clear-cut delineations of general objectives, as well as well-defined statements of long-range and immediate goals for the specific project. Many projects might be planned to achieve the same broad general objectives. For example, these objectives might be (1) to help each individual to solve problems and to communicate quantitative facts and ideas through the use of mathematical language and forms; (2) to inform children and youth of vocational and professional opportunities in the field of mathematics; (3) to provide young citizens with the background and understanding necessary to make their contributions in a world which is becoming more technical and more mechanical.

In addition to the general objectives, each project should clearly define its immediate and its long-range goals. For example, a certain school district discovered that in grades four, five, and six pupils were weak in understanding measurement. This district then prepared a project which was submitted to the California State Department of Education under Public Law 864. The project was to improve instruction pertaining to measurement in these grades. The following objectives were stated for the project.

The immediate objectives to help girls and boys in grades four, five, and six are (1) to understand concepts and acquire skill in the measurement of space, weight, time, temperature, and value; (2) to be able to use this understanding and skill in problem solving; (3) to meet individual differences by making available a wide variety of books, charts, manipulative devices, and other audio-visual materials.

The long-range objectives to help girls and boys in grades four, five, and six are (1) to gain the ability to solve increasingly difficult problems in measurement; (2) to develop interest in instruments of measurement, new and old; (3) to acquire interest and skill in precision of measurement; (4) to develop a greater interest in mathematics in general and a desire to continue its study; (5) to appreciate the importance of measurement in everyday life.

Many projects have possibilities for research which should not be overlooked. It is only through research that better methods of instruction can be determined. For example, in the preceding project, the personnel of the school district, including curriculum co-ordinators, principals, and teachers met together to develop a definite program for the teaching of measurement. After discussion and study, they decided that they did not know for how long at a time or how often measurement should be taught to obtain best results. At this point a planned research project was set up. It was agreed that one-third of the teachers at each grade level would follow the California State text exactly, teaching measurement only as it came in the book and for the length of time indicated. One-third of the teachers would teach measurement for one 45-minute period per week, while the final third would teach measurement for ten minutes each day for a specified number of weeks. All teachers would have a carefully worked out plan to follow as to content and sequence, so that they would be teaching the same material, but only the time element would be different. Each teacher would be asked to used measurement in the total program throughout the day whenever possible. At the end of the experiment, carefully prepared tests would be given to all the children to discover differences in learning. At the beginning of the following year, more tests would be given to determine differences in retention. Improvement in instruction should result from such carefully planned research studies.

PROCEDURES SHOULD BE DETAILED

Any program for the improvement of instruction will not likely be successful if it is developed without the co-operation of the teachers. Methods and instructional materials and equipment should be decided upon with the help of the teachers in order that their involvement may contribute to the success of the program. Detailed plans for conducting the program as worked out by committees of teachers and other personnel are an important part of any project. Such plans should be submitted with project applications.

For example, the project on measurement in grades four, five, and six might be as follows:

It was ascertained that the local course of study in mathematics and the state texts were in agreement as to grade placement of content as related to measurement. The teachers were especially interested in methods of instruction, length of time, and frequency of instruction, and in materials and equipment.

Committees of teachers recommended certain methods of instruction in measurement as being most successful. Paper work and the actual use of instruments were considered essential. Grouping within the classroom was strongly advised, making it possible for the slow-learners to spend much time with manipulative devices, while some groups were actually measuring and solving problems, and others were having opportunities to read and explore their own interests in measurement. Children were encouraged to work in groups and to help one another, but each child was given time to think and work by himself when he needed it.

The length of time and the frequency of instruction in measurement will be decided definitely after continued study. Plans were made to include the concepts and skills of measurement whenever possible in other areas of the school curriculum. The social studies, and other areas of the curriculum offer many such opportunities. Understanding comes with use.

The following materials were placed in each fourth, fifth and sixth grade classroom: yardsticks, foot rulers, tape measures, liquid and dry measure kits, odometers, Fahrenheit thermometers, clock faces with both Arabic and Roman numerals, flannel boards, models of one square foot, models of one square yard, globes, play money, plain cubes, and wall maps showing standard time zones. These materials were to be used by the children to help them understand measurement and gain skill in using measurements. A stop watch, sundial, sand glass, weight scales, English and metric systems, meter bar or stick, perimeter area board, clinical, meat, centigrade, and candy thermometers, and a thermostat were made available in each school. These would be used by the pupils to deepen their understanding of mathematical concepts.

A large number of books on all phases of mathematics and on all levels of difficulty was purchased to be circulated among the classrooms. Kits of 15 books were sent to each class room and rotated periodically. The pupils were encouraged to read these books to broaden their interests in mathematics.

Audio-visual aids were considered to be of great help in enriching a mathematics program. Each school was provided sufficient audio-visual equipment so that projectors were available when needed. Teachers were encouraged to become familiar with the films and film strips on various phases of measurement. Teachers were cautioned to use these aids as part of an integrated instructional program so that the material would be meaningful to the children.

SUPERVISION AND IN-SERVICE TRAINING SHOULD BE PROVIDED

An absolute essential for the success of any project is qualified personnel to co-ordinate and direct the project. In the project on measurement the qualifications of the curriculum co-ordinator who would be in charge of the program should be included in the application. It is desirable that this person should have worked with the teachers in planning the program and in selecting the instructional materials and audio-visual equipment. The curriculum co-ordinator, or his assistants, would then observe the teachers and assist them in the classroom on a regular basis. He would also conduct periodic workshops to exchange ideas, to discuss problems, and to demonstrate materials and equipment.

The project also requires someone in charge of research to plan, direct, and evaluate with the teachers involved. The exact number of personnel required to make a project function successfully depends upon the number of schools involved. It would be necessary for small districts to call for assistance from the office of the county superintendent of schools. However, it is important that each person knows his job and carries through with it. Too often a project begins with enthusiasm and then dies out due to lack of carry-through by those in charge.

In-service training of teachers is of great importance to the success of any program, and definite plans should be submitted with all projects. For example, plans for in-service training in the illustrative project on measurement might be submitted as follows:

General plans for training the teachers involved in the project were suggested by the teacher planning committee. These plans made provisions for (1) each teacher to be given an opportunity to observe the teaching of measurement by a master teacher; (2) workshops to be conducted and demonstrations to be given by experts; and (3) regular meetings scheduled with the project co-ordinator in charge. During these meetings, successful methods and worth-while materials will be discussed and displayed. Bulletin boards and interest centers will be set up. These meetings will be for the purpose of offering all possible help and encouragement to teachers.

EVALUATION SHOULD BE CAREFULLY PLANNED

It is only through carefully planned evaluation that it is possible to determine whether or not any project is successfully meeting its objective. Evaluation techniques should be decided upon at the time of the initial planning. Ongoing evaluation is helpful to the teacher in improving instruction as needed. Evaluation at stated intervals in the progress of a project is of great importance in that it points up weaknesses in the total program and makes it possible to revise plans and objectives. It is important that all test scores and the results of other evaluative instruments be carefully tabulated with this purpose in mind.

In the suggested project on measurement for grades four, five, and six the plans for the section on evaluation were as follows:

1. Ongoing evaluation will be accomplished by teacher-prepared tests and textbook tests which will be given about once every six weeks. The results of these tests will be used by the teacher to improve the instructional program.

2. Scores from the problems on measurement in the standardized tests will be tabulated.

3. Objective tests devised by a teacher committee with the help of an evaluation consultant will be used for final evaluation. These tests will be devised to determine understanding of concepts of measurement, the ability to work with measures, and problem solving. These results will be used to find weaknesses and thus to improve instruction.

4. Teachers will keep anecdotal records to show the extent of growth in understanding of concepts of measurement and to show how well the children can apply what they have learned.

5. At the end of each school year, carefully-devised interest inventories will be given to the pupils to determine whether their interest in mathematics has increased. The results of interest inventories, the implication of anecdotal records, and all test scores will be evaluated by a specialist to make certain that the best possible interpretation is secured.

CONTINUITY AND ARTICULATION

Continuity is necessary to the success of teaching in any area. It is therefore advisable that teachers in higher grades be aware of a special project that is underway. In the case of the project in measurement, meetings with teachers of grades seven and eight, and with personnel of the high school, should be planned for the purpose of explaining the program and making plans for continuity of experience. Articulation of this kind among the grades and with the high school will promote understanding and therefore eliminate duplication of effort, increase interest, and result in an enriched program of instruction throughout the district.

SUMMARY

All school districts should be interested in improving instruction in mathematics. Districts are urged to evaluate their present programs and to work on plans for improvement and enrichment. Only through careful planning and organization can desired results be obtained, and therefore specific plans must be submitted as part of each project. Projects which show promise of being successful usually have the following characteristics:

1. The project itself is limited to one definite phase of mathematics.
2. Both immediate and long-range objectives are clearly stated.
3. Planning has taken place with the teachers to assure enthusiastic and co-operative teaching.
4. A carefully thought out instructional plan includes methods to be used and worth-while materials and equipment.

5. Use of audio-visual aids is limited to those items which will contribute to an integrated program of instruction.

6. The district has qualified personnel to direct the program.

7. A program for in-service training of teachers has been planned.

8. Definite plans for evaluation of the program have been made, making possible the revision of methods or materials as weaknesses appear.

9. Provision has been made for continuity through the grades and for articulation of the work done in the elementary school with that done in the high school.

SUGGESTIONS FOR POSSIBLE PROJECTS IN MATHEMATICS

The following suggestions are offered to stimulate thinking about possibilities in the improvement of mathematics:

1. A school district might plan to utilize resources of the education and the mathematics departments of a nearby college or university in co-operation with staff members of the school system to review the entire problem of the preservice and in-service education of professional personnel in order to design a program of mathematics together with essential materials and equipment and thus combine teacher education with curriculum development for the district.

2. A school district might plan a project including one or more mobile units of 20 (more or less) books with interesting mathematics content which could be made available to classrooms serving fifth, sixth, seventh, and eighth grade children.

3. Exhibits of books with interesting mathematics content and carefully annotated bibliographies of the material could be made available through the office of a county school superintendent or a district superintendent. The project might be objectively evaluated on the basis of the number of children reading each title as well as on subjective evidence of increased interest in mathematics.

4. A project might be designed at a specific grade level with appropriate materials designed to improve children's concepts of place value.

5. A project might be designed at specific grade levels to show development of children's concepts of fractions, decimals, and percentage.

6. A project might be designed at specific grade levels to show growth and to improve children's understanding of measurement.

7. A project might be designed to teach children at grades six, seven, and eight the use of the slide rule.

8. A project might be designed to improve children's concepts of place value by use of the comptometer.

9. A project might be designed to show how geometrical concepts could be taught through grades six, seven, and eight.

10. Projects might be designed to develop resource units at appropriate grade levels on time, money, and foreign exchange, measurement, space travel and celestial navigation, and the like.

11. A project might be designed to measure the growth of mathematical concepts and ability in reading mathematical material through extended reading of appropriate books at various grade levels.

12. A project might be designed to develop self-teaching units to enable the mathematically talented to progress at their own rate.

13. A project might be designed to use specific manipulative materials and firsthand experience to improve the achievement of slow learners.

14. A project might be designed to determine the actual number knowledge (time, space, volume, number) of children at school entrance and at subsequent developmental levels.

10

Issues in Elementary School Mathematics

It appears that issues are necessary in order for a discipline to refresh itself. "Necessity is the mother of invention." Issues raised and issues researched contribute to the developmental nature of mathematics education, each step adding a greater degree of refinement. Through the continued discussion of issues, research is generated, direction unfolds, and the values in mathematics education are placed in a conspicuous position. Issues are synonymous with growth and tend to reflect the state of health of mathematics education. It causes the practitioner, the researcher, and the education organizer to look at mathematics either sympathetically or critically, and causes us to examine all other related aspects as they influence the direction of mathematics education. As we agree or disagree with the issues, this dialogue tends to generate new ideas and further research and development in mathematics education at the elementary school level.

Does "Modern Math" Ignore Learning Theory?

David Rappaport

The mathematics curriculum at all levels of the elementary school is undergoing rapid and radical change. The emphasis on "modern" or newer mathematics reflects great concern for abstract principles and other content formerly reserved for the more mature student. Although the arithmetic

Reprinted from *Phi Delta Kappan* (June 1963), 445–447, by permission of the publisher.

curriculum needs to be changed, it is my contention that this new emphasis has introduced concepts and practices in violation of sound principles of learning theory.

The interest in modern mathematics represents a third phase in the changing elementary school curriculum in this century. From 1900 to 1935 the main emphasis in the teaching of arithmetic was on speed and accuracy. Children were graded on the number of correct answers they could get in a limited time. Standardized tests were administered in wholesale fashion, norms were set up, and children were graded and classified according to their arithmetic skills. Teachers resorted to drill and more drill as a teaching technique in order to insure high scores.

After 1935, under the influence of such educational leaders as Brownell, Wheat, Spitzer, McSwain, Morton, and Van Engen, the emphasis shifted to a concern for meaning and understanding. Discovery replaced drill as a teaching technique. The concept of "meaningful arithmetic" was widely accepted in the United States. There was general agreement that children should learn the arithmetic skills, but at the same time there was recognition that drill did not always achieve the desired goal. It was argued that meaningful learning would result in better skills and that it would stimulate the children to further mathematical learning. It became necessary to revise the arithmetic curriculum so that the "why" would be as important as the "how."

In recent years emphasis has shifted once more to a concern for content. For many years math professors complained that high-school students were inadequately prepared for the study of college mathematics. During the last fifty years mathematics knowledge has developed by leaps and bounds, but the high-school curriculum did not reflect this fact. The result was a big gap between the old curriculum and the new mathematics. Teachers took sides in a debate between the "traditionalists" and the "modernists." The College Entrance Examination Board, the National Council of Teachers of Mathematics, mathematics professors, textbook publisers, and various other groups joined in an effort to narrow the gap. The result was a virtual revolution in the mathematics curriculum.

First, the high-school curriculum had to be changed. But it soon became apparent that high schools could not do an effective job because students needed earlier training in mathematics. Children trained in traditional ways could not adapt themselves to the new concepts and ways of thinking. The result was a continuing effort to bring the newer concepts into earlier grades. The curriculum first introduced into the high school was soon introduced into the junior high school, then into the middle elementary grades, and now into the first grade.

Changes in content are necessary and should be supported, but it is also necessary to warn against extreme attitudes that are being developed.[1] The new emphasis is bringing sophisticated mathematics to children at too early an age. I fear that often "logic" has become predominant over psychology, at the expense of learning.

Logic is the formulation or deduction of valid conclusions that are consistent with a set of undefined terms, defined terms, and postulates. All logical systems must have these three elements. Postulates are statements accepted as true without proof. A conclusion is logical if it agrees with the postulates or definitions. A change in definitions or postulates results in new conclusions which are different from the old. Thus non-Euclidian geometry, based on definitions and postulates that are different from those of Euclidian geometry, contains theorems that are not found in Euclidian geometry and often conflict with it. Nevertheless, Euclidian and non-Euclidian geometry are both logical systems.

The mathematician continually refines his definitions and postulates. He tries to make his logical system more general and more inclusive. Man began to postulate before recorded history began. Today we consider many of the definitions and postulates of early mathematicians inadequate. It takes a great deal of understanding of the elements of a logical system to appreciate the refinements.

How do children learn? Do they begin with a set of undefined terms, definitions, and postulates? Of course not. They must first experience concrete relationships. Abstract thinking comes later. The definitions that children learn must be based on their own experiences and understanding. These may not meet the test of logical rigor, but as a child's knowledge, experience, and understanding grow, he will be able to follow the more sophisticated definitions and postulates. It is my belief that the present trend emphasizes the sophisticated refinements before the child has matured enough to appreciate them.

The following examples illustrate some of the extreme attitudes which, if not modified, may undo the progress that has been made in making arithmetic meaningful to children.

The number line has been used by algebra teachers to demonstrate addition and subtraction of signed numbers. But now the number line is being introduced into the first grade as an example of the newer mathematics program. Just how is it being used? I observed a mathematics consultant teaching the new mathematics. She asked a first grade class why 9 is greater than 8. The answer she sought was that 9 is the greater number because it is found to the right of 8 on the number line.

I recalled one of the dialogues of Plato in which the government prosecutor was rushing past Socrates. He was in too big a hurry even to say hello. He was rushing to court to have his father hanged. When Socrates asked him why he wanted to have his father hanged, he answered that his father had committed an evil act and must be punished. The father had done some-

---

[1] David Rappaport, "Mathematics—Logical, Psychological, Pedagogical," *The Arithmetic Teacher*, February, 1962, pp. 67–70.

thing that displeased the gods. Socrates persisted in questioning the young man. Was the father's act evil because it displeased the gods, or were the gods displeased because the act was evil? We learn from Plato that the young prosecutor was so stunned by this question that he spent the rest of the day philosophizing with Socrates on the nature of evil.

A similar question may be asked of the mathematics consultant. Is 9 greater than 8 because it is to the right of 8 on the number line, or is 9 placed to the right of 8 on the number line because it is greater than 8? Does the child accept the number line and apply it to the concept of number, or must he first learn about number and then apply this knowledge to the number line? The number line is a physical model that can be used to illustrate number ideas, but it should not precede learning about number.

At the annual meeting of the National Council of Teachers of Mathematics held in Chicago in 1961, one of the speakers described the School Mathematics Study Group material developed for the fourth, fifth, and sixth grades. This group, generally known as SMSG, is one of the leaders in the movement to introduce the newer mathematics into the elementary school. The speaker had taught this material to a sixth grade class. In her presentation she said, "We no longer teach multiplication as the addition of equal sized groups, but as the Cartesian product of two sets." A Cartesian product of two sets is the pairing of the elements of one set with the elements of another set. Thus, if a girl has 8 blouses and 6 skirts, she could have 48 outfits by pairing one blouse with one skirt, assuming that there is no clash of color or material that would prevent the combination of any blouse with any skirt. This is considered to be an improvement over the traditional concept of multiplication in which the child learned that 8×6 was found by adding 8 sixes. But how does the child learn that 8×6 is equal to 48 by pairing 8 blouses with 6 skirts? When asked this question, the speaker answered, "By counting, I suppose."

The child does not count 48 individual pairs. He sees that each blouse can be paired with 6 skirts. Therefore, there are 8 groups of 6 pairs. In other words, he learns the Cartesian product of two sets by adding equal sized groups. Would it not be better to have the child learn the multiplication facts as the sum of equal sized groups and then apply this knowledge to the concept of Cartesian cross-products?

Van Engen goes beyond the definition of multiplication as the cross-product of two sets. He advocates the teaching of multiplication as a mapping process. He writes,

Multiplication is a way of associating two numbers with a third number. Thus, the pair $(2, 3)$ is associated with 6. In mathematics, we say $(2, 3)$ is mapped onto 6 and write

$$(2, 3) \longrightarrow 6$$

But this is not enough. Addition also associates two numbers with a third.

So we must say something more if multiplication is to be differentiated from addition. We have the key idea, namely, that of mapping a pair of numbers onto another number (associating a pair of numbers with a single number).[2]

This association, according to Van Engen, can be shown by means of a multiplication table. But how does the child learn how to map? How does the child learn to associate 48 with the number pair (8, 6)? Although Van Engen admits that the third grade child is not ready for this kind of definition, he suggests that the concept be developed by many situations to convince the child that it is sensible to associate numbers with number pairs. Thus, multiplication is taught as a mapping process rather than as an addition process.

If the child is to learn these multiplicative mappings, he still must learn the multiplication facts by adding equal sized groups. How does multiplication as a mapping process really help the third grader, or older child, to understand the meaning of multiplication? If multiplication as a mapping process is a clarifying concept for mathematicians, is it, necessarily, a clarifying concept for children?

One final illustration. A consultant made this statement: "It is wrong for teachers to teach the children that 7 sheep plus 5 sheep equal 12 sheep. You cannot add sheep. Addition is a mathematical process that can be performed only with abstract numbers. You can add 7 and 5 but not sheep."

Is this a clarifying concept?

I believe that the introduction of highly sophisticated mathematical concepts in the early elementary grades will take the child away from the meaningful understanding of basic arithmetic concepts needed in his everyday, practical experiences and also in his preparation for further learning in other areas. Though the current trend may help a few to become abstract mathematicians, the large majority of elementary school children will, I think, be confused by many elements of the program as it is now being developed.

---

[2] Henry Van Engen, "The Reform Movement in Arithmetic and the Verbal Problem," *The Arithmetic Teacher*, January, 1963, p. 4.

Mathematics in Kindergarten—Formal or Informal?

Dorothy M. Roberts and Irving Bloom

The use of formal teaching materials in kindergarten has stirred much controversy. Kindergarten teachers in the Scotch Plains-Fanwood District have tended to resist the use of any workbook or worksheet-type materials. The researchers decided to invite the teachers to take part in a pilot study. When the study was explained to the teachers, much of their apprehension subsided.

The purpose of our study was to analyze and to compare growth patterns in skills, concepts, and general readiness developed by three different mathematics programs in kindergarten. The study covered a period from February through May, or about fourteen weeks. The materials used were the Silver Burdett *Modern Arithmetic through Discovery, Beginner's Book* (1) SRA's *Greater Cleveland Mathematics Program, Grade K Book* (2) and the Scotch Plains *Kindergarten Handbook* (3) which contains a series of informal number readiness activities. The local handbook (3) describes a variety of number activities: games, finger plays, and songs. These activities are designed to develop concepts of number; the ability to count rationally, to recognize geometric shapes, and the ability to recognize sets of objects and to count them accurately. The activities are also designed to help the children learn the ordinals—*first, second, third,* and *last*—and the meanings of words like *larger, smaller, more than, less than, taller, shorter, longer,* and *as big as.*

The concepts are taught informally. The children are not expected to sit quietly in rows and listen to the teacher's presentation at a prescribed time and place each day. Rather, the children are taught through simple activities, when and where they seem ready to engage in them successfully and happily. The teacher works to help each child develop his powers of reason, to note relations, to observe his environment, and to make simple generalizations.

The activities are not limited to number work, but often encompass language and listening skills, counting, working in groups—all in one teacher-directed activity or discussion.

Usually, little or no written work is done in connection with the mathematics activities—at least there is no textbook or workbook for the child to use. Experience with textbooks and workbooks is reserved for first grade. This was the situation in the typical kindergarten at the time the study was undertaken.

Reprinted from "Mathematics in Kindergarten—Formal or Informal?" *The Elementary School Journal*, Vol. 67, No. 6 (March 1967), pp. 338–341, by Dorothy M. Roberts and Irving Bloom, by permission of The University of Chicago Press.

Initial meetings were held with the teachers to discuss the aims and the procedures of the program and to plan for the part that each teacher and each class group would play. Measurement techniques and devices were discussed, and a plan of organization was agreed on. Five groups of children were involved in the experiment. The first group was a morning kindergarten of twenty-one children, some not yet five years of age; this group was assigned to the Silver Burdett program. The second group was an afternoon kindergarten of twenty-three children five years of age or older who worked with the same program as Group 1. The third group was a morning kindergarten group of twenty-three children similar in age to Group 1. Group 3 used the Greater Cleveland Mathematics program for kindergarten. The group which used the informal program, the local kindergarten handbook, was a morning kindergarten, designated Group 4. This was our control group. There were twenty-three children in the class. The ages were similar to those in Groups 1 and 3. The Silver Burdett program was also used by an afternoon kindergarten with children of the same age and class size as Group 2. Only the three morning groups were comparable. Their test results were considered significant.

Thus, each of the three teachers had the opportunity to work with one of the new programs, and one class, Group 4, served as a control group.

It was our plan to measure the growth of each child in some way. Since no commercially prepared test seemed to suit our needs, the researchers compiled a test of nineteen items designed to measure most aspects of number readiness. . . .

At the beginning of the study the teachers administered the test in one sitting to a group of six to eight children. The teachers were assisted by a student teacher and several first-grade teachers, who arranged to have small groups of kindergartners visit in their rooms, thus freeing the kindergarten teacher for testing. The same test was administered in a similar fashion at the end of the study, fourteen weeks later. The strengths and the weaknesses of the children as shown by the test results were compared and analyzed before and after the program. A careful item-by-item analysis was made for each of the three groups, 1, 3, and 4, and mean gains of the three groups were compared. Not only were gains by individual children measured, but group gains under different teaching-learning programs were compared.

An analysis of the data obtained on the pre-test indicated the following patterns:

In the three morning groups (1, 3, and 4) of sixty-seven younger children (ages four years and ten months to five years and four months), thirty children had three or fewer errors out of nineteen items. Nineteen of the thirty children had one error or none.

The scores below the median score had a greater range than the scores above the median. The range below the median was three times as great as the range above it. The finding may indicate that within similar chronological age levels slow maturers show more deviation from the average than faster maturers.

In the two afternoon groups (Groups 2 and 5) of older children (ages five years and four months to five years and ten months), out of a total of forty-six, a third missed one question or none. Twelve children had perfect scores. The range of the scores below the median was five times as great as the range of the scores above the median. Had a more difficult test been used, or had the test been given at a time other than midyear, the results might have been quite different.

After the pre-test the teachers began the math work of their respective programs. They followed the manuals as closely as possible and used the workbook and worksheet materials under the direction and the supervision of the researchers.

It was agreed that no pressures were to be put on those children who showed a definite lack of readiness to follow the directions required to complete the worksheets. Nor was there to be any urgency to complete any certain number of worksheets during the experimental period. Some days the children omitted the work entirely. We kept uppermost in our minds the effects that the new programs with worksheets would have on the children.

Statistically the outcomes of the study may be summarized as follows:

1. The chronologically older groups (the afternoon classes) showed higher test scores on pre-tests as well as post-tests. Test administration was more easily managed with these groups.

2. The three morning groups, 1, 3, and 4, showed no significant differences in their scores. The mean gains per child in each program were nearly equal.

3. Although the control group tested lower on the pre- and post-tests, the mean gain for this group was 2.8 points.

4. Of the sixty-seven children in Groups 1, 3, and 4, the mean gain between the pre- and post-tests was 2.7. On the final test, thirty-three had all nineteen questions correct, and ten more missed only one question.

5. The test was not difficult enough to measure adequately the achievement of the bright kindergartners. Had the test been administered earlier in the year, results would have been quite different.

6. The greatest improvement in test scores was apparent in two areas: recognition of the numbers of objects in a set (cardinality) and recognition of ordinals.

7. All but nine of the sixty-seven children showed gains in scores, but of the nine who showed no gain, seven had perfect scores on the pre-test.

Teachers' comments on the experiment indicate a positive response:

"I feel I am prepared to do a much better math program in kindergarten. I feel more secure in our new math. I have many new ideas. I am very enthusiastic."

"I am more conscious of the possibilities of providing a background for future number work in the kindergarten."

"I would like to try another program. It was most rewarding to be able to use my own judgment and to move along when I felt the children were ready."

"I am more aware of the different concepts and skills I am teaching. Also I have new ideas for group and flannel board work."

"Each lesson is well-organized to develop specific concepts. There are always many supplemental experiences suggested for each concept so that the children are very much interested in the program. These suggestions can also be used in social studies, language arts, music, and physical education."

One teacher reported that the manual helped her see a planned sequential development of concepts, which the average teacher in kindergarten might not be aware of in an informal, more incidental kind of program.

These comments clearly indicate that the experiment contributed to the teachers' professional growth. The experience also helped familiarize them with the new programs. When they read about them or heard them discussed in meetings, they had a clearer understanding of what these programs really were.

The highly structured mathematics materials used in this experiment did not produce significant differences in achievement. The regular program produced as much learning as either of the two newer programs. Teachers were willing to try "something new" without prejudgment. The mathematics materials did not achieve significant results, but other kindergarten teachers in the district, interested in supplementing the regular program, are asking for the teachers' manuals of the two series tested.

REFERENCES

1. MERLE GRAY, ANTOINETTE K. SINARD. *Modern Arithmetic through Discovery, Beginner's Book.* Morristown, New Jersey: Silver Burdett Company, 1964.
2. Educational Research Council of Greater Cleveland. *Greater Cleveland Mathematics Program, K.* Chicago: Science Research Associates, 1962.
3. *Kindergarten Handbook.* Scotch Plains, New Jersey: Scotch Plains–Fanwood Public Schools, 1963.

Teaching Arithmetic by Concrete Analogy

J. D. Williams

INTRODUCTION

The previous articles in this series (2) will have acquainted the reader with a variety of kinds of arithmetic apparatus, and opinions relating to how and why it should be used. Between some of these approaches there is little to

Reprinted from *Educational Research* (February 1963), 120–131, by permission of the National Foundation for Educational Research in England and Wales.

choose, and, further, where they do not cover the same part of the curriculum, a choice is not necessary. All the same, the teacher is left with many decisions to take concerning the kind of apparatus to use, and the best way of using it—if, that is, he decides in the first place in favour of this *kind* of approach.

On what grounds can such decisions be based? When we look to fellow teachers, we find that each recommends the method he uses, for he can see the scope of this, but not of others. When we look to objective research we are confronted with one or two small studies whose results, even if they were not in themselves quite equivocal, would be difficult to align to any particular teacher's classroom problems. If we look to psychological *theory*, in its present state, we can find some justification for any decision we like— *and* some for its diametrical opposite.

However, we can be sure of one thing—that before a decision is made, we must be aware of the issues involved. This article aims to make explicit some of these issues, to describe how 'structuralists' have solved some of the relevant problems, and to classify some of the arguments for and against various points of view. No special attempt to arrive at any conclusions will be made —the object is merely to expose facets of the questions. In the end, the teacher will have to come to his *own* conclusions, for only *he* knows the full requirements of his teaching situation.

Four issues will be discussed: (*i*) 'structural' versus 'environmental' teaching, (*ii*) whether many or few different devices should be used, (*iii*) counting versus measuring, and (*iv*) the difficulties involved in weaning the pupil from the apparatus. Certainly there are other issues which could be examined—many, for example, arising out of the details of apparatus-design. But this article will be devoted to an examination of points that are fairly general in implication.

"STRUCTURAL" VERSUS "ENVIRONMENTAL"

Those we might call the 'environmentalists' hold that arithmetic should be taught in a 'real life' context—using shopping situations, for example. Their main arguments are:

1. Children should learn arithmetic in a context that already has meaning for them. It is only in terms of the familiar that they will grasp new.
2. When used for dealing with situations that are already interesting, arithmetic will itself become so;
3. What is the purpose of learning arithmetic? To cope with 'real life' problems. What better a way to teach it, then, than as a tool for doing just this?
4. Where a special set of apparatus is used consistently for most arithmetic-teaching, the apparatus is likely to become mistaken for the arithmetic. Because of the great diversity of the experiences available in the natural environment, this medium is not likely so to restrict the child's conception of arithmetic.

For the 'structuralists' it might be argued that their 'artificial' environment, consisting of specially-devised apparatus, has the following advantages.

1. In the natural environment, the arithmetic in any situation is likely masked by other features. It *might* be more interesting to add together prices of things than to combine pieces of wood, but the interest in a game of shopping might *distract* attention from the arithmetically-relevant aspects. In structural arithmetic the non-arithmetical features of the situation are simpler and sufficiently constant to be ignored.

2. Although a great deal of arithmetic can be illustrated by examples from real life, the scope of this medium is in some ways more limited than that of specially-devised apparatus. By artificially grouping 'real-life' objects, one can, of course, illustrate most of the things that one can illustrate with structured material, although with much less convenience and in a much less succinct manner. If, on the other hand, as many environmentalists do, one uses naturally-arising situations which are more 'convincingly real,' it is unlikely that one will be able to find illustrations for more than a few fragments of the arithmetic to be taught.

3. Arithmetic is a system, and, since they are constructed out of elements that are analogous to the elements of arithmetic, the structures built with a set of apparatus form parts of an analogous system. Before children can really appreciate what is happening in arithmetic, they must see how its parts interrelate; they must have the opportunity, for example, of realising that when they add 4×3, and 2×3 on one occasion, they are doing something that in some ways resembles what they are doing when they multiply 6 by 3 on another. If different parts of the system are illustrated in widely different media, the interrelations are less likely to be seen than if, as is possible with structured apparatus, the medium remains constant. This point will be discussed at greater length later.

Of course, many teachers, and the proponents of some teaching systems, recommend the use of structured material *in conjunction with* environmental teaching. Three different views are taken on how this should be done:

1. Structured material should be introduced *before* the introduction of real-life situations. Users of the Cuisenaire material often introduce such situations only after a long period of using the material itself. Otherwise, they maintain, children might resort to unit counting of discrete objects, which would inhibit the appreciation of the cardinal properties of numbers that is fostered by use of the material.

2. Some claim that structured material should be introduced only *after* arithmetic has been used in real-life situations. The material should be used as a bridge between the environment and symbolic arithmetic, as a 'semi-concrete' means of systematising experiences that the child has already gained from the environment.

3. Probably the most common view is that structured material should be used alongside real-life experiences. There are several ways of following this course:

a. what the one lacks the other has; the material is used to show the relationships *within* the arithmetical system, while 'real-life' situations can be used to show how the system is related to the outside world;

b. Dienes, and many others, recommend that mathematics should be taught in as many different media as possible—it is only when the child has seen the mathematics in a diversity of contexts that he can distinguish between the mathematics and the context;

    c. one kind of use to which structured material can be put is that of 'describing' the natural environment. This can be done very conveniently with the Shaw material. Components are first of all matched with 'real-life' situations just as numerals normally might be. The components are then structured and the structures related. This constitutes a way of dealing with the numerical properties of the environment, but by using rods instead of symbols.

THE USE OF MORE THAN ONE MODEL

The inventors of two of the methods we are considering have intentionally included in their apparatus many different kinds of model. First we shall consider their reasons for doing this.

Montessori believed that the most efficient way of teaching an arithmetical operation was to break it down into component skills, and allow the child to master these, before requiring of him a performance of the whole operation. Rather than devise a single multi-purpose piece of apparatus, it was her policy to use, for each component skill, whichever kind of apparatus she thought would afford the best illustration. Thus she used several different kinds of apparatus for different stages in the child's development.

Dienes, on the other hand, recommends the use of several different kinds of apparatus at *each* stage throughout the child's development. His reason for this has been mentioned before: acquaintance with a variety of embodiments of a concept helps the child to distinguish between the concept and the medium in which it is embodied, and thus helps with the *abstraction* of the concept.

Both Montessori and Dienes seem to have good reasons for the use of a multiplicity of devices, and Montessori has, further, the excuse that, over the age-range for which her materials were devised, it is unlikely that she could have found a single kind of apparatus that was flexible enough to cope with all stages. However, both can be criticised.

Where, in her method, Montessori uses different devices for different parts of arithmetic, she is conspicuously open to the criticism levelled earlier against the use of 'real-life' situations—that parts of the arithmetical system learnt with one device are, perhaps, less likely to be seen to be relevant to parts learnt with a different device. Because his many devices are *each* used for illustrating most parts of the arithmetical system, we cannot fault Dienes in this particular way. Dienes' pupils are given the opportunity of seeing inter-relationships within several different media.

But this does not mean that his method is beyond criticism. In his M.A.B., Dienes presents the child with a variety of number systems so that the mathematical generalities underlying number systems will be abstracted. But at what expense? These generalities are by no means *all* that the child needs to learn at this age. It will be necessary for him to learn particular statements *within* the decimal system (like '3 × 4 = 12') and relationships between such statements (like 'because 3 × 4 = 12, $\frac{12}{3}$ = 4'). Now, where the child's experience is confined to the decimal system, these statements are limited in number and meaning. However, as soon as the child begins to work in other systems as well, the number of such statements increases manyfold—e.g. 3 × 4 = 12 (base 10), 3 × 4 = 20 (base 6), 3 × 4 = 22 (base 5), and so on, so that, for example, the response '12' to the stimulus '3 × 4' will have many rivals, and probably will not be learnt so well. Again, relationship *between* such statements might also be less apparent, e.g., if 3 × 4 always equals 12, then the relationship between this and $\frac{12}{3}$ = 4 is much more likely to be seen than if 3 × 4 sometimes equals 20 (base 6) or 22 (base 5) and so on.

Perhaps, when they have appreciated that each statement is relative to a particular number-system, children will be capable of coping with this multitude of statements; probably the *bright* will be able to manage. But perhaps also the luxury of understanding the nature of number systems can be afforded, in the case of many children, only by sacrificing the sureness of their grasp of the decimal system—which, because of its practical usefulness might by some teachers be thought to have more of the status of a *necessity*.

Now we shall consider the A.E.M. Here, the variation does not affect the mathematics to be learnt, for only the *perceptual* characteristics of the representations are varied.

Dienes claims that, presented with several perceptually-different representations of a mathematical idea, the child will abstract the idea as the one common component. It seems plausible to assume that these representations should (*a*) be *perspicuous*—that is, embody the idea in a way that enables it easily to be seen, and (*b*) conduce to *refinement* of the idea, thus increasing its abstractness' and its range of applicability. A more precise meaning will be given to these requirements in the following discussion, in which the role played by variants in a system such as that of Dienes is questioned.

Wheeler (1) points out that children find it easier to abstract mathematical concepts from some variants of the A.E.M. than from others, and suggests that the child usually *discovers* a mathematical structure in one of the more perspicuous situations and then *applies* it in understanding the others. This is convincing for two reasons. As Wheeler argues—the child's attention is likely to be attracted to the perceptual *differences* between the variants rather than the mathematical similarities. Again, once the child has used one of the variants for abstracting mathematical ideas he will realise that there are certain features of the representation that can usually be discounted as irrelevant to the mathematics, and that the mathematics represented can usually be applied in other situations. In other words he will have learnt to interpret the variant as merely an *exemplar* of concepts, and consequently will be able to derive quite abstract concepts from this one variant.

However, even if the main part of the child's insight into an idea *is* derived from a representation in terms of only one of the variants, could not this insight be further refined, (and the 'concept' be said to become *more* 'abstract') by what Wheeler would call its 'application' in the understanding of other kinds of representation? If so, then perceptual variation would at least be 'putting the finishing touches' to the abstraction of the concept.

Let us now, then, consider some of the factors determining the value of using certain of the less perspicuous variants as 'refiners' of concepts which the child has already grasped to some extent. Naturally, *any* further representation would demonstrate that the concept applied beyond the situation in which it had been learnt, so, whatever the representation, one could say *this* in its favour. Yet some kinds of representation could be more useful than others, for different representations will reveal different classes of situation in which the concept applies, and some of these classes will be more generally relevant than others. Compare, for example, the usefulness of representing the concept in terms of groups of things, on the one hand, and triangles, on the other. What else, apart from the apparatus used, will the child be able to conceive of in terms of groups?—just about everything; and what else in terms of triangular patterns?—hardly anything. Thus we could condemn the triangles, on the grounds that they are neither perspicuous enough to reveal the concept nor general enough in relevance to be of great use in refining and extending it.

There is, however, a place for even *this* variant in Dienes' system, for, although, in the abstracting process, its *direct* contribution (even as a 'refiner') might be small, it certainly provides the child with an interesting new set of opportunities for *exercising* the concepts he has acquired.

We may summarise this series of arguments as follows:

Where different parts of the mathematical system are represented by different kinds of device, there is a danger that the child will not interrelate these parts.

Where the difference involves a change in mathematical variables, as in the M.A.B., the advantages of increasing the generality of what is to be learnt must be weighed against the possible disadvantages of increasing the complexity of the information to be absorbed.

The manner in which the variation of perceptual representations operates to facilitate abstraction might not be quite as Dienes suggests. Some variants might best serve to *reveal* a structure, others might serve to *refine* it, while others might function only to provide opportunity for its *application*.

COUNTING, OR MEASURING?

One of the main advantages that Stern sees in her apparatus is that it encourages children to *measure* rather than count—a *direct* comparison of size is made, without resort to counting the units of each group compared. On the Cuisenaire and the Colour Factor rods no units are marked, lest there should be counting. Why should measurement be favoured so? First, let us examine the advantages that measuring might have over counting.

The identity of each number and number operation becomes lost by assimilation to the process of counting. Where the answer to $4 + 3$ can always be found by counting up to 4, and then counting on 3, there is no need to remember that $4 + 3 = 7$. In fact, where this resort is constantly employed the child does not need to retain much of an idea of the peculiarities of any number—even the size of the group it symbolises, for example.

In measuring, you match a combination of groups of aligned units with another, thus:

If there has been any error in the matching, this is immediately apparent. In counting you match the units of a combination of groups with an ordered series of symbols. In the latter case, unless you use some means of recording each symbol-unit matching, there is no indication at the end of the process of whether there has been an error. So that they should have confidence in their arithmetical endeavours and should learn by their mistakes, it is of cardinal importance that children should be able to trace their errors.

The simple, well-organised perceptual configurations produced by measuring-devices permit speedy imaginal manipulation.

In counting, the members of a group are surveyed, or scanned, one by one. Counting is a series of responses: 'one,' 'two,' 'three,' etc. In measuring, the groups to be compared are presented entire, and their components can be surveyed, as it were, *simultaneously*. This perceptual configuration:

is, in a sense, a *static* presentation of what, in terms of counting, would be a dynamic process. When the situation is surveyed visually, it can be seen at a glance that $2 + 4 = 6$. When, on the other hand, the surveyance is in terms of a series of actions, the whole series (taking *more* than a moment) must be completed. But this is not all. A static, visual presentation facilitates what might be called 'multi-directional' and 'multi-selective' scanning. In the diagram above you can see more than that $2 + 4 = 6$; you can also see at a glance that $4 + 2 = 6$ and indeed, that $6 - 2 = 4$ and $6 - 4 = 2$. Since counting is a *directed* activity, and since it involves *successive*, not *simultaneous* surveyance of the elements of groups, it does not afford this flexibility of direction and purpose in scanning. Thus, in a measuring situation, a greater number of arithmetical implications is likely to be available for the child to appreciate.

Finally, the manipulation of rods to which (as in the case of the Cuisenaire material) are assigned no definite numerical values gives the child an acquaintance with the mathematical generalities *underlying* arithmetic. This, of course, is an excellent introduction to algebra.

Despite the foregoing objections to counting, the use of this technique as the child's main means of approaching arithmetic is still being encouraged by some very progressively-minded teachers. The environmentalists often encourage its use, and one of our structuralists—Bass—has made it the cornerstone of his method. There is by no means a dearth of arguments *for* counting; some of these follow.

How is it possible to give the child a *justification* for naming groups of various sizes by their respective number-symbols? How can we give a reason for assigning a number name to a group of a certain size? The most obvious way is by counting, that is matching the elements of the group with successive members of the series until each element in the group is matched with a member of the series; the number with which the last element is matched can then be taken to be the number of elements in the group. Unless the child's awareness of this is maintained, he is likely to lose sight of the essential similarity of the widely different situations in which numerical values are assigned.

The applicability of measuring to arithmetic is limited in ways in which counting is not. A counting, but not a measuring procedure, can easily be extended to apply to directed numbers. Likewise, operators can be represented by counting, but hardly by lengths.

Counting, constituting an *action* model of arithmetic, rather than a *visual* model, can be applied with greater versatility and directness. Before measurement can be employed directly, of course, a situation needs to be conceived in terms of units; very few naturally-arising situations are already in these terms, or, indeed, admit of realistic translation into them. The counting procedure can have just about anything as its content, and, because of this, the arithmetic learnt by its means can be shown to have relevance to a wide variety of situations.

Since counting and measuring both have their merits it would seem to be a good idea that the child's learning should incorporate both. Measuring could be used in order to provide an understanding of arithmetical relationships, while counting would be useful in helping the child to relate his arithmetic to the environment.

WEANING FROM THE CONCRETE TO THE ABSTRACT

Since, in structural arithmetic, manipulations in a *concrete* medium will eventually have to be replaced by manipulations of a *symbolic* nature, the problem arises of whether it is possible to wean the child from one medium to the other, and, if so, how this is to be done.

THE DIFFICULTY

It is sometimes feared that children who have been taught arithmetic with concrete aids will be unable to dispense with them. Most evidence indicates that this is not justified. Bright children soon find that they can short-circuit the actual manipulation of materials, and either visualise these manipulations or rely upon symbols alone. Dull children will, of course, take longer to reach this stage, but perhaps this is just as well. Perhaps, if they had not been brought up on concrete materials, some children certainly might not have become dependent upon such materials for their understanding of mathematics—but this, perhaps, would be because they had no understanding of *any* sort. Generally, children will turn to the concrete only when they cannot cope with the symbolic, and generally it is as well that they should be able to use this resort.

A subtler fear is that apparatus-reared children will become dependent upon the use of imagery. It is easy to see how such imagery might be harmful. To some areas of mathematics the possibilities of a particular imaginal model might not extend. In this territory the child might be at a loss to know how to proceed. (E.g. x^2 can be depicted by a square slab, x by x; x^3 by a cube, x by x by x; but we cannot continue to depict powers beyond this by using further spatial dimensions, for we have exhausted them all.)

In some areas the model might even be misleading, and constitute an *obstacle* to further learning. (E.g. for positive numbers the statement $6 - 2 = +4$ can be paralleled quite accurately by taking 2 units from a 6-rod. But in imagining the use of this device for negative numbers, what more natural and misleading a conclusion to draw than that $6 - 2 = -4$?)

Perhaps, too, the constant reference to imagery will reduce the child's speed in manipulating symbols—perhaps it is better that *some* symbolic manipulations *should* become completely mechanised. Should one *always* remain thoughtful about one's multiplication tables? (Perhaps one should. Well, in this case, it might be worth-while to sacrifice some speed for the sake of vigilance of insight).

Despite all this, visual imagery might well be a *good* thing. We have seen in a previous section how this kind of imagery permits a kind of multi-directional and multi-selective scanning that is likely to be of supreme usefulness in exposing possibilities of a mathematical situation that are not explicit in its symbolic formulation. We know, too, that the mathematically able often resort to spatial visualisation, and that the capacity for engaging in this has been found to accompany mathematical ability.

In conclusion, then, it seems that our 'difficulty' might not be of very great importance. However, attempts have been made to cope with various aspects of the passage from the concrete to the abstract, and some of these are examined below.

WEANING STRATEGIES

There are various ways in which the child has to be weaned from manipulation of concrete materials, and the means used for effecting this development vary somewhat from method to method.

The Direct Introduction of Notation. Usually, numerals are introduced soon after the child has been allowed to engage in some exploratory manipulation of the materials. However, in the case of the Cuisenaire and Colour Factor methods this introduction is deferred until the child has become well used to the colour notation. In some cases, notation is introduced as follows: (*i*) the child learns to speak the numerals and then to count small numbers of separate units; (*ii*) the units are structured into blocks which are then referred to by number names; (*iii*) cards bearing numerals are matched with appropriate blocks; (*iv*) devices for familiarising the child with the kinaesthetic sensations derived from writing numerals (like sandpaper numerals or number insets) can be used as a means of teaching the child how to write the numerals, which are then used for recording operations. Usually, at a stage before the child is able to *write* a record, operations will be recorded by the arrangement of numeral cards.

The methods differ in the extent to which symbols are used. For Bass, of course, symbols are of great importance, for counting cannot be carried out without them. In the Shaw apparatus, the guiding devices (cards, showing the value of the structures built) require that the child should be acquainted with numerals, while, in the Stern, physical guides (like the size of a container) are more often employed. Jones' flat number-pieces have appropriate numerals on their undersides, so that children are continually reminded of the notational aspect of their manipulations. Likewise, little tags bearing numerals can be attached to the Unifix structures.

Positional notation might be introduced directly by a device such as Montessori's superimposable cards. In these, units cards bearing numerals 0-9 are narrow enough to rest on the right-hand side of the numerals of a similar set of wider tens cards, which, in turn, are narrow enough to rest on the right-hand side of the numerals of a similar set of wider hundreds cards, thus:

hundreds card: | 5   0   0 |

tens card: | 2   0 |

units card: | 7 |

Superimposed, each card in place, these would compose

| 5 | 2 | 7 |

However, *positional* notation is introduced *indirectly* by most structuralists, including Montessori, and a means of doing this will be described in the next section.

THE INDIRECT INTRODUCTION OF NOTATION THROUGH COLOUR

Colour is sometimes used as a preliminary notation before numerals are introduced, and as a means of distinguishing between different orders of ten, before positional notation is introduced. In both cases it can be said that the quality is being used 'semi-symbolically,' but in each the justification for using this description would be different.

As a Preliminary Notation. Because different colours can be made regularly to accompany different sizes of object, colour can be used in *concrete* representations of numerical operations. Because, on the other hand, colour can be *detached* from regular concomitance with size, it can also be used for purely *symbolic* representation. Therefore, in this case, we can dub colour 'semi-symbolic' by virtue of the fact that it can be used in this dual role.

The use of *colour,* instead of attaching *numerals* to the objects used in concrete representation has certain advantages.

1. Colour is a *pervasive* quality, which enables immediate discrimination between objects—even if only a *glimpse* of the objects is caught, or if they are seen from a considerable distance. A numeral, on the other hand, is difficult to recognise at a distance, or if only part of it is seen, or if it is seen from an unusual angle. For this reason, in the case of the latter, the child would be liable to lose sight of the notational significance of the manipulations he performed, and the teacher would be less easily able to comunicate about them with the child at a distance.

2. Colour readily becomes integrated into the child's images of the objects and thus gives imaginal manipulations a notational significance.

3. Children take readily to the use of colour words, for they have already become accustomed to categorising and describing in terms of this quality.

4. In both the Cuisenaire and the Colour Factor methods, which are the two methods that use a preliminary colour notation, it is a major aim to teach the

child mathematical relationships between sizes before he is introduced to numerical values. This is a way of discouraging him from counting; since he will not have learnt to relate colour names in a series as a counting device, the colour notation does not conduce to this approach to number operations.

5. Although it does not lend itself to the representation of number quite so readily as does size, colour has certain properties which can be exploited to some extent for this purpose: groups of similar colours can represent groups of similar numbers; colour combinations can represent number combinations; colours can be ordered in series on a basis of wavelength or intensity.

Introducing Positional Notation. Here colour can again be regarded as a 'semi-symbolic' property, but in a different sense. It can be regarded thus, simply by virtue of the fact that it is a physical property which is given a conventional numerical significance. In this case, objects alike in other respects (counters, plaques, beads, etc.) are identifiable by virtue of their *colour* as representing units of different orders of ten. Thus, greens may stand for 'ones,' blues for 'tens,' reds for 'hundreds,' and so on, without there being any indication of this numerical significance in terms of *size* of object. After children have learnt the quantitative significance of these colours they learn that objects of certain colours are placed in certain positions, and thence that the quantitative significance of numerals depends upon their positioning.

It is not difficult to find justification for using colour for this purpose. Position is not readily accepted as a quality *intrinsic* to objects (or to numerals, for that matter) so some other property must be used to *introduce* the idea that different objects are different in quantitative significance. Physical size would, of course, be the property that would indicate the most clearly the quantitative value of an object, and this is, indeed, used in the *first* stages of introducing positional notation. But the representation of higher orders of ten in terms of physical size is a clumsy and expensive business, and, anyway, would take us very little of the way from a concrete to a symbolic representation. Colour, however, is eminently suitable, for it *is* readily accepted as a property intrinsic to the object and yet, by itself, can represent quantity only symbolically.

An illustration will show more fully how colour can be used for this purpose. In the Montessori method, experience with apparatus consisting of single beads, structures of ten, a hundred and a thousand beads, gives the child a concrete notion of the composition of the decimal number system. At the same time, however, the 'stamp game' is played. In this, the child learns to arrange in columns and exchange small plaques, marked '1' '10' '100' and '1000,' and coloured, respectively, green, blue, red and green again. This contributes to experiences leading to the use of counting frames on which beads representing different orders of ten are coloured according to the same scheme. When, eventually, operations are recorded on paper, this bears vertical lines of appropriate colours to indicate where units, tens, hundreds, etc., should go.

Dienes, also, recommends the use of a 'colour-bridge' in progressing from purely concrete to symbolic positional operations, and the Shaw apparatus lends itself very well to the development of a learning sequence that passes from the concrete to the symbolic via colour.

THREE ROUTES FROM BLOCKS TO REALITY

In this section we shall consider three different ways in which structuralists have attempted to encourage the child to see the relevance of block-manipulations to other mathematical situations.

Structured Problems. Stern attempts to gear structural learning to real-life situations by arranging these situations so that they will fall into visual patterns that are similar to those with which the child has become familiar in his manipulations of blocks. Particularly useful to build upon here, are the child's experiences with the pattern boards.

Coding Real-Life Situations in Terms of Structural Materials. Stern gives some attention to the possibility of allowing structures to 'stand for' components of real-life problem situations, but this can be done much more elegantly with the Shaw apparatus. The latter is particularly suitable for use in the gearing of *matching* and *counting* to measuring. Pegs can be plugged individually (or in groups) into holes in the base, and matched with objects or counted. They can then be plugged into one another to form structures suitable for measuring. Either directly, by one-to-one correspondence, or indirectly, via a counting procedure, the elements of a structure can be matched with those of a real-life situation. Thus, by either of these simple procedures, the situation can be 'coded' into structures, in which form the mathematical properties of the situation are more clearly seen.

Developing Abstract Ideas which will Generalise. Dienes aims to develop in the child mathematical concepts which are sufficiently abstract to be independent of any one kind of medium. Theoretically, if the media in which a concept is learnt are varied sufficiently, the media in which it can be seen to apply will be sufficiently various. We have seen how Dienes goes systematically about the task of reducing the likelihood that the embodiment of a concept will be mistaken for the concept itself. For instance, in his A.E.M., x^2 can be represented by an equal number of rows and columns of square blocks, or pegs on a pegboard, but lest the rectangular shape thus produced should be thought to be a necessary feature of embodiments of mathematical 'squareness,' a triangular representation can be given, and, finally, the child can be weaned away from geometrical imagery by the use of the balance, or non-geometrical groups of objects (x matchboxes each containing x buttons, for example).

SUMMARY AND COMMENT

It will have been noticed that the four issues we have considered have been dealt with in different ways. In the case of the structural-versus-environmental and the counting-versus-measuring controversies, arguments for opposing points of view and possible compromises have been examined. Educationists have taken stands on both of these issues, and the main purpose here was to summarise, elaborate and clarify their arguments.

The section on diversity was devoted mainly to questioning Montessori's use of and Dienes' arguments for multiple embodiment. Dienes' is a very cogent argument which meets with little articulate opposition; here, an attempt was made at showing that there *could* be other points of view.

The final section—'Weaning from the Concrete to the Abstract,' was given to a discussion of how the child will pass from manipulating apparatus to manipulating symbols and *applying* arithmetic. Fears concerning the insularity of structural learning, and provisions made for coping with this difficulty were considered.

The foregoing does not leave the teacher with a very tidy scheme of things, but this it is not meant to do. If it has *un*tidied some schemes, its achievement will have come nearer to its aim.

Too often, a teaching scheme is swallowed whole. Too often, when this happens, the teacher's appetite is satisfied. The scheme shows him what to do, and gives him reasons for doing it. Light at last shines on the teacher's problems. At last he feels he can see the picture clearly. But in proportion to the extent to which this light is coloured by some special bias, so are *some* parts of the picture *dis*coloured by it. Only by introducing a multitude of different lights can we approximate to the clear light of day and only then can we hope to see, in anything like their full complexity, the subtle combinations of hues that go to make up the picture.

REFERENCES

1. Wheeler, D., 'Experiment in Leicestershire Schools: the Dienes Material', *Mathematics Teaching*, No. 17, 1961.
2. Williams, J. D., Teaching arithmetic by concrete analogy: I—Miming Devices, *Educational Research*, Vol. III, Nos. 2 and 3. II—Structural Systems, *Educational Research*, Vol. IV, No. 3.

Questions on Improving Elementary School Mathematics

C. Alan Riedesel

The previous chapters have dealt with specific suggestions for teaching elementary school mathematics. In this chapter several more general questions often asked by teachers are considered.

How can a teacher bring herself up-to-date and/or keep up-to-date? Keeping up-to-date in any area of the curriculum requires first a desire on the part of the teacher to keep up-to-date. Like the proverbial horse being led to water, only the teacher who has a real desire to improve her competence in mathematics and the teaching of mathematics will do so. The suggestions that follow are offered as an aid to teachers and administrators who wish to up-date their knowledge and wish to keep up-to-date.

1. Read periodicals such as *The Arithmetic Teacher, The Mathematics Teacher, School Science and Mathematics, The Grade Teacher,* and *The Instructor,* which contain monthly articles concerned with the teaching of elementary school mathematics. *The Arithmetic Teacher* is of particular help since it contains book reviews and reviews of new materials. Since it is not feasible for every teacher to belong to the National Council of Teachers of Mathematics (although it would be very helpful if all elementary teachers were members), it is suggested either that the principal obtain *The Arithmetic Teacher* for the teachers' reading room or that several teachers pool their resources in joining professional organizations. For example, each of five teachers can join a different organization, and all can share the magazines they receive. In this way each has easy access to journals on mathematics, language arts, reading, social studies, and science.

2. Attend credit and noncredit courses offered for the improvement of elementary teachers' mathematics background. Increasingly, educational television stations are providing programs on mathematics for teachers; universities are offering extension work in mathematics; and elementary schools are providing resource persons to offer in-service classes. Also, federal agencies sponsor summer institutes and in-service institutes for the development of leadership personnel for in-service work.

3. Form small discussion groups, pick a topic, and share information.

4. Obtain and work with materials for improving mathematics content and materials for improving the teaching of elementary school mathematics, such as those listed in the Selected Bibliography.

5. Try new ideas in the classroom. Probably the best way to stay up-to-date is to get involved in change. Try out new materials as they are published and try out "experimental" suggestions given in *The Arithmetic Teacher.*

6. The administrator can
   a. Provide released time for in-service mathematics courses.

b. Provide materials for independent study.
c. Obtain films designated for in-service work.
d. Seek assistance from the state department of education.
e. Consult nearby colleges and universities.
f. Study needs, wants, and background of teachers.
g. Provide new materials for teacher evaluation.
h. Disseminate information concerning courses, National Science Foundation Institutes, workshops, and meetings that are available to teachers
i. Plan cooperatively with nearby schools to bring in consultants and speakers on topics in mathematics.
j. Set up mathematics laboratories to be used for in-service education.
k. Keep parents informed of curriculum developments in mathematics.
l. Provide for representation from the school district at national meetings concerned with mathematics education.
m. Provide for reports from national meetings on mathematics education.

There is a great deal of discussion about fostering creativity through school subjects. Does mathematics lend itself to creative thinking? Normally the layman does not think of mathematics as an area that lends itself well to the development of creative thinking. However, a discussion with a research mathematician might lead one to believe that all of mathematics centers around developing thought patterns that lead to creativity.

In the past, the methods used to teach mathematics were of a variety that did little to encourage creative thinking. In fact, they may well have discouraged most high-level thought processes. Typically the teacher would say, "Your answer is wrong because you have not worked the problem in the way I taught in class." Today there is ever-increasing attention to the development of creative mathematical thinking, and with it, greater numbers of pupils are finding mathematics to be an interesting and rewarding field of intellectual endeavor. Projects in which pupils develop their own notational system, mathematical models for physical world situations, "magic squares" and similar pattern arrangements, and mathematical systems can be used to foster creativity.

How well do pupils like mathematics as compared to the other subjects in the curriculum? Contrary to the subjective judgment of most laymen, in surveys of pupil preference of subjects, mathematics usually rates number one.[1]

Teaching procedures that use a guided discovery approach take much longer to develop new topics. Doesn't it take longer to teach mathematics in this manner? While the "idea developing" phases take much longer in a guided discovery approach than in an explanatory approach, the better understanding of mathematical principles developed using the guided discovery approach reduces the time necessary for practice or drill. Thus, the

---

[1] Claire E. Faust, "A Study of The Relationship Between Attitude and Achievement in Selected Elementary School Subjects" (Unpublished Ph.D. dissertation, State University of Iowa, 1962).

time taken for either approach is about the same. Also, two recent studies support the contention that for maximum achievement, more than half of mathematics class time should be devoted to developmental-meaningful activities.[2]

What can I do with intermediate-grade level pupils who move into our "modern math" program from another school using traditional content and traditional teaching procedures? Transfer pupils pose a real problem. The following ideas have proved useful in bringing a pupil up-to-date.

1. Programmed materials such as *Mathematics Enrichment, A, B, C, and D,* published by Harcourt, Brace & World, offer modern content in a format of small-step programmed materials. Pupils can up-date themselves with these materials.

2. If the pupil is willing, it is often a useful thing for the teacher to provide the pupil with the text for the grade level below and to suggest selected exercises that will help in up-dating the pupil.

3. The problem is not as acute as it appears on the surface to be, since the majority of mathematics teaching materials follows a spiral approach to mathematical topics. Thus, topics from previous years' work are reviewed. During the review periods the teacher should devote extra time to pupils who are new to the system.

4. A few publishers provide paperback workbooks that contain portions of the content from previous years. The selection is directed to pupils who have been using a more traditional program.

There is an emphasis upon correct vocabulary today. How much vocabulary should be developed? Should correct vocabulary always be used? The number of technical mathematical terms taught in the elementary school is increasing. An example of this increase can be noted by examining the materials developed by the School Mathematics Study Group.[3] In the beginning one-third of the first-grade program the following terms occur: set, set member, collection, subset, review set, empty set, joining sets, union of sets, remove, remainder set, shape, round, face, edge, corner, inside, outside, surface, circle, rectangle, triangle, circular region, rectangular region, triangular region, pair, equivalent, as many as, more than, fewer than, and partition. Each of these terms is used in a mathematical manner.

In addition to the acquisition of new terms, there is an emphasis upon "cleaning up" the present vocabulary of elementary school mathematics. Terms such as "cancellation" may be quite misleading. Other words such as "borrow," "carry," and "goes into" should probably be replaced by more precise terms.

---

[2] Donald E. Shipp and George H. Deer, "The Use of Class Time in Arithmetic," *The Arithmetic Teacher,* Vol. 7, No. 3 (March 1960), pp. 117–121; and Albert H. Shuster and Fred L. Pigge, "Retention Efficiency of Meaningful Teaching," *The Arithmetic Teacher,* Vol. 12, No. 1 (January 1965).

[3] School Mathematics Study Group, *Mathematics for the Elementary School,* preliminary ed. (Stanford, California: Leland Stanford Junior College, 1963).

Most elementary school pupils are interested in learning new terms, and there is little reason to begin with an incorrect term. For maximum success in vocabulary development, the following suggestions are offered:

1. Give pupils an opportunity to familiarize themselves with a mathematical concept before learning the name. Thus, pupils should have wide experience using the commutative property of addition before naming it.
2. Avoid the "matching type" of vocabulary drill exercises. Concentrate on correct use of vocabulary in situations in which correct vocabulary helps a discussion.
3. Remember the mathematical idea is more important than the name.

How can "meaning" be maintained? Often teachers introduce new topics in mathematics with an emphasis upon understanding and then quickly proceed to efficient computational processing without a review of meaning. It is strongly suggested that periodically the teacher ask questions such as "I noted that you all renamed in this subtraction situation without writing any changes in the numerals. Can you tell me what the basic principles of this process are?" "You've been inverting and multiplying when you divide fractions. Why does this work? What mathematical principles are involved?" "You multiplied the measure of the length by the measure of the width to find the area of this rectangle. Why?"

Very little mention has been made of money in this book. Isn't the use of money in teaching elementary school mathematics important? The use of money in teaching elementary school mathematics is quite important. However, the author feels that money situations should follow the mathematical understanding of a topic. If money situations are used in introductory work, the mathematical ideas are often clouded. For example, with money pupils think of ones (pennies), tens (dimes), and then ones again (dollars). Also the use of nickels and quarters often detracts from the development of tens and ones. If money is used in subtracting, 43¢ − 27¢ for example, pupils will subtract 2 dimes, 1 nickel and 2 pennies.

43¢	3 dimes	2 nickels	3 pennies
−27¢	2 dimes	1 nickel	2 pennies
	1 dime	1 nickel	1 penny

After each new topic is developed, it is *very* worthwhile to use money situations in problem solving.

Should I allow pupils to use "crutches" such as counting on their fingers? Many "crutches" are good examples of correct mathematical thinking. They may be immature methods of computing, but they often illustrate basic mathematical principles. Pupils will normally discard the practice of finger counting, for example, when they find more economical ways of thinking.[4]

---

[4] John R. Clark, "The Use of Crutches in Teaching Arithmetic," *The Arithmetic Teacher*, Vol. 1, No. 1 (October 1954), pp. 6–10.

McConnell's statement made in 1941 still has much merit today. He said: [5]

Repeating the final form of a response from the very beginning may actually encourage the habituation of immature procedures and seriously impede necessary growth.

Intermediate steps such as the use of the "crutch" in subtraction, aid the learner both to understand the process and to compute accurately. With proper guidance, these temporary reactions may be expected to give way to more direct responses in later stages of learning.

How much time per day should be devoted to mathematical instruction? This is a difficult question to answer. The importance of mathematics in the world today is greatly increasing. Also, there is evidence that an increase in the mathematics time allotment does increase achievement.[6] If class discussion and time for pupil work are considered, a valid argument can be made for a time allotment of approximately forty minutes per day in grades one and two and at least sixty minutes per day in grades three through six.

I believe that it is important for average and bright pupils to understand mathematical processes, but isn't it better for slow pupils to learn their mathematics by practicing without understanding? This is a commonly held belief and, on the surface, appears to have some merit. But, a strong case can and should be made for slow learners being taught to understand mathematics. If the slow learner is only taught that $5 \times 7 = 35$ and then forgets this multiplication fact, there are no means for him to obtain an answer. If, on the other hand, the multiplication fact has been developed through the understanding of multiplication as a series of equal additions and as forming a 7 by 5 array pattern, the pupil can go back to these forms to find an answer. Having this understanding is important for the slow learner since he normally possesses a poor memory.

Teachers often ask children to "prove" their answer. Is proof in the mathematical sense used in the elementary school? In the primary grades when a teacher asks a pupil to prove that his answer is correct, she is using prove as a synonym for verify. The teacher wishes the pupil to give several other similar examples in which the property or idea holds true. This is not proof in the mathematical sense, but it is a good learning procedure for primary school pupils. Also, opportunities should be given to children to discover that just because something works once or twice doesn't mean it will always work.

As the pupil moves up the educational ladder, he should have the oppor-

[5] T. R. McConnell, "Recent Trends in Learning Theory," *Arithmetic in General Education,* Sixteenth Yearbook, National Council of Teachers of Mathematics (New York: Bureau of Publications, Teachers College, Columbia University, 1941), p. 279.

[6] Oscar T. Jarvis, "Time Allotment Relationships to Pupils Achievement in Arithmetic," *The Arithmetic Teacher,* Vol. 10, No. 5 (May 1963), pp. 248–250.

tunity to study some simple mathematical proofs. The use of a modular system such as the one illustrated in chapter 1 gives pupils an opportunity to prove a mathematical property by testing all possible cases. Pupils may also be presented with situations in which they can use direct proof. The example below illustrates such a procedure.

Given: Commutative property, associate property, basic addition facts, place value [7]

Find: $23 + 45 = N$

$$
\begin{aligned}
(20 + 3) + (40 + 5) &= (20 + 3) + (5 + 40) && \text{commutative property} \\
&= 20 + 3 + (5 + 40) && \text{associative property} \\
&= 20 + (3 + 5) + 40 && \text{associative property} \\
&= 20 + 8 + 40 && \text{addition fact} \\
&= 20 + 40 + 8 && \text{commutative property} \\
&= (20 + 40) + 8 && \text{associative property} \\
&= 60 + 8 && \text{addition of } 20 + 40 \\
&= 68 && \text{addition of } 60 + 8
\end{aligned}
$$

The opportunities to use mathematical proof should become more frequent as a pupil progresses in his mathematical maturity. Yet, extreme care should be taken to prevent elementary school mathematics from becoming highly abstract. If the pupils involved are at the third-grade level, the use of tens and ones blocks to verify that $23 + 45 = 68$ is to be preferred to a long listing of commutative property, associative property, place value, etc.

Should pupils memorize number facts? A few people working in the field of mathematics education have suggested that it is not necessary for pupils to learn the basic addition, subtraction, multiplication, and division facts "by heart." Even with the large number of automatic computers available today and with future increases in the number of easily portable computers, the citizen of tomorrow will still be required to use many basic number facts in his everyday activities. A great deal of time is saved if persons "just know" the basic number facts. However, the study for mastery should occur after pupils understand the basic ideas.

What about homework? Mathematics has traditionally been the elementary school subject most used for homework assignments. Yet the value of mathematical homework assignments is questionable. Some of the best mathematics teaching occurs when pupils are working on assignments and the teacher is observing, questioning, and helping. It is suggested that the majority of homework assignments in mathematics occurs at the end of units when pupils are practicing and fixing concepts, not when concepts are being developed.

[7] Note: at a higher level properties of exponent would be used.

I have trouble with parents when I give homework. They often use different procedures and make confusing suggestions to pupils. What can be done to alleviate this difficulty? Parents should be informed concerning recent changes in mathematics curriculum. Many school systems have offered courses in modern mathematics for parents, with outstanding success. In many small communities attendance at these meetings has numbered over one hundred. In larger communities several sections of classes for parents are offered each semester. In addition, several books on modern mathematics for parents have been written, and individual teachers and groups of teachers may well prepare periodic letters explaining the attack used on a particular topic.

If New Programs Are to Be Effective, Parents Must Understand Their Goals. If several teachers at a grade level work together in preparing these letters, it is quite possible to provide the parents with a math bulletin every two weeks. One letter written by a fourth-grade teacher is presented below.

Dear Mr. and Mrs. Martin:

Recently a parent asked me, "Why do you ask the children to think or figure out things for themselves? You're supposed to teach them." This was a very legitimate question, and I believe you might be interested in my answer.

What is the purpose of teaching mathematics? Is there just one purpose—to teach the basic facts of the four operations? Or are there multiple purposes—teaching the basic facts, developing imagination, developing an understanding of math as a whole, and developing a good attitude toward mathematics?

Our children are growing up in a very complex world. Today, it is more important than ever to have the ability to think for ourselves. We have decisions to make every day. When a child goes shopping, he needs to think and reason. In everyday situations reasoning for ourselves is very important. Problems arise where we need not just add, subtract, multiply, and divide, but where we must decide which process to use before we can do the computation.

As for reasoning and discovery—do you think this is something new? The answer is, no. The Egyptian scribe Ahmes left this challenge: to find ten ways to solve one problem rather than one way to solve ten problems. . . . This is what we as teachers are trying to accomplish today.

If you have been following educational development, you will see that discovery is important not only in mathematics but also in science and other subjects. How do scientists solve a problem for which there is no present answer? Yes, they experiment and try to DISCOVER their answer.

There have been many controlled experiments in using the "thinking" method versus the "tell to" method when teaching mathematics. These experiments show us that discovery gives true knowledge that stays with the child.

Answer this question for yourself, and it should give you the answer to your inquiry. Which do you remember longer—a fact or statement that someone tells you or one which you must discover, compute, figure out, or look up for yourself?

Obviously, each of the pupils cannot "discover" every new concept in mathematics for himself. But, I like to give him the opportunity before "telling him."

Sincerely,
Mrs. M. Campbell

In addition to periodic letters and parent conferences, the school may stock several copies of books designed to up-date parents in modern mathematics. Several paperback books can be made available to parents or suggested to them.[8]

Unresolved Issues

Donovan A. Johnson and Robert Rahtz

We have now come to the end of this brief tour of the new mathematics, and we trust that you have an appreciation of its content, its spirit, its objectives, and its special point of view. Perhaps you will not remember all of the details of every topic that was discussed in the preceding chapters, but we hope that you have acquired an understanding of modern mathematics' concern with basic mathematical ideas, underlying principles, and the unity of mathematics. Hopefully, modern mathematics no longer seems so outlandish to you as it did when you first examined your child's new mathematics textbook or were first asked by him to help with his homework in mathematics. Hopefully, too, you can appreciate how remarkable mathematics is as an intellectual discipline.

But it is entirely possible that you still have some lingering doubts about the appropriateness of the new mathematics programs. It is understandably difficult for an adult to revise his long-held notions about a subject and accept a new version with immediate, unrestrained enthusiasm. Perhaps your youngster's own enthusiasm for his work in mathematics will gradually remove whatever doubts remain in your own mind.

Actually, we should examine the evidence at hand and use good judgment in our acceptance of the new programs. As a nation, we would be foolish indeed if we permitted ourselves to accept without question any new curriculum, no matter how positive and enthusiastic its creators may be. It is no secret that many school systems have yielded to outside pressures in installing the new programs, in order to jump on the mathematics bandwagon. Not all school systems have used good judgment in installing the new

[8] For example, Francis J. Mueller, *Understanding the New Elementary School Mathematics* (Belmont, California: The Dickenson Publishing Co., 1965); Ralph T. Heimer, and Miriam S. Newman, *The New Mathematics for Parents* (New York: Holt, Rinehart and Winston, 1965); and Evelyn Sharp, *A Parent's Guide to the New Mathematics* (New York: Dutton, 1964).

courses. Some schools have probably moved too quickly into the new programs, asking teachers to handle them without having made proper provision for training them in the new courses. Some programs have been accepted without asking where they lead or for whom they were designed.

It is no wonder, then, that significant questions have been raised about certain aspects of these programs. One need not be considered an enemy of the new mathematics to raise questions about the programs. Many proponents of the new programs, even including some of their creators themselves, are willing to admit that all may not be perfect in this new world of mathematics.

What are some of these significant questions?

First, do we really know which mathematical topics can be most effectively developed at a given grade level? Experimental programs have shown that sophisticated ideas can be learned by young children. Anyone who has seen, for example, a lesson in an intuitive approach to quadratic equations taught to a fifth-grade class by Dr. Robert Davis, founder of the Madison Project, can only marvel at the ability of the youngsters to grasp the ideas presented in the space of a single class period. But is this reason enough to include the subject in the fifth-grade curriculum? The new programs have consistently pushed topics formerly taught in one grade down a year or more below that grade. Does the fact that a certain topic *can* be taught necessarily mean that it *ought* to be taught? This question arouses sharp differences of opinion. Some educators believe that youngsters deserve to be taught as much as they can possibly absorb, and to do otherwise is to deny them a fundamental educational right. Furthermore, say these educators, our world becomes more and more complicated. Our children will have to know considerably more about mathematics—and at an earlier age—than we have been willing to let them know in order to cope with this world. In 1963 a conference of mathematicians, mathematics educators, mathematics users, and psychologists met in Cambridge, Massachusetts, to consider a new framework for mathematics education. One of the most important outcomes of this Cambridge conference was a recommendation that the "ideal" mathematics program would be one which would complete by grade 6 work now not studied until the third year of high school and which by grade 12 would have covered work that is the equivalent of three years of present-day college mathematics. By grade 12 the college-bound student would be expected to have mastered the equivalent of two years of calculus and one semester each of modern algebra and probability theory.

The report of the Cambridge conference was met with equal degrees of enthusiastic advocacy and startled consternation. Debate waxed hot—and still does—about its recommendations. Administrators who were still struggling to get their modern mathematics courses off the ground have wondered what changes would next be expected of them.

But the issue still remains: should we move in the direction of the Cambridge report's recommendations or would we be better advised to make sure that what we teach is well taught to pupils who can master the ideas and skills involved. To answer this we must have clearly in mind the goals we are striving to attain. What do we want our children to know? How does a student who has become competent differ in his behavior from the student who has not reached this goal? What is an ideal product of our schools? Only when we answer questions such as these can we rate the quality of a new program. Only when we relate content to outcomes can we render good judgment in evaluating the content.

A second important issue concerns the question of which of the new topics should become a permanent part of the new mathematics curriculum. Are we wise, for example, in spending as much time as some programs do on numeration systems in various bases? Is it necessary for youngsters beginning in grade one to learn how to operate in base five, base two, base eight, as well as base ten? Certainly, to adults who have been base-ten bound for almost all of their lives, the notion of operating in another base is intriguing. But perhaps there are other ways to build an understanding of numeration and computation. Perhaps there are topics that are not now taught which might achieve the same purpose. Here, clearly, is an area where some clear-headed research is needed.

Then there is the question of emphasis on structure in mathematics. How fruitful is it for so much stress to be placed on the basic axioms of our number systems, such as commutativity, associativity, distributivity? And if these basic ideas are to be taught, what is the best time to teach them? Some educators believe that youngsters must have many years of experience with numbers before they can truly comprehend the significance of these principles. Others say that these ideas must be brought to the fore early so that youngsters might be fully conscious at all times of how the wheels of the number systems go round. Still others say that teaching these principles at all is a complete waste of time. After all, they point out, mathematics is like a building. A building is meant to be lived in and worked in; one does not spend one's time boasting about the high quality of the foundation. To this the advocates of teaching structure reply hotly that one really does not understand the nature of mathematics unless he can appreciate these deeply embedded principles. Mathematics, they say, is an abstract structure, a model for thinking, and the earlier one recognizes this the sooner can one cope with mathematics.

Related to this problem is another: what degree of rigor or mathematical precision in definitions and proofs is appropriate at various grade levels? Should mathematical ideas be presented in language that may be simple, yet, by virtue of its simplicity be somewhat lacking in exactness? Hopefully common sense will prevail here and mathematics will heed the admonition, "Sufficient unto the day is the rigor thereof." In other words, what may be rigorous for grade three need not be considered rigorous in grade nine.

Certainly, we have not heard of any mathematics curriculum maker who would advocate, for example, that before youngsters in grade two can work with counting numbers they must understand the Peano postulates upon which the number system is based. Discussion of these postulates might be reserved for the high-school years. But then again, there are those who would say that any discussion of the Peano postulates below the college level is pointless.

Another aspect of this problem concerns the language that is to be used in presenting mathematical ideas. What vocabulary and symbolism are appropriate? The Peano postulates come to mind again as an example in this connection. You will recall that Peano stated in effect that every natural number has a successor—that the successor of 1 is 2, the successor of 2 is 3, and so on. This idea, stated in this sort of informal language, would certainly be clear even to an elementary-school youngster. But Peano carried his logical processes much further. He used his postulate regarding consecutive numbers to define addition. He said that addition on the natural numbers is a binary operation designated by the symbol $+$ for which

$$1 + x = x^*$$
$$x^* + y = (x + y)^*$$

where x and y are natural numbers and x^* and $(x + y)^*$ stand for the successors of these numbers. This definition of addition is rigorous and mathematically useful. But this does not appear to be the idea of addition that ought to be presented to an elementary youngster. Virtually all curriculum reformers would agree that Peano's definition had best be left for later years of school, but the reformers have not always used the same degree of common sense in analogous situations.

In the same family of unresolved issues is the question of which applications of mathematical ideas should be included in school mathematics. The new programs include few applications to everyday life. If the traditional mathematics course went overboard in its concern with the use of mathematics in shopping, installment buying, insurance, and banking, the new programs, in their eagerness to get at mathematical ideas, have slighted the applications of mathematical ideas. Many curriculum reformers are already at work changing this situation.

But the problem may be somewhat more complicated than appears at first glance, for one must consider what is meant by "applications" and "everyday life." Do we mean only the world of the supermarket, the bank, the utility company, the lumberyard, the hardware store? Certainly these are part of our everyday life. But it could well be that if our applications were limited to such areas of utility, we would be giving youngsters trivial exercises in mathematics. Furthermore, isn't it true that our everyday world today includes as well the world of science, engineering, the computer? Shouldn't mathematics be applied in these settings as well? If the answer is yes, then one must consider the further question of how problems involving scientific ideas can be presented without having to teach not only the mathematics involved but the science as well? This is a challenging problem that some mathematics educators are diligently trying to face up to.

Another unresolved issue relates to the level of computational skill that should be expected of students. To many people knowing mathematics means merely being able to do a calculation like 24×16 rapidly and correctly. We have seen in this book that mathematics involves much more than skill in handling this kind of problem. But just where do computational skills fit into the total picture? Should computational skills receive continued emphasis? In the automated world of tomorrow based on electronic computers, will a student have to be as skillful in computation as the student of a generation ago? If it is agreed that computational skills are still necessary, what are the best means of helping students attain them?

It should be recognized that the new programs admit the importance of computational skill. The argument that these skills are outdated is a specious one. These skills are still needed, so that when a student is learning new subject matter, he can concentrate on the new ideas rather than on the computations involved. Furthermore, skill in the mechanics of mathematics is likely to facilitate productive thinking in problem solving and in research and creative activities.

The position of many of the new curriculum groups is typified by this statement from the *Program for College Preparatory Mathematics* of the College Entrance Examination Board:

> Strong skills are surely needed but they must be based on understanding and not merely on rote memorization. Once meaning has been achieved, then drill should be provided to establish skills—skills that can be performed, as Whitehead says, "without thinking." In this way, the mind is liberated to grapple with new ideas.

But there is some concern that in the emphasis of the new courses on ideas little time will be left for the development of skills. Some educators fear that this situation might develop with teachers who are not at home with the new content. Such teachers may have so much difficulty developing the new ideas that they find themselves with little time to spend on skill development. (On the other hand, one also hears the fear expressed that the teacher to whom mathematics has always meant only computational skill will find the new emphasis on ideas so uncongenial that she will spend almost all of her time drilling on skills.)

Another point of view holds that drill as such is incompatible with the spirit of the new mathematics—that the deadly nature of drill will kill off any taste for the new mathematics, just as it did for the old mathematics. Educators of this persuasion are looking for new ways to insure accuracy and skill in computation. A new and admittedly extreme solution to the problem is offered by the Cambridge report referred to earlier:

Lest there be any misunderstanding concerning our viewpoint, let it be stated that reasonable proficiency in arithmetic calculation and algebraic manipulation is essential to the study of mathematics. However, the means of imparting such skill need not rest on methodical drill. We believe that entirely adequate technical practice can be woven into the acquisition of new concepts. But our belief goes farther. It is not merely that adequate practice can be given along with more mathematics; we believe that this is the only truly effective way to impart technical skills. Pages of drill sums and repetitious "real-life" problems have less than no merit; they impede the learning process. We believe that arithmetic as it has been taught in grade schools until quite recently has such a meagre intellectual content that the oft-noted reaction against the subject is not an unfortunate rebellion against a difficult subject, but a perfectly proper response to a pre-occupation with triviality.

We are not saying that some drill problems may not be appropriate for the individual student whose technical skill is behind, but we do believe that this should be the exception, not the rule. We are definitely opposed to the view that the main objective is arithmetic proficiency and that new, interesting concepts are being introduced primarily to sugar-coat the bitter pill of computational practice.

We propose to gain three years through a new organization of the subject matter and the virtually total abandonment of drill for drill's sake, replacing the unmotivated drill of classical arithmetic by problems which illustrate new mathematical concepts.*

In the long run, perhaps, the conflict between skills and ideas will prove to be illusory. If skills support the learning of new ideas and ideas make skill meaningful, there is no reason why a good program in mathematics should not accommodate both aspects of the subject.

The final unresolved issue that we bring up concerns the ability level of the students for whom the new courses have been designed. Are these courses intended for all students or are they in fact only for college-capable students? If the answer is that they are chiefly for the latter group, what is being done, or should be done, for the non-college-bound student? In what ways should the content of courses for these students differ from that of the college-capable?

As far as the new elementary school courses are concerned, our experience with them is yet too limited to be able to answer with any degree of assurance the question of the type of student for whom they are suitable. Officially these courses are intended for all students. Whether this intention will be carried out in practice remains to be seen. We may expect that students will continue to show the same range of ability in mathematics that they have in the past and that adjustments in the course content, method, and materials will have to be made to take care of individual differences. Mathematics educators are firm in their belief that the answer to the problem

---

* *Goals for School Mathematics* (Boston: Houghton Mifflin Company, 1963).

of taking care of slower students does *not* call for a return to traditional mathematics.

On the secondary school level, we have evidence that the newer courses are not suitable for all students. Early in its existence the SMSG recognized the problem and prepared a special algebra course for students who were not capable of college preparatory work. This course was characterized by the same spirit as was the standard course and covered most of the same topics. But it did so more slowly with simple language, easy problems, and in less depth; it was not in any sense a traditional course. Despite this SMSG course, the problem of preparing courses in modern mathematics for the nonacademic student and the slow student is only now beginning to be faced, and we may expect to see considerable production in this area in the near future.

There are also questions about the discovery method. Must all the ideas of mathematics be discovered by all students? Of course, this is impossible. How then shall the teacher know when to encourage his students to discover an idea, what students have discovered it, and when the student should verbalize his discovery? The search for efficient ways to develop ideas will need to continue for some time.

These are the major unresolved questions about modern mathematics that are being discussed by mathematicians and mathematics educators today. As schools acquire more and more experience with the new courses, additional important questions are sure to be raised. The most encouraging thing about the present situation is that the questions *are* being asked and ways to answer them being found. The American educational community has never been willing to think of its curriculums as fixed and immutable, and it is clear that the new mathematics programs will continue to change even as more and more schools convert to the new world of mathematics.

11

Elementary School Mathematics: Tomorrow

The changes that have occurred in mathematics education during the past decade are but a prelude to the possibilities of the future. We shall continue to witness an inundation of programs, books, and other materials along with a concern for continued professional growth. One burning question will continue to be asked: "How can we better teach mathematics to the children who are attending our elementary schools?"

If you are able to predict the future of elementary school mathematics, you control the destiny of mathematics education. If you had the vision to look ahead, if, indeed, you could predict, what effect would it have upon you? How would it change you at this point? What changes would you effect if you really knew what mathematics is essential ten to twenty years from now? What would you be doing right now with regard to changing your preparation, or with working with children? Would this knowledge change your teaching, or would you wait for the change?

Emerging Trends in Mathematics

Sister M. Anne

Everyone seems to accept that change in the elementary arithmetic curriculum is inevitable. The changes recommended by the College Entrance Ex-

Reprinted from *The Catholic School Journal* (January 1966), 32–34, by permission of the publisher.

amination Board which spurred the revolution in the secondary curriculum have necessitated corresponding changes at the elementary level. Reasons for the initial changes at the high school level have been well explained by others, particularly in two booklets: *Revolution in School Mathematics* from the National Council of Teachers of Mathematics and *Elementary School Mathematics, New Directions*, a pamphlet from the United States Office of Education. The following experimental projects in elementary arithmetic, described briefly here, will indicate the trends now becoming apparent.

Many groups have contributed to the changes in arithmetic at the elementary level. The University of Illinois Committee on School Mathematics, the School Mathematics Study Group, Ball State, and Boston College have applied the theories that they developed while working out their secondary programs to experimental elementary school programs. The experimenters of the Ball State Program are responsible for the series, *Elementary School Mathematics*.[1] Other groups have confined their experimentation to the elementary level. Noteworthy among these is the Greater Cleveland Mathematics Program[2] which started at kindergarten and worked upward. The Cleveland experimentation, at the primary level, has shown that children can learn more mathematics in the primary grades than had hitherto been required of them.

The inclusion of geometry into the curriculum received impetus from the successful experiments with geometry in the primary grades which Patrick Suppes and Newton Hawley directed at Stanford University in California. Charles Davis, working with the Madison Project at Webster College and Syracuse University, has demonstrated that children can discover quite sophisticated mathematical ideas even at an early age. The films available on the Madison Project give concrete evidence of this.

The University of Maryland Mathematics Project aimed at investigating what mathematics seventh- and eighth-grade children *could* learn and what they *should* learn. The School Mathematics Study Group writers were greatly influenced by the findings of the University of Maryland Project. *Exploring Modern Mathematics*[3] is based very much on the University of Maryland Project.

Another series, *Seeing Through Arithmetic*,[4] experiments with teaching for understanding, especially through pupil discovery. This is achieved in the Grades 1 through 6 series through carefully chosen pictures. In the seventh- and eighth-grade texts, the authors strive for discovery through questions so carefully chosen that the texts resemble programed instruction.

[1] Published by Addison Wesley, Palo Alto, Calif.
[2] Published by Science Research Associates, Inc., Chicago, Ill.
[3] Published by Holt, Rinehart and Winston, Inc., New York, N. Y.
[4] Published by Scott, Foresman and Co., Chicago, Ill.

SEVEN EMERGING TRENDS

The results of the experimentation of these groups are now appearing in the elementary school textbooks, a study of which reveals the following emerging trends.

1. The emphasis throughout is on understanding. I will discuss six methods or devices which promote understanding.

There is much use of the number line to make mathematical ideas more concrete. For example:

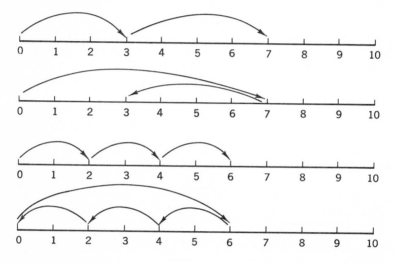

$3 + 4 = \square$ Move forward on the number line the distance indicated by each addend.

$7 - 4 = \square$ Move backward on the number line the amount to be subtracted.

$3 \times 2 = \square$ Move forward in equal moves as indicated by the factors.

$6 \div 2 = \square$ Move backward in equal moves as indicated by the divisor.

Discussion of numbers in other bases is included early to promote interest in the base 10 system. Showing that just as place value in base 10 is founded on powers of 10, so also place value in base 5 is founded on powers of 5 helps to emphasize this important property of the base 10 system, e.g.:

Place value in base 10:

thousands	hundreds	tens	ones
10^3	10^2	10^1	10^0

Place value in base 5:

one hundred twenty-fives	twenty-fives	fives	ones
5^3	5^2	5^1	5^0

Computation in other bases is included in the texts for the sole purpose of encouraging students to analyze comparable examples in our base 10 number system.

To promote understanding *multiplication is approached from several viewpoints.* It is introduced early (by second grade in many cases) and concretely, as repeated addition, with no emphasis on the multiplication facts as such, e.g.:

$$2 + 2 + 2 = 6$$
three 2's are 6

It is reintroduced—following a spiral approach, using more ideas and demanding mastery of the facts—in third and succeeding grades.

Division is approached as repeated subtraction.

Many of the new texts introduce long division by a method popularized by Scott, Foresman. In this method, in the beginning stages of long division, you are unconcerned about whether you choose the right quotient figure the first time. By repeated subtraction, you will finally arrive at the correct quotient figure, e.g., in dividing 855 by 15, you might approximate the quotient as 40. Subtract forty 15's from the dividend. This done, subtract ten more 15's. Keep subtracting until there is no further remainder.

Subtract until the remainder is less than the divisor.

$$
\begin{array}{rr}
15\ \overline{855} & 40 \\
40 \times 15 = 600 & \\
\overline{255} & 10 \\
10 \times 15 = 150 & \\
\overline{105} & 7 \\
7 \times 15 = 105 & \\
\overline{} & \overline{57}
\end{array}
$$

Add these
partial quotients.

As another aid to understanding, *the structure of the whole number system is carefully built up.* Included in this structure are the fundamental laws governing the operations of arithmetic, i.e., the commutative, associative, and distributive laws as they affect addition, subtraction, multiplication, and division. For example, children begin learning the commutative principle as the "order principle" even in the first grade when they learn that:

$$2 + 3 = 3 + 2$$

Later they learn that:

$$2 \times 3 = 3 \times 2$$

Primary children understand the associative principle as the grouping principle in such examples as:

$$2 + (3 + 4) = (2 + 3) + 4$$

Somewhat later they notice that:

$$2 \times (3 \times 4) = (2 \times 3) \times 4$$

The properties of 1 and 0 are similarly tested. As children progress, this same structure is applied to fractions, decimals, and negative integers.

As an example of the way the order principle (or commutative principle) is successively applied to new number systems, we have:

WHOLE NUMBERS:	$2 + 3 = 3 + 2$
FRACTIONS:	$\frac{1}{2} + \frac{1}{4} = \frac{1}{4} + \frac{1}{2}$
NEGATIVE INTEGERS:	$(-1) + (-3) = (-3) + (-1)$

Relationships are constantly emphasized to insure understanding. For example, the relationship between addition and subtraction:

$$6 + 4 = n$$
$$n - 4 = 6$$

The relationship between multiplication and division:

$$3 \times 4 = 12$$
$$12 \div 4 = 3$$

Both of these are examples of inverse operations.

2. A trend now emerging is that new topics are being introduced. Mathematicians are working on showing that *all of mathematics can be expressed in terms of sets.* Hence, the topic, sets, is considered the topic which can best unify—and hence simplify—the mathematics we teach.

Sets are used to define the operations. If you are unfamiliar with set language these are the words we are using:

A SET is a collection of objects.

Anything which belongs to a set is a MEMBER of the set.

DISJOINT SETS are sets which have no members in common.

The UNION of two sets is the set consisting of all the elements belonging to either of the sets.

The notion of disjoint sets is used to introduce addition and multiplication:

$2 + 3 = 5$

Addition is the union
of two disjoint sets.

Nonmetric geometry (geometry other than that based on measurement: geometry beyond the usual length, area, and volume problems) is being incorporated into the curriculum. Among the topics included are: construction of geometric figures, parallel and perpendicular lines, space geometry, closed curves and simple closed curves. In many of the geometric sections, the student is given definitions such as those below and asked to apply them in exercises.

A Closed Curve
and
Simple Closed
Curve.

A closed curve is a curve that returns to its starting point. A simple closed curve is a curve that returns to its starting point without crossing itself at any point. Students may be asked to identify figures according to these definitions.

3. *Another trend is that there is more material in the primary grades* as well as more and different material in the intermediate and advanced grades. Many of the newer texts carry addition facts with sums of 17 and subtraction facts with minuends to 17 in the first grade, in contrast to the former custom of sums and minuends to 10 only. Most newer books have units on geometry, starting even with the kindergarten. Multiplication is begun in an experimental way in the second grade.

4. *There is a radical change in the seventh- and eighth-grade curriculum.* Educators have long thought that the discount, commission, insurance and tax problems which have been a part of the seventh- and eighth-grade curriculum were a remnant of the days when a person's education was completed in the eighth grade, and these topics were needed for meeting life situations soon to be encountered. (Modern business really conducts its affairs much more efficiently than the elementary school texts would seem to indicate.) The new seventh- and eighth-grade curriculum is more mathematical in content and a much better preparation for the mathematics being advocated in high school.

5. *Another emerging trend is the incorporation of new ideas from the psychology of learning into our teaching methods.* Some very strong views have been proposed on children's learning. Jerome Bruner in his book, *The Process*

of Education, said, "The foundations of any subject may be taught to anybody at any age in some form." [5] He justifies this statement by saying that the fundamental ideas of any subject are usually quite simple. Such statements have given experimenters courage to reach out boldly.

One major contribution of the psychology of learning to arithmetic is in the recommendation for the use of the "discovery method" of teaching. An axiom of teaching is that children learn best when they are involved in the learning. Teachers are encouraged to have the children "discover" mathematical ideas. However, this discovery process can be very time-consuming; hence the alternative of "guided discovery" has become very acceptable. In this method, the teacher guides the pupil, by careful questioning, to the discovery of the desired concept.

In connection with discovery, Gertrude Hendrix of the University of Illinois Mathematics Program has made a valuable contribution.[6] She contends that there is a nonverbal awareness stage in learning. Students who have discovered the desired concept may not have the language facility or the mathematical maturity to verbalize the discovery. She suggests that a teacher watch carefully the children who are trying to discover a new concept. When the teacher detects an animated, enthusiastic attack of a problem, he may conclude that the child has discovered the concept, even if the child cannot explain exactly why his system works.

6. *Another trend is the use of programed instruction.* Many textbook companies are publishing supplementary programed material. This material has various uses. It can provide extra help for those who may need more instruction; it can help the one absent from school to catch up with the class; it is invaluable material to acquaint the teacher with the new content she must teach the child; and it can help parents help their children.

7. *A final emerging trend is the teacher and pupil enthusiasm which is engendered.* Very apparent wherever the new mathematics has been introduced is the interest that the students take in their work and the consequent pleasure that the teachers experience in their teaching. The appeal to the understanding, the more challenging methods of teaching as well as weeding out the "dead wood" in the content have resulted in a curriculum much more satisfactory to everyone.

Where are we going now? The Cambridge Conference on School Mathematics which met in Cambridge, Mass., in the summer of 1963, proposed a very revolutionary curriculum for K–6 and 7–12.[7] Their suggestions include such topics as logic and trigonometry for the elementary school. Perhaps their proposals indicate new directions. As teachers become more

[5] Jerome Bruner, *The Process of Education* (Cambridge: Harvard University Press, 1961), p. 12.

[6] Gertrude Hendrix, "Learning by Discovery," *The Mathematics Teacher,* LIV (May, 1961), pp. 290–299.

[7] *Goals for School Mathematics,* The Report of the Cambridge Conference on School Mathematics (Boston: Houghton Mifflin Co., 1963).

proficient in the content and methods now being advocated, they will probably be able to handle the sophisticated material proposed.

SOME USEFUL REFERENCES ON THE NEW MATHEMATICS

Books for Teachers

DEANS, EDWINA, *Elementary School Mathematics, New Directions,* Government Bulletin OE-29042 (Washington, D.C.: U.S. Government Printing Office, 1963).

EDUCATIONAL RESEARCH COUNCIL OF GREATER CLEVELAND, *Key Topics in Mathematics for the Primary Teacher* (Chicago: Science Research Associates, Inc., 1962).

HEDDENS, JAMES W., *Today's Mathematics* (Chicago: Science Research Associates, Inc., 1964).

NATIONAL COUNCIL OF TEACHERS OF MATHEMATICS, *Topics in Mathematics for Elementary School Teachers,* 29th Yearbook (Washington, D.C.: National Council of Teachers of Mathematics, 1964; available in eight pamphlets or hardbound book).

Books for Parents

HEIMER, RALPH T., and NEWMAN, M. S., *The New Mathematics for Parents* (New York: Holt, Rinehart and Winston, Inc., 1965).

LAWRENCE, SISTER MARY, S.S.J., and COLLETTA, SISTER, S.S.M.N., *Exploring New Mathematics* (Buffalo: Department of Education, Diocese of Buffalo, 1964).

Programed Material

NELSON, CHARLES W., "Programed Supplement" to *Exploring Modern Mathematics* by Keedy, Jameson, and Johnson, Books 1 and 2 (New York: Holt, Rinehart and Winston, Inc., 1964).

SPOONER, GEORGE, *Mathematics Enrichment,* Programs A, B, and C (New York: Harcourt, Brace, and World, Inc., 1962).

Textbook Evaluation

NATIONAL COUNCIL OF TEACHERS OF MATHEMATICS, "Aids for Evaluators of Mathematics Textbooks," *Arithmetic Teacher,* Vol. 12, May, 1965, pp. 388–394. (Available also as a reprint from the National Council of Teachers of Mathematics.)

Movie

MATHEMATICS FOR TOMORROW, 29-min., 16mm. color film produced by Mathematical Association of America and the National Council of Teachers of Mathematics. Available from: Audiovisual Sound Studio, National Education Association, 1201 16th St. N.W., Washington, D.C. 20036.

Next Steps in Elementary-School Mathematics

Maurice L. Hartung

Reform movements have a life history that seems to follow a discernible pattern not unlike that of many other phenomena. There usually is a fairly long initial period of gestation. During this time, the reformers are occupied with formulating ideas, planning, recruiting workers, seeking financial support, and other preliminaries.

Following this, there is a period of furious activity as the movement actually gets under way. This is the phase which often becomes so conspicuous that almost everybody begins to notice that reform is taking place. Some people resist the changes. Others climb on the bandwagon. Inevitably the movement attracts a certain number of individuals who seek, through the unrest and uncertainty of many people, to promote their personal panacea, or some distorted version of the reform.

Eventually this period of rapid expansion starts to subside and a new phase begins. This is the sobering-up period, the time for careful evaluation, the time to consolidate gains, the time to modify or eliminate the extreme versions that were experimented with during the preceding period.

It seems to me that we are now in this third phase of the present reform movement in mathematics education. The next steps should be in the direction of making more effective and widespread use of the promising ideas and research findings that we now have. This does not mean, of course, that the search for new and better ideas should not be continued by qualified persons.

ORGANIZATION OF CONTENT

One of the major tasks ahead is to give more careful attention to the *organization* of content. It is true that there has been mention of the "spiral" organization of learning activities—i.e., an idea is introduced in one grade with the expectation that it will receive more mature consideration at one or more later grades. This concept, while not new, does represent a recognition of the importance of organization. Nevertheless, over-all organization of content has received relatively little attention recently.

Much of the recent experimentation has involved teaching selected mathematical ideas at younger ages than would have been considered possible—or wise—a few years ago. In its simplest form, this is done by merely moving

Reprinted from *Theory into Practice* (April 1964), 66–70, by permission of the publisher.

topics down a year or two in the course of study but leaving the instruction largely unchanged. For example, the algebra course formerly taken by ninth graders is given in the eighth grade. An extreme example is found in the Geometry Project of Professor Hawley of Stanford University. In this project, children in the primary grades made geometric constructions with straight-edge and compass; and the standards of accuracy required in the drawings were, in general, higher than those demanded at the junior- and senior-high school levels in which this content is normally taught. Many, many other examples could be given of teaching content to children at younger ages than formerly. Such innovations, if widely adopted, would bring about a radical change in the traditional organization of mathematical content.

We ought to think of the mathematics curriculum as a continuous, se-quential, and integrated program that extends over the thirteen years from kindergarten to grade twelve. It is obvious immediately that most of the recent experimentation has not seriously attempted to build a program in this sense. Instead, we have a variety of so-called programs, or projects. One of the best known of these is the Syracuse University–Webster College Madi-son Project, directed by Professor Robert B. Davis. In a recent bulletin pub-lished by the National Council of Teachers of Mathematics, Professor Davis wrote as follows:

This material provides a supplementary program in algebra and coordinate geom-etry, with some applications in physical science. Although the material is not tied to specified school grade levels, it can be started at least as early as grade 2 (age: 7 years), and can be used at least as late as grade 8. However, most schools first introduce the material in grades 5, 6, and 7; as the school itself acquires more experience with the Madison Project materials, these materials begin to be used, in appropriate places, in earlier and later grades.

.   .   .

Consequently, the curriculum of a school using the Madison Project materials in Phase I would look generally like this:

Grades K–3: Mainly the school's original arithmetic program, hardly changed at all by the use of Madison Project materials. (Possibly Madison Project materials might find some small use here.)
Grades 4–7: Mainly the school's original arithmetic and science programs, but with a supplemental use of Madison Project materials—perhaps on a one-lesson-per-week basis.

A school using such a program would then need to follow this with a carefully designed course sequence for grades 8–12 that would take advantage of the stronger background of the children emerging from grade 7.[1]

I have no doubt that this project and other projects of this sort have a number of beneficial outcomes. For example, if properly used, the materials

---

[1] "The Syracuse University–Webster College Madison Project," *An Analysis of New Mathematics Programs.* Washington, D.C.: National Council of Teachers of Mathematics, 1963, pp. 16, 18–19.

will lead the pupils to the self-discovery of mathematical ideas under the guidance of a skilled teacher. I have singled out this program for specific mention because I could quote a published report by Professor Davis himself to make my point—namely, that the project materials do not claim to be a continuous, sequential, and integrated program, even for a limited grade span.

If I were asked to state the criterion for an ideal or perfect program, I would reply as follows: The ideal program is such that we could not substitute a single activity for the ones already selected, or could not change the order of presentation of any of the activities, without adversely affecting the average achievement of the pupils. In other words, the activities have been perfectly selected and perfectly organized to achieve the objectives of the program. One may realize, perhaps, how far mathematics education has yet to go before it develops an ideal program, if one recalls how teachers are often urged to substitute one activity for another or one development of a given idea for another, or how free they feel to change the order of some of the activities in their present programs. With a perfect program, such changes would result in lowered achievement.

One of the tendencies noticeable in the present state of mathematics teaching is for teachers or schools to attempt to deal with the situation by substituting "enrichment" for actual reform, or to "try out" a new unit (e.g., on sets, equations, geometry, or inequalities) "experimentally." Generally, this means that one or more classes are selected for the tryout, materials are purchased, and a few days or weeks are authorized for the teaching. There is usually an informal and sometimes a formal evaluation of the experience. Such efforts, even if very successful, fall far short of what we should aim for in mathematical education—a program in the sense defined earlier.

A unit on sets, for example, although it is new, modern, and interesting, may not increase the mathematical maturity of pupils to any great extent. The idea of sets is important because so many other ideas or concepts can be defined and developed in terms of this idea. Thus, if properly developed, the idea of sets can serve as a *unifying idea* for the entire mathematical curriculum. When it is used in this way, its frequent recurrence in diverse situations can help the pupils see continuity, sequence, and integration in the mathematical curriculum. Thus, it can contribute to building a program, in contrast to the stringing together of a comparatively loosely connected and loosely organized series of units. One of the logical next steps, therefore, is the introduction of material on sets, not as an isolated unit, but as a *fundamental building block* of the entire mathematics curriculum.

Another fundamental idea that is being worked into some of the new materials is commonly called structure. Briefly, to emphasize the structure of a mathematical system means to bring to the focus of attention the set of objects (numbers, points, or whatever) with which one deals, the set of mathematical operations that one uses, and the small number of fundamental properties that suffice for the development of the entire system. For example, if we are dealing with the set of natural numbers, we have a few fundamental operations (such as addition and multiplication), and a few properties (such as the commutative and associative) in terms of which all other things that are done with the natural numbers are explained and justified. The idea of structure, like the idea of set, is well suited to be a unifying idea for the entire curriculum. It is fundamental and permeates mathematics through and through.

In particular, in teaching children how to multiply 32 by 6, for example, the distributive property is used. The number 32 is expressed in terms of the base-ten system as $30 + 2$, so that $6 \times 32 = 6 (30 + 2)$. By the distributive property, this is equal to $6 \times 30 + 6 \times 2$ or $180 + 12$, which is 192. In traditional arithmetical teaching, the distributive property is almost never explicitly stated and applied. In some of the newer materials, however, it is explicitly taught and used to explain and justify the computational procedure.

As I have pointed out elsewhere, an important question is: What is the optimum time for such properties to be formalized for and by the pupil—that is, to be explicitly stated and used? [2] If the attempt is made too soon, these properties may be viewed by the pupil as just another set of meaningless rules. If, on the other hand, they are understood and their role as part of the structure is at least faintly seen, they can bring about a truly remarkable economy and efficiency in the learning of arithmetic.

I return now to my main point. The major task of curriculum builders for the next few years should be to weld fundamental ideas such as *set* and *structure*, and a host of other ideas that depend upon them (or can be developed from them), into a continuous, coherent, sequential program. This goal need not inhibit further experimentation to find out just what children can learn at a given age. But a collection of things that children can learn is not a curriculum. Some elements have to be selected, and the whole has to be carefully organized before a program (in the sense defined earlier) emerges.

IMPROVEMENTS IN INSTRUCTIONAL METHODS

One of the most noticeable things about so-called modern mathematics is not really mathematics at all. It is the instructional method used. Much of the success of introducing material at earlier ages is due to the fact that the

[2] See Maurice L. Hartung, "Formalism in Arithmetic Programs," *The Arithmetic Teacher*, November, 1962, 9, 371–75.

experimenters adopted some form of what is now widely called "the discovery method." It has long been known that children understand better and retain longer if they acquire knowledge by a thinking process (*cognitive* is the popular term nowadays) rather than by mere memorization or habituation. This method has now suddenly become popular. I hope it remains so. At the same time, I hope that mathematics teachers learn to use "the discovery method" with wisdom and restraint. For the pupil to discover everything is obviously futile because it would take too long. He needs to be told some things so he can get on with the job of learning other things. Consequently, curriculum workers in the next few years should give much attention to the selection of those topics that yield optimum results when approached by the discovery method. Once these are better known, we can relax a bit and stop riding the discovery horse to death.

In this connection, some experimenters claim to have shown that very young children can discover (with a little guidance) the basic ideas of certain fundamental structures—for example, the idea of a special kind of set called a mathematical group. The methods used often employ specially devised games in which the elements (i.e., children) go through certain operations (i.e., moves of the game) subject to certain rules (i.e., generalizations about the properties). These are called premathematical experiences. In these early stages, the teachers are careful not to formalize the structure. For example, pupils are said to understand the structure called a group if they can play the game according to the rules. But many teachers would hesitate to call this mathematics until some formalization has occurred. These games are played as *games,* just as certain games were played long before it was discovered by mature mathematicians that they could be formalized in mathematical terms.

There is no question that children can carry out such activities with interest and even enthusiasm. As stated earlier, the point of this discussion is that a collection of such activities does not necessarily constitute a program. The persons who are experimenting along these lines would, I am sure, be the first to admit this. However, many teahers and administrators who read and hear about the marvelous results being achieved in a particular project feel that they should be doing the same thing, or something similar. They forget that many such projects, if put together in a disorganized bundle, may not in the long run ensure that mathematical achievement is maximized.

Some experiences of the discovery type are extremely valuable. Some "unverbalized awareness" is undoubtedly valuable also. But surely all learning activities need not be of the discovery type, and surely the pupil may eventually be expected to verbalize and formalize what he has learned. When instructional methods are being considered, therefore, one of the next steps is to achieve a balance between inductive and heuristic modes of attack (discovery methods) on the one hand, and deductive methods, practice for the acquisition of skill, and other traditional methods on the other hand.

I shall mention one other bothersome aspect of the current scene. A few years ago it was feasible (but not always wise) to use several different textbooks in one class. In fact, teachers were often urged to do so. Also, textbooks by different authors and publishers could be used at various grade levels; the traditional curriculum was so standardized that materials could be used like interchangeable machine parts. Under current conditions, these practices are not nearly as feasible as they once were. Emerging programs are much more diverse than the older ones they displace. One can no longer depend upon finding several sets of materials designed for use in one grade and finding in them the same subject organized in essentially the same manner. This means, it seems to me, that school systems have increasingly to commit themselves to one program for a period of years, and stick to it. Otherwise, there may be both serious gaps in the experience of children and extensive overlapping of some material. This situation also makes the problem of transfer students much more serious than it formerly was. Sooner or later there will have to be a decision based on informed judgment as to what is to be expected at various stages of mathematical development; otherwise, the difficulties that teachers and administrators face as a result of the mobility of the American people will become insurmountable.

CONCLUSION

The recent strains upon school people as they try to adjust to a new era in mathematical education are symptomatic of the distance many schools still have to go before the ideal program emerges. Once it does emerge, we can be reasonably sure it will not remain ideal for long. New ideas will be stimulating curriculum workers, and there will again be demands for change. In times like this, there are two extremes that lead to difficulties. On the one hand, some persons are inflexible, traditional, and conservative when all the rest of the world is changing and, hopefully, moving forward. On the other hand, other persons are so flexible and ready to change that every new proposal that comes along strikes their fancy. These persons tend to jump about, trying out this and that sort of thing indiscriminately. They seem to have no long-range program and to use few, if any, criteria for deciding what to do except that the thing *must* be new and different.

The reasonably secure person in a changing situation has a clearly formulated set of objectives that conform to modern ideas and needs. He has some good criteria for selecting and organizing learning activities, and he has effective means of evaluation. He then devotes his efforts to developing a program of mathematical education that is more than a mere assemblage of somewhat random learning experiences and activities.

How Parents Can Help

Donovan A. Johnson and Robert Rahtz

Finally, we wish to consider briefly the role of parents in the mathematical education of their youngsters. The role of parents cannot be overemphasized. It is the parents who fashion the future by the influence they exercise on their children. It is the parents who largely determine a child's interests, habits, vocational choice, and values. It is the parents who provide the setting, the stimulus, and the resources for a child's development and education. It is the parents who develop the three c's—conscience, curiosity, and character.

The new mathematics programs have re-emphasized the importance of the students' attitudes in learning mathematical ideas. These attitudes include the interests, values, appreciations, and prejudices of the pupil. Research on the development of attitudes toward mathematics indicates that the parent is a key person. As parents we transfer our attitudes to our children by what we say, do, and think. One way to nourish a poor attitude toward mathematics is to say:

"I feel sorry for you, having to study algebra."
"No wonder you can't understand it, I never could get the hang of mathematics either."
"You'll never be any good in mathematics doing it that way."
"You don't need any more mathematics to run the business."

Instead we might foster a favorable attitude by saying such encouraging things as:

"Sure math is hard, but it's a powerful tool that has many uses."
"If you get the idea, you'll enjoy it, like winning a game."
"Keep thinking and you'll find the solution."
"Nobody ever lost a job because he knew too much mathematics."

Progress in mathematics requires that the child complete assignments, read books, think independently, and be curious about mathematical ideas. To help our child study we should provide him with the space, the time, and the tools which he needs for his lessons. If at all possible, see that the study place is quiet, pleasant, and comfortable, with adequate light and a reasonable temperature. And we should encourage our children to study at a specific time. Mathematics books, programmed texts, models, toys, slide rules, computer kits are learning aids which you could provide.

To promote independent thinking we should use good judgment in giving help with homework. When questions are asked abotut problems on homework we should first express interest. Then we should try to ask questions which will help our child discover the answer rather than answering the question directly. Having the child explain the problem itself to you makes him think about the situation in such a way that the solution may be suggested. If you too can't solve the problem, don't express disgust but rather enjoy the problem as a challenge, a puzzle, or a game. Help your child to accept the challenge of difficult problems. If the answer is obvious there is no satisfaction in solving the problem.

In order to nourish curiosity we ourselves should enjoy to explore new ideas. Whenever we find unusual news items, facts, puzzles, cartoons, or tricks related to mathematics we should express our pleasure in them by sharing them with the family. We should encourage our children to read recreational mathematics books, view TV programs which have mathematical or scientific aspects, visit science fairs, and use library facilities. There is a wealth of material about mathematics in pamphlets and books written in a language that can be enjoyed by children and adults.

Competence in mathematics also requires reasonable facility in computation. Rather than continue the drill activities of the arithmetic text, parents can set up competitions, number games, and mental arithmetic in a recreational setting. Many commercial games are available at school supply stores and toy shops. Guessing games such as Twenty Questions and Password, and counting games like Nim and Buzz are described in the publication *Games for Learning Mathematics,* published by Walch Publishing Company, Portland, Maine.

If your child has a natural talent for mathematics, be sure that he capitalizes on this potential. The demand for mathematicians and mathematics teachers is great and is likely to increase. As a parent you should encourage your child, whether a boy or a girl, to consider mathematics as a career. Watch the newspaper ads to learn the demand for mathematically competent persons. Visit the school counselor to find the best courses for your child. Study college catalogs to make sure that your child will have the background for the college of his choice. Explore the possibilities of summer camps, seminars, advanced placement, acceleration, or summer institutes for superior students. Encourage your child to participate in science fairs or to complete optional projects for his mathematics class.

If your child is having difficulty with his mathematics try to give him help at an early date. The sequential nature of mathematics tends to compound difficulties with topics taught in earlier grades. Remedial instruction may be available in the form of tutors, special courses, summer courses, or programmed texts. Consult with your child's teacher or the school counselor for the identification of the source of difficulty and for information as to ways of providing for deficiencies.

To make a contribution to your child's progress in mathematics, you need to be informed of the current trends in mathematics education. To do this, discuss your child's school activities with him. Study his texts. Continue to inform yourself about the new mathematics (see the list of suggested books on this page). If your community has an adult education course on modern mathematics, join it. Most important of all, discover that learning mathematics can be a satisfying, pleasant experience.

SUGGESTED READING

ADLER, IRVING. *Mathematics*. New York: Golden Press, Inc., 1958. A colorful, well-illustrated treatment of the history and applications of elementary mathematics.

————. *The New Mathematics*. New York: New American Library of World Literature, Inc., 1958. A popular discussion of many of the new discoveries in mathematics.

BERGAMINI, DAVID. *Mathematics*. New York: Time, Inc., 1963. A beautifully illustrated book about mathematicians, mathematical ideas, and applications of mathematics.

COURANT, RICHARD, and HERBERT ROBBINS. *What Is Mathematics?* New York: Oxford University Press, 1941. A scholarly treatment, but a very readable book on the nature of mathematics, its topics, and its structure.

DEANS, EDWINA. *Elementary School Mathematics*. Washington, D.C.: U.S. Office of Education, 1963. A discussion of the new programs in mathematics.

JOHNSON, DONOVAN, and WILLIAM H. GLENN. *Exploring Mathematics on Your Own*. New York: Doubleday & Company, Inc., 1961. Readable presentations of many topics mentioned in this volume.

————. *Invitation to Mathematics*. New York: Doubleday & Company, Inc., 1961. Popular treatment of interesting topics in mathematics.

KASNER, EDWARD, and JAMES NEWMAN. *Mathematics and the Imagination*. New York: Simon and Schuster, Inc., 1940. A classic in its presentation of some of the dramatic sidelights of mathematics in popular language.

NATIONAL COUNCIL OF TEACHERS OF MATHEMATICS. *The Revolution in School Mathematics*. Washington, D.C.: National Council of Teachers of Mathematics, 1960.

————. *New Mathematics Programs*. Washington, D.C.: National Council of Teachers of Mathematics, 1963. Discussions and evaluations of experimental mathematics programs.

REID, CONSTANCE. *Introduction to Higher Mathematics*. New York: Thomas Y. Crowell Company, 1959. A layman's discussion of some of the ideas of contemporary mathematics.

SAWYER, W. W. *Vision in Elementary Mathematics*. Baltimore, Md.: Penguin Books, Inc., 1964. An ingenious presentation of the ideas and processes of elementary mathematics.